Order of Public Worship

NOTE.—The Methodist Episcopal Church and the Methodist Episcopal Church, South, have adopted a Common Order of Worship as given below.

[PARTS IN BRACKETS MAY BE OMITTED.]

Let all our services begin exactly at the time appointed, and let all our people kneel in silent prayer on entering the sanctuary.

[**I. VOLUNTARY,** instrumental or vocal.]

II. SINGING FROM THE COMMON HYMNAL,

the people standing.

[**III. THE APOSTLES' CREED,** recited by all, still standing.]

I BELIEVE in God the Father Almighty, Maker of heaven and earth: And in Jesus Christ, his only Son our Lord; who was conceived by the Holy Ghost, born of the Virgin Mary; suffered under Pontius Pilate, was crucified, dead, and buried; the third day he rose again from the dead; he ascended into heaven, and sitteth at the right hand of God the Father Almighty; from thence he shall come to judge the quick and the dead.

I believe in the Holy Ghost; the holy catholic Church, the communion of saints; the forgiveness of sins; the resurrection of the body; and the life everlasting. Amen.

IV. PRAYER, concluding with the Lord's Prayer, repeated audibly by all, both minister and people kneeling.

[**V. ANTHEM OR VOLUNTARY.**]

VI. LESSON FROM THE OLD TESTAMENT,

which, if from the Psalms, may be read responsively.*

[**VII. THE GLORIA PATRI.**]

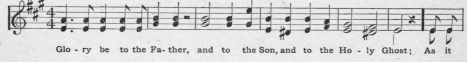

Glo - ry be to the Fa - ther, and to the Son, and to the Ho - ly Ghost; As it

was in the be-gin-ning, is now, and ev - er shall be, world without end. A -men, A -men.

VIII. LESSON FROM THE NEW TESTAMENT.

IX. NOTICES, FOLLOWED BY COLLECTION;

during or after which an offertory may be rendered.

X. SINGING FROM THE COMMON HYMNAL,

the people standing.

XI. THE SERMON.

XII. PRAYER, the people kneeling. †

XIII. SINGING FROM THE COMMON HYMNAL,

the people standing. ‡

XIV. DOXOLOGY AND THE APOSTOLIC BENEDICTION

(2 Cor. 13. 14).

---

* In the afternoon or evening the Lesson from the Old Testament may be omitted.
† The order of prayer and singing after sermon may be reversed.
‡ An invitation to come to Christ or to unite with the Church should be given when this hymn is announced.

The
Methodist Hymnal

OFFICIAL HYMNAL
OF THE
METHODIST EPISCOPAL CHURCH
AND THE
METHODIST EPISCOPAL CHURCH, SOUTH

———

Cincinnati: Jennings & Graham
New York: Eaton & Mains

Historic Note

In accordance with authority given by the General Conference of the Methodist Episcopal Church and the General Conference of the Methodist Episcopal Church, South, the Bishops of the respective churches appointed as members of the Joint Commission for the preparation of a common Hymnal the following persons:

Of the Methodist Episcopal Church

BISHOP D. A. GOODSELL,
S. F. UPHAM,
C. M. STUART,
C. M. COBERN,
R. J. COOKE,
C. S. NUTTER,
W. A. QUAYLE,
H. G. JACKSON,
C. W. SMITH,
C. T. WINCHESTER,
J. M. BLACK.

Of the Methodist Episcopal Church, South

BISHOP E. E. HOSS,
GEORGE B. WINTON,
H. M. Du BOSE,
W. F. TILLETT,
PAUL WHITEHEAD,
JOHN M. MOORE,
EDWIN MIMS,
II. N. SNYDER,
F. S. PARKER,
JAMES CAMPBELL,
R. T. KERLIN.

v

Preface

THIS Hymnal is the result of the labors of a joint Commission of twenty-two ministers and laymen appointed in equal numbers by the Methodist Episcopal Church and the Methodist Episcopal Church, South; the double purpose being to provide a worthy manual of song for use in the public and private worship of Almighty God, and to testify to the world the essential unity of the two great branches of Episcopal Methodism.

The fruit of their toil we now lay before the churches with confidence and joy: with confidence because we feel warranted in saying that the book is an admirable compilation of sacred lyrics; and with joy because we trust that for many long years it will prove to be a visible and potent bond of union among all our people.

We gladly note that the hymns of the Wesleys are given the prominence which justly belongs to them in any collection to be used by Methodists. But the book will be found to contain also the choicest work of the other hymn writers of the eighteenth century, namely, Doddridge, Watts, Cowper, Newton, Montgomery, and a very considerable number of new hymns selected after a wide examination of the body of religious verse produced during the last seventy-five years. The hymns admitted have been selected from the ancient and modern treasuries of religious poetry. They are the expression of sound doctrine and healthful Christian experience, and it is believed will greatly enrich our worship and bring us into closer fellowship with believers in all lands and in all ages.

Such verbal changes as have been made in the hymns are in most cases a return to the original and preferable forms. Some stanzas have been wholly excluded on the ground that they contain imagery offensive to modern taste, and others have been omitted to secure desirable brevity. The Commission did not venture to make arbitrary or capricious alterations.

In only a very few cases have hymns been divorced from the tunes to which long use has wedded them. For some familiar hymns alternate tunes have been provided, either with a view to please both branches of the church or to secure a better musical expression for the words than is given by the tune now familiar. Many new tunes by the more eminent modern composers of church music have been introduced. Much care has been given to the selection of these tunes, which we are assured will be found to be devotional in spirit, well fitted to the hymns to which they are set, and adapted to use by the great congregation.

And now, praying that this Hymnal, prepared by a joint Commission whose brotherly harmony was never once broken and whose final meeting was a Pentecost, may be abundantly blessed of God to the edification of believing souls and to the glory of his name, we commend it to our churches, and we earnestly hope that it may everywhere supplant those unauthorized publications which often teach what organized Methodism does not hold, and which, by excluding the nobler music of the earlier and later days, prevent the growth of a true musical taste.

Your servants in Christ,

THOMAS BOWMAN,
S. M. MERRILL,
E. G. ANDREWS,
H. W. WARREN,
C. D. FOSS,
J. M. WALDEN,
W. F. MALLALIEU,
C. H. FOWLER,
J. H. VINCENT,
J. N. FITZGERALD,
I. W. JOYCE,
D. A. GOODSELL,
C. C. McCABE,
EARL CRANSTON,
D. H. MOORE,
J. W. HAMILTON,
J. F. BERRY,
HENRY SPELLMEYER,
W. F. McDOWELL,
J. W. BASHFORD,
WILLIAM BURT,
L. B. WILSON
T. B. NEELY,
Bishops Methodist Episcopal Church.

J. C. KEENER,
A. W. WILSON,
J. C. GRANBERY,
R. K. HARGROVE,
W. W. DUNCAN,
C. B. GALLOWAY,
E. R. HENDRIX,
J. S. KEY,
O. P. FITZGERALD,
W. A. CANDLER,
H. C. MORRISON,
E. E. HOSS,
A. C. SMITH,
Bishops Methodist Episcopal Church, South.

Classification

The Methodist Hymnal

Worship

Adoration and Praise

I AZMON C. M.   CARL G. GLASER. Arr. by LOWELL MASON

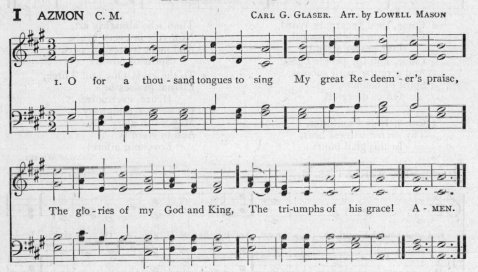

1. O for a thou-sand tongues to sing My great Re-deem-er's praise,

The glo-ries of my God and King, The tri-umphs of his grace! A - MEN.

2 My gracious Master and my God,
   Assist me to proclaim,
   To spread through all the earth abroad,
   The honors of thy name.

3 Jesus! the name that charms our fears,
   That bids our sorrows cease;
   'Tis music in the sinner's ears,
   'Tis life, and health, and peace.

4 He breaks the power of canceled sin,
   He sets the prisoner free;

His blood can make the foulest clean;
His blood availed for me.

5 He speaks, and, listening to his voice,
   New life the dead receive;
   The mournful, broken hearts rejoice;
   The humble poor believe.

6 Hear him, ye deaf; his praise, ye dumb,
   Your loosened tongues employ;
   Ye blind, behold your Saviour come;
   And leap, ye lame, for joy.
                                   CHARLES WESLEY

2 ITALIAN HYMN 6. 6. 4. 6. 6. 6. 4.

FELICE GIARDINI

1. Come, thou al-might-y King, Help us thy name to sing, Help us to praise! Fa-ther all-glo-ri-ous, O'er all vic-to-ri-ous, Come, and reign o-ver us, Ancient of days! A-MEN.

2 Come, thou Incarnate Word,
　Gird on thy mighty sword,
　　Our prayer attend;
　Come, and thy people bless,
　And give thy word success:
　Spirit of holiness,
　　On us descend!

3 Come, Holy Comforter,
　Thy sacred witness bear,
　　In this glad hour:

Thou who almighty art,
Now rule in every heart,
　And ne'er from us depart,
　　Spirit of power!

4 To the great One and Three,
Eternal praises be
　　Hence, evermore:
His sovereign majesty
May we in glory see,
And to eternity
　　Love and adore!

CHARLES WESLEY

3 SILVER STREET S. M.

ISAAC SMITH

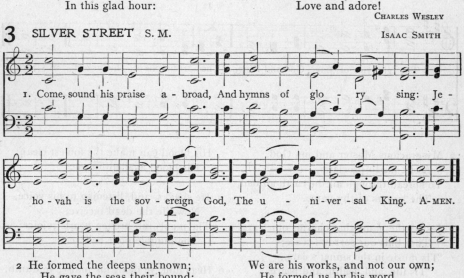

1. Come, sound his praise a-broad, And hymns of glo-ry sing: Je-ho-vah is the sov-ereign God, The u-ni-ver-sal King. A-MEN.

2 He formed the deeps unknown;
　He gave the seas their bound;
　The watery worlds are all his own,
　　And all the solid ground.

3 Come, worship at his throne,
　Come, bow before the Lord;

We are his works, and not our own;
　He formed us by his word.

4 To-day attend his voice,
　Nor dare provoke his rod;
　Come, like the people of his choice,
　　And own your gracious God.

ISAAC WATTS

Adoration and Praise

4 LEONI 6. 6. 8. 4. D.

Hebrew Melody

1. The God of Abraham praise, Who reigns enthroned a - bove; An-cient of ev - er -
last-ing days, And God of love; Je - ho-vah, great I AM, By earth and heav'n confessed;
I bow and bless the sa - cred name, For - ev - er blest. A-MEN.

2 The God of Abraham praise,
    At whose supreme command
From earth I rise, and seek the joys
    At his right hand:
I all on earth forsake,
    Its wisdom, fame, and power;
And him my only portion make,
    My shield and tower.

3 He by himself hath sworn.
    I on his oath depend;
I shall, on eagles' wings upborne,
    To heaven ascend:
I shall behold his face,
    I shall his power adore,
And sing the wonders of his grace
    For evermore.

4 The goodly land I see,
    With peace and plenty blest;
A land of sacred liberty,
    And endless rest.

There milk and honey flow,
    And oil and wine abound;
And trees of life forever grow,
    With mercy crowned.

5 Before the great Three-One
    They all exulting stand,
And tell the wonders he hath done
    Through all their land:
The listening spheres attend,
    And swell the growing fame;
And sing, in songs which never end,
    The wondrous name.

6 The whole triumphant host
    Give thanks to God on high;
"Hail, Father, Son, and Holy Ghost,"
    They ever cry:
Hail, Abraham's God and mine! —
    I join the heavenly lays, —
All might and majesty are thine,
    And endless praise.

THOMAS OLIVERS

3

Worship

5 DUKE STREET L. M.
JOHN HATTON

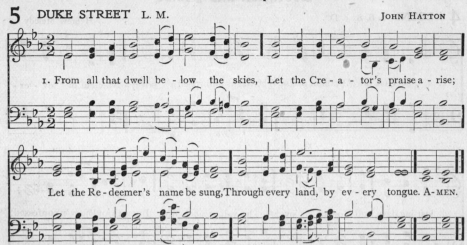

1. From all that dwell be-low the skies, Let the Cre-a-tor's praise a-rise;

Let the Re-deemer's name be sung, Through every land, by ev-ery tongue. A-MEN.

2 Eternal are thy mercies, Lord;
Eternal truth attends thy word:
Thy praise shall sound from shore to shore,
Till suns shall rise and set no more.

3 Your lofty themes, ye mortals, bring;
In songs of praise divinely sing;

The great salvation loud proclaim,
And shout for joy the Saviour's name.

4 In every land begin the song;
To every land the strains belong:
In cheerful sounds all voices raise,
And fill the world with loudest praise.

ISAAC WATTS and JOHN WESLEY

6 OLD HUNDRED L. M.
Genevan Psalter

1. Be-fore Je-ho-vah's aw-ful throne, Ye na-tions, bow with sa-cred joy;

Know that the Lord is God a-lone, He can cre-ate, and he de-stroy. A-MEN.

2 His sovereign power, without our aid,
Made us of clay, and formed us men;
And when like wandering sheep we strayed,
He brought us to his fold again.

3 We'll crowd thy gates with thankful songs,
High as the heavens our voices raise;

And earth with her ten thousand tongues,
Shall fill thy courts with sounding praise.

4 Wide as the world is thy command;
Vast as eternity thy love;
Firm as a rock thy truth shall stand,
When rolling years shall cease to move.

ISAAC WATTS. Alt. by JOHN WESLEY

4

Adoration and Praise

7 TRURO L. M.

CHARLES BURNEY

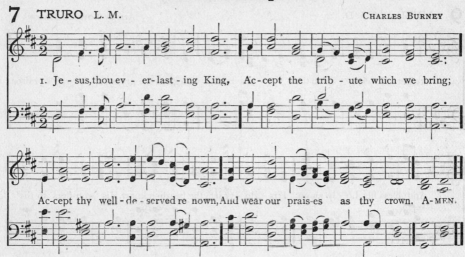

1. Je-sus, thou ev-er-last-ing King, Ac-cept the trib-ute which we bring;

Ac-cept thy well-de-served re nown, And wear our prais-es as thy crown. A-MEN.

2 Let every act of worship be
Like our espousals, Lord, to thee;
Like the blest hour, when from above
We first received the pledge of love.

3 The gladness of that happy day,
O may it ever, ever stay!

Nor let our faith forsake its hold,
Nor hope decline, nor love grow cold.

4 Let every moment, as it flies,
Increase thy praise, improve our joys,
Till we are raised to sing thy name,
At the great supper of the Lamb.

ISAAC WATTS

8 MARLOW C. M.

JOHN CHETHAM

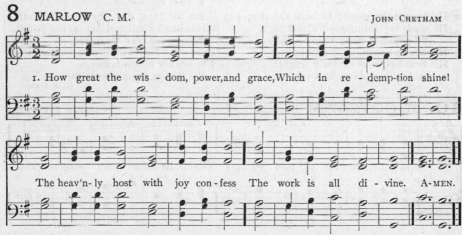

1. How great the wis-dom, power, and grace, Which in re-demp-tion shine!

The heav'n-ly host with joy con-fess The work is all di-vine. A-MEN.

2 Before his feet they cast their crowns,
Those crowns which Jesus gave,
And, with ten thousand thousand tongues,
Proclaim his power to save.

3 They tell the triumphs of his cross,
The sufferings which he bore;

How low he stooped, how high he rose,
And rose to stoop no more.

4 With them let us our voices raise,
And still the song renew;
Salvation well deserves the praise
Of men and angels too.

BENJAMIN BEDDOME

5

Worship

9 ARIEL 8. 8. 6. D.

Arr. by LOWELL MASON

1. Let all on earth their voi - ces raise, To sing the great Je - ho-vah's praise, And bless his ho - ly name: His glo - ry let the heathen know, His won-ders to the nations show, His sav - ing grace proclaim, His sav-ing grace pro - claim. A - MEN.

2 He framed the globe; he built the sky;
He made the shining worlds on high,
  And reigns in glory there:
His beams are majesty and light;
His beauties, how divinely bright!
  His dwelling place, how fair!

3 Come the great day, the glorious hour,
When earth shall feel his saving power,
  All nations fear his name.
Then shall the race of men confess
The beauty of his holiness,
  His saving grace proclaim.

ISAAC WATTS

10 ST. CHRYSOSTOM L. M. 6l.

JOSEPH BARNBY

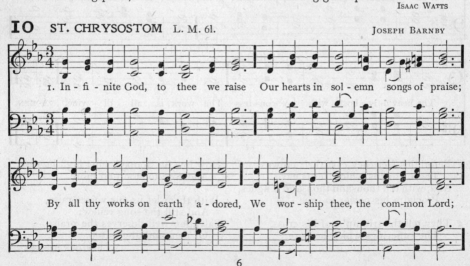

1. In - fi - nite God, to thee we raise Our hearts in sol - emn songs of praise; By all thy works on earth a - dored, We wor - ship thee, the com-mon Lord;

6

Adoration and Praise

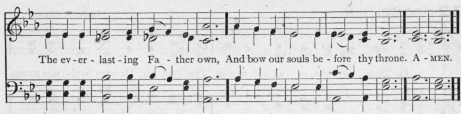

The ev - er - last-ing Fa - ther own, And bow our souls be - fore thy throne. A - MEN.

2 Thee all the choir of angels sings,
The Lord of hosts, the King of kings;
Cherubs proclaim thy praise aloud,
And seraphs shout the Triune God;
And "Holy, holy, holy," cry,
"Thy glory fills both earth and sky."

3 Father of endless majesty,
All might and love we render thee;
Thy true and only Son adore,
The same in dignity and power;
And God the Holy Ghost declare,
The saints' eternal Comforter.

CHARLES WESLEY

II HANOVER 10. 10. 11. 11.   WILLIAM CROFT

1. Ye ser-vants of God, your Mas-ter pro-claim, And pub-lish a - broad his won-der-ful name; The name all - vic - to - rious of Je - sus ex - tol; His king-dom is glo-rious, and rules o - ver all. A - MEN.

2 God ruleth on high, almighty to save;
And still he is nigh; his presence we have:
The great congregation his triumph shall sing,
Ascribing salvation to Jesus, our King.

3 "Salvation to God, who sits on the throne,"
Let all cry aloud, and honor the Son:
The praises of Jesus the angels proclaim,
Fall down on their faces, and worship the Lamb.

4 Then let us adore, and give him his right,
All glory and power, all wisdom and might,
All honor and blessing, with angels above,
And thanks never ceasing for infinite love.

CHARLES WESLEY

Worship

12 DOANE L. M.
JOHN B. CALKIN

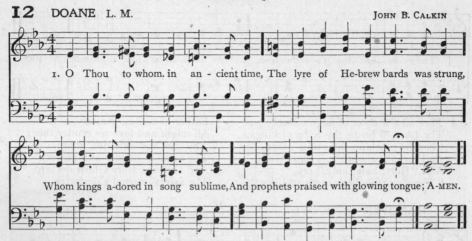

1. O Thou to whom, in an-cient time, The lyre of He-brew bards was strung,

Whom kings a-dored in song sublime, And prophets praised with glowing tongue; A-MEN.

2 Not now on Zion's height alone
   The favored worshiper may dwell,
Nor where, at sultry noon, thy Son
   Sat weary by the patriarch's well.

3 From every place below the skies,
   The grateful song, the fervent prayer,

The incense of the heart, may rise
   To heaven, and find acceptance there.

4 O Thou to whom, in ancient time,
   The lyre of prophet bards was strung,
To thee at last in every clime,
   Shall temples rise and praise be sung.

JOHN PIERPONT

13 HOLY HILL L. M.
WILLIAM H. PONTIUS

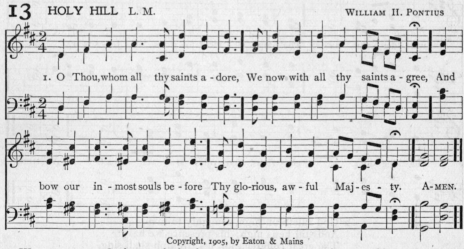

1. O Thou, whom all thy saints a-dore, We now with all thy saints a-gree, And

bow our in-most souls be-fore Thy glo-rious, aw-ful Maj-es-ty. A-MEN.

2 We come, great God, to seek thy face,
   And for thy loving-kindness wait;
And O how dreadful is this place!
   'Tis God's own house, 'tis heaven's gate.

3 Tremble our hearts to find thee nigh;
   To thee our trembling hearts aspire;
And lo! we see descend from high
   The pillar and the flame of fire.

4 Still let it on the assembly stay,
   And all the house with glory fill;
To Canaan's bounds point out the way,
   And lead us to thy holy hill.

5 There let us all with Jesus stand,
   And join the general church above,
And take our seats at thy right hand,
   And sing thine everlasting love.

CHARLES WESLEY

14 GILDER L. M.   ARNE OLDBERG

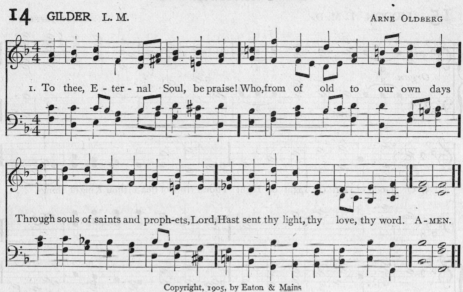

1. To thee, E - ter - nal Soul, be praise! Who, from of old to our own days

Through souls of saints and proph-ets, Lord, Hast sent thy light, thy love, thy word. A-MEN.

2 We thank thee for each mighty one
Through whom thy living light hath shone;
And for each humble soul and sweet
That lights to heaven our wandering feet.

3 We thank thee for the love divine
Made real in every saint of thine;
That boundless love itself that gives
In service to each soul that lives.

4 We thank thee for the word of might
Thy Spirit spake in darkest night.
Spake through the trumpet voices loud
Of prophets at thy throne who bowed.

5 Eternal Soul, our souls keep pure,
That like thy saints we may endure;
Forever through thy servants, Lord,
Send thou thy light, thy love, thy word.

RICHARD W. GILDER

14 WORSHIP L. M. (*Second Tune*)   KARL P. HARRINGTON

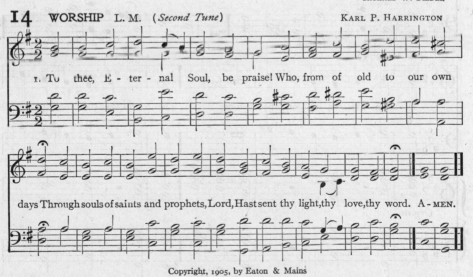

1. To thee, E - ter - nal Soul, be praise! Who, from of old to our own

days Through souls of saints and prophets, Lord, Hast sent thy light, thy love, thy word. A-MEN.

15 LIDDON L. M. D.

J. ALBERT JEFFERY

Organ

1. O God of God! O Light of Light! Thou Prince of Peace, thou King of kings, . .

Organ

To thee, where an-gels know no night, The song of praise for-ev-er rings:

(IN UNISON)

To him who sits up-on the throne, The Lamb once slain for sin-ful

Organ

Adoration and Praise

men, Be hon - or, might; all by him won;

Glo - ry and praise! A - men, A - men! A - MEN.

2 Deep in the prophets' sacred page,
   Grand in the poets' wingèd word,
Slowly in type, from age to age,
   Nations beheld their coming Lord;
Till through the deep Judean night
   Rang out the song, "Good will to men!"
Hymned by the firstborn sons of light,
   Re-echoed now, "Good will!" Amen!

3 That life of truth, those deeds of love,
   That death of pain, 'mid hate and scorn;
These all are past, and now above, [thorn.
   He reigns our King! once crowned with
"Lift up your heads, ye heavenly gates;"
   So sang his hosts, unheard by men;
"Lift up your heads, for you he waits."
   "We lift them up! Amen, Amen!"

4 Nations afar in ignorance deep;
   Isles of the sea, where darkness lay;
These hear his voice, they wake from sleep,
   And throng with joy the upward way,
They cry with us, "Send forth thy light,"
   O Lamb, once slain for sinful men;
Burst Satan's bonds, O God of might;
   Set all men free! Amen, Amen!

5 Sing to the Lord a glorious song,
   Sing to his name, his love forth tell;
Sing on, heaven's hosts, his praise prolong;
   Sing, ye who now on earth do dwell;
Worthy the Lamb for sinners slain, [men.
   From angels, praise; and thanks from
Worthy the Lamb, enthroned to reign,
   Glory and power! Amen, Amen!

JOHN JULIAN

16 OLD HUNDRED L. M.

Genevan Psalter

1. All peo-ple that on earth do dwell, Sing to the Lord with cheer-ful voice;

Him serve with fear, his praise forth tell, Come ye be-fore him, and re-joice. A-MEN.

2 The Lord, ye know, is God indeed,
  Without our aid he did us make;
  We are his flock, he doth us feed,
  And for his sheep he doth us take.

3 O enter then his gates with praise,
  Approach with joy his courts unto:

Praise, laud, and bless his name always,
  For it is seemly so to do.

4 For why? the Lord our God is good,
  His mercy is forever sure;
  His truth at all times firmly stood,
  And shall from age to age endure.

WILLIAM KETHE

17 MILLER L. M.

CARL P. E. BACH. Arr. by EDWARD MILLER

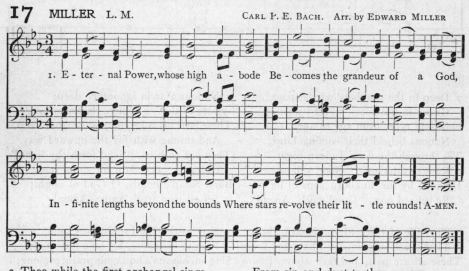

1. E-ter-nal Power, whose high a-bode Be-comes the grandeur of a God,

In-fi-nite lengths beyond the bounds Where stars re-volve their lit-tle rounds! A-MEN.

2 Thee while the first archangel sings,
  He hides his face behind his wings,
  And ranks of shining thrones around
  Fall worshiping, and spread the ground.

3 Lord, what shall earth and ashes do?
  We would adore our Maker too;

From sin and dust to thee we cry,
  The Great, the Holy, and the High.

4 God is in heaven, and men below:
  Be short our tunes; our words be few:
  A solemn reverence checks our songs,
  And praise sits silent on our tongues.

ISAAC WATTS

18 GREENLAND 7s. 6s. D.   Lausanne Psalter

1. O God, the Rock of A - ges, Who ev - er - more hast been,

What time the tem - pest ra - ges, Our dwell - ing place se - rene;

Be - fore thy first cre - a - tions, O Lord, the same as now,

To end - less gen - e - ra - tions The ev - er - last - ing Thou! A - MEN.

2 Our years are like the shadows
  On sunny hills that lie,
Or grasses in the meadows
  That blossom but to die:
A sleep, a dream, a story
  By strangers quickly told,
An unremaining glory
  Of things that soon are old.

3 O Thou, who canst not slumber,
  Whose light grows never pale,
Teach us aright to number
  Our years before they fail.

On us thy mercy lighten,
  On us thy goodness rest,
And let thy Spirit brighten
  The hearts thyself hast blessed.

4 Lord, crown our faith's endeavor
  With beauty and with grace,
Till, clothed in light forever,
  We see thee face to face:
A joy no language measures;
  A fountain brimming o'er;
An endless flow of pleasures;
  An ocean without shore.

EDWARD H. BICKERSTETH

19 NETTLETON 8s. 7s. D.

JOHN WYETH

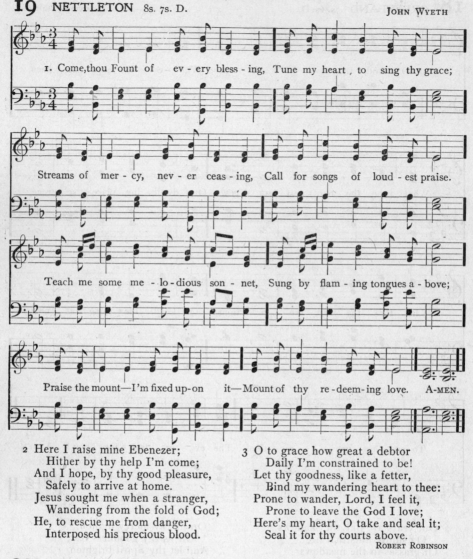

1. Come, thou Fount of ev-ery bless-ing, Tune my heart to sing thy grace;

Streams of mer-cy, nev-er ceas-ing, Call for songs of loud-est praise.

Teach me some me-lo-dious son-net, Sung by flam-ing tongues a-bove;

Praise the mount—I'm fixed up-on it—Mount of thy re-deem-ing love. A-MEN.

2 Here I raise mine Ebenezer;
    Hither by thy help I'm come;
And I hope, by thy good pleasure,
    Safely to arrive at home.
Jesus sought me when a stranger,
    Wandering from the fold of God;
He, to rescue me from danger,
    Interposed his precious blood.

3 O to grace how great a debtor
    Daily I'm constrained to be!
Let thy goodness, like a fetter,
    Bind my wandering heart to thee:
Prone to wander, Lord, I feel it,
    Prone to leave the God I love;
Here's my heart, O take and seal it;
    Seal it for thy courts above.

ROBERT ROBINSON

20 PRAISE 11s. 10s.

KARL P. HARRINGTON

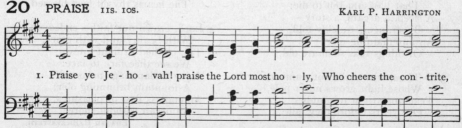

1. Praise ye Je-ho-vah! praise the Lord most ho-ly, Who cheers the con-trite,

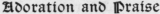

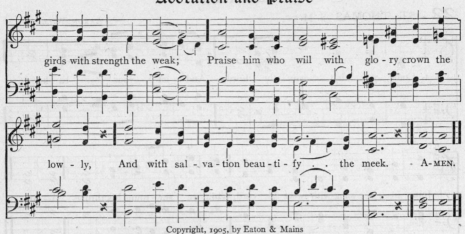

girds with strength the weak; Praise him who will with glo - ry crown the

low - ly, And with sal - va - tion beau - ti - fy . . the meek. A-MEN.

2 Praise ye Jehovah! for his loving-kindness,
   And all the tender mercy he hath shown;
Praise him who pardons all our sin and blindness,
   And calls us sons, and takes us for his own.

3 Praise ye Jehovah! source of all our blessings,
   Before his gifts earth's richest boons wax dim;
Resting in him, his peace and joy possessing,
   All things are ours, for we have all in him.

4 Praise ye the Father! God the Lord, who gave us,
   With full and perfect love, his only Son;
Praise ye the Son! who died himself to save us;
   Praise ye the Spirit! praise the Three in One!

MARGARET C. CAMPBELL

21 DUKE STREET L. M.
JOHN HATTON

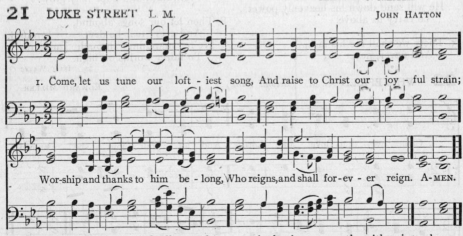

1. Come, let us tune our loft - iest song, And raise to Christ our joy - ful strain;

Wor-ship and thanks to him be - long, Who reigns, and shall for-ev - er reign. A-MEN.

2 His sovereign power our bodies made,
   Our souls are his immortal breath;
And when his creatures sinned, he bled,
   To save us from eternal death.

3 Burn every breast with Jesus' love;
   Bound every heart with rapturous joy;

And saints on earth, with saints above,
   Your voices in his praise employ.

4 Extol the Lamb with loftiest song,
   Ascend for him our cheerful strain;
Worship and thanks to him belong,
   Who reigns, and shall forever reign.

ROBERT A. WEST

22 ST. THOMAS S. M.

AARON WILLIAMS

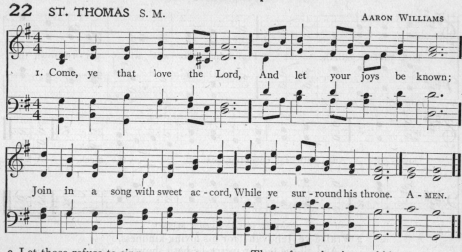

1. Come, ye that love the Lord, And let your joys be known;
Join in a song with sweet ac-cord, While ye sur-round his throne. A-MEN.

2 Let those refuse to sing
   Who never knew our God,
But servants of the heavenly King
   May speak their joys abroad.

3 The God that rules on high,
   That all the earth surveys,
That rides upon the stormy sky,
   And calms the roaring seas;

4 This awful God is ours,
   Our Father and our Love;
He will send down his heavenly powers,
   To carry us above.

5 There we shall see his face,
   And never, never sin;

There, from the rivers of his grace,
   Drink endless pleasures in:

6 Yea, and before we rise
   To that immortal state,
The thoughts of such amazing bliss
   Should constant joys create.

7 The men of grace have found
   Glory begun below;
Celestial fruit on earthly ground
   From faith and hope may grow.

8 Then let our songs abound,
   And every tear be dry; [ground,
We're marching through Immanuel's
   To fairer worlds on high.

ISAAC WATTS

22 WHITEFIELD S. M. (*Second Tune*)

EDWARD MILLER

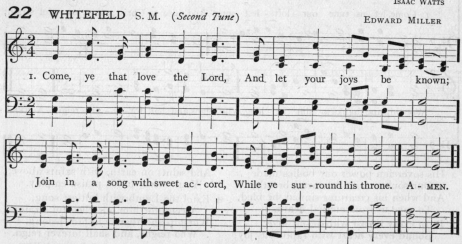

1. Come, ye that love the Lord, And let your joys be known;
Join in a song with sweet ac-cord, While ye sur-round his throne. A-MEN.

23 PARK STREET L. M.   FREDERICK M. A. VENUA

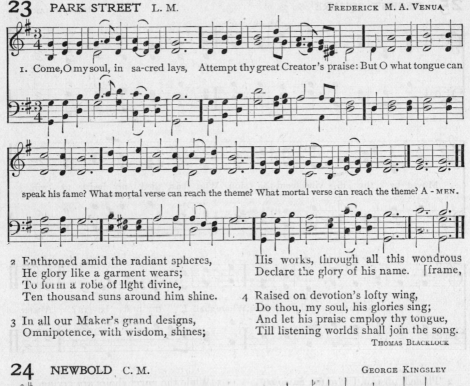

1. Come, O my soul, in sa-cred lays, Attempt thy great Creator's praise: But O what tongue can speak his fame? What mortal verse can reach the theme? What mortal verse can reach the theme? A-MEN.

2 Enthroned amid the radiant spheres,
He glory like a garment wears;
To form a robe of light divine,
Ten thousand suns around him shine.

3 In all our Maker's grand designs,
Omnipotence, with wisdom, shines;

His works, through all this wondrous frame,
Declare the glory of his name.

4 Raised on devotion's lofty wing,
Do thou, my soul, his glories sing;
And let his praise employ thy tongue,
Till listening worlds shall join the song.

THOMAS BLACKLOCK

24 NEWBOLD C. M.   GEORGE KINGSLEY

1. Come, let us join our cheerful songs With an-gels round the throne; Ten thousand thousand are their tongues, But all their joys are one, But all their joys are one. A-MEN.

2 "Worthy the Lamb that died," they cry,
"To be exalted thus!"
"Worthy the Lamb!" our hearts reply,
"For he was slain for us."

3 Jesus is worthy to receive
Honor and power divine;

And blessings more than we can give,
Be, Lord, forever thine.

4 The whole creation join in one,
To bless the sacred name
Of him that sits upon the throne,
And to adore the Lamb.

ISAAC WATTS

25 REGENT SQUARE 8s. 7s. 6l.   HENRY SMART

1. O thou God of my sal-va-tion, My Re-deem-er from all sin;

Moved by thy di-vine com-pas-sion, Who hast died my heart to win,

I will praise thee; I will praise thee; Where shall I thy praise be-gin? A-MEN.

2 Though unseen, I love the Saviour;
  He hath brought salvation near;
Manifests his pardoning favor;
  And when Jesus doth appear,
    Soul and body
Shall his glorious image bear.

3 While the angel choirs are crying,
  "Glory to the great I AM,"
I with them will still be vying —
  Glory! glory to the Lamb!
    O how precious
Is the sound of Jesus' name!

4 Angels now are hovering round us,
  Unperceived amid the throng;
Wondering at the love that crowned us,
  Glad to join the holy song:
    Hallelujah,
Love and praise to Christ belong!

THOMAS OLIVERS

26 DARWALL 6. 6. 6. 6. 8. 8.   JOHN DARWALL

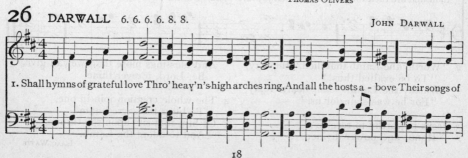

1. Shall hymns of grateful love Thro' heav'n's high arches ring, And all the hosts a-bove Their songs of

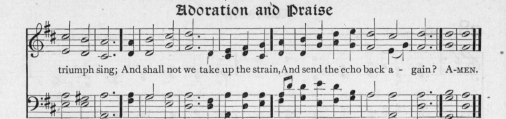

triumph sing; And shall not we take up the strain, And send the echo back a - gain? A-MEN.

2 Shall they adore the Lord,
   Who bought them with his blood,
And all the love record
   That led them home to God;
And shall not we take up the strain,
And send the echo back again?

3 O spread the joyful sound,
   The Saviour's love proclaim,
And publish all around
   Salvation through his name;
Till all the world take up the strain,
And send the echo back again.

JAMES J. CUMMINS

27 ANGEL VOICES 8. 5. 8. 5. 8. 4. 3.   ARTHUR S. SULLIVAN

1. An - gel voi - ces, ev - er sing - ing Round thy throne of light,

An - gel harps for - ev - er ring ing, Rest not day nor night,

Thousands on - ly live to bless thee, And con - fess thee Lord of might. A-MEN.

2 Thou who art beyond the farthest
   Mortal eye can scan,
Can it be that thou regardest
   Songs of sinful man?
Can we feel that thou art near us,
   And wilt hear us?
Yea, we can.

3 Here, great God, to-day we offer
   Of thine own to thee;
And for thine acceptance proffer,
   All unworthily,

Hearts and minds, and hands and voices,
   In our choicest
Melody.

4 Honor, glory, might, and merit,
   Thine shall ever be,
Father, Son, and Holy Spirit,
   Blessèd Trinity:
Of the best that thou hast given
   Earth and heaven
Render thee.

FRANCIS POTT

28 DIX 7s. 6l.

CONRAD KOCHER

1. For the beau-ty of the earth, For the beau-ty of the skies,

For the love which from our birth O-ver and a-round us lies,—

Christ our God, to thee we raise This our hymn of grate-ful praise. A-MEN.

2 For the beauty of each hour
   Of the day and of the night,
Hill and vale, and tree and flower,
   Sun and moon, and stars of light,—
Christ our God, to thee we raise
This our hymn of grateful praise.

3 For the joy of ear and eye;
   For the heart and mind's delight;
For the mystic harmony
   Linking sense to sound and sight,—
Christ our God, to thee we raise
This our hymn of grateful praise.

4 For the joy of human love,
   Brother, sister, parent, child,
Friends on earth, and friends above;
   For all gentle thoughts and mild,—

Christ our God, to thee we raise
This our hymn of grateful praise.

5 For thy church, that evermore
   Lifteth holy hands above,
Offering up on every shore
   Its pure sacrifice of love,—
Christ our God, to thee we raise
This our hymn of grateful praise.

6 For thyself, best Gift Divine!
   To our race so freely given;
For that great, great love of thine,
   Peace on earth, and joy in heaven,—
Christ our God, to thee we raise
This our hymn of grateful praise.

FOLLIOTT S. PIERPOINT

29 WENTWORTH 8s. 4s. 6l.

FREDERICK C. MAKER

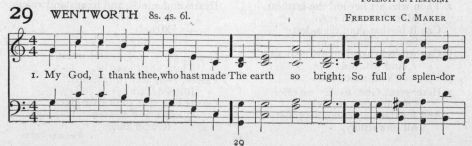

1. My God, I thank thee, who hast made The earth so bright; So full of splen-dor

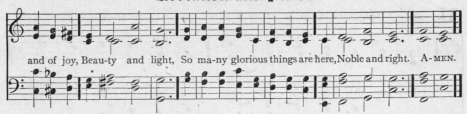

and of joy, Beau-ty and light, So ma-ny glorious things are here, Noble and right. A-MEN.

2 I thank thee, too, that thou hast made
    Joy to abound;
  So many gentle thoughts and deeds
    Circling us round;
  That in the darkest spot of earth
    Some love is found.

3 I thank thee more that all our joy
    Is touched with pain;
  That shadows fall on brightest hours,
    That thorns remain;
  So that earth's bliss may be our guide,
    And not our chain.

4 I thank thee, Lord, that thou hast kept
    The best in store;
  We have enough, yet not too much,
    To long for more;
  A yearning for a deeper peace
    Not known before.

5 I thank thee, Lord, that here our souls
    Though amply blest,
  Can never find, although they seek,
    A perfect rest;
  Nor ever shall, until they lean
    On Jesus' breast.

ADELAIDE A. PROCTER

30   NUN DANKET   6. 7. 6. 7. 6. 6. 6. 6.

JOHANN CRÜGER

1. Now thank we all our God With heart and hands and voi - ces, Who

wondrous things hath done, In whom his world re - joi - ces; Who, from our mothers' arms,

Hath bless'd us on our way With countless gifts of love, And still is ours to - day. A - MEN.

2 O may this bounteous God,
    Through all our life be near us,
  With ever joyful hearts
    And blessèd peace to cheer us;
  And keep us in his grace,
    And guide us when perplexed,
  And free us from all ills
    In this world and the next.

MARTIN RINKART. Tr. by CATHERINE WINKWORTH

31

ST. THEODULPH 7s. 6s. *With Refrain* MELCHIOR TESCHNER

1. All glo - ry, laud, and hon - or To thee, Re - deem - er, King,
   To whom the lips of chil - dren Made sweet ho - san - nas ring!

The 2d and following verses

2. Thou art the King of Is - ra - el, Thou Da - vid's roy - al Son,

Who in the Lord's name com - est, The King and Bless - èd One.

After each verse

All glo - ry, laud, and hon - or To thee, Re - deem - er, King,
To whom the lips of chil - dren Made sweet ho - san - nas ring! A - MEN.

3 The company of angels
    Are praising thee on high;
And mortal men, and all things
    Created, make reply.
      All glory, etc.

4 The people of the Hebrews
    With palms before thee went:
Our praise and prayers and anthems
    Before thee we present.
      All glory, etc.

5 To thee, before thy passion,
    They sang their hymns of praise;
To thee, now high exalted,
    Our melody we raise.
      All glory, etc.

6 Thou didst accept their praises;
    Accept the prayers we bring,
Who in all good delightest,
    Thou good and gracious King.
      All glory, etc.

THEODULPH. Tr. by JOHN M. NEALE

32 LAUDES DOMINI 6s. 6l.

JOSEPH BARNBY

1. When morn-ing gilds the skies, . My heart a-wak-ing cries,

May Je-sus Christ be praised! A-like at work and prayer,

To Je-sus I re-pair; .. May Je-sus Christ be praised! A-MEN.

2 Whene'er the sweet church bell
Peals over hill and dell,
   May Jesus Christ be praised!
O hark to what it sings,
As joyously it rings,
   May Jesus Christ be praised!

3 My tongue shall never tire
Of chanting with the choir,
   May Jesus Christ be praised!
This song of sacred joy,
It never seems to cloy,
   May Jesus Christ be praised!

4 When sleep her balm denies,
My silent spirit sighs,
   May Jesus Christ be praised!
When evil thoughts molest,
With this I shield my breast,
   May Jesus Christ be praised!

5 Does sadness fill my mind?
A solace here I find,
   May Jesus Christ be praised!

Or fades my earthly bliss?
My comfort still is this,
   May Jesus Christ be praised!

6 The night becomes as day,
When from the heart we say,
   May Jesus Christ be praised!
The powers of darkness fear,
When this sweet chant they hear,
   May Jesus Christ be praised!

7 In heaven's eternal bliss
The loveliest strain is this,
   May Jesus Christ be praised!
Let earth, and sea, and sky,
From depth to height reply,
   May Jesus Christ be praised!

8 Be this, while life is mine,
My canticle divine,
   May Jesus Christ be praised!
Be this the eternal song
Through ages all along,
   May Jesus Christ be praised!

From the German. Tr. by EDWARD CASWALL

33 ST. AGNES C. M.
JOHN B. DYKES

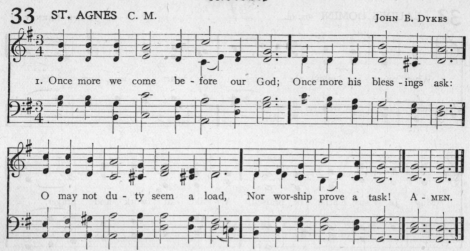

1. Once more we come be-fore our God; Once more his bless-ings ask:

O may not du-ty seem a load, Nor wor-ship prove a task! A-MEN.

2 Father, thy quickening Spirit send
   From heaven in Jesus' name,
To make our waiting minds attend,
   And put our souls in frame.

3 May we receive the word we hear,
   Each in an honest heart,

And keep the precious treasure there,
   And never with it part!

4 To seek thee all our hearts dispose,
   To each thy blessings suit,
And let the seed thy servant sows
   Produce abundant fruit.

JOSEPH HART

34 LAUD C. M.
JOHN B. DYKES

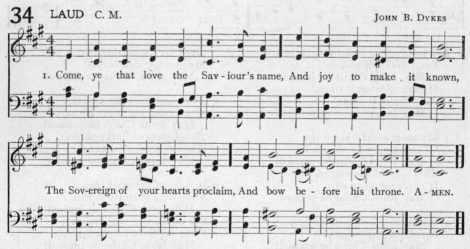

1. Come, ye that love the Sav-iour's name, And joy to make it known,

The Sov-ereign of your hearts proclaim, And bow be-fore his throne. A-MEN.

2 Behold your Lord, your Master, crowned
   With glories all divine;
And tell the wondering nations round
   How bright those glories shine.

3 When, in his earthly courts, we view
   The glories of our King,

We long to love as angels do,
   And wish like them to sing.

4 And shall we long and wish in vain?
   Lord, teach our songs to rise:
Thy love can animate the strain,
   And bid it reach the skies.

ANNE STEELE

Opening

35 PLEYEL'S HYMN 7s.

IGNACE J. PLEYEL

1. Lord, we come be-fore thee now, At thy feet we hum-bly bow;

O do not our suit dis-dain; Shall we seek thee, Lord, in vain? A-MEN.

2 Lord, on thee our souls depend;
In compassion now descend;
Fill our hearts with thy rich grace,
Tune our lips to sing thy praise.

3 In thine own appointed way,
Now we seek thee, here we stay;
Lord, we know not how to go,
Till a blessing thou bestow.

4 Send some message from thy word,
That may joy and peace afford;
Let thy Spirit now impart
Full salvation to each heart.

5 Grant that all may seek and find
Thee, a gracious God and kind:
Heal the sick, the captive free;
Let us all rejoice in thee.

WILLIAM HAMMOND

36 BELMONT C. M.

W. GARBLINE

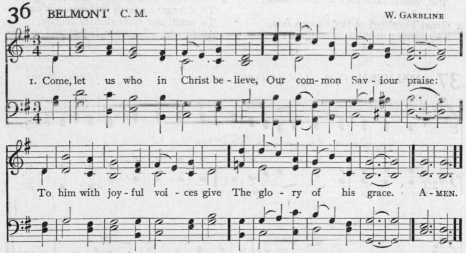

1. Come, let us who in Christ be-lieve, Our com-mon Sav-iour praise:

To him with joy-ful voi-ces give The glo-ry of his grace. A-MEN.

2 He now stands knocking at the door
Of every sinner's heart:
The worst need keep him out no more,
Nor force him to depart.

3 Through grace we hearken to thy voice,
Yield to be saved from sin;

In sure and certain hope rejoice,
That thou wilt enter in.

4 Come quickly in, thou heavenly Guest,
Nor ever hence remove;
But sup with us, and let the feast
Be everlasting love.

CHARLES WESLEY

37 WESTCOTT L. M. JOSEPH BARNBY

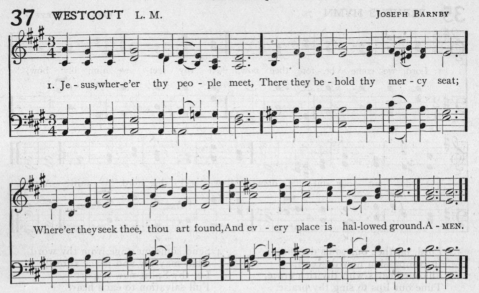

1. Je - sus, wher-e'er thy peo - ple meet, There they be-hold thy mer - cy seat;
Where'er they seek thee, thou art found, And ev - ery place is hal-lowed ground. A - MEN.

2 For thou, within no walls confined,
Dost dwell with those of humble mind;
Such ever bring thee where they come,
And, going, take thee to their home.

3 Great Shepherd of thy chosen few,
Thy former mercies here renew;

Here, to our waiting hearts, proclaim
The sweetness of thy saving name.

4 Here may we prove the power of prayer
To strengthen faith and sweeten care;
To teach our faint desires to rise,
And bring all heaven before our eyes.

WILLIAM COWPER

37 MALVERN L. M. (*Second Tune*) LOWELL MASON

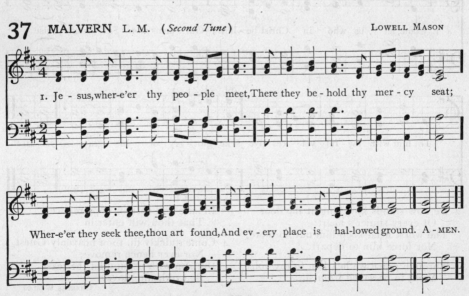

1. Je - sus, wher-e'er thy peo - ple meet, There they be - hold thy mer - cy seat;
Wher-e'er they seek thee, thou art found, And ev - ery place is hal-lowed ground. A - MEN.

Closing

38   ELLERS   10s.   EDWARD J. HOPKINS

1. Sav-iour, a-gain to thy dear name we raise With one ac-cord our part-ing hymn of praise; We stand to bless thee ere our wor-ship cease, Then, low-ly kneel-ing, wait thy word of peace. A-MEN.

2 Grant us thy peace upon our homeward way;
With thee began, with thee shall end the day;
Guard thou the lips from sin, the hearts from shame,
That in this house have called upon thy name.

3 Grant us thy peace, Lord, through the coming night,
Turn thou for us its darkness into light;
From harm and danger keep thy children free,
For dark and light are both alike to thee.

4 Grant us thy peace throughout our earthly life,
Our balm in sorrow, and our stay in strife;
Then, when thy voice shall bid our conflict cease,
Call us, O Lord, to thine eternal peace.

JOHN ELLERTON

27

Worsbip

39 ETON 8. 7. 8. 7. 4. 7.   JOSEPH BARNBY

1. Lord, dis-miss us with thy bless-ing, Fill our hearts with joy and peace;

Let us each, thy love pos-sess-ing, Tri-umph in re-deem-ing grace;

O re-fresh us, Trav-eling through this wil-der-ness. A-MEN.

2 Thanks we give, and adoration,
 For thy gospel's joyful sound;
May the fruits of thy salvation
 In our hearts and lives abound;
 May thy presence
With us evermore be found.

3 So, whene'er the signal's given
 Us from earth to call away,
Borne on angels' wings to heaven,
 Glad the summons to obey,
 May we ever
Reign with Christ in endless day.

JOHN FAWCETT

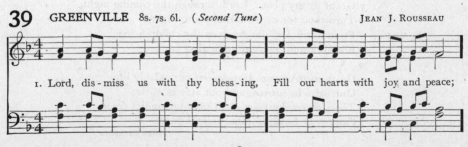

39 GREENVILLE 8s. 7s. 6l. (*Second Tune*)   JEAN J. ROUSSEAU

1. Lord, dis-miss us with thy bless-ing, Fill our hearts with joy and peace;

28

Closing

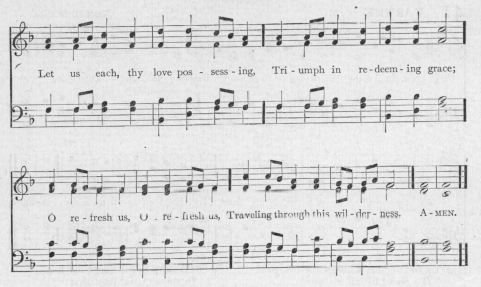

Let us each, thy love pos - sess - ing, Tri - umph in re - deem - ing grace;

O re - fresh us, O re - fresh us, Traveling through this wil - der - ness. A - MEN.

40 SARDIS 8s. 7s.

LUDWIG VAN BEETHOVEN

1. May the grace of Christ our Sav - iour, And the Fa - ther's boundless love,

With the Ho - ly Spir - it's fa - vor, Rest up - on us from a - bove. A - MEN.

2 Thus may we abide in union
With each other and the Lord,
And possess, in sweet communion,
Joys which earth cannot afford.

JOHN NEWTON

29

41 WARWICK C. M.   SAMUEL STANLEY

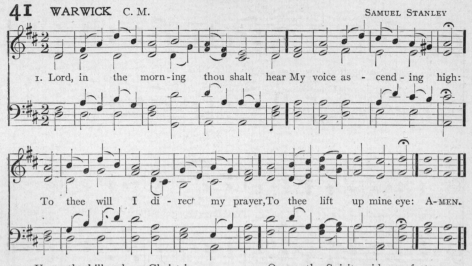

1. Lord, in the morn-ing thou shalt hear My voice as-cend-ing high:
To thee will I di-rect my prayer, To thee lift up mine eye: A-men.

2 Up to the hills where Christ is gone
   To plead for all his saints,
   Presenting, at the Father's throne,
   Our songs and our complaints.

3 O may thy Spirit guide my feet
   In ways of righteousness;
   Make every path of duty straight,
   And plain before my face.
                                    ISAAC WATTS

42 CANONBURY L. M.   ROBERT SCHUMANN

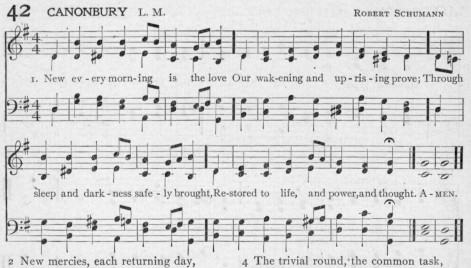

1. New ev-ery morn-ing is the love Our wak-ening and up-ris-ing prove; Through
sleep and dark-ness safe-ly brought, Re-stored to life, and power, and thought. A-men.

2 New mercies, each returning day,
   Hover around us while we pray;
   New perils past, new sins forgiven,
   New thoughts of God, new hopes of heaven.

3 If on our daily course our mind
   Be set to hallow all we find,
   New treasures still of countless price
   God will provide for sacrifice.

4 The trivial round, the common task,
   Will furnish all we ought to ask,—
   Room to deny ourselves, a road
   To bring us daily nearer God.

5 Only, O Lord, in thy dear love
   Fit us for perfect rest above;
   And help us this and every day
   To live more nearly as we pray.
                                    JOHN KEBLE

43 CONSOLATION 11s. 10s.   Arr. from FELIX MENDELSSOHN-BARTHOLDY

1. Still, still with Thee, when pur-ple morn-ing break-eth, When the bird wak-eth, and the shad-ows flee; Fair-er than morn-ing, love-li-er than day-light, Dawns the sweet con-scious-ness, I am with thee. A-MEN.

2 Alone with thee, amid the mystic shadows,
　The solemn hush of nature newly born;
　Alone with thee in breathless adoration,
　In the calm dew and freshness of the morn.

3 As in the dawning o'er the waveless ocean,
　The image of the morning-star doth rest,
　So in this stillness, thou beholdest only
　Thine image in the waters of my breast.

4 Still, still to thee! as to each newborn morning,
　A fresh and solemn splendor still is given,
　So does this blessèd consciousness awaking,
　Breathe each day nearness unto thee and heaven.

5 When sinks the soul, subdued by toil, to slumber,
　Its closing eyes look up to thee in prayer;
　Sweet the repose beneath thy wings o'ershading,
　But sweeter still, to wake and find thee there.

6 So shall it be at last, in that bright morning,
　When the soul waketh, and life's shadows flee;
　O in that hour, fairer than daylight dawning,
　Shall rise the glorious thought — I am with thee.

HARRIET B. STOWE

44 MORNING HYMN L. M.

FRANÇOIS H. BARTHÉLÉMON

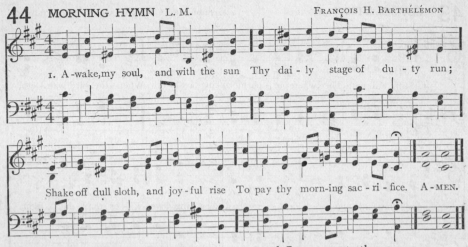

1. A-wake, my soul, and with the sun Thy dai-ly stage of du-ty run;

Shake off dull sloth, and joy-ful rise To pay thy morn-ing sac-ri-fice. A-MEN.

2 Wake, and lift up thyself, my heart,
And with the angels bear thy part,
Who all night long unwearied sing
High praise to the eternal King.

3 All praise to thee, who safe hast kept,
And hast refreshed me while I slept:
Grant, Lord, when I from death shall wake,
I may of endless life partake.

4 Lord, I my vows to thee renew:
Disperse my sins as morning dew;
Guard my first springs of thought and will,
And with thyself my spirit fill.

5 Direct, control, suggest, this day,
All I design, or do, or say;
That all my powers, with all their might,
In thy sole glory may unite.

THOMAS KEN

45 MORNINGTON S. M.

Earl of MORNINGTON

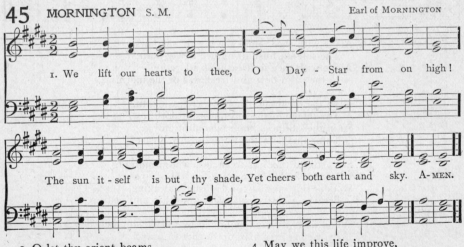

1. We lift our hearts to thee, O Day-Star from on high!

The sun it-self is but thy shade, Yet cheers both earth and sky. A-MEN.

2 O let thy orient beams
The night of sin disperse,
The mists of error and of vice
Which shade the universe!

3 How beauteous nature now!
How dark and sad before!
With joy we view the pleasing change,
And nature's God adore.

4 May we this life improve,
To mourn for errors past;
And live this short revolving day
As if it were our last.

5 To God, the Father, Son,
And Spirit — One in Three —
Be glory; as it was, is now,
And shall forever be.

JOHN WESLEY

46 PARKER C. M.

KARL P. HARRINGTON

1. Now from the al - tar of my heart Let in - cense flames a - rise:

As - sist me, Lord, to of - fer up Mine eve - ning sac - ri - fice. A-MEN.

2 This day God was my Sun and Shield,
My Keeper and my Guide;
His care was on my frailty shown,
His mercies multiplied.

3 Minutes and mercies multiplied
Have made up all this day:

Minutes came quick, but mercies were
More fleet and free than they.

4 New time, new favor, and new joys
Do a new song require;
Till I shall praise thee as I would,
Accept my heart's desire.

JOHN MASON

47 HURSLEY L. M.

PETER RITTER. Arr. by WILLIAM H. MONK

1. Sun of my soul, thou Sav - iour dear, It is not night if thou be near:

O may no earthborn cloud a - rise To hide thee from thy serv - ant's eyes. A-MEN.

2 When the soft dews of kindly sleep
My wearied eyelids gently steep,
Be my last thought, how sweet to rest
Forever on my Saviour's breast.

3 Abide with me from morn till eve,
For without thee I cannot live;
Abide with me when night is nigh,
For without thee I dare not die.

4 If some poor wandering child of thine
Have spurned, to-day, the voice divine,

Now, Lord, the gracious work begin;
Let him no more lie down in sin.

5 Watch by the sick; enrich the poor
With blessings from thy boundless store;
Be every mourner's sleep to-night,
Like infant's slumbers, pure and light.

6 Come near and bless us when we wake,
Ere through the world our way we take;
Till, in the ocean of thy love,
We lose ourselves in heaven above.

JOHN KEBLE

3

48 ABENDS L. M.

HERBERT S. OAKELEY

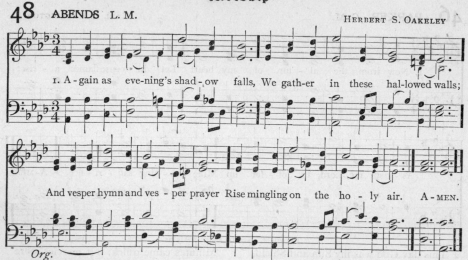

1. A-gain as eve-ning's shad-ow falls, We gath-er in these hal-lowed walls;

And vesper hymn and ves - per prayer Rise mingling on the ho - ly air. A-MEN.

Org.

2 May struggling hearts that seek release
Here find the rest of God's own peace;
And, strengthened here by hymn and
prayer,
Lay down the burden and the care.

3 O God, our light! to thee we bow;
Within all shadows standest thou;

Give deeper calm than night can bring;
Give sweeter songs than lips can sing.

4 Life's tumult we must meet again,
We cannot at the shrine remain;
But in the spirit's secret cell
May hymn and prayer forever dwell.

SAMUEL LONGFELLOW

49 EVENING HYMN L. M.

THOMAS TALLIS

1. Glo - ry to thee, my God, this night, For all the bless-ings of the light:

Keep me, O keep me, King of kings, Be-neath the shad-ow of thy wings. A-MEN.

2 Forgive me, Lord, for thy dear Son,
The ill which I this day have done;
That with the world, myself, and thee,
I, ere I sleep, at peace may be.

3 Teach me to live, that I may dread
The grave as little as my bed;

Teach me to die, that so I may
Rise glorious at the judgment day.

4 O let my soul on thee repose,
And may sweet sleep mine eyelids close;
Sleep, which shall me more vigorous make,
To serve my God, when I awake.

THOMAS KEN

Evening

EVENTIDE 10s.

WILLIAM H. MONK

1. A - bide with me! Fast falls the e - ven - tide, The dark - ness
deep - ens— Lord, with me a - bide! When oth - er help - ers
fail, and com-forts flee, Help of the help-less, O a - bide with me! A-MEN.

2 Swift to its close ebbs out life's little day;
　Earth's joys grow dim, its glories pass away;
　Change and decay in all around I see;
　O thou, who changest not, abide with me!

3 I need thy presence every passing hour;
　What but thy grace can foil the tempter's power?
　Who, like thyself, my guide and stay can be?
　Through cloud and sunshine, Lord, abide with me!

4 I fear no foe, with thee at hand to bless;
　Ills have no weight, and tears no bitterness;
　Where is death's sting? where, grave, thy victory?
　I triumph still, if thou abide with me.

5 Hold thou thy cross before my closing eyes;
　Shine through the gloom and point me to the skies;
　Heaven's morning breaks, and earth's vain shadows flee;
　In life, in death, O Lord, abide with me!

HENRY F. LYTE

Worship

51 HEBRON L. M.
LOWELL MASON

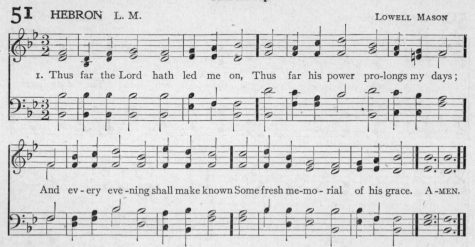

1. Thus far the Lord hath led me on, Thus far his power pro-longs my days;

And ev-ery eve-ning shall make known Some fresh me-mo-rial of his grace. A-MEN.

2 Much of my time has run to waste,
  And I, perhaps, am near my home;
But he forgives my follies past,
  And gives me strength for days to come.

3 I lay my body down to sleep;
  Peace is the pillow for my head;

While well-appointed angels keep
  Their watchful stations round my bed.

4 Thus, when the night of death shall come,
  My flesh shall rest beneath the ground,
And wait thy voice to rouse my tomb,
  .With sweet salvation in the sound.

ISAAC WATTS

52 STOCKWELL 8s. 7s.
DARIUS E. JONES

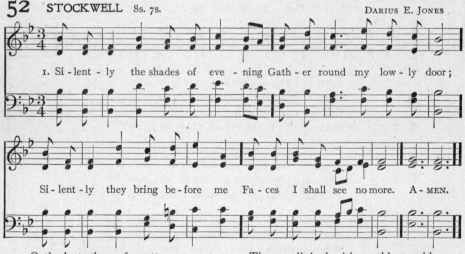

1. Si-lent-ly the shades of eve-ning Gath-er round my low-ly door;

Si-lent-ly they bring be-fore me Fa-ces I shall see no more. A-MEN.

2 O the lost, the unforgotten,
  Though the world be oft forgot!
O the shrouded and the lonely,
  In our hearts they perish not!

3 Living in the silent hours,
  Where our spirits only blend,

They, unlinked with earthly trouble,
  We, still hoping for its end.

4 How such holy memories cluster,
  Like the stars when storms are past,
Pointing up to that fair heaven
  We may hope to gain at last.

CHRISTOPHER C. COX

53 MERCY 7s.

LOUIS M. GOTTSCHALK. Arr. by EDWIN P. PARKER

1. Soft - ly now the light of day Fades up - on our sight a - way;
Free from care, from la - bor free, Lord, we would commune with thee. A - MEN.

2 Thou, whose all-pervading eye
  Naught escapes, without, within,
  Pardon each infirmity,
  Open fault, and secret sin.

3 Soon from us the light of day
  Shall forever pass away;
  Then, from sin and sorrow free,
  Take us, Lord, to dwell with thee.
  GEORGE W. DOANE

54 ABENDS L. M.

HERBERT S. OAKELEY

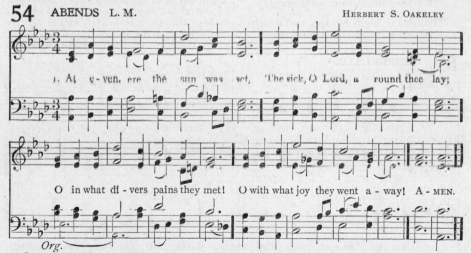

1. At e - ven, ere the sun was set, The sick, O Lord, a - round thee lay;
O in what di - vers pains they met! O with what joy they went a - way! A - MEN.

2 Once more 'tis eventide, and we,
  Oppressed with various ills, draw near;
  What if thy form we cannot see?
  We know and feel that thou art here.

3 O Saviour Christ, our woes dispel;
  For some are sick, and some are sad,
  And some have never loved thee well,
  And some have lost the love they had.

4 And none, O Lord, have perfect rest,
  For none are wholly free from sin;

And they who fain would serve thee best,
  Are conscious most of wrong within.

5 O Saviour Christ, thou too art Man;
  Thou hast been troubled, tempted, tried;
  Thy kind but searching glance can scan
  The very wounds that shame would hide.

6 Thy touch has still its ancient power,
  No word from thee can fruitless fall;
  Hear in this solemn evening hour,
  And in thy mercy heal us all.
  HENRY TWELLS

55 EVENING PRAYER 8s. 7s.

GEORGE C. STEBBINS

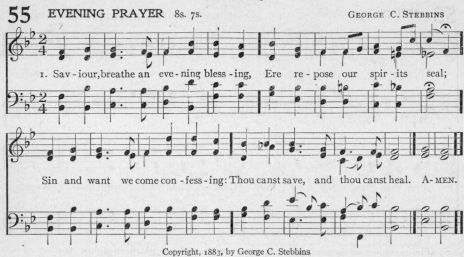

1. Sav-iour, breathe an eve-ning bless-ing, Ere re-pose our spir-its seal;

Sin and want we come con-fess-ing: Thou canst save, and thou canst heal. A-MEN.

Copyright, 1883, by George C. Stebbins

2 Though destruction walk around us,
　Though the arrows past us fly,
Angel guards from thee surround us;
　We are safe, if thou art nigh.

3 Though the night be dark and dreary,
　Darkness cannot hide from thee;

Thou art he who, never weary,
　Watchest where thy people be.

4 Should swift death this night o'ertake us,
　And our couch become our tomb,
May the morn in heaven awake us,
　Clad in light and deathless bloom.
　　　　　　　　　JAMES EDMESTON

56 VESPERI LUX 7. 7. 7. 5.

JOHN B. DYKES

1. Ho-ly Fa-ther, cheer our way With thy love's per-pet-ual ray;

Grant us ev-ery clos-ing day Light at eve-ning time. A-MEN.

2 Holy Saviour, calm our fears
When earth's brightness disappears;
Grant us in our later years
　Light at evening time.

3 Holy Spirit, be thou nigh
When in mortal pains we lie;

Grant us, as we come to die,
　Light at evening time.

4 Holy, blessed Trinity,
Darkness is not dark to thee;
Those thou keepest always see
　Light at evening time.
　　　　　　RICHARD H. ROBINSON

Evening

57 EVENING PRAISE 7. 7. 7. 7. 4.   WILLIAM F. SHERWIN

1. Day is dy-ing in the west; Heaven is touch-ing earth with rest:

Wait and wor-ship while the night Sets her eve-ning lamps a-light Through all the

sky. Ho-ly, ho-ly, ho-ly Lord God of Hosts! Heaven and earth are

full of thee! Heaven and earth are prais-ing thee, O Lord most high! A-MEN.

Copyright, 1877, by J. H. Vincent

2 Lord of life, beneath the dome
Of the universe, thy home,
Gather us who seek thy face
To the fold of thy embrace,
    For thou art nigh.
Holy, holy, holy Lord God of Hosts!
Heaven and earth are full of thee!
Heaven and earth are praising thee,
    O Lord most high!

MARY A. LATHBURY

58 NIGHTFALL 11. 11. 11. 5.   Joseph Barnby

1. Now God be with us, for the night is clos-ing; The light and
dark-ness are of his dis-pos-ing, And 'neath his shad-ow

Slower

here to rest we yield us, For he will shield us. A-men.

2 Let evil thoughts and spirits flee before us;
   Till morning cometh, watch, O Master, o'er us;
   In soul and body thou from harm defend us,
   Thine angels send us.

3 Let holy thoughts be ours when sleep o'ertakes us;
   Our earliest thoughts be thine when morning wakes us.
   All sick and mourners we to thee commend them,
   Do thou befriend them.

4 We have no refuge, none on earth to aid us
   But thee, O Father, who thine own hast made us.
   Keep us in life; forgive our sins; deliver
   Us now and ever.

5 Praise be to thee through Jesus our salvation,
   God, Three in One, the ruler of creation,
   High throned, o'er all thine eye of mercy casting,
   Lord everlasting.

PETRUS HERBERT. Tr. by CATHERINE WINKWORTH

59 MERRIAL 6s. 5s.

JOSEPH BARNBY

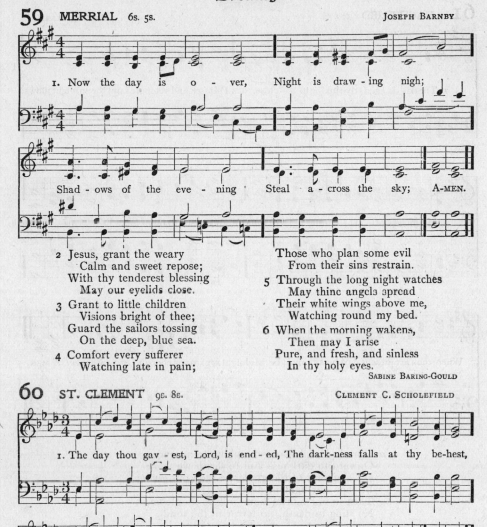

1. Now the day is o-ver, Night is draw-ing nigh;
Shad-ows of the eve-ning Steal a-cross the sky; A-MEN.

2 Jesus, grant the weary
Calm and sweet repose;
With thy tenderest blessing
May our eyelids close.

3 Grant to little children
Visions bright of thee;
Guard the sailors tossing
On the deep, blue sea.

4 Comfort every sufferer
Watching late in pain;

Those who plan some evil
From their sins restrain.

5 Through the long night watches
May thine angels spread
Their white wings above me,
Watching round my bed.

6 When the morning wakens,
Then may I arise
Pure, and fresh, and sinless
In thy holy eyes.

SABINE BARING-GOULD

60 ST. CLEMENT 9s. 8s.

CLEMENT C. SCHOLEFIELD

1. The day thou gav-est, Lord, is end-ed, The dark-ness falls at thy be-hest,
To thee our morn-ing hymns as-cended, Thy praise shall hallow now our rest. A-MEN.

2 We thank thee that thy church unsleeping,
While earth rolls onward into light,
Through all the world her watch is keeping,
And rests not now by day or night.

3 As o'er each continent and island
The dawn leads on another day,

The voice of prayer is never silent,
Nor dies the strain of praise away.

4 So be it, Lord; thy throne shall never,
Like earth's proud empires, pass away;
But stand and rule and grow forever,
Till all thy creatures own thy sway.

JOHN ELLERTON

61 NACHTLIED 10s. 6l.

HENRY SMART

1. The day is gen-tly sinking to a close, Faint-er and yet more faint the sunlight glows:

O Brightness of thy Father's glory, thou E-ter-nal Light of Light, be with us now:

Where thou art present, darkness cannot be; Midnight is glorious noon, O Lord, with thee. A-MEN.

2 Our changeful lives are ebbing to an end;
Onward to darkness and to death we tend;
O Conqueror of the grave, be thou our guide;
Be thou our light in death's dark eventide:
Then in our mortal hour will be no gloom,
No sting in death, no terror in the tomb.

3 Thou, who in darkness walking didst appear
Upon the waves, and thy disciples cheer,
Come, Lord, in lonesome days, when storms assail,
And earthly hopes and human succors fail:
When all is dark may we behold thee nigh
And hear thy voice, "Fear not, for it is I."

4 The weary world is moldering to decay,
Its glories wane, its pageants fade away;
In that last sunset when the stars shall fall,
May we arise awakened by thy call,
With thee, O Lord, forever to abide
In that blest day which has no eventide.

CHRISTOPHER WORDSWORTH

62 ST. LEONARD C. M. D.

HENRY HILES

1. The shad-ows of the eve-ning hours Fall from the dark-ening sky;

Up-on the fra-grance of the flowers The dews of eve-ning lie.

Be-fore thy throne, O Lord of heaven, We kneel at close of day;

Look on thy chil-dren from on high, And hear us while we pray. A-MEN.

2 The sorrows of thy servants, Lord,
   O do not thou despise,
But let the incense of our prayers
   Before thy mercy rise.
The brightness of the coming night
   Upon the darkness rolls;
With hopes of future glory chase
   The shadows from our souls.

3 Slowly the rays of daylight fade:
   So fade within our heart
The hopes in earthly love and joy,
   That one by one depart.

Slowly the bright stars, one by one,
   Within the heavens shine:
Give us, O Lord, fresh hopes in heaven,
   And trust in things divine.

4 Let peace, O Lord, thy peace, O God,
   Upon our souls descend;
From midnight fears, and perils, thou
   Our trembling hearts defend.
Give us a respite from our toil;
   Calm and subdue our woes;
Through the long day we labor, Lord,
   O give us now repose.

ADELAIDE A. PROCTER

63 CHESTERFIELD C. M.

THOMAS HAWEIS

1. Come, let us join with one ac-cord In hymns a-round the throne! This
is the day . our ris-ing Lord Hath made and called his own. A-MEN.

2 This is the day which God hath blest,
  The brightest of the seven,
Type of that everlasting rest
  The saints enjoy in heaven.

3 Then let us in his name sing on,
  And hasten to that day

When our Redeemer shall come down,
And shadows pass away.

4 Not one, but all our days below,
  Let us in hymns employ;
And in our Lord rejoicing, go
  To his eternal joy.

CHARLES WESLEY

64 LISBON S. M.

DANIEL READ

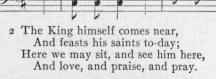

1. Wel-come, sweet day of rest, That saw the Lord a-rise;
Wel-come to this re-viv-ing breast, And these re-joic-ing eyes! A-MEN.

2 The King himself comes near,
  And feasts his saints to-day;
Here we may sit, and see him here,
  And love, and praise, and pray.

3 One day in such a place,
  Where thou, my God, art seen,

Is sweeter than ten thousand days
Of pleasurable sin.

4 My willing soul would stay
  In such a frame as this,
And sit and sing herself away
  To everlasting bliss.

ISAAC WATTS

44

The Lord's Day

65 MOUNT CALVARY C. M.
ROBERT P. STEWART

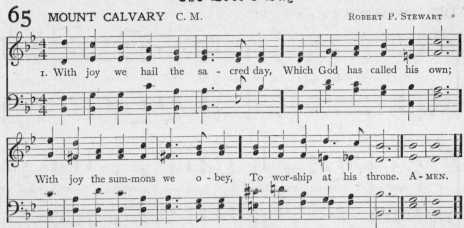

1. With joy we hail the sa - cred day, Which God has called his own;

With joy the sum-mons we o - bey, To wor-ship at his throne. A - MEN.

2 Thy chosen temple, Lord, how fair!
  As here thy servants throng
To breathe the humble, fervent prayer,
  And pour the grateful song.

3 Spirit of grace! O deign to dwell
  Within thy church below;
Make her in holiness excel,
  With pure devotion glow.

4 Let peace within her walls be found;
  Let all her sons unite,
To spread with holy zeal around
  Her clear and shining light.

5 Great God, we hail the sacred day
  Which thou hast called thine own;
With joy the summons we obey
  To worship at thy throne.
HARRIET AUBER

66 SCHUMANN S. M.
Arr. from ROBERT SCHUMANN

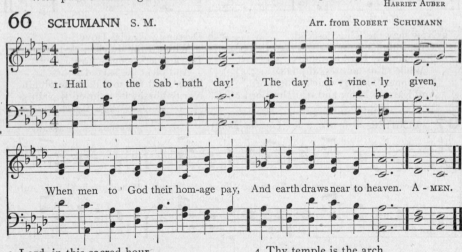

1. Hail to the Sab - bath day! The day di - vine - ly given,

When men to God their hom-age pay, And earth draws near to heaven. A - MEN.

2 Lord, in this sacred hour,
  Within thy courts we bend,
And bless thy love, and own thy power,
  Our Father and our Friend.

3 But thou art not alone
  In courts by mortals trod;
Nor only is the day thine own
  When man draws near to God:

4 Thy temple is the arch
  Of yon unmeasured sky;
Thy Sabbath, the stupendous march
  Of vast eternity.

5 Lord, may that holier day
  Dawn on thy servants' sight;
And purer worship may we pay
  In heaven's unclouded light.
STEPHEN G. BULFINCH

67 WARSAW 6. 6. 6. 6. 8. 8.

THOMAS CLARK

1. Wel - come, de - light - ful morn, Thou day of sa - cred rest!
I hail thy kind re - turn; Lord, make these mo - ments blest: From the low
train of mor - tal toys, I soar to reach im - mor - tal joys. A - MEN.

2 Now may the King descend,
   And fill his throne with grace;
Thy scepter, Lord, extend,
   While saints address thy face:
Let sinners feel thy quickening word,
And learn to know and fear the Lord.

3 Descend, celestial Dove,
   With all thy quickening powers;
Disclose a Saviour's love,
   And bless the sacred hours:
Then shall my soul new life obtain,
Nor Sabbaths be enjoyed in vain.

HAYWARD, in Dobell's Selection

67 LISCHER 6. 6. 6. 6. 8. 8. (*Second Tune*)

FRIEDRICH SCHNEIDER

1. Wel-come, de-light-ful morn, Thou day of sa - cred rest! I hail thy kind re - turn;
Lord, make these moments blest: From the low train of mor - tal toys, I soar to reach im -

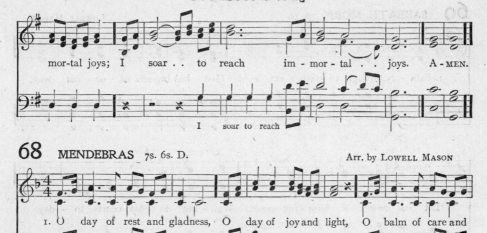

mor-tal joys; I soar .. to reach im - mor - tal .. joys. A - MEN.

I soar to reach

68 MENDEBRAS 7s. 6s. D.

Arr. by LOWELL MASON

1. O day of rest and gladness, O day of joy and light, O balm of care and

sad-ness, Most beau - ti - ful, most bright: On thee, the high and low - ly, Through

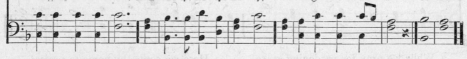

a - ges joined in tune, Sing "Ho - ly, ho - ly, ho - ly," To the great God Tri - une. A - MEN.

2 On thee, at the creation,
  The light first had its birth;
On thee, for our salvation,
  Christ rose from depths of earth;
On thee, our Lord, victorious,
  The Spirit sent from heaven;
And thus on thee, most glorious,
  A triple light was given.

3 To-day on weary nations
  The heavenly manna falls;
To holy convocations
  The silver trumpet calls,

Where gospel light is glowing
  With pure and radiant beams,
And living water flowing
  With soul-refreshing streams.

4 New graces ever gaining
  From this our day of rest,
We reach the rest remaining
  To spirits of the blest;
To Holy Ghost be praises,
  To Father, and to Son;
The church her voice upraises
  To thee, blest Three in One.

47

CHRISTOPHER WORDSWORTH

69 SABBATH MORN 7s. 61.

LOWELL MASON

1. Safely through another week, God has brought us on our way;
Let us now a blessing seek, Waiting in his courts to-day:
Day of all the week the best, Emblem of eternal rest.
Day of all the week the best, Emblem of eternal rest. A-MEN.

2 While we pray for pardoning grace,
  Through the dear Redeemer's name,
Show thy reconcilèd face,
  Take away our sin and shame;
From our worldly cares set free,
May we rest this day in thee.

3 Here we come thy name to praise;
  May we feel thy presence near:
May thy glory meet our eyes,
  While we in thy house appear:
Here afford us, Lord, a taste
Of our everlasting feast.

4 May thy gospel's joyful sound
  Conquer sinners, comfort saints;
Make the fruits of grace abound,
  Bring relief for all complaints:
Thus may all our Sabbaths prove,
Till we join the church above.

JOHN NEWTON

70 BROOKFIELD L. M.　　　　　　　　　　　THOMAS B. SOUTHGATE

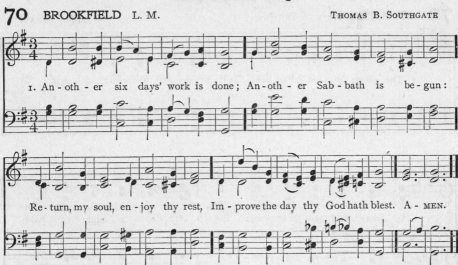

1. An-oth-er six days' work is done; An-oth-er Sab-bath is be-gun:

Re-turn, my soul, en-joy thy rest, Im-prove the day thy God hath blest. A-MEN.

2 O that our thoughts and thanks may rise,
As grateful incense, to the skies;
And draw from Christ that sweet repose
Which none but he that feels it knows!

3 This heavenly calm within the breast
Is the dear pledge of glorious rest,

Which for the church of God remains,
The end of cares, the end of pains.

4 In holy duties let the day,
In holy comforts, pass away;
How sweet, a Sabbath thus to spend,
In hope of one that ne'er shall end!
　　　　　　　　　　　　JOSEPH STENNETT

71 ROCKINGHAM L. M.　　　　　　　　　　　LOWELL MASON

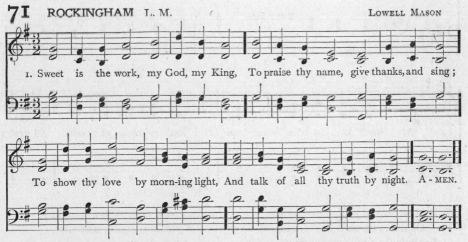

1. Sweet is the work, my God, my King, To praise thy name, give thanks, and sing;

To show thy love by morn-ing light, And talk of all thy truth by night. A-MEN.

2 Sweet is the day of sacred rest;
No mortal cares shall seize my breast;
O may my heart in tune be found,
Like David's harp of solemn sound.

3 When grace has purified my heart,
Then I shall share a glorious part;

And fresh supplies of joy be shed,
Like holy oil, to cheer my head.

4 Then shall I see, and hear, and know
All I desired or wished below;
And every power find sweet employ
In that eternal world of joy.
　　　　　　　　　　　　ISAAC WATTS

72 ST. ANSELM 7s. 6s. D.

JOSEPH BARNBY

1. The dawn of God's dear Sab-bath Breaks o'er the earth a-gain, As some sweet sum-mer morn-ing Aft-er a night of pain; It comes as cool-ing show-ers To some ex-haust-ed land, As shade of clus-tered palm trees 'Mid wea-ry wastes of sand. A-MEN.

2 And we would bring our burden
   Of sinful thought and deed,
 In thy pure presence kneeling,
   From bondage to be freed;
 Our heart's most bitter sorrow
   For all thy work undone;
 So many talents wasted!
   So few bright laurels won!

3 And with that sorrow mingling,
   A steadfast faith, and sure,
 And love so deep and fervent,
   That tries to make it pure:
 In his dear presence finding
   The pardon that we need;
 And then the peace so lasting,
   Celestial peace indeed!

ADA C CROSS

73 MARTHAM L. M.

J. H. MAUNDER

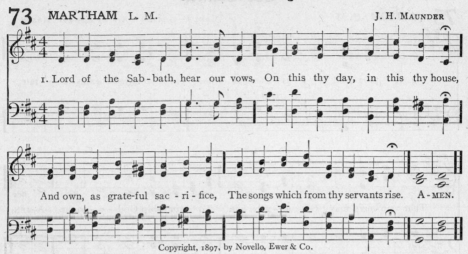

1. Lord of the Sab-bath, hear our vows, On this thy day, in this thy house,

And own, as grate-ful sac-ri-fice, The songs which from thy servants rise. A-MEN.

Copyright, 1897, by Novello, Ewer & Co.

2 Thine earthly Sabbaths, Lord, we love;
But there's a nobler rest above;
To that our laboring souls aspire,
With ardent hope and strong desire.

3 No more fatigue, no more distress,
Nor sin nor hell, shall reach the place;

No sighs shall mingle with the songs,
Which warble from immortal tongues.

4 No rude alarms of raging foes,
No cares to break the long repose;
No midnight shade, no clouded sun,
But sacred, high, eternal noon.

PHILIP DODDRIDGE

74 HOLLEY 7s.

GEORGE HEWS

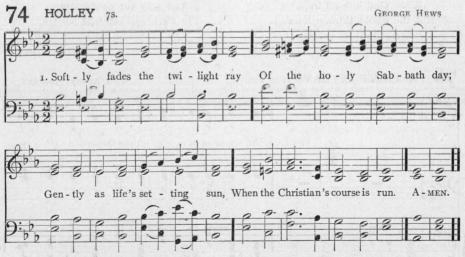

1. Soft-ly fades the twi-light ray Of the ho-ly Sab-bath day;

Gen-tly as life's set-ting sun, When the Christian's course is run. A-MEN.

2 Peace is on the world abroad,
'Tis the holy peace of God,
Symbol of the peace within
When the spirit rests from sin.

3 Saviour, may our Sabbaths be
Days of joy and peace in thee,
Till in heaven our souls repose,
Where the Sabbath ne'er shall close.

SAMUEL F. SMITH

The Trinity

75 AZMON C. M.

CARL G. GLASER. Arr. by LOWELL MASON

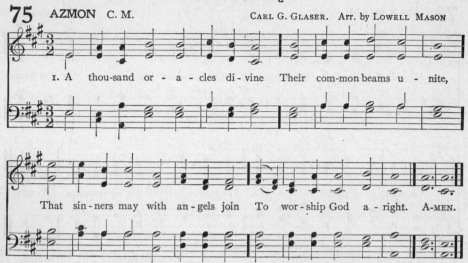

1. A thou-sand or - a - cles di - vine Their com-mon beams u - nite,

That sin-ners may with an - gels join To wor-ship God a - right. A-MEN.

2 Triumphant host! they never cease
  To laud and magnify
The Triune God of holiness,
  Whose glory fills the sky;

3 Whose glory to this earth extends,
  When God himself imparts,
And the whole Trinity descends
  Into our faithful hearts.

4 By faith the upper choir we meet,
  And challenge them to sing
Jehovah, on his shining seat,
  Our Maker and our King.

5 But God made flesh is wholly ours,
  And asks our nobler strain:
The Father of celestial powers,
  The Friend of earthborn man.

CHARLES WESLEY

76 ANCIENT OF DAYS 11s. 10s.

J. ALBERT JEFFERY

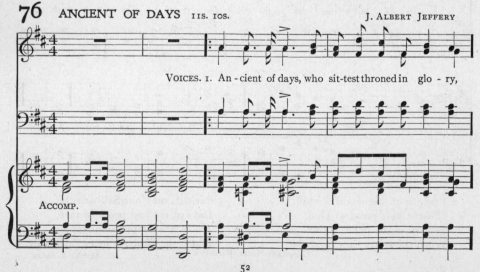

VOICES. 1. An - cient of days, who sit-test throned in glo - ry,

ACCOMP.

The Trinity

To thee all knees are bent, all voi - ces pray; Thy love has blest the wide world's wondrous sto - ry With light and life since E-den's dawn-ing day. A - MEN.

2 O Holy Father, who hast led thy children
  In all the ages, with the fire and cloud,
Through seas dry-shod, through weary wastes bewildering;
  To thee, in reverent love, our hearts are bowed.

3 O Holy Jesus, Prince of Peace and Saviour,
  To thee we owe the peace that still prevails,
Stilling the rude wills of men's wild behavior,
  And calming passion's fierce and stormy gales.

4 O Holy Ghost, the Lord and the Life-giver,
  Thine is the quickening power that gives increase;
From thee have flowed, as from a pleasant river,
  Our plenty, wealth, prosperity, and peace.

5 O Triune God, with heart and voice adoring,
  Praise we the goodness that doth crown our days;
Pray we, that thou wilt hear us, still imploring
  Thy love and favor, kept to us always.

WILLIAM C. DOANE

53

The Trinity

77 **ST. ATHANASIUS** 7s. 6l.

EDWARD J. HOPKINS

1. Ho - ly, ho - ly, ho - ly, Lord God of Hosts e - ter - nal King, By the heavens and earth a - dored! An - gels and arch - an - gels sing, Chant-ing ev - er - last - ing - ly To the bless - èd Trin - i - ty. A-MEN.

2 Thousands, tens of thousands, stand,
   Spirits blest, before thy throne,
Speeding thence at thy command,
   And, when thy behests are done,
Singing everlastingly
To the blessèd Trinity.

3 Cherubim and seraphim
   Veil their faces with their wings;
Eyes of angels are too dim
   To behold the King of kings,
While they sing eternally
To the blessèd Trinity.

4 Thee apostles, prophets thee,
   Thee the noble martyr band,
Praise with solemn jubilee;
   Thee, the church in every land;
Singing everlastingly
To the blessèd Trinity.

5 Hallelujah! Lord, to thee,
   Father, Son, and Holy Ghost,
Godhead one, and persons three,
   Join we with the heavenly host,
Singing everlastingly
To the blessèd Trinity.

CHRISTOPHER WORDSWORTH

The Trinity

JOHN B. DYKES

1. Holy, holy, ho-ly, Lord God Al-might-y! Ear-ly in the morn-ing our song shall rise to thee; Ho-ly, ho-ly, ho-ly, mer-ci-ful and might-y, God in Three Per-sons, blessèd Trin-i-ty. A-MEN.

2 Holy, holy, holy! all the saints adore thee,
   Casting down their golden crowns around the glassy sea;
   Cherubim and seraphim falling down before thee,
   Which wert, and art, and evermore shalt be.

3 Holy, holy, holy! though the darkness hide thee,
   Though the eye of sinful man thy glory may not see;
   Only thou art holy; there is none beside thee,
   Perfect in power, in love, and purity.

4 Holy, holy, holy, Lord God Almighty!
   All thy works shall praise thy name, in earth, and skỳ, and sea;
   Holy, holy, holy, merciful and mighty,
   God in Three Persons, blessèd Trinity!

REGINALD HEBER

The Father

Being and Attributes

79 BEATITUDO C. M.   JOHN B. DYKES

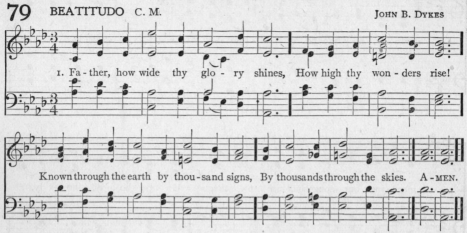

1. Fa-ther, how wide thy glo-ry shines, How high thy won-ders rise!

Known through the earth by thou-sand signs, By thousands through the skies. A-MEN.

2 Those mighty orbs proclaim thy power;
  Their motions speak thy skill:
  And on the wings of every hour
  We read thy patience still.

3 But when we view thy strange design
  To save rebellious worms,
  Where vengeance and compassion join
  In their divinest forms;

4 Our thoughts are lost in reverent awe;
  We love and we adore:
  The first archangel never saw
  So much of God before.

5 Here the whole Deity is known,
  Nor dares a creature guess
  Which of the glories brighter shone,
  The justice or the grace.

6 Now the full glories of the Lamb
  Adorn the heavenly plains;
  Bright seraphs learn Immanuel's name,
  And try their choicest strains.

7 O may I bear some humble part
  In that immortal song!
  Wonder and joy shall tune my heart,
  And love command my tongue.

ISAAC WATTS

80 JANES L. M.   From JOHANN C. W. A. MOZART

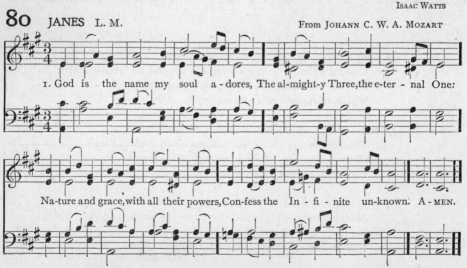

1. God is the name my soul a-dores, The al-might-y Three, the e-ter-nal One:

Na-ture and grace, with all their powers, Con-fess the In-fi-nite un-known. A-MEN.

Being and Attributes

2 Thy voice produced the sea and spheres,
  Bade the waves roar, the planets shine;
But nothing like thyself appears
  Through all these spacious works of thine.

3 Still restless nature dies and grows;
  From change to change the creatures run:
Thy being no succession knows,
  And all thy vast designs are one.

4 A glance of thine runs through the globe,
  Rules the bright worlds, and moves their
    frame;

Of light thou form'st thy dazzling robe;
  Thy ministers are living flame.

5 How shall polluted mortals dare
  To sing thy glory or thy grace?
Beneath thy feet we lie afar,
  And see but shadows of thy face.

6 Who can behold the blazing light?
  Who can approach consuming flame?
None but thy wisdom knows thy might;
  None but thy word can speak thy name.

ISAAC WATTS

81 MILLENNIUM 6. 6. 6. 6. 8. 8.

Composer Unknown

1. The Lord Jehovah reigns, His throne is built on high; The garments he assumes Are light and majesty: His glories shine with beams so bright, No mortal eye can bear the sight. A-MEN.

2 The thunders of his hand
  Keep the wide world in awe;
His wrath and justice stand
  To guard his holy law;
And where his love resolves to bless,
His truth confirms and seals the grace.

3 Through all his mighty works
  Amazing wisdom shines;
Confounds the powers of hell,
  And all their dark designs;
Strong is his arm, and shall fulfill
His great decrees and sovereign will.

4 And will this sovereign King
  Of glory condescend,
And will he write his name,
  My Father and my Friend?
I love his name, I love his word;
Join all my powers to praise the Lord!

ISAAC WATTS

82 KEBLE L. M.

JOHN B. DYKES

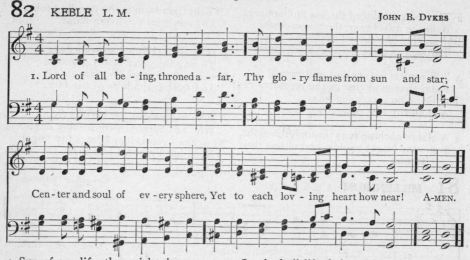

1. Lord of all be - ing, throned a - far, Thy glo - ry flames from sun and star;

Cen - ter and soul of ev - er - y sphere, Yet to each lov - ing heart how near! A-MEN.

2 Sun of our life, thy quickening ray
Sheds on our path the glow of day;
Star of our hope, thy softened light
Cheers the long watches of the night.

3 Our midnight is thy smile withdrawn;
Our noontide is thy gracious dawn;
Our rainbow arch thy mercy's sign;
All, save the clouds of sin, are thine!

4 Lord of all life, below, above,
Whose light is truth, whose warmth is love,
Before thy ever-blazing throne
We ask no luster of our own.

5 Grant us thy truth to make us free,
And kindling hearts that burn for thee,
Till all thy living altars claim
One holy light, one heavenly flame.

OLIVER W. HOLMES

83 MARTHAM L. M.

J. H. MAUNDER

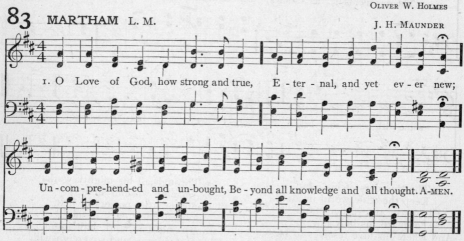

1. O Love of God, how strong and true, E - ter - nal, and yet ev - er new;

Un - com - pre - hend - ed and un-bought, Be - yond all knowledge and all thought. A-MEN.

2 O heavenly Love, how precious still,
In days of weariness and ill,
In nights of pain and helplessness,
To heal, to comfort, and to bless!

3 O wide-embracing, wondrous Love,
We read thee in the sky above;
We read thee in the earth below,
In seas that swell and streams that flow.

4 We read thee best in Him who came
To bear for us the cross of shame,
Sent by the Father from on high,
Our life to live, our death to die.

5 O Love of God, our shield and stay
Through all the perils of our way;
Eternal Love, in thee we rest,
Forever safe, forever blest.

HORATIUS BONAR

84 CREATION L M.D.

FRANCIS J. HAYDN

1. The spa-cious fir-ma-ment on high, With all the blue e-the-real sky,
And span-gled heavens, a shin-ing frame, Their great O-rig-i-nal pro-claim.
The un-wea-ried sun, from day to day, Does his Cre-a-tor's power dis-play,
And pub-lish-es to ev-ery land The work of an al-might-y hand. A-MEN.

2 Soon as the evening shades prevail,
The moon takes up the wondrous tale,
And nightly, to the listening earth,
Repeats the story of her birth;
While all the stars that round her burn,
And all the planets in their turn,
Confirm the tidings as they roll,
And spread the truth from pole to pole.

3 What though in solemn silence all
Move round the dark terrestrial ball?
What though no real voice nor sound
Amid the radiant orbs be found?
In reason's ear they all rejoice,
And utter forth a glorious voice;
Forever singing as they shine,
"The hand that made us is divine."

JOSEPH ADDISON

85 CARLTON 8s. 7s. D.

JOSEPH BARNBY

1. Might-y God! while an-gels bless thee, May a mor-tal lisp thy name? Lord of men, as well as an-gels, Thou art ev-ery creature's theme: Lord of every land and nation, Ancient of e-ter-nal days! Sounded through the wide cre-a-tion Be thy just and aw-ful praise. A - MEN.

2 For the grandeur of thy nature,
   Grand beyond a seraph's thought;
For the wonders of creation,
   Works with skill and kindness wrought;
For thy providence, that governs
   Through thine empire's wide domain,
Wings an angel, guides a sparrow;
   Blessèd be thy gentle reign!

3 For thy rich, thy free redemption,
   Bright, though veiled in darkness long,
Thought is poor, and poor expression;
   Who can sing that wondrous song?

Brightness of the Father's glory!
   Shall thy praise unuttered lie?
Break, my tongue, such guilty silence,
   Sing the Lord who came to die.

4 From the highest throne of glory,
   To the cross of deepest woe;
Thou didst come to ransom sinners:
   Flow, my praise, forever flow!
Reascend, immortal Saviour;
   Leave thy footstool, take thy throne;
Thence return and reign forever;
   Be the kingdom all thine own!

ROBERT ROBINSON

86 ST. STEPHEN C. M.

WILLIAM JONES

1. My God, how won - der - ful thou art, Thy maj - es - ty how bright,

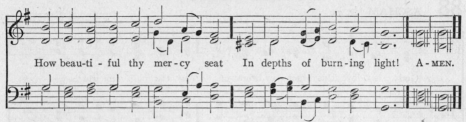

How beau-ti-ful thy mer-cy seat In depths of burn-ing light! A-MEN.

2 How dread are thine eternal years,
   O everlasting Lord,
By prostrate spirits day and night
Incessantly adored!

3 How beautiful, how beautiful,
   The sight of thee must be,
Thine endless wisdom, boundless power,
And awful purity!

4 O how I fear thee, living God,
   With deepest, tenderest fears,
And worship thee with trembling hope,
And penitential tears.

5 Yet I may love thee too, O Lord,
   Almighty as thou art;
For thou hast stooped to ask of me
The love of my poor heart.

6 No earthly father loves like thee,
   No mother half so mild
Bears and forbears, as thou hast done
With me, thy sinful child.

7 Father of Jesus, love's reward!
   What rapture will it be,
Prostrate before thy throne to lie,
And gaze, and gaze on thee!

FREDERICK W. FABER

87 BARNBY C. M.

JOSEPH BARNBY

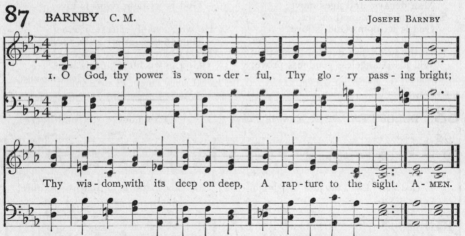

1. O God, thy power is won-der-ful, Thy glo-ry pass-ing bright;

Thy wis-dom, with its deep on deep, A rap-ture to the sight. A-MEN.

2 I see thee in the eternal years
   In glory all alone,
Ere round thine uncreated fires
Created light had shone.

3 I see thee walk in Eden's shade,
   I see thee all through time;
Thy patience and compassion seem
New attributes sublime.

4 I see thee when the doom is o'er,
   And outworn time is done,

Still, still incomprehensible,
   O God, yet not alone.

5 Angelic spirits, countless souls,
   Of thee have drunk their fill;
And to eternity will drink
Thy joy and glory still.

6 O little heart of mine! shall pain
   Or sorrow make thee moan,
When all this God is all for thee,
A Father all thine own?

FREDERICK W. FABER

The Father

88 ASCHAM 8s. 7s.

EDMUND S. CARTER

1. God is love; his mer-cy bright-ens All the path in which we rove;

Bliss he wakes and woe he light-ens; God is wis-dom, God is love. A-MEN.

2 Chance and change are busy ever;
   Man decays, and ages move;
 But his mercy waneth never;
   God is wisdom, God is love.

3 E'en the hour that darkest seemeth,
   Will his changeless goodness prove;

From the gloom his brightness streameth,
   God is wisdom, God is love.

4 He with earthly cares entwineth
   Hope and comfort from above;
 Everywhere his glory shineth;
   God is wisdom, God is love.

JOHN BOWRING

88 DULCETTA 8s. 7s. (*Second Tune*)

FROM LUDWIG VAN BEETHOVEN

1. God is love; his mer-cy bright-ens All the path in which we rove;

Bliss he wakes and woe he light-ens; God is wis-dom, God is love. A-MEN.

89 MAKER C. M.

FREDERICK C. MAKER

1. Be-gin, my tongue, some heaven-ly theme, And speak some bound-less thing, The might-y works or might-ier name Of our e-ter-nal King. A-MEN.

2 Tell of his wondrous faithfulness,
  And sound his power abroad;
Sing the sweet promise of his grace
  And the performing God.

3 His very word of grace is strong,
  As that which built the skies;

The voice that rolls the stars along,
  Speaks all the promises.

4 O might I hear thy heavenly tongue
  But whisper, "Thou art mine!"
Those gentle words should raise my song
  To notes almost divine.

ISAAC WATTS

90 CHURCH TRIUMPHANT L. M.

JAMES W. ELLIOTT

1. The Lord is King! lift up thy voice, O earth, and all ye heavens, re-joice! From world to world the joy shall ring, "The Lord om-nip-o-tent is King!" A-MEN.

2 The Lord is King! child of the dust,
  The Judge of all the earth is just;
Holy and true are all his ways:
  Let every creature speak his praise.

3 He reigns! ye saints, exalt your strains;
  Your God is King, your Father reigns;
And he is at the Father's side,
  The Man of Love, the Crucified.

4 Come, make your wants, your burdens
    known,
He will present them at the throne;
And angel bands are waiting there
  His messages of love to bear.

5 O when his wisdom can mistake,
  His might decay, his love forsake,
Then may his children cease to sing,
  The Lord omnipotent is King.

JOSIAH CONDER

The Father

91 ZION 8. 7. 8. 7. 4. 7.   THOMAS HASTINGS

1. Guide me, O thou great Je-ho-vah, Pilgrim through this bar-ren land: I am

weak, but thou art might-y; Hold me with thy powerful hand: Bread of heav-en, Feed me

till I want no more. Bread of heav-en, Feed me till I want no more. A-MEN.

2 Open now the crystal fountain,
  Whence the healing waters flow;
Let the fiery, cloudy pillar
Lead me all my journey through:
  Strong Deliverer,
Be thou still my strength and shield.

3 When I tread the verge of Jordan,
  Bid my anxious fears subside;
Bear me through the swelling current;
Land me safe on Canaan's side:
  Songs of praises
I will ever give to thee.

WILLIAM WILLIAMS

92 COBERN 10. 10. 11. 11.   HENRY J. GAUNTLETT

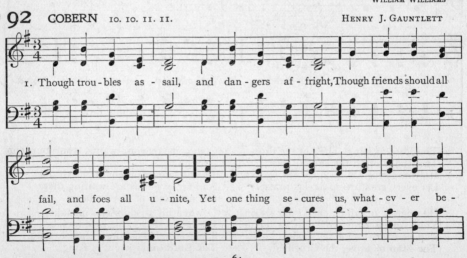

1. Though trou-bles as-sail, and dan-gers af-fright, Though friends should all

fail, and foes all u-nite, Yet one thing se-cures us, what-ev-er be-

Providence and Grace

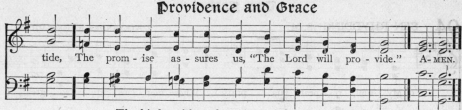

tide, The prom-ise as-sures us, "The Lord will pro-vide." A-MEN.

2 The birds, without barn or storehouse, are fed;
From them let us learn to trust for our bread:
His saints what is fitting shall ne'er be denied,
So long as 'tis written, " The Lord will provide."

3 No strength of our own, nor goodness we claim;
Our trust is all thrown on Jesus's name:
In this our strong tower for safety we hide;
The Lord is our power, "The Lord will provide."

4 When life sinks apace, and death is in view,
The word of his grace shall comfort us through:
Not fearing or doubting, with Christ on our side,
We hope to die shouting, "The Lord will provide."

JOHN NEWTON

93 DECIUS 8. 7. 8. 7. 8. 8. 7.

NICOLAUS DECIUS

1. To God on high be thanks and praise For mer-cy ceas-ing nev-er, Where-
by no foe a hand can raise, Nor harm can reach us ev-er. With joy to him our
hearts as-cend, The source of peace that knows no end, A peace that none can sev-er. A-MEN.

2 The honors paid thy holy name
To hear thou ever deignest!
Thou God the Father, still the same
Unshaken ever reignest.
Unmeasured stands thy glorious might;
Thy thoughts, thy deeds, outstrip the light,
Our heaven thou, Lord, remainest.

NICOLAUS DECIUS. Tr. by CATHERINE WINKWORTH

94 BEN RHYDDING S. M.

ALEXANDER R. REINAGLE

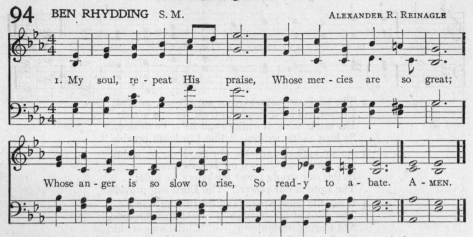

1. My soul, re-peat His praise, Whose mer-cies are so great;

Whose an-ger is so slow to rise, So read-y to a-bate. A-MEN.

2 High as the heavens are raised
  Above the ground we tread,
So far the riches of his grace
  Our highest thoughts exceed.

3 His power subdues our sins;
  And his forgiving love,
Far as the east is from the west,
  Doth all our guilt remove.

4 The pity of the Lord,
  To those that fear his name,

Is such as tender parents feel;
  He knows our feeble frame.

5 Our days are as the grass,
  Or like the morning flower:
If one sharp blast sweep o'er the field
  It withers in an hour.

6 But thy compassions, Lord,
  To endless years endure;
And children's children ever find
  Thy words of promise sure.

ISAAC WATTS

95 MELCOMBE L. M.

SAMUEL WEBBE

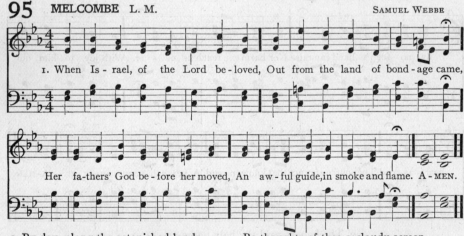

1. When Is-rael, of the Lord be-loved, Out from the land of bond-age came,

Her fa-thers' God be-fore her moved, An aw-ful guide, in smoke and flame. A-MEN.

2 By day, along the astonished lands
  The cloudy pillar glided slow;
By night, Arabia's crimsoned sands
  Returned the fiery column's glow.

3 Thus present still, though now unseen,
  When brightly shines the prosperous day,

Be thoughts of thee a cloudy screen,
  To temper the deceitful ray.

4 And O, when gathers on our path,
  In shade and storm, the frequent night,
Be thou, long-suffering, slow to wrath,
  A burning and a shining light.

WALTER SCOTT

Providence and Grace

96 DUNDEE C. M. Scotch Psalter

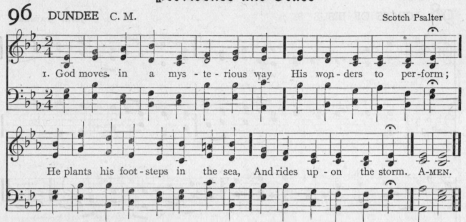

1. God moves in a mys-te-rious way His won-ders to per-form;
He plants his foot-steps in the sea, And rides up-on the storm. A-MEN.

2 Deep in unfathomable mines
Of never-failing skill,
He treasures up his bright designs,
And works his sovereign will.

3 Ye fearful saints, fresh courage take;
The clouds ye so much dread
Are big with mercy, and shall break
In blessings on your head.

4 Judge not the Lord by feeble sense,
But trust him for his grace;
Behind a frowning providence
He hides a smiling face.

5 His purposes will ripen fast,
Unfolding every hour:
The bud may have a bitter taste,
But sweet will be the flower.

6 Blind unbelief is sure to err,
And scan his work in vain:
God is his own interpreter,
And he will make it plain.
WILLIAM COWPER

97 ST. PETER L. M. Arr. from NICOLAUS DECIUS

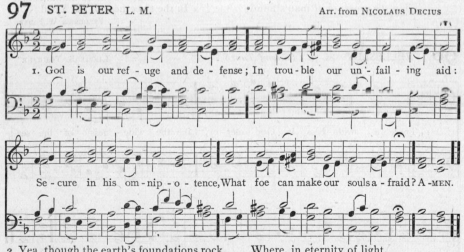

1. God is our ref-uge and de-fense; In trou-ble our un-fail-ing aid:
Se-cure in his om-nip-o-tence, What foe can make our souls a-fraid? A-MEN.

2 Yea, though the earth's foundations rock,
And mountains down the gulf be hurled,
His people smile amid the shock:
They look beyond this transient world.

3 There is a river pure and bright, [plains;
Whose streams make glad the heavenly

Where, in eternity of light,
The city of our God remains.

4 Built by the word of his command,
With his unclouded presence blest,
Firm as his throne the bulwarks stand;
There is our home, our hope, our rest.
JAMES MONTGOMERY

98 CROSS OF JESUS 8s. 7s.

JOHN STAINER

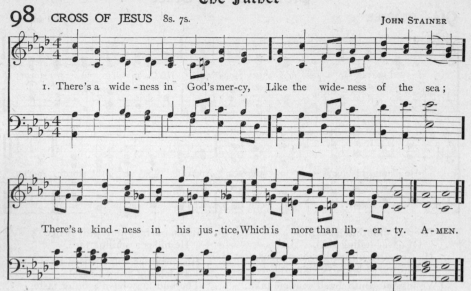

1. There's a wide-ness in God's mer-cy, Like the wide-ness of the sea;

There's a kind-ness in his jus-tice, Which is more than lib-er-ty. A-MEN.

2 There is welcome for the sinner,
  And more graces for the good;
There is mercy with the Saviour;
  There is healing in his blood.

3 For the love of God is broader
  Than the measure of man's mind;

And the heart of the Eternal
  Is most wonderfully kind.

4 If our love were but more simple,
  We should take him at his word;
And our lives would be all sunshine
  In the sweetness of our Lord.

FREDERICK W. FABER

98 WELLESLEY 8s. 7s. (Second Tune)

LIZZIE S. TOURJÉE

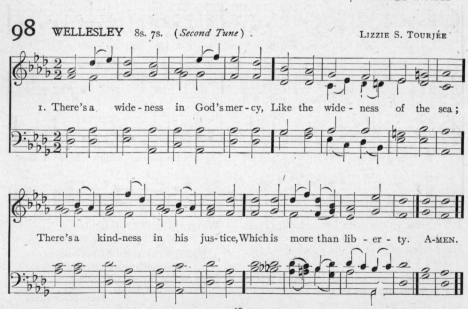

1. There's a wide-ness in God's mer-cy, Like the wide-ness of the sea;

There's a kind-ness in his jus-tice, Which is more than lib-er-ty. A-MEN.

Providence and Grace

99 TAPPAN C. M.

GEORGE KINGSLEY

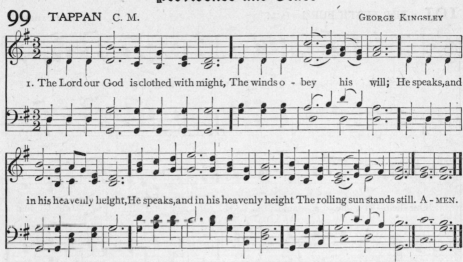

1. The Lord our God is clothed with might, The winds o-bey his will; He speaks, and in his heavenly height, He speaks, and in his heavenly height The rolling sun stands still. A-MEN.

2 Rebel, ye waves, and o'er the land
   With threatening aspect roar;
   The Lord uplifts his awful hand,
   And chains you to the shore.

3 Ye winds of night, your force combine;
   Without his high behest,
   Ye shall not, in the mountain pine,
   Disturb the sparrow's nest.

4 His voice sublime is heard afar;
   In distant peals it dies;
   He yokes the whirlwind to his car,
   And sweeps the howling skies.

5 Ye nations, bend, in reverence bend;
   Ye monarchs, wait his nod;
   And bid the choral song ascend
   To celebrate our God.

H. KIRKE WHITE

100 DENNIS S. M.

Arr. from HANS G. NAEGELI

1. How gen-tle God's com-mands! How kind his pre-cepts are!
   Come, cast your bur-dens on the Lord, And trust his con-stant care. A-MEN.

2 Beneath his watchful eye
   His saints securely dwell;
   That hand which bears all nature up
   Shall guard his children well.

3 Why should this anxious load
   Press down your weary mind?

Haste to your heavenly Father's throne,
   And sweet refreshment find.

4 His goodness stands approved,
   Unchanged from day to day;
   I'll drop my burden at his feet,
   And bear a song away.

PHILIP DODDRIDGE

101 EIN' FESTE BURG P. M.

MARTIN LUTHER

1. A might-y fort-ress is our God, A bul-wark nev-er fail-ing:
Our help-er he, a-mid the flood Of mor-tal ills pre-vail-ing.
For still our an-cient foe Doth seek to work us woe; His craft and power are great,
And, armed with cru-el hate, On earth is not his e-qual. A-MEN.

2 Did we in our own strength confide,
    Our striving would be losing;
  Were not the right Man on our side,
    The Man of God's own choosing.
  Dost ask who that may be?
  Christ Jesus, it is he;
  Lord Sabaoth is his name,
  From age to age the same,
    And he must win the battle.

3 And though this world, with devils filled,
    Should threaten to undo us;
  We will not fear, for God hath willed
    His truth to triumph through us.

The prince of darkness grim —
We tremble not for him;
His rage we can endure,
For lo! his doom is sure,
    One little word shall fell him.

4 That word above all earthly powers —
    No thanks to them — abideth;
  The Spirit and the gifts are ours
    Through Him who with us sideth.
  Let goods and kindred go,
  This mortal life also.
  The body they may kill:
  God's truth abideth still,
    His kingdom is forever.

MARTIN LUTHER. Tr. by FREDERICK H. HEDGE.

Providence and Grace

102 AVON C. M.

HUGH WILSON

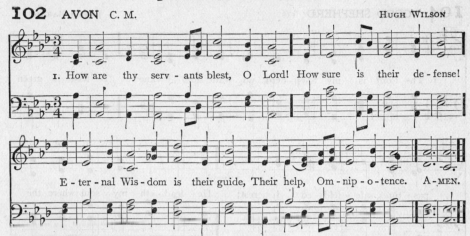

1. How are thy serv - ants blest, O Lord! How sure is their de - fense!

E - ter - nal Wis - dom is their guide, Their help, Om - nip - o - tence. A - MEN.

2 In foreign realms, and lands remote,
   Supported by thy care,
Through burning climes they pass unhurt,
   And breathe in tainted air.

3 When by the dreadful tempest borne
   High on the broken wave,
They know thou art not slow to hear,
   Nor impotent to save.

4 The storm is laid, the winds retire,
   Obedient to thy will;

   The sea, that roars at thy command,
   At thy command is still.

5 In midst of dangers, fears, and deaths,
   Thy goodness we adore;
We praise thee for thy mercies past,
   And humbly hope for more.

6 Our life, while thou preservest life,
   A sacrifice shall be;
And death, when death shall be our lot,
   Shall join our souls to thee.

JOSEPH ADDISON

103 NUREMBERG 7s.

JOHANN R. AHLE

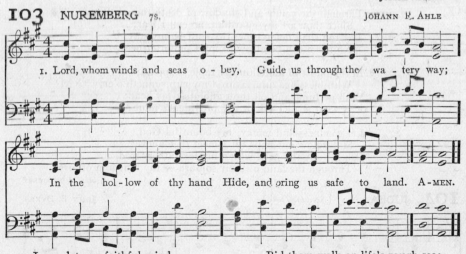

1. Lord, whom winds and seas o - bey, Guide us through the wa - tery way;

In the hol - low of thy hand Hide, and bring us safe to land. A - MEN.

2 Jesus, let our faithful mind
   Rest, on thee alone reclined:
Every anxious thought repress;
   Keep our souls in perfect peace.

3 Keep the souls whom now we leave,
   Bid them to each other cleave;

   Bid them walk on life's rough sea;
   Bid them come by faith to thee.

4 Save, till all these tempests end,
   All who on thy love depend;
Waft our happy spirits o'er;
   Land us on the heavenly shore.

CHARLES WESLEY

104 GOOD SHEPHERD 11s.

JOSEPH BARNBY

1. The Lord is my Shep-herd, no want shall I know; I feed in green pas - tures, safe - fold - ed I rest; He lead - eth my soul where the still wa - ters flow, Re-stores me when wandering, redeems when op - pressed. A - MEN.

2 Through the valley and shadow of death though I stray,
    Since thou art my guardian, no evil I fear;
  Thy rod shall defend me, thy staff be my stay;
    No harm can befall, with my Comforter near.

3 In the midst of affliction my table is spread;
    With blessings unmeasured my cup runneth o'er;
  With perfume and oil thou anointest my head;
    O what shall I ask of thy providence more?

4 Let goodness and mercy, my bountiful God,
    Still follow my steps till I meet thee above;
  I seek — by the path which my forefathers trod,
    Through the land of their sojourn — thy kingdom of love.

JAMES MONTGOMERY

104 JUDEA 11s. (*Second Tune*)

JOHN B. DYKES

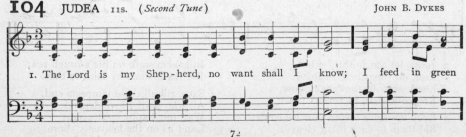

1. The Lord is my Shep-herd, no want shall I know; I feed in green

pas-tures, safe-fold-ed I rest; He lead-eth my soul where the still wa-ters

flow, Re-stores me when wan-dering, re-deems when op - pressed. A - MEN.

105 MANOAH C. M.   From GIOACHINO A. ROSSINI

1. When all thy mer - cies, O my God, My ris - ing soul sur - veys,

Trans-port-ed with the view, I'm lost In won - der, love, and praise. A - MEN.

2 O how can words with equal warmth
  The gratitude declare,
That glows within my ravished heart?
  But thou canst read it there.

3 Ten thousand thousand precious gifts
  My daily thanks employ;
Nor is the least a cheerful heart
  That tastes those gifts with joy.

4 When in the slippery paths of youth,
  With heedless steps I ran,
Thine arm, unseen, conveyed me safe,
  And led me up to man.

5 Through hidden dangers, toils, and
  It gently cleared my way;   [deaths,
And through the pleasing snares of vice,
  More to be feared than they.

6 Through every period of my life
  Thy goodness I'll pursue;
And after death, in distant worlds,
  The glorious theme renew.

7 Through all eternity to thee
  A grateful song I'll raise;
For O, eternity's too short
  To utter all thy praise.

JOSEPH ADDISON

106 LYONS 10. 10. 11. 11.

FRANCIS J. HAYDN

1. O wor-ship the King, all-glo-rious a-bove, O grate-ful-ly sing his
power and his love; Our Shield and De-fend-er, the An-cient of days,
Pa - vil-ioned in splen-dor, and gird-ed with praise. A-MEN.

2 O tell of his might, O sing of his grace,
Whose robe is the light, whose canopy space;
His chariots of wrath the deep thunderclouds form,
And dark is his path on the wings of the storm.

3 Thy bountiful care what tongue can recite?
It breathes in the air, it shines in the light,
It streams from the hills, it descends to the plain,
And sweetly distills in the dew and the rain.

4 Frail children of dust, and feeble as frail,
In thee do we trust, nor find thee to fail;
Thy mercies how tender! how firm to the end!
Our Maker, Defender, Redeemer, and Friend.

ROBERT GRANT

The Son

Incarnation and Advent

107 COPENHAGEN C. M.

PETER C. LUTKIN

1. Joy to the world! the Lord is come; Let earth re - ceive her King;

Let ev - ery heart pre-pare him room, And heaven and na - ture sing A MEN.

Copyright, 1905, by Eaton & Mains

2 Joy to the world! the Saviour reigns;
Let men their songs employ;
While fields and floods, rocks, hills and [plains,
Repeat the sounding joy.

3 No more let sin and sorrow grow,
Nor thorns infest the ground;

He comes to make his blessings flow
Far as the curse is found.

4 He rules the world with truth and grace,
And makes the nations prove
The glories of his righteousness,
And wonders of his love.

ISAAC WATTS

107 ANTIOCH C. M. (*Second Tune*)

Arr. from GEORGE F. HÄNDEL

1. Joy to the world! the Lord is come; Let earth re - ceive her King; Let

ev - ery heart pre - pare him room, And heaven and na - ture sing, And

And heaven, And heaven and na - ture

heaven and na - ture sing, And heaven, And heaven and na - ture sing. A - MEN.

sing, And heaven and na - ture sing,

75

108 NATIVITY C. M.

HENRY LAHEE

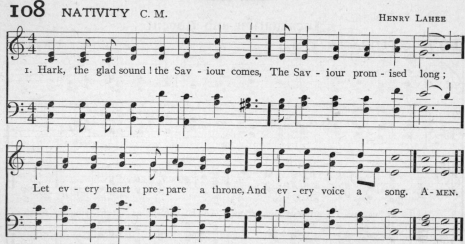

1. Hark, the glad sound ! the Sav - iour comes, The Sav - iour prom - ised long ;

Let ev - ery heart pre - pare a throne, And ev - ery voice a song. A - MEN.

2 He comes, the prisoner to release,
   In Satan's bondage held;
   The gates of brass before him burst,
   The iron fetters yield.

3 He comes, from thickest films of vice
   To clear the mental ray,
   And on the eyes oppressed with night
   To pour celestial day.

4 He comes, the broken heart to bind,
   The wounded soul to cure,
   And, with the treasures of his grace,
   To enrich the humble poor.

5 Our glad hosannas, Prince of Peace,
   Thy welcome shall proclaim;
   And heaven's eternal arches ring
   With thy belovèd name.

PHILIP DODDRIDGE

109 ST. OSWALD 8s. 7s.

JOHN B. DYKES

1. Hark ! what mean those ho - ly voi - ces, Sweet - ly sound - ing through the skies?

Lo ! the an - gel - ic host re - joi - ces ; Heavenly hal - le - lu - jahs rise. A - MEN.

2 Listen to the wondrous story,
   Which they chant in hymns of joy:
   "Glory in the highest, glory,
   Glory be to God most high!

3 "Peace on earth, good will from heaven,
   Reaching far as man is found;
   Souls redeemed and sins forgiven!
   Loud our golden harps shall sound.

4 "Christ is born, the great Anointed;
   Heaven and earth his praises sing;
   O receive whom God appointed,
   For your Prophet, Priest, and King.

5 "Hasten, mortals, to adore him;
   Learn his name, and taste his joy;
   Till in heaven ye sing before him,
   'Glory be to God most high!'"

JOHN CAWOOD

Incarnation

110 CAROL C. M. D.

RICHARD S. WILLIS

1. It came up-on the mid-night clear, That glo-rious song of old,
From an-gels bend-ing near the earth To touch their harps of gold;
"Peace on the earth, good will to men, From heaven's all-gra-cious King." The
world in sol-emn still-ness lay To hear the an-gels sing. A-MEN.

2 Still through the cloven skies they come
With peaceful wings unfurled,
And still their heavenly music floats
O'er all the weary world;
Above its sad and lowly plains
They bend on hovering wing,
And ever o'er its Babel sounds
The blessèd angels sing.

3 Yet with the woes of sin and strife
The world hath suffered long;
Beneath the angel-strain have rolled
Two thousand years of wrong;
And man, at war with man, hears not
The love song which they bring:
O hush the noise, ye men of strife,
And hear the angels sing!

4 And ye, beneath life's crushing load,
Whose forms are bending low,
Who toil along the climbing way
With painful steps and slow,
Look now! for glad and golden hours
Come swiftly on the wing:
O rest beside the weary road,
And hear the angels sing!

5 For lo! the days are hastening on
By prophet-bards foretold,
When with the ever-circling years
Comes round the age of gold;
When peace shall over all the earth
Its ancient splendors fling,
And the whole world send back the song
Which now the angels sing.

EDMUND H. SEARS

III MENDELSSOHN 7s. D.   FELIX MENDELSSOHN-BARTHOLDY

1. Hark! the her-ald an-gels sing, "Glo-ry to the newborn King; Peace on earth, and mer-cy mild; God and sin-ners rec-on-ciled." Joy-ful, all ye na-tions, rise, Join the tri-umph of the skies; With an-gel-ic hosts proclaim, "Christ is born in Beth-le-hem." Hark! the her-ald an-gels sing, "Glo-ry to the new-born King." A-MEN.

2 Christ, by highest heaven adored,
Christ, the everlasting Lord:
Late in time behold him come,
Offspring of a virgin's womb.
Veiled in flesh the Godhead see,
Hail the incarnate Deity!
Pleased as man with men to appear,
Jesus our Immanuel here.
    Hark! the herald angels sing,
    " Glory to the newborn King."

3 Hail the heaven-born Prince of Peace!
Hail the Sun of righteousness!
Light and life to all he brings,
Risen with healing in his wings:
Mild he lays his glory by,
Born that man no more may die;
Born to raise the sons of earth;
Born to give them second birth.
    Hark! the herald angels sing,
    " Glory to the newborn King."

4 Come, Desire of nations, come!
Fix in us thy humble home:
Rise, the woman's conquering seed,
Bruise in us the serpent's head;
Adam's likeness now efface,
Stamp thine image in its place:
Second Adam from above,
Reinstate us in thy love.
    Hark! the herald angels sing,
    " Glory to the newborn King."
                            CHARLES WESLEY

Incarnation

112 STELLA 6. 6. 6. 6. 12. 12.   ALFRED G. WATHALL

1. There's a song in the air! There's a star in the sky! There's a mother's deep prayer,
And a ba-by's low cry! And the star rains its fire while the beau-ti-ful sing,

Small notes for 3d and 4th verses

For the man-ger of Beth-le-hem cra-dles a King. A-MEN.

2 There's a tumult of joy
　　O'er the wonderful birth,
　For the Virgin's sweet boy
　　Is the Lord of the earth.
Ay! the star rains its fire while the beautiful sing,
For the manger of Bethlehem cradles a King!

3 In the light of that star
　　Lie the ages impearled;
　And that song from afar
　　Has swept over the world.
Every hearth is aflame, and the beautiful sing
In the homes of the nations that Jesus is King!

4 We rejoice in the light,
　　And we echo the song
　That comes down through the night
　　From the heavenly throng.
Ay! we shout to the lovely evangel they bring,
And we greet in his cradle our Saviour and King!

JOSIAH G. HOLLAND

112 CHRISTMAS SONG 6. 6. 6. 6. 12. 12. (*Second Tune*) KARL P. HARRINGTON

Andante con moto

1. There's a song in the air! There's a star in the sky! There's a moth-er's deep prayer, And a ba-by's low cry! And the star rains its fire while the beau-ti-ful sing, For the man-ger of Beth-le-hem cra-dles a King! A-MEN.

ritard · *piu mosso* · *ritard*

2 There's a tumult of joy
    O'er the wonderful birth,
  For the Virgin's sweet boy
    Is the Lord of the earth.
Ay! the star rains its fire while the beautiful sing,
For the manger of Bethlehem cradles a King!

3 In the light of that star
    Lie the ages impearled;
  And that song from afar
    Has swept over the world.
Every hearth is aflame, and the beautiful sing
In the homes of the nations that Jesus is King!

4 We rejoice in the light,
    And we echo the song
  That comes down through the night
    From the heavenly throng.
Ay! we shout to the lovely evangel they bring,
And we greet in his cradle our Saviour and King!

JOSIAH G. HOLLAND

112 KOLDING 6. 6. 6. 6. 12. 12 (*Third Tune*) PETER C. LUTKIN

mp

1. There's a song in the air! There's a star in the sky! There's a

Incarnation

dim. e rit.   *a tempo, cres.*

mother's deep prayer, And a ba-by's low cry! And the star rains its fire while the

beau-ti-ful sing, For the man-ger of Beth-le-hem cra-dles a King! A-MEN.

113 REGENT SQUARE 8s. 7s. 6l.

HENRY SMART

1. An-gels, from the realms of glo-ry, Wing your flight o'er all the earth;

Ye who sang cre-a-tion's sto-ry, Now pro-claim Mes-si-ah's birth:

Come and wor-ship, Come and wor-ship, Wor-ship Christ, the new-born King. A-MEN.

2 Shepherds, in the field abiding,
  Watching o'er your flocks by night,
God with man is now residing;
  Yonder shines the infant light:
    Come and worship,
Worship Christ, the newborn King.

3 Sages, leave your contemplations,
  Brighter visions beam afar;
Seek the great Desire of nations;
  Ye have seen his natal star:
    Come and worship,
Worship Christ, the newborn King.

4 Saints, before the altar bending,
  Watching long in hope and fear,
Suddenly the Lord, descending,
  In his temple shall appear:
    Come and worship,
Worship Christ, the newborn King.

5 Sinners, wrung with true repentance,
  Doomed for guilt to endless pains,
Justice now revokes the sentence,
  Mercy calls you, break your chains:
    Come and worship,
Worship Christ, the newborn King.

JAMES MONTGOMERY

114 MORNING STAR 11s. 10s.

J. P. HARDING

1. Bright-est and best of the sons of the morn-ing, Dawn on our dark-ness and lend us thine aid; Star of the East, the ho-ri-zon a-dorn-ing, Guide where our in-fant Re-deem-er is laid. A-MEN.

2 Cold on his cradle the dewdrops are shining;
   Low lies his head with the beasts of the stall;
   Angels adore him, in slumber reclining,
   Maker, and Monarch, and Saviour of all.

3 Say, shall we yield him, in costly devotion,
   Odors of Edom and offerings divine?
   Gems of the mountain, and pearls of the ocean,
   Myrrh from the forest, and gold from the mine?

4 Vainly we offer each ample oblation;
   Vainly with gifts would his favor secure;
   Richer by far is the heart's adoration;
   Dearer to God are the prayers of the poor.

5 Brightest and best of the sons of the morning,
   Dawn on our darkness and lend us thine aid;
   Star of the East, the horizon adorning,
   Guide where our infant Redeemer is laid.

REGINALD HEBER

Incarnation

115 CHRISTMAS C. M.

From George F. Händel

1. While shepherds watched their flocks by night, All seat-ed on the ground, The an-gel of the Lord came down, And glory shone a-round, And glory shone a-round. A-men.

2 "Fear not!" said he; for mighty dread
  Had seized their troubled mind,
"Glad tidings of great joy I bring,
  To you and all mankind.

3 "To you, in David's town, this day
  Is born, of David's line,
The Saviour, who is Christ the Lord;
  And this shall be the sign:

4 "The heavenly babe you there shall find
  To human view displayed,

All meanly wrapped in swathing-bands,
  And in a manger laid."

5 Thus spake the seraph; and forthwith
  Appeared a shining throng
Of angels praising God on high,
  Who thus addressed their song:

6 "All glory be to God on high,
  And to the earth be peace:
Good will henceforth from heaven to men,
  Begin and never cease."

Tate and Brady

116 WILSON 8s. 7s.

From Felix Mendelssohn-Bartholdy

1. Come, thou long ex-pect-ed Je-sus, Born to set thy peo-ple free: From our fears and sins re-lease us, Let us find our rest in thee. A-men.

2 Israel's strength and consolation,
  Hope of all the earth thou art;
Dear Desire of every nation,
  Joy of every longing heart.

3 Born thy people to deliver,
  Born a child, and yet a King,

Born to reign in us forever,
  Now thy gracious kingdom bring.

4 By thine own eternal Spirit,
  Rule in all our hearts alone;
By thine all-sufficient merit,
  Raise us to thy glorious throne.

Charles Wesley

117 CHOPE P. M.

Chope's Carols

1. In the field with their flocks a - bid - ing, They lay on the dew - y ground;

And glimmering un - der the star - light, The sheep lay white a - round;

When the light of the Lord streamed o'er them, And lo! from the heaven a - bove,

Incarnation

An an-gel leaned from the glo - ry, And sang his song of love.

REFRAIN

He sang, that first sweet Christ-mas, The song that shall nev-er cease,

"Glo-ry to God in the high-est, On earth good will and peace." A-MEN.

2 "To you in the city of David
  A Saviour is born to-day!"
And sudden a host of the heavenly ones
  Flashed forth to join the lay.
O never hath sweeter message
  Thrilled home to the souls of men,
And the heavens themselves had never heard
  A gladder choir till then.

  REFRAIN
For they sang that Christmas carol
  That never on earth shall cease,
"Glory to God in the highest,
  On earth good will and peace."

3 And the shepherds came to the manger,
  And gazed on the Holy Child;
And calmly o'er that rude cradle
  The virgin mother smiled;
And the sky in the starlit silence,
  Seemed full of the angel lay:
"To you in the city of David
  A Saviour is born to-day!"

  REFRAIN
O they sang, and I ween that never
  The carol on earth shall cease.
"Glory to God in the highest,
  On earth good will and peace."

FREDERICK W. FABER

85

118 CRUSADER'S HYMN 5. 6. 8. 5. 5. 8.

Arr. by Richard S. Willis

1. Fair-est Lord Je - sus! Rul - er of all na - ture! O thou of God and man the Son!

Thee will I cher - ish, Thee will I hon - or, Thee, my soul's glo-ry, joy, and crown. A-MEN.

2 Fair are the meadows,
   Fairer still the woodlands,
Robed in the blooming garb of spring;
   Jesus is fairer,
   Jesus is purer,
Who makes the woeful heart to sing.

3 Fair is the sunshine,
   Fairer still the moonlight,
And all the twinkling starry host;
   Jesus shines brighter,
   Jesus shines purer
Than all the angels heaven can boast.

From the German

119 AVISON 11S. 12S. With Refrain

Charles Avison

REFRAIN

Shout the glad ti-dings, ex - ult - ing - ly sing, . . . Je - ru - sa - lem triumphs, Mes-

VERSE

si - ah is King! 1. Zi - on, the mar - vel - ous sto - ry be tell - ing, The

Incarnation

Son of the High-est, how low-ly his birth! The bright-est arch-an-gel in glo-ry ex-cell-ing, He stoops to re-deem thee, he reigns up-on earth!

Refrain after the last verse

Shout the glad ti-dings, ex-ult-ing-ly sing, . . . Je-ru-sa-lem triumphs, Mes-si-ah is King, Mes-si-ah is King, Mes-si-ah is King! A-MEN.

2 Tell how he cometh; from nation to nation,
   The heart-cheering news let the earth echo round;
How free to the faithful he offers salvation,
   How his people with joy everlasting are crowned.
REFRAIN Shout the glad tidings, exultingly sing;
   Jerusalem triumphs, Messiah is King!

3 Mortals, your homage be gratefully bringing,
   And sweet let the gladsome hosanna arise;
Ye angels, the full hallelujah be singing,
   One chorus resound through the earth and the skies.
REFRAIN Shout the glad tidings, exultingly sing;
   Jerusalem triumphs, Messiah is King!

WILLIAM A. MUHLENBURG

120 FESTGESANG 8s. 6s. D.

ALFRED G. WATHALL

1. Long years ago o'er Bethlehem's hills Was seen a wondrous thing; As shepherds watched their sleeping flocks They heard the angels sing. The anthem rolled among the clouds When earth was hushed and still; Its notes proclaimed sweet peace on earth, To all mankind good will. "Glory to God in the high-est," The an-gels' song resounds, "Glo-ry to God in the high - est!" A-MEN.

2 That song is sung by rich and poor,
  Where'er the Christ is known;
'Tis sung in words, and sung in deeds,
  Which bind all hearts in one.
Angels are still the choristers,
  But we the shepherds are,
To bear the message which they bring,
  To those both near and far:
" Glory to God in the highest,"
  The angels' song resounds,
" Glory to God in the highest!"

C. WHITNEY COOMBS

Incarnation

120 WEIHNACHT 8s. 6s. D. (*Second Tune*) KARL P. HARRINGTON

1. Long years a-go o'er Bethlehem's hills Was seen a won-drous thing; As
shepherds watched their sleeping flocks They heard the an-gels sing. The an-them rolled a-
mong the clouds When earth was hushed and still; Its notes proclaimed sweet peace on earth,
To all man kind good will. "Glo-ry to God in the high-est," The
an-gels' song re-sounds, "Glo-ry to God in the high - est!" A-MEN.

121 ST. LOUIS 8s. 6s. D. Irregular.

LEWIS H. REDNER

1. O lit - tle town of Beth - le - hem, How still we see thee lie!

A - bove thy deep and dream - less sleep The si - lent stars go by;

Yet in thy dark streets shin - eth The ev - er - last - ing Light;

The hopes and fears of all the years Are met in thee to - night. A - MEN.

2 For Christ is born of Mary,
 And gathered all above,
While mortals sleep, the angels keep
 Their watch of wondering love.
O morning stars, together
 Proclaim the holy birth,
And praises sing to God the King,
 And peace to men on earth!

3 How silently, how silently,
 The wondrous gift is given!
So God imparts to human hearts
 The blessings of his heaven.
No ear may hear his coming,
 But in this world of sin,
Where meek souls will receive him still,
 The dear Christ enters in.

Incarnation

4 O holy Child of Bethlehem!
   Descend to us, we pray;
   Cast out our sin, and enter in,
   Be born in us to-day.

We hear the Christmas angels
The great glad tidings tell;
O come to us, abide with us,
Our Lord Immanuel!

Phillips Brooks

121 BETHLEHEM 8s. 6s. D. Irregular. (*Second Tune*)   Joseph Barnby

1. O lit-tle town of Beth-le-hem, How still we see thee lie! ...

A - bove thy deep and dream-less sleep The si-lent stars go by;

Yet in thy dark streets shin-eth The ev-er-last-ing Light;

The hopes and fears of all the years Are met in thee to-night. A-MEN.

122 ELLIOTT P. M.

TIMOTHY R. MATTHEWS

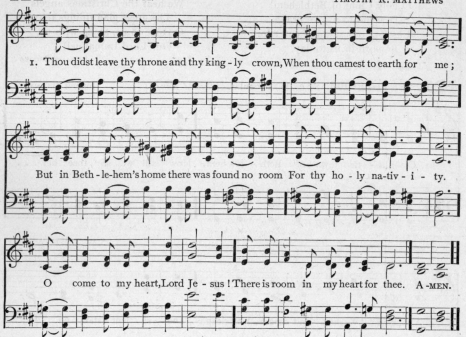

1. Thou didst leave thy throne and thy king-ly crown, When thou camest to earth for me;

But in Beth-le-hem's home there was found no room For thy ho-ly na-tiv-i-ty.

O come to my heart, Lord Je-sus! There is room in my heart for thee. A-MEN.

2 Heaven's arches rang when the angels sang,
Proclaiming thy royal degree;
But in lowly birth didst thou come to earth,
And in great humility.
O come to my heart, Lord Jsus!
There is room in my heart for thee.

3 The foxes found rest, and the birds their nest
In the shade of the forest tree;
But thy couch was the sod, O thou Son of God,
In the deserts of Galilee.
O come to my heart, Lord Jesus!
There is room in my heart for thee.

4 Thou camest, O Lord, with the living word,
That should set thy people free;
But with mocking scorn, and with crown of thorn,
They bore thee to Calvary.
O come to my heart, Lord Jesus!
Thy cross is my only plea.

5 When heaven's arches ring, and her choirs shall sing
At thy coming to victory,
Let thy voice call me home, saying, "Yet there is room,
There is room at my side for thee."
And my heart shall rejoice, Lord Jesus,
When thou comest and callest for me.

EMILY E. S. ELLIOTT

123 SILENT NIGHT P. M.

FRANZ GRUBER

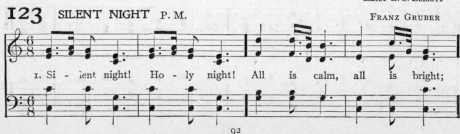

1. Si-lent night! Ho-ly night! All is calm, all is bright;

Round yon vir - gin moth - er and Child! Ho - ly In - fant, so ten - der and mild,

Sleep in heav - en - ly peace, Sleep in heav - en - ly peace. A - MEN.

2 Silent night! Holy night!
Shepherds quake at the sight!
Glories stream from heaven afar,
Heavenly hosts sing Alleluia.
Christ, the Saviour, is born!
Christ, the Saviour, is born!

3 Silent night! Holy night!
Son of God, love's pure light
Radiant beams from thy holy face,
With the dawn of redeeming grace,
Jesus, Lord, at thy birth,
Jesus, Lord, at thy birth.

JOSEPH MOHR

124 CRIMEA L. M.

THORO HARRIS

1. When, mar shaled on the night - ly plain, The glit-tering hosts be - stud the sky,

One star a - lone of all the train Can fix the sin - ner's wandering eye. A - MEN.

2 Hark! hark! to God the chorus breaks,
From every host, from every gem;
But one alone the Saviour speaks,
It is the Star of Bethlehem.

3 It is my guide, my light, my all;
It bids my dark forebodings cease;

And through life's storm and danger's thrall,
It leads me to the port of peace.

4 Thus, safely moored, my perils o'er,
I'll sing first in night's diadem,
Forever, and for evermore,
The Star! the Star of Bethlehem!

H. KIRKE WHITE

125 PORTUGUESE HYMN 11s.   Composer Unknown

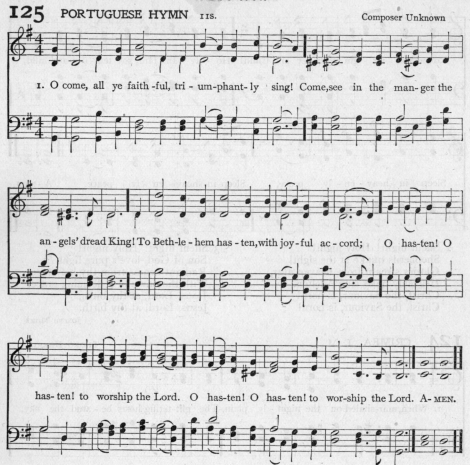

1. O come, all ye faith-ful, tri-um-phant-ly sing! Come, see in the man-ger the an-gels' dread King! To Beth-le-hem has-ten, with joy-ful ac-cord; O has-ten! O has-ten! to worship the Lord. O has-ten! O has-ten! to wor-ship the Lord. A-MEN.

2 True Son of the Father, he comes from the skies;
The womb of the Virgin he doth not despise;
To Bethlehem hasten, with joyful accord;
O hasten! O hasten! to worship the Lord.

3 O hark to the angels, all singing in heaven,
"To God in the highest, all glory be given!"
To Bethlehem hasten, with joyful accord,
O hasten! O hasten! to worship the Lord.

4 To thee, then, O Jesus, this day of thy birth,
Be glory and honor through heaven and earth;
True Godhead Incarnate, Omnipotent Word!
O hasten! O hasten! to worship the Lord.

From the Latin. Tr. by EDWARD CASWALL

126 DENNY C. M.

LOWELL MASON

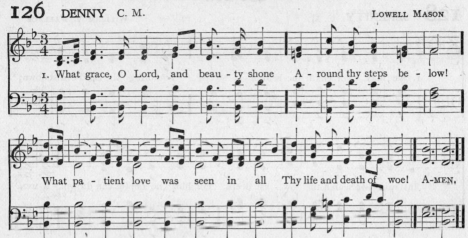

1. What grace, O Lord, and beau-ty shone A-round thy steps be-low!
What pa-tient love was seen in all Thy life and death of woe! A-MEN.

2 For, ever on thy burdened heart
   A weight of sorrow hung;
   Yet no ungentle, murmuring word
   Escaped thy silent tongue.

3 Thy foes might hate, despise, revile,
   Thy friends unfaithful prove;
   Unwearied in forgiveness still,
   Thy heart could only love.

4 O give us hearts to love like thee,
   Like thee, O Lord, to grieve
   Far more for others' sins, than all
   The wrongs that we receive.

5 One with thyself, may every eye
   In us, thy brethren, see
   That gentleness and grace that spring
   From union, Lord, with thee.

EDWARD DENNY

127 CANONBURY L. M.

ROBERT SCHUMANN

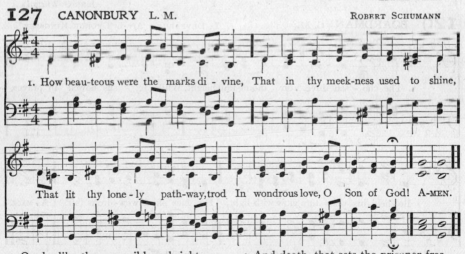

1. How beau-teous were the marks di-vine, That in thy meek-ness used to shine,
That lit thy lone-ly path-way, trod In wondrous love, O Son of God! A-MEN.

2 O who like thee, so mild, so bright,
   Thou Son of man, thou Light of Light?
   O who like thee did ever go
   So patient, through a world of woe?

3 O who like thee so humbly bore
   The scorn, the scoffs of men, before?
   So meek, so lowly, yet so high,
   So glorious in humility?

4 And death, that sets the prisoner free,
   Was pang, and scoff, and scorn to thee;
   Yet love through all thy torture glowed,
   And mercy with thy lifeblood flowed.

5 O wondrous Lord, my soul would be
   Still more and more conformed to thee,
   And learn of thee, the lowly One,
   And like thee, all my journey run.

A. CLEVELAND COXE

128 SERENITY C. M.

WILLIAM V. WALLACE

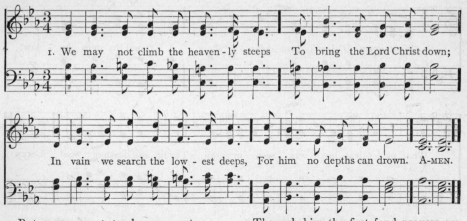

1. We may not climb the heaven-ly steeps To bring the Lord Christ down;
In vain we search the low-est deeps, For him no depths can drown. A-men.

2 But warm, sweet, tender, even yet
A present help is he;
And faith has still its Olivet,
And love its Galilee.

3 The healing of the seamless dress
Is by our beds of pain;
We touch him in life's throng and press,
And we are whole again.

4 Through him the first fond prayers are
Our lips of childhood frame;   [said
The last low whispers of our dead
Are burdened with his name.

5 O Lord and Master of us all,
Whate'er our name or sign,
We own thy sway, we hear thy call,
We test our lives by thine!

JOHN G. WHITTIER

129 BOARDMAN C. M.

L. DEVEREUX. Arr. by GEORGE KINGSLEY

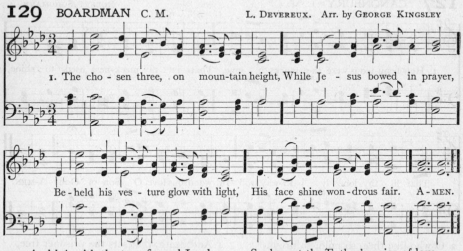

1. The cho-sen three, on moun-tain height, While Je-sus bowed in prayer,
Be-held his ves-ture glow with light, His face shine won-drous fair. A-men.

2 And lo! with the transfigured Lord,
Leader and seer they saw;
With Carmel's hoary prophet stood
The giver of the law.

3 From the low-bending cloud above,
Whence radiant brightness shone,

Spake out the Father's voice of love,
"Hear my belovèd Son!"

4 Lord, lead us to the mountain height;
To prayer's transfiguring glow;
And clothe us with the Spirit's might
For grander work below.

DAVID H. ELA

130 WESTON 8s. 7s. D.

JOHN E. ROE

1. Friend of sin-ners! Lord of Glo-ry! Low-ly, Might-y! Broth-er, King!
Mus-ing o'er thy won-drous sto-ry, Grate-ful we thy prais-es sing:
Friend to help us, com-fort, save us, In whom power and pit-y blend—
Praise we must the grace which gave us Je-sus Christ, the sin-ners' Friend! A-MEN.

2 Friend who never fails nor grieves us,
  Faithful, tender, constant, kind! —
Friend who at all times receives us,
  Friend who came the lost to find: —
Sorrow soothing, joys enhancing,
  Loving until life shall end —
Then conferring bliss entrancing,
  Still, in heaven, the sinners' Friend!

3 O to love and serve thee better!
  From all evil set us free;
Break, Lord, every sinful fetter;
  Be each thought conformed to thee:
Looking for thy bright appearing,
  May our spirits upward tend;
Till no longer doubting, fearing,
  We behold the sinners' Friend!

C. NEWMAN HALL.

5

131 HAYES L. M. D.

From Ludwig van Beethoven

1. O Mas - ter, it is good to be High on the moun-tain here with thee,

Where stand re - vealed to mor - tal gaze Those glo - rious saints of oth - er days,

Who once re - ceived on Ho - reb's height The e - ter - nal laws of truth and right,

Or caught the still small whisper, higher Than storm, than earthquake, or than fire. A-MEN.

2 O Master, it is good to be
Entranced, enwrapt, alone with thee;
And watch thy glistering raiment glow
Whiter than Hermon's whitest snow;
The human lineaments that shine
Irradiant with a light divine;
Till we too change from grace to grace,
Gazing on that transfigured face.

3 O Master, it is good to be
Here on the holy mount with thee:
When darkling in the depths of night,
When dazzled with excess of light,
We bow before the heavenly voice
That bids bewildered souls rejoice,
Though love wax cold, and faith be dim,
"This is my Son, O hear ye him."

Arthur P. Stanley

132 ST. JOSEPH 8. 7. 8. 7. 7. 7.

H. H. Statham

1. Je - sus wept! those tears are o - ver, But his heart is still the same;

Life, Character, and Ministry

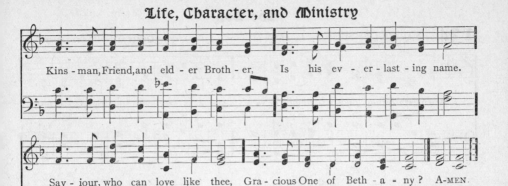

Kins-man, Friend, and eld-er Broth-er, Is his ev-er-last-ing name.

Sav-iour, who can love like thee, Gra-cious One of Beth-a-ny? A-MEN.

2 When the pangs of trial seize us,
    When the waves of sorrow roll,
  I will lay my head on Jesus,
    Refuge of the troubled soul.
      Surely, none can feel like thee,
      Weeping One of Bethany!

3 Jesus wept! and still in glory,
    He can mark each mourner's tear;
  Loving to retrace the story
    Of the hearts he solaced here.
      Lord, when I am called to die,
      Let me think of Bethany,

4 Jesus wept! that tear of sorrow
    Is a legacy of love;
  Yesterday, to-day, to-morrow,
    He the same doth ever prove.
      Thou art all in all to me,
      Loving One of Bethany!

JOHN R. MACDUFF

I33 ST. BERNARD C. M.

JOHN RICHARDSON

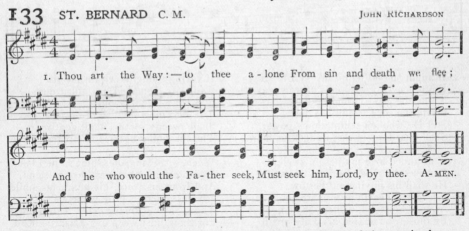

1. Thou art the Way: — to thee a-lone From sin and death we flee;

And he who would the Fa-ther seek, Must seek him, Lord, by thee. A-MEN.

2 Thou art the Truth: — thy word alone
    True wisdom can impart;
  Thou only canst inform the mind,
    And purify the heart.

3 Thou art the Life: — the rending tomb
    Proclaims thy conquering arm;

And those who put their trust in thee
  Nor death nor hell shall harm.

4 Thou art the Way, the Truth, the Life;
    Grant us that way to know,
  That truth to keep, that life to win,
    Whose joys eternal flow.

GEORGE W. DOANE

The Son

134 ST. PETERSBURG L. M. 6l.

DIMITRI S. BORTNIANSKY

1. When gath-ering clouds a-round I view, And days are dark, and friends are few,

On Him I lean who not in vain Ex-pe-rienced ev-ery hu-man pain;

He sees my wants, al-lays my fears, And counts and treasures up my tears. A-MEN.

2 If aught should tempt my soul to stray
From heavenly wisdom's narrow way,
To fly the good I would pursue,
Or do the sin I would not do,
Still He, who felt temptation's power,
Shall guard me in that dangerous hour.

3 If wounded love my bosom swell,
Deceived by those I prized too well,
He shall his pitying aid bestow,
Who felt on earth severer woe,—
At once betrayed, denied, or fled,
By those who shared his daily bread.

4 If vexing thoughts within me rise,
And, sore dismayed, my spirit dies,
Still He, who once vouchsafed to bear
The sickening anguish of despair,
Shall sweetly soothe, shall gently dry,
The throbbing heart, the streaming eye.

5 When, sorrowing, o'er some stone I bend
Which covers what was once a friend,
And from his voice, his hand, his smile,
Divides me for a little while, —
Thou, Saviour, mark'st the tears I shed,
For thou didst weep o'er Lazarus dead.

6 And O, when I have safely past
Through every conflict but the last,
Still, still unchanging, watch beside
My painful bed, for thou hast died,
Then point to realms of cloudless day
And wipe the latest tear away.

ROBERT GRANT

135 ORTONVILLE C. M.

THOMAS HASTINGS

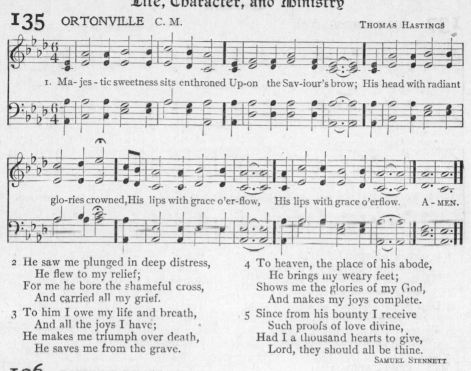

1. Ma- jes - tic sweetness sits enthroned Up-on the Sav-iour's brow; His head with radiant glo-ries crowned, His lips with grace o'er-flow, His lips with grace o'erflow. A - MEN.

2 He saw me plunged in deep distress,
  He flew to my relief;
For me he bore the shameful cross,
  And carried all my grief.

3 To him I owe my life and breath,
  And all the joys I have;
He makes me triumph over death,
  He saves me from the grave.

4 To heaven, the place of his abode,
  He brings my weary feet;
Shows me the glories of my God,
  And makes my joys complete.

5 Since from his bounty I receive
  Such proofs of love divine,
Had I a thousand hearts to give,
  Lord, they should all be thine.

SAMUEL STENNETT

136 DOMINUS REGIT ME 8s. 7s.

JOHN B. DYKES

1. The King of love my Shep-herd is, Whose good-ness fail-eth nev-er; I noth-ing lack if I am his, And he is mine for - ev - er. A - MEN.

2 Where streams of living water flow,
  My ransomed soul he leadeth,
And, where the verdant pastures grow,
  With food celestial feedeth.

3 Perverse and foolish oft I strayed,
  But yet in love he sought me,
And on his shoulder gently laid,
  And home, rejoicing, brought me.

4 In death's dark vale I fear no ill
  With thee, dear Lord, beside me;
Thy rod and staff my comfort still,
  Thy cross before to guide me.

5 And so through all the length of days,
  Thy goodness faileth never;
Good Shepherd, may I sing thy praise
  Within thy house forever.

HENRY W. BAKER

The Son

137 HOLY CROSS C. M.

Arranged by JAMES C. WADE

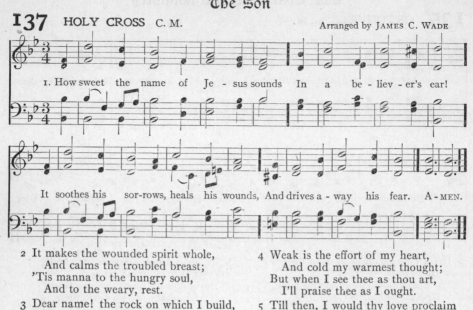

1. How sweet the name of Je - sus sounds In a be - liev - er's ear!

It soothes his sor-rows, heals his wounds, And drives a - way his fear. A - MEN.

2 It makes the wounded spirit whole,
    And calms the troubled breast;
'Tis manna to the hungry soul,
    And to the weary, rest.

3 Dear name! the rock on which I build,
    My shield and hiding place;
My never-failing treasury, filled
    With boundless stores of grace!

4 Weak is the effort of my heart,
    And cold my warmest thought;
But when I see thee as thou art,
    I'll praise thee as I ought.

5 Till then, I would thy love proclaim
    With every fleeting breath;
And may the music of thy name
    Refresh my soul in death.
                 JOHN NEWTON

138 COPELAND L. M.

KARL P. HARRINGTON

1. Christ's life our code, his cross our creed, Our com-mon, glad con - fes - sion be;

Our deep-est wants, our high - est aims, Find their ful-fill - ment, Lord, in thee. A - MEN.

2 Dear Son of God! thy blessèd will
    Our hearts would own, with saints above;
All life is larger for thy law,
    All service sweeter for thy love.

3 Thy life our code! in letters clear
    We read our duty, day by day,
Thy footsteps tracing eagerly,
    Who art the truth, the life, the way.

4 Thy cross our creed! thy boundless love
    A ransomed world at last shall laud,
And crown thee their eternal King,
    O Lord of Glory! Lamb of God!

5 Till then, to thee our souls aspire
    In ardent prayer and earnest deed,
With love like thine, confessing, still,
    Christ's life our code! his cross our creed!
              BENJAMIN COPELAND

139 GROSTETTE L. M. HENRY W. GREATOREX

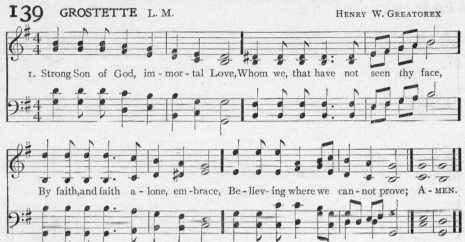

1. Strong Son of God, im-mor-tal Love, Whom we, that have not seen thy face,
By faith, and faith a-lone, em-brace, Be-liev-ing where we can-not prove; A-MEN.

2 Thou wilt not leave us in the dust:
Thou madest man, he knows not why,
He thinks he was not made to die:
And thou hast made him: thou art just.

3 Thou seemest human and divine,
The highest, holiest manhood, thou:

Our wills are ours, we know not how;
Our wills are ours, to make them thine.

4 Our little systems have their day;
They have their day and cease to be:
They are but broken lights of thee,
And thou, O Lord, art more than they.

ALFRED TENNYSON

140 KIEL L. M. PETER C. LUTKIN

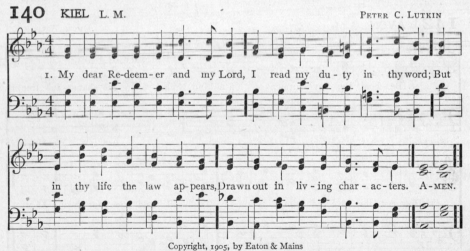

1. My dear Re-deem-er and my Lord, I read my du-ty in thy word; But
in thy life the law ap-pears, Drawn out in liv-ing char-ac-ters. A-MEN.

Copyright, 1905, by Eaton & Mains

2 Such was thy truth, and such thy zeal,
Such deference to thy Father's will,
Such love and meekness so divine,
I would transcribe and make them mine.

3 Cold mountains and the midnight air
Witnessed the fervor of thy prayer;

The desert thy temptations knew,
Thy conflict and thy victory too.

4 Be thou my pattern; make me bear
More of thy gracious image here;
Then God, the Judge, shall own my name
Among the followers of the Lamb.

ISAAC WATTS

141 EUCHARIST L. M.

ISAAC B. WOODBURY

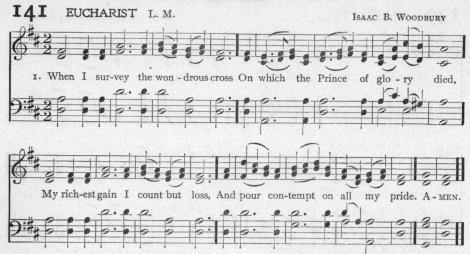

1. When I sur-vey the won-drous cross On which the Prince of glo-ry died,

My rich-est gain I count but loss, And pour con-tempt on all my pride. A-MEN.

2 Forbid it, Lord, that I should boast,
    Save in the death of Christ, my God;
All the vain things that charm me most,
    I sacrifice them to his blood.

3 See, from his head, his hands, his feet,
    Sorrow and love flow mingled down!

Did e'er such love and sorrow meet,
    Or thorns compose so rich a crown?

4 Were the whole realm of nature mine,
    That were a present far too small;
Love so amazing, so divine,
    Demands my soul, my life, my all.

ISAAC WATTS

142 AVON C. M.

HUGH WILSON

1. Be-hold the Sav-iour of man-kind Nailed to the shame-ful tree!

How vast the love that him in-clined To bleed and die for thee! A-MEN.

2 Hark, how he groans! while nature shakes,
    And earth's strong pillars bend!
The temple's veil in sunder breaks,
    The solid marbles rend.

3 'Tis done! the precious ransom's paid!
    "Receive my soul!" he cries;

See where he bows his sacred head!
    He bows his head, and dies!

4 But soon he'll break death's envious
    And in full glory shine: [chain,
O Lamb of God, was ever pain,
    Was ever love, like thine?

SAMUEL WESLEY, Sr.

Sufferings and Death

143 ASBURY 8s. 7s.   CLAUDE W. HARRINGTON

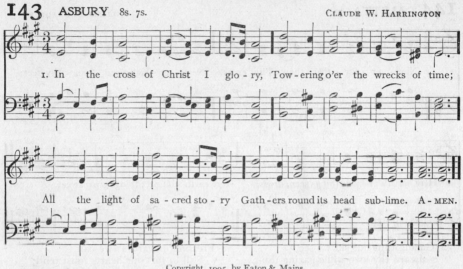

1. In the cross of Christ I glo-ry, Tow-ering o'er the wrecks of time;

All the light of sa-cred sto-ry Gath-ers round its head sub-lime. A-MEN.

Copyright, 1905, by Eaton & Mains

2 When the woes of life o'ertake me,
   Hopes deceive, and fears annoy,
Never shall the cross forsake me;
   Lo! it glows with peace and joy.

3 When the sun of bliss is beaming
   Light and love upon my way,
From the cross the radiance streaming
   Adds more luster to the day.

4 Bane and blessing, pain and pleasure,
   By the cross are sanctified;
Peace is there, that knows no measure,
   Joys that through all time abide.

5 In the cross of Christ I glory,
   Towering o'er the wrecks of time;
All the light of sacred story
   Gathers round its head sublime.

JOHN BOWRING

143 RATHBUN 8s. 7s. (*Second Tune*)   ITHAMAR CONKEY

1. In the cross of Christ I glo-ry, Tow-ering o'er the wrecks of time;

All the light of sa-cred sto-ry Gath-ers round its head sub-lime. A-MEN.

144 ALETTA 7s.

WILLIAM B. BRADBURY

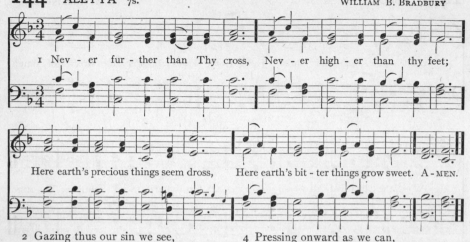

1 Nev - er fur - ther than Thy cross, Nev - er high - er than thy feet;

Here earth's precious things seem dross, Here earth's bit - ter things grow sweet. A - MEN.

2 Gazing thus our sin we see,
    Learn thy love while gazing thus;
Sin, which laid the cross on thee,
    Love, which bore the cross for us.

3 Here we learn to serve and give,
    And, rejoicing, self deny;
Here we gather love to live,
    Here we gather faith to die.

4 Pressing onward as we can,
    Still to this our hearts must tend;
Where our earliest hopes began,
    There our last aspirings end;

5 Till amid the hosts of light,
    We in thee redeemed, complete,
Through thy cross made pure and white,
    Cast our crowns before thy feet.

ELIZABETH R. CHARLES

145 BELOIT L. M.

CARL G. REISSIGER

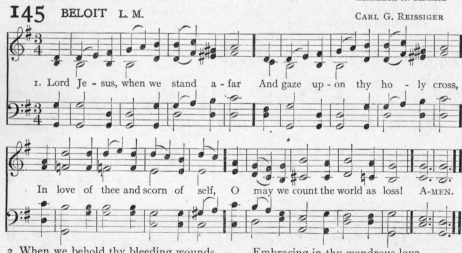

1. Lord Je - sus, when we stand a - far And gaze up - on thy ho - ly cross,

In love of thee and scorn of self, O may we count the world as loss! A - MEN.

2 When we behold thy bleeding wounds,
    And the rough way that thou hast trod,
Make us to hate the load of sin
    That lay so heavy on our God.

3 O holy Lord! uplifted high
    With outstretched arms, in mortal woe,

Embracing in thy wondrous love
    The sinful world that lies below!

4 Give us an ever-living faith
    To gaze beyond the things we see;
And in the mystery of thy death
    Draw us and all men after thee!

WILLIAM W. HOW

146 COMMUNION C. M.

STEPHEN JENKS

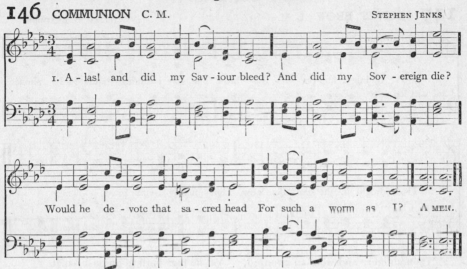

1. A - las! and did my Sav - iour bleed? And did my Sov - ereign die?

Would he de - vote that sa - cred head For such a worm as I? A - men.

2 Was it for crimes that I have done,
   He groaned upon the tree?
   Amazing pity! grace unknown!
   And love beyond degree!

3 Well might the sun in darkness hide,
   And shut his glories in,
   When Christ, the mighty Maker, died
   For man the creature's sin.

4 Thus might I hide my blushing face
   While his dear cross appears;
   Dissolve my heart in thankfulness,
   And melt mine eyes to tears.

5 But drops of grief can ne'er repay
   The debt of love I owe:
   Here, Lord, I give myself away, —
   'Tis all that I can do.

ISAAC WATTS

146 AVON C. M. (Second Tune)

HUGH WILSON

1. A - las! and did my Sav - iour bleed? And did my Sov - ereign die?

Would he de - vote that sa - cred head For such a worm as I? A - men.

147 OLIVES' BROW L. M.

WILLIAM B. BRADBURY

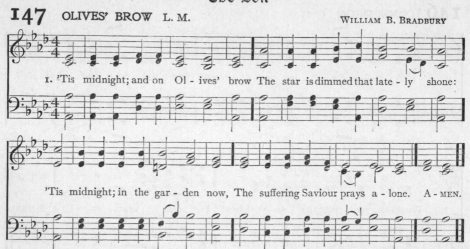

1. 'Tis midnight; and on Ol - ives' brow The star is dimmed that late - ly shone:

'Tis midnight; in the gar - den now, The suffering Saviour prays a - lone. A - MEN.

2 'Tis midnight; and from all removed,
The Saviour wrestles lone with fears;
E'en that disciple whom he loved
Heeds not his Master's grief and tears.

3 'Tis midnight; and for others' guilt
The Man of sorrows weeps in blood;

Yet he that hath in anguish knelt
Is not forsaken by his God.

4 'Tis midnight; and from ether-plains
Is borne the song that angels know;
Unheard by mortals are the strains
That sweetly soothe the Saviour's woe.

WILLIAM B. TAPPAN

148 MALVERN L. M.

LOWELL MASON

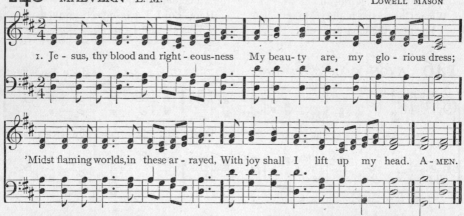

1. Je - sus, thy blood and right - eous-ness My beau - ty are, my glo - rious dress;

'Midst flaming worlds, in these ar - rayed, With joy shall I lift up my head. A - MEN.

2 Bold shall I stand in thy great day,
For who aught to my charge shall lay?
Fully absolved through these I am,
From sin and fear, from guilt and shame.

3 The holy, meek, unspotted Lamb,
Who from the Father's bosom came,
Who died for me, e'en me to atone,
Now for my Lord and God I own.

4 Lord, I believe thy precious blood,
Which, at the mercy seat of God,
Forever doth for sinners plead,
For me, e'en for my soul, was shed.

5 Lord, I believe were sinners more
Than sands upon the ocean shore,
Thou hast for all a ransom paid,
For all a full atonement made.

NICOLAUS L. ZINZENDORF. Tr. by JOHN WESLEY

Sufferings and Death

149 WESTCOTT L. M.   JOSEPH BARNBY

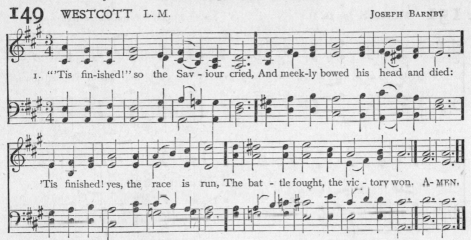

1. "'Tis fin-ished!" so the Sav-iour cried, And meek-ly bowed his head and died: 'Tis finished! yes, the race is run, The bat - tle fought, the vic - tory won. A - MEN.

2 'Tis finished! all that heaven foretold
By prophets in the days of old;
And truths are opened to our view,
That kings and prophets never knew.

3 'Tis finished! Son of God, thy power
Hath triumphed in this awful hour;

And yet our eyes with sorrow see
That life to us was death to thee.

4 'Tis finished! let the joyful sound
Be heard through all the nations round;
'Tis finished! let the triumph rise
And swell the chorus of the skies!

SAMUEL STENNETT. Alt.

150 ST. DROSTANE L. M.   JOHN B. DYKES

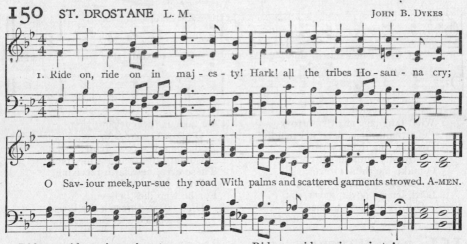

1. Ride on, ride on in maj - es - ty! Hark! all the tribes Ho-san - na cry; O Sav-iour meek, pur-sue thy road With palms and scattered garments strowed. A - MEN.

2 Ride on, ride on in majesty!
In lowly pomp ride on to die:
O Christ, thy triumphs now begin
O'er captive death and conquered sin.

3 Ride on, ride on in majesty!
The wingèd squadrons of the sky
Look down with sad and wondering eyes
To see the approaching sacrifice.

4 Ride on, ride on in majesty!
Thy last and fiercest strife is nigh;
The Father, on his sapphire throne,
Expects his own anointed Son.

5 Ride on, ride on in majesty!
In lowly pomp ride on to die;
Bow thy meek head to mortal pain,
Then take, O God, thy power, and reign.

HENRY H. MILMAN

The Son

151 MUNICH 7s. 6s. D. Arr. by FELIX MENDELSSOHN-BARTHOLDY

1. O sa-cred Head, now wound-ed, With grief and shame weighed down,
Now scorn-ful-ly sur-round-ed With thorns, thine on-ly crown;
O sa-cred Head, what glo-ry, What bliss, till now was thine!
Yet, though de-spised and go-ry, I joy to call thee mine. A-MEN.

2 What language shall I borrow
  To thank thee, dearest Friend,
For this, thy dying sorrow,
  Thy pity without end?
O make me thine forever;
  And should I fainting be,
Lord, let me never, never,
  Outlive my love to thee.

3 Be near me when I'm dying,
  O show thy cross to me;
And, for my succor flying,
  Come, Lord, and set me free:
These eyes, new faith receiving,
  From Jesus shall not move;
For he who dies believing,
  Dies safely, through thy love.

BERNARD of Clairvaux, PAUL GERHARDT
Tr. by J. W. ALEXANDER

151 PASSION CHORALE 7s. 6s. D. (*Second Tune*) HANS L. HASSLER

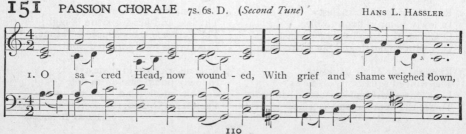

1. O sa-cred Head, now wound-ed, With grief and shame weighed down,

Now scorn-ful-ly sur-round-ed With thorns, thine on-ly crown;

O sa-cred Head, what glo-ry, What bliss, till now was thine!

Yet, though de-spised and go-ry, I joy to call thee mine. A-MEN.

152 ST. CROSS L. M.   JOHN B. DYKES

1. O come and mourn with me a-while; O come ye to the Sav-iour's side;

O come, to-geth-er let us mourn; Je-sus, our Lord, is cru-ci-fied. A-MEN.

2 Have we no tears to shed for him,
   While soldiers scoff and Jews deride?
Ah! look how patiently he hangs;
   Jesus, our Lord, is crucified.

3 Seven times he spake, seven words of love;
   And all three hours his silence cried

For mercy on the souls of men;
   Jesus, our Lord, is crucified.

4 O love of God! O sin of man! [tried;
   In this dread act your strength is
And victory remains with love;
   Jesus, our Lord, is crucified.

FREDERICK W. FABER

153 SELENA L. M. 6l.

Isaac B. Woodbury

1. O Love di - vine, what hast thou done! The incar-nate God hath died for me!

The Fa-ther's co - e - ter - nal Son Bore all my sins up - on the tree!

The Son of God for me hath died: My Lord, my Love, is cru - ci - fied. A - MEN.

2 Behold him, all ye that pass by,
   The bleeding Prince of life and peace!
Come, sinners, see your Saviour die,
   And say, was ever grief like his?
Come, feel with me his blood applied:
My Lord, my Love, is crucified:

3 Is crucified for me and you,
   To bring us rebels back to God:
Believe, believe the record true,
   Ye all are bought with Jesus' blood:
Pardon for all flows from his side:
My Lord, my Love, is crucified.

4 Then let us sit beneath his cross,
   And gladly catch the healing stream;
All things for him account but loss,
   And give up all our hearts to him:
Of nothing think or speak beside:
My Lord, my Love, is crucified.

CHARLES WESLEY

154 STABAT MATER 8. 8. 7. D.

H. KNIGHT

1. Near the cross was Ma - ry weep-ing, There her mourn-ful sta - tion keep - ing,

Sufferings and Death

Gaz-ing on her dy-ing Son: There in speech-less an-guish groan-ing,

Yearn-ing, trembling, sigh-ing, moaning, Through her soul the sword had gone. A-MEN.

2 When no eye its pity gave us,
   When there was no arm to save us,
     He his love and power displayed:
   By his stripes he wrought our healing,
   By his death, our life revealing,
     He for us the ransom paid.

3 Jesus, may thy love constrain us,
   That from sin we may refrain us,
     In thy griefs may deeply grieve:
   Thee our best affections giving,
   To thy glory ever living,
     May we in thy glory live.

JACOPONE DA TODI. Tr. by JAMES W. ALEXANDER

155   ABER S. M.

WILLIAM H. MONK

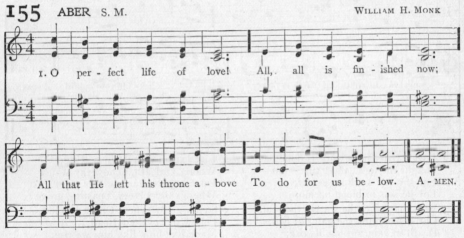

1. O per-fect life of love! All, all is fin-ished now;

All that He left his throne a-bove To do for us be-low. A-MEN.

2 No work is left undone
   Of all the Father willed;
   His toil, his sorrows, one by one,
     The Scripture have fulfilled.

3 No pain that we can share
   But he has felt its smart;
   All forms of human grief and care
     Have pierced that tender heart.

4 And on his thorn-crowned head,
   And on his sinless soul,
   Our sins in all their guilt were laid,
     That he might make us whole.

5 In perfect love he dies;
   For me he dies, for me:
   O all-atoning Sacrifice,
     I cling by faith to thee.

6 In every time of need,
   Before the judgment throne,
   Thy work, O Lamb of God, I'll plead,
     Thy merits, not my own.

7 Yet work, O Lord, in me,
   As thou for me hast wrought;
   And let my love the answer be
     To grace thy love has brought.

HENRY W. BAKER

156 EASTER HYMN 7s. *With Hallelujah*

Lyra Davidica

1. Christ the Lord is risen to-day, Hal - - le - lu - jah!
Sons of men and an-gels say: Hal - - le - lu - jah!
Raise your joys and tri - umphs high, Hal - - le - lu - jah!
Sing, ye heavens, and earth re - ply, Hal - - le - lu - jah! A-MEN.

2 Love's redeeming work is done;
  Fought the fight, the battle won:
  Lo! the sun's eclipse is o'er;
  Lo! he sets in blood no more.

3 Vain the stone, the watch, the seal,
  Christ has burst the gates of hell:
  Death in vain forbids his rise;
  Christ hath opened paradise.

4 Lives again our glorious King;
  Where, O death, is now thy sting?
  Once he died our souls to save;
  Where's thy victory, boasting grave?

5 Soar we now where Christ has led,
  Follow our exalted Head;
  Made like him, like him we rise;
  Ours the cross, the grave, the skies!

CHARLES WESLEY

156 PASCHALE GAUDIUM 7s. *With Hallelujah*
(Second Tune)

JOHN STAINER

1. Christ the Lord is risen to-day, Hal - le - lu - jah! Sons of men and an-gels say:

Resurrection

Hal - le - lu - jah! Raise your joys and triumphs high, Hal - le - lu - jah!

Sing, ye heavens, and earth re - ply. Hal - le - lu - jah! A - MEN.

157 RIALTO S. M.

GEORGE F. ROOT

1. The Lord is risen in - deed; The grave hath lost its prey;

With him shall rise the ran-somed seed, To reign in end - less day. A-MEN.

2 The Lord is risen indeed;
   He lives, to die no more;
   He lives, the sinner's cause to plead,
   Whose curse and shame he bore.

3 The Lord is risen indeed;
   Attending angels, hear!

Up to the courts of heaven, with speed,
   The joyful tidings bear:

4 Then wake your golden lyres,
   And strike each cheerful chord;
   Join, all ye bright celestial choirs,
   To sing our risen Lord.

THOMAS KELLY

158 JORDAN L. M. D.

JOSEPH BARNBY

1. Our Lord is ris-en from the dead; Our Je-sus is gone up on high;

The powers of hell are cap-tive led, Dragged to the por-tals of the sky:

Voices in Unison   *In Harmony*

There his tri-umph-al char-iot waits, And an-gels chant the sol-emn lay:

Voices in Unison   *In Harmony*

"Lift up your heads, ye heaven-ly gates; Ye ev-er-last-ing doors, give way!" A-MEN.

2 "Loose all your bars of massy light,
   And wide unfold the ethereal scene;
He claims these mansions as his right;
   Receive the King of glory in!"
"Who is the King of glory? Who?"
   "The Lord, that all our foes o'ercame;
The world, sin, death, and hell o'erthrew;
   And Jesus is the Conqueror's name."

3 Lo, his triumphal chariot waits,
   And angels chant the solemn lay:
"Lift up your heads, ye heavenly gates;
   Ye everlasting doors, give way!"
"Who is the King of glory? Who?"
   "The Lord, of glorious power possessed;
The King of saints and angels too;
   God over all, forever blest!"

CHARLES WESLEY

Resurrection

EPIPHANY 10s. 11s. D. Irregular.   WILLIAM C. FILBY

1. Lift your glad voi - ces in tri-umph on high, For Je-sus hath ris-en, and man can-not die; .. Vain were the ter-rors that gath-ored a-round him, And short the do-min-ion of death and the grave; He burst from the fet-ters of darkness that bound him, Re-splendent in glo-ry to live and to save! Loud was the cho-rus of an-gels on high, The Saviour hath ris-en, and man shall not die. A-MEN.

2 Glory to God, in full anthems of joy;
    The being he gave us death cannot destroy:
Sad were the life we must part with to-morrow,
    If tears were our birthright, and death were our end;
But Jesus hath cheered the dark valley of sorrow,
    And bade us, immortal, to heaven ascend:
Lift then your voices in triumph on high,
For Jesus hath risen, and man shall not die.

                                        HENRY WARE Jr.

160 HYMN OF JOY 8s. 7s. D.

From LUDWIG VAN BEETHOVEN

1. Sing with all the sons of glo - ry, Sing the res - ur - rec-tion song! Death and sor-row, earth's dark story, To the former days belong: All around the clouds are breaking, Soon the storms of time shall cease, In God's likeness, man a-wak-ing, Knows the ev - er - last-ing peace. A - MEN.

2 O what glory, far exceeding
　All that eye has yet perceived!
　Holiest hearts for ages pleading,
　　Never that full joy conceived.
　God has promised, Christ prepares it,
　　There on high our welcome waits;
　Every humble spirit shares it,
　　Christ has passed the eternal gates.

3 Life eternal! heaven rejoices,
　Jesus lives who once was dead;
　Join, O man, the deathless voices,
　　Child of God, lift up thy head!

　　Patriarchs from the distant ages,
　　Saints all longing for their heaven,
　　Prophets, psalmists, seers, and sages,
　　　All await the glory given.

4 Life eternal! O what wonders
　Crowd on faith; what joy unknown,
　When, amidst earth's closing thunders,
　　Saints shall stand before the throne!
　O to enter that bright portal,
　　See that glowing firmament,
　Know, with thee, O God immortal,
　　"Jesus Christ whom thou hast sent!"

WILLIAM J. IRONS

161 DORT 6. 6. 4. 6. 6. 6. 4.

LOWELL MASON

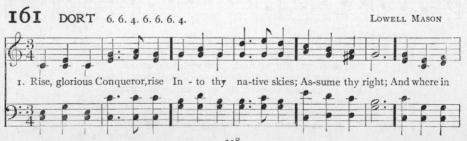

1. Rise, glorious Conqueror, rise In - to thy na-tive skies; As-sume thy right; And where in

Resurrection

many a fold The clouds are backward rolled, Pass through those gates of gold, And reign in light. A - MEN.

2 Victor o'er death and hell,
　Cherubic legions swell
　　The radiant train:
　Praises all heaven inspire;
　Each angel sweeps his lyre,
　And claps his wings of fire,
　　Thou Lamb once slain!

3 Enter, incarnate God!
　No feet but thine have trod
　　The serpent down:
　Blow the full trumpets, blow,
　Wider yon portals throw,
　Saviour, triumphant, go,
　　And take thy crown!

4 Lion of Judah, hail!
　And let thy name prevail
　　From age to age:
　Lord of the rolling years,
　Claim for thine own the spheres,
　For thou hast bought with tears
　　Thy heritage.

MATTHEW BRIDGES

162 ESSEX 7s.

THOMAS CLARK

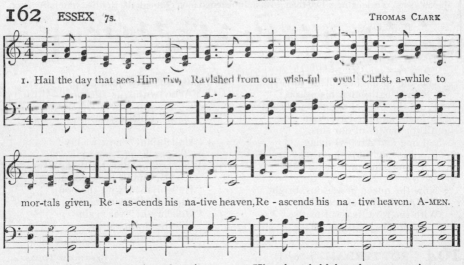

1. Hail the day that sees Him rise, Ravished from our wishful eyes! Christ, a-while to

mor-tals given, Re - as-cends his na-tive heaven, Re - ascends his na - tive heaven. A-MEN.

2 There the pompous triumph waits:
　Lift your heads, eternal gates;
　Wide unfold the radiant scene;
　Take the King of glory in!

3 Circled round with angel powers,
　Their triumphant Lord and ours,
　Conqueror over death and sin,
　Take the King of glory in!

4 Him though highest heaven receives,
　Still he loves the earth he leaves;
　Though returning to his throne,
　Still he calls mankind his own.

5 Saviour, parted from our sight,
　High above yon azure height,
　Grant our hearts may thither rise,
　Following thee beyond the skies.

CHARLES WESLEY

163 ST. KEVIN 7s. 6s. D.
ARTHUR S. SULLIVAN

1. Come, ye faith-ful, raise the strain Of tri-umph-ant glad - ness! God hath brought his Is - ra - el In - to joy from sad - ness, Loosed from Pharaoh's bit - ter yoke Jacob's sons and daughters, Led them with unmoistened foot Through the Red Sea waters. A - MEN.

2 'Tis the spring of souls to-day:
  Christ hath burst his prison,
From the frost and gloom of death
  Light and life have risen.
All the winter of our sins,
  Long and dark, is flying
From his light to whom we give
  Thanks and praise undying.

3 Now the queen of seasons, bright
  With the day of splendor,
With the royal feast of feasts,
  Comes its joy to render;

Comes to glad Jerusalem,
  Who, with true affection,
Welcomes in unwearied strains
  Jesus' resurrection!

4 "Hallelujah!" now we cry
  To our King Immortal,
Who, triumphant, burst the bars
  Of the tomb's dark portal;
"Hallelujah!" with the Son,
  God the Father praising;
"Hallelujah!" yet again
  To the Spirit raising.

JOHN of Damascus. Tr. by JOHN M. NEALE

164 ROTTERDAM 7s. 6s. D.
BERTHOLD TOURS

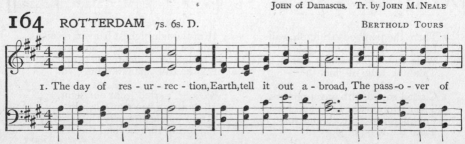

1. The day of res - ur - rec - tion, Earth, tell it out a - broad, The pass - o - ver of

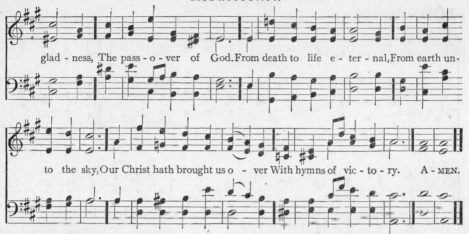

glad - ness, The pass - o - ver of God. From death to life e - ter - nal, From earth un - to the sky, Our Christ hath brought us o - ver With hymns of vic - to - ry. A - MEN.

2 Our hearts be pure from evil,
That we may see aright
The Lord in rays eternal
Of resurrection light;
And, listening to his accents,
May hear, so calm and plain,
His own "All hail!" and, hearing,
May raise the victor-strain.

3 Now let the heavens be joyful!
Let earth her song begin!
Let the round world keep triumph,
And all that is therein!
Invisible and visible,
Their notes let all things blend,
For Christ the Lord hath risen,
Our joy that hath no end.

JOHN of Damascus. Tr. by JOHN M. NEALE

165　STORRS L. M.

TIMOTHY R. MATTHEWS

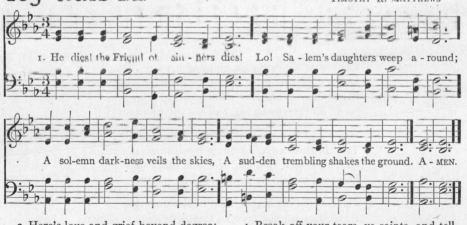

1. He dies! the Friend of sin - ners dies! Lo! Sa - lem's daughters weep a - round;
A sol-emn dark-ness veils the skies, A sud-den trembling shakes the ground. A - MEN.

2 Here's love and grief beyond degree:
The Lord of Glory dies for man!
But lo! what sudden joys we see,
Jesus, the dead, revives again!

3 The rising God forsakes the tomb;
In vain the tomb forbids his rise;
Cherubic legions guard him home,
And shout him welcome to the skies.

4 Break off your tears, ye saints, and tell
How high your great Deliverer reigns;
Sing how he spoiled the hosts of hell,
And led the monster death in chains!

5 Say, "Live forever, wondrous King!
Born to redeem, and strong to save;"
Then ask the monster, "Where's thy sting?"
And, "Where's thy victory, boasting grave?"

　ISAAC WATTS. Alt. by MARTIN MADAN

166 BAPTISTE 11s.

JOHN B. CALKIN

1. Wel - come, hap - py morn - ing! age to age shall say: Hell to - day is
van-quished, heaven is won to - day! Lo, the Dead is liv - ing,
God for ev - er-more! Him their true Cre-a - tor, all his works a - dore. A-MEN.

2 Earth with joy confesses, clothing her for spring,
All good gifts returned with her returning King.
Bloom in every meadow, leaves on every bough,
Speak his sorrows ended, hail his triumph now.

3 Maker and Redeemer, life and health of all,
Thou, from heaven beholding human nature's fall,
Of the Father's Godhead true and only Son,
Manhood to deliver, manhood didst put on.

4 Thou, of life the author, death didst undergo,
Tread the path of darkness, saving strength to show;
Come then, true and faithful, now fulfill thy word,
'Tis thine own third morning, rise, O buried Lord!

5 Loose the souls long-prisoned, bound with Satan's chain;
All that now is fallen raise to life again;
Show thy face in brightness, bid the nations see,
Bring again our daylight; day returns with thee!

VENANTIUS FORTUNATUS. Tr. by JOHN ELLERTON

167 MILES' LANE C. M.

WILLIAM SHRUBSOLE

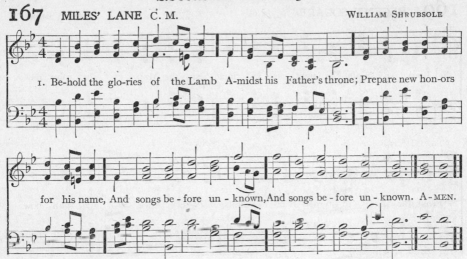

1. Be-hold the glo-ries of the Lamb A-midst his Father's throne; Prepare new hon-ors for his name, And songs be-fore un-known, And songs be-fore un-known. A-MEN.

2 Let elders worship at his feet,
The church adore around;
With vials full of odors sweet,
And harps of sweetest sound.

3 Those are the prayers of all the saints,
And these the hymns they raise:
Jesus is kind to our complaints,
He loves to hear our praise.

4 Now to the Lamb that once was slain
Be endless blessings paid:
Salvation, glory, joy, remain
Forever, on thy head.

5 Thou hast redeemed our souls with blood,
Hast set the prisoners free;
Hast made us kings and priests to God;
And we shall reign with thee.

ISAAC WATTS

168 TRURO L. M.

CHARLES BURNEY

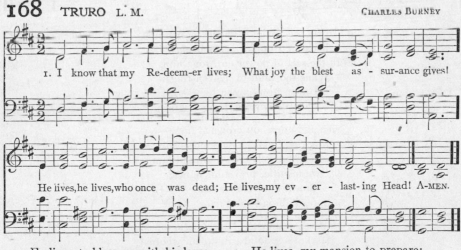

1. I know that my Re-deem-er lives; What joy the blest as-sur-ance gives! He lives, he lives, who once was dead; He lives, my ev-er-last-ing Head! A-MEN.

2 He lives, to bless me with his love;
He lives, to plead for me above;
He lives, my hungry soul to feed;
He lives, to help in time of need.

3 He lives, and grants me daily breath;
He lives, and I shall conquer death;

He lives, my mansion to prepare;
He lives, to bring me safely there.

4 He lives, all glory to his name;
He lives, my Saviour, still the same;
What joy the blest assurance gives,
I know that my Redeemer lives!

SAMUEL MEDLEY

The Son

REGENT SQUARE 8s. 7s. 6l.   HENRY SMART

1. Look, ye saints, the sight is glo-rious, See the Man of sor-rows now;

cres.

From the fight re-turned vic-to-rious, Ev-ery knee to him shall bow:

Crown him, crown him! Crown him, crown him! Crowns become the Vic-tor's brow. A-MEN.

2 Crown the Saviour, angels, crown him:
  Rich the trophies Jesus brings:
In the seat of power enthrone him,
  While the vault of heaven rings:
    Crown him, crown him!
  Crown the Saviour King of kings.

3 Sinners in derision crowned him,
  Mocking thus the Saviour's claim;
Saints and angels crowd around him,
  Own his title, praise his name:
    Crown him, crown him!
  Spread abroad the Victor's fame.

4 Hark, those bursts of acclamation!
  Hark, those loud triumphant chords!
Jesus takes the highest station:
  O what joy the sight affords!
    Crown him, crown him,
  King of kings, and Lord of lords!

THOMAS KELLY

170 **STANLEY** 7s. D.

JOSEPH BARNBY

1. He is gone; a cloud of light Has re-ceived him from our sight;

High in heaven, where eye of men Fol-lows not, nor an-gels' ken;

Through the veils of time and space, Passed in-to the ho-liest place;

All the toil, the sor-row done, All the bat-tle fought and won. A-MEN.

2 He is gone; towards their goal
World and church must onward roll:
Far behind we leave the past;
Forward are our glances cast:
Still his words before us range
Through the ages, as they change:
Wheresoe'er the truth shall lead,
He will give whate'er we need.

3 He is gone; but we once more
Shall behold him as before;
In the heaven of heavens the same,
As on earth he went and came.
In the many mansions there,
Place for us he will prepare:
In that world unseen, unknown,
He and we shall yet be one.

ARTHUR P. STANLEY

171 AUTUMN 8s. 7s. D.

LOUIS VON ESCH

1. Hail, thou once de-spis-èd Je-sus! Hail, thou Gal-i-le-an King!

Thou didst suf-fer to re-lease us; Thou didst free sal-va-tion bring.

Hail, thou ag-o-niz-ing Sav-iour, Bear-er of our sin and shame!

By thy mer-its we find fa-vor; Life is giv-en through thy name. A-MEN.

2 Paschal Lamb, by God appointed,
   All our sins on thee were laid:
By almighty love anointed,
   Thou hast full atonement made.
All thy people are forgiven,
   Through the virtue of thy blood;
Opened is the gate of heaven;
   Peace is made 'twixt man and God.

3 Jesus, hail! enthroned in glory,
   There forever to abide;
All the heavenly hosts adore thee,
   Seated at thy Father's side:

There for sinners thou art pleading;
   There thou dost our place prepare:
Ever for us interceding,
   Till in glory we appear.

4 Worship, honor, power, and blessing,
   Thou art worthy to receive;
Loudest praises, without ceasing,
   Meet it is for us to give.
Help, ye bright angelic spirits;
   Bring your sweetest, noblest lays;
Help to sing our Saviour's merits;
   Help to chant Immanuel's praise!

JOHN BAKEWELL

Ascension and Reign

172 FERGUSON S. M.

GEORGE KINGSLEY

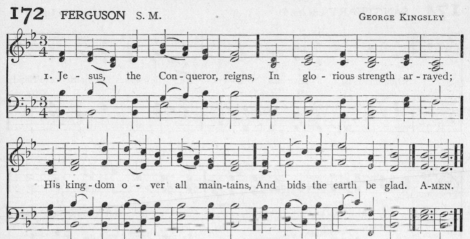

1. Je - sus, the Con - queror, reigns, In glo - rious strength ar - rayed;
His king - dom o - ver all main-tains, And bids the earth be glad. A-MEN.

2 Ye sons of men, rejoice
In Jesus' mighty love;
Lift up your heart, lift up your voice,
To him who rules above.

3 Extol his kingly power;
Kiss the exalted Son,

Who died, and lives to die no more,
High on his Father's throne:

4 Our Advocate with God,
He undertakes our cause,
And spreads through all the earth abroad
The victory of his cross.

CHARLES WESLEY

173 LAUD C. M.

JOHN B. DYKES

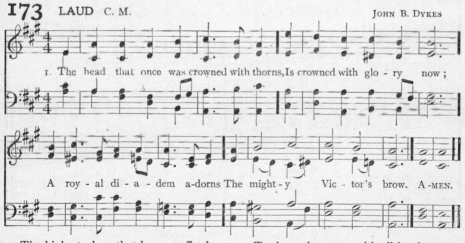

1. The head that once was crowned with thorns, Is crowned with glo - ry now;
A roy - al di - a - dem a-dorns The might-y Vic - tor's brow. A -MEN.

2 The highest place that heaven affords
Is his, is his by right,
The King of kings, and Lord of lords,
And heaven's eternal Light:

3 The joy of all who dwell above,
The joy of all below,
To whom he manifests his love,
And grants his name to know.

4 To them the cross, with all its shame,
With all its grace, is given;
Their name, an everlasting name,
Their joy, the joy of heaven.

5 They suffer with their Lord below,
They reign with him above;
Their everlasting joy to know
The mystery of his love.

THOMAS KELLY

The Son

JOHN B. DYKES

1. One there is, a-bove all oth-ers, Well de-serves the name of Friend;

His is love be-yond a broth-er's, Cost-ly, free, and knows no end.

Which of all our friends, to save us, Could or would have shed his blood?

But the Sav-iour died to have us Rec-on-ciled in him to God. A-MEN.

2 When he lived on earth abasèd,
 Friend of sinners was his name;
Now, above all glory raisèd,
 He rejoices in the same.
O for grace our hearts to soften!
 Teach us, Lord, at length to love;
We, alas! forget too often
 What a Friend we have above.

JOHN NEWTON

Ascension and Reign

175 HERMAS 6s. 5s. D. *With Refrain*   FRANCES R. HAVERGAL

1. Gold-en harps are sound-ing, An-gel voi-ces ring, Pearl-y gates are o-pened, O-pened for the King. Christ, the King of glo-ry, Je-sus, King of love, Is gone up in tri-umph To his throne a-bove.

REFRAIN

All his work is end-ed; Joy-ful-ly we sing, Je-sus hath as-cend-ed, Glo-ry to our King! A-MEN.

2 He who came to save us,
  He who bled and died,
Now is crowned with glory,
  At his Father's side.
Never more to suffer,
  Never more to die;
Jesus, King of glory,
  Is gone up on high.

3 Pleading for his children
  In that blessèd place,
Calling them to glory,
  Sending them his grace,
His bright home preparing,
  Faithful ones, for you,
Jesus ever liveth,
  Ever loveth too.

FRANCES R. HAVERGAL

176 CARLTON 8s. 7s. D.

JOSEPH BARNBY

1. Hal - le - lu - jah! sing to Je - sus! His the scep - ter, his the throne;

Hal - le - lu - jah! his the tri - umph, His the vic - to - ry a - lone;

Hark! the songs of peace - ful Zi - on Thun - der like a might - y flood;

Je - sus out of ev - ery na - tion Hath re-deemed us by his blood. A - MEN.

2 Hallelujah! not as orphans
    Are we left in sorrow now;
Hallelujah! he is near us,
    Faith believes, nor questions how:
Though the cloud from sight received him,
    When the forty days were o'er;
Shall our hearts forget his promise,
    "I am with you evermore"?

3 Hallelujah! Bread of heaven,
    Thou on earth our food, our stay!
Hallelujah! here the sinful
    Flee to thee from day to day;

Intercessor, Friend of sinners,
    Earth's Redeemer, plead for me,
Where the songs of all the sinless
    Sweep across the crystal sea.

4 Hallelujah! sing to Jesus!
    His the scepter, his the throne;
Hallelujah! his the triumph,
    His the victory alone:
Hark! the songs of peaceful Zion
    Thunder like a mighty flood;
Jesus, out of every nation,
    Hath redeemed us by his blood.

WILLIAM C. DIX

Ascension and Reign

177 HARWELL 8. 7. 8. 7. 7. 7.   LOWELL MASON

1. Hark, ten thou - sand harps and voi - ces Sound the note of praise a - bove!

Je - sus reigns, and heaven re - joi - ces; Je - sus reigns, the God of love;

See, he sits on yon - der throne; Je - sus rules the world a - lone.

Hal - le - lu - jah! hal - le - lu - jah! Hal - le - lu - jah! A - men! A - MEN.

2 Jesus, hail! whose glory brightens
　　All above, and gives it worth;
　Lord of life, thy smile enlightens,
　　Cheers, and charms thy saints on earth:
　　　When we think of love like thine,
　　　Lord, we own it love divine.
　　　　Hallelujah. hallelujah!
　　　　Hallelujah! Amen!

3 Saviour, hasten thine appearing;
　　Bring, O bring the glorious day,
　When, the awful summons hearing,
　　Heaven and earth shall pass away;
　　　Then with golden harps we'll sing,
　　　"Glory, glory to our King!"
　　　　Hallelujah! hallelujah!
　　　　Hallelujah! Amen!

THOMAS KELLY

131

178 CHRIST CHURCH 6. 6. 6. 6. 8. 8.

CHARLES STEGGALL

1. Re - joice, the Lord is King! Your Lord and King a - dore;
Mor - tals, give thanks and sing, And tri - umph ev - er - more; Lift up your heart, lift
up your voice; Re - joice, a - gain I say, re - joice. A - MEN.

2 Jesus, the Saviour, reigns,
  The God of truth and love;
When he had purged our stains,
  He took his seat above;
Lift up your heart, lift up your voice;
Rejoice, again I say, rejoice.

3 His kingdom cannot fail,
  He rules o'er earth and heaven;
The keys of death and hell
  Are to our Jesus given;
Lift up your heart, lift up your voice;
Rejoice, again I say, rejoice.

4 He sits at God's right hand
  Till all his foes submit,
And bow to his command,
  And fall beneath his feet;
Lift up your heart, lift up your voice;
Rejoice, again I say, rejoice.

5 He all his foes shall quell,
  And all our sins destroy;
Let every bosom swell
  With pure seraphic joy;
Lift up your heart, lift up your voice;
Rejoice, again I say, rejoice.

6 Rejoice in glorious hope;
  Jesus the Judge shall come,
And take his servants up
  To their eternal home;
We soon shall hear the archangel's voice;
The trump of God shall sound, Rejoice!

CHARLES WESLEY

179 DIADEMATA S. M. D.   GEORGE J. ELVEY

1. Crown him with ma - ny crowns, The Lamb up - on his throne;

Hark! how the heaven - ly an - them drowns All mu - sic but its own:

A - wake, my soul, and sing, Of him who died for thee,

And hail him as thy match - less King Through all e - ter - ni - ty. A-MEN.

2 Crown him the Lord of love;
  Behold his hands and side,
Rich wounds, yet visible above,
  In beauty glorified:
No angel in the sky
Can fully bear that sight,
But downward bends his burning eye
At mysteries so bright.

3 Crown him the Lord of peace,
  Whose power a scepter sways
From pole to pole, that wars may cease,
  And all be prayer and praise:

His reign shall know no end,
  And round his piercèd feet
Fair flowers of paradise extend
  Their fragrance ever sweet.

4 Crown him the Lord of years,
  The Potentate of time,
Creator of the rolling spheres,
  Ineffably sublime!
All hail! Redeemer, hail!
For thou hast died for me;
Thy praise shall never, never fail
Throughout eternity.

MATTHEW BRIDGES

180 CORONATION C. M. OLIVER HOLDEN

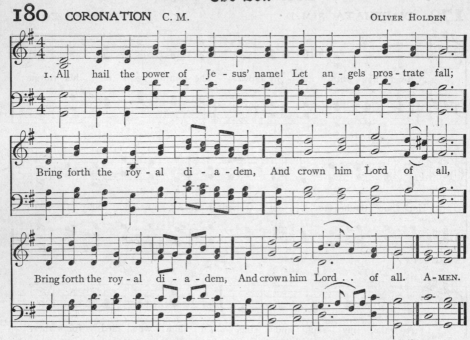

1. All hail the power of Je - sus' name! Let an - gels pros - trate fall;
Bring forth the roy - al di - a - dem, And crown him Lord of all,
Bring forth the roy - al di - a - dem, And crown him Lord .. of all. A-MEN.

2 Ye chosen seed of Israel's race,
　Ye ransomed from the fall,
　Hail him who saves you by his grace,
　And crown him Lord of all.

3 Sinners, whose love can ne'er forget
　The wormwood and the gall;
　Go, spread your trophies at his feet,
　And crown him Lord of all.

4 Let every kindred, every tribe
　On this terrestrial ball,
　To him all majesty ascribe,
　And crown him Lord of all.

5 O that, with yonder sacred throng,
　We at his feet may fall!
　We'll join the everlasting song,
　And crown him Lord of all.
　　　　　　　　EDWARD PERRONET. Alt.

180 MILES' LANE C. M. (*Second Tune*) WILLIAM SHRUBSOLE

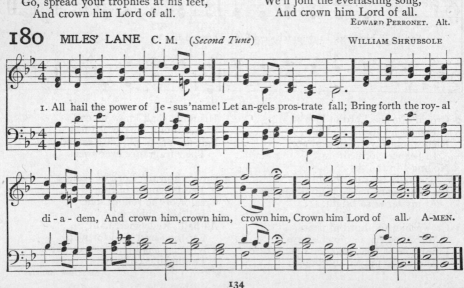

1. All hail the power of Je - sus' name! Let an-gels pros-trate fall; Bring forth the roy-al
di - a - dem, And crown him, crown him, crown him, Crown him Lord of all. A-MEN.

The Holy Spirit

181 WINCHESTER OLD C. M.

G. KIRBYE

1. Come, Ho - ly Ghost, our hearts in - spire, Let us thine in - fluence prove;
Source of the old pro - phet - ic fire, Foun - tain of life and love. A - MEN.

2 Come, Holy Ghost, for moved by thee
   The prophets wrote and spoke;
   Unlock the truth, thyself the key,
   Unseal the sacred book.

3 Expand thy wings, celestial Dove,
   Brood o'er our nature's night;

   On our disordered spirits move,
   And let there now be light.

4 God, through himself, we then shall know,
   If thou within us shine;
   And sound, with all thy saints below,
   The depths of love divine.

CHARLES WESLEY

182 THATCHER S. M.

GEORGE F. HÄNDEL

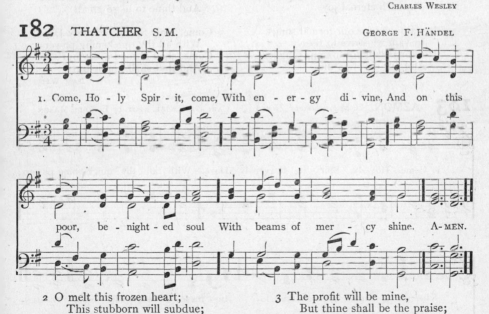

1. Come, Ho - ly Spir - it, come, With en - er - gy di - vine, And on this
poor, be - night - ed soul With beams of mer - cy shine. A - MEN.

2 O melt this frozen heart;
   This stubborn will subdue;
   Each evil passion overcome,
   And form me all anew!

3 The profit will be mine,
   But thine shall be the praise;
   And unto thee will I devote
   The remnant of my days.

BENJAMIN BEDDOME

The Holy Spirit

183 ST. MARTIN'S C. M.

WILLIAM TANSUR

1. Come, Ho - ly Spir - it, heaven - ly Dove, With all thy quickening powers;

Kin - dle a flame of sa - cred love In these cold hearts of ours. A - MEN.

2 Look how we grovel here below,
  Fond of these earthly toys;
  Our souls, how heavily they go,
  To reach eternal joys.

3 In vain we tune our formal songs,
  In vain we strive to rise;
  Hosannas languish on our tongues,
  And our devotion dies.

4 And shall we then forever live
  At this poor dying rate?
  Our love so faint, so cold to thee,
  And thine to us so great!

5 Come, Holy Spirit, heavenly Dove,
  With all thy quickening powers;
  Come, shed abroad a Saviour's love,
  And that shall kindle ours.

ISAAC WATTS

183 AZMON C. M. (*Second Tune*)

CARL G. GLÄSER. Arr. by LOWELL MASON

1. Come, Ho - ly Spir - it, heaven - ly Dove, With all thy quick-ening powers;

Kin - dle a flame of sa - cred love In these cold hearts of ours. A - MEN.

The Holy Spirit

184 BETHEL 6. 6. 4. 6. 6. 6. 4.

JOHN H. CORNELL

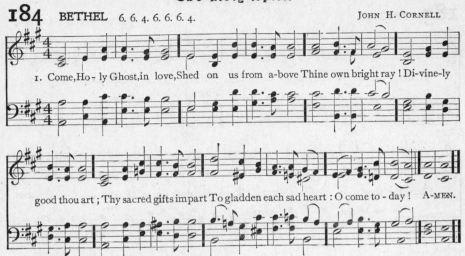

1. Come, Ho - ly Ghost, in love, Shed on us from a-bove Thine own bright ray ! Di - vine-ly
good thou art ; Thy sacred gifts impart To gladden each sad heart : O come to - day ! A-MEN.

2 Come, tenderest Friend, and best,
Our most delightful Guest,
   With soothing power:
Rest, which the weary know,
Shade, 'mid the noontide glow,
Peace, when deep griefs o'erflow,
   Cheer us, this hour!

3 Come, Light serene, and still
Our inmost bosoms fill,
   Dwell in each breast;
We know no dawn but thine,
Send forth thy beams divine,
On our dark souls to shine,
   And make us blest!

4 Come, all the faithful bless;
Let all who Christ confess
   His praise employ;
Give virtue's rich reward,
Victorious death accord,
And, with our glorious Lord,
   Eternal joy!

ROBERT II, King of France. Tr. by RAY PALMER

184 OLIVET 6. 6. 4. 6. 6. 6. 4. *(Second Tune)*

LOWELL MASON

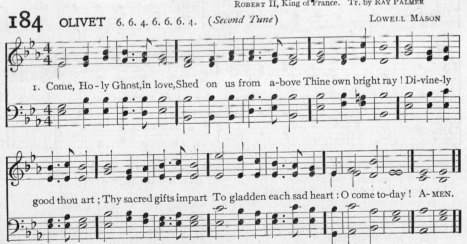

1. Come, Ho - ly Ghost, in love, Shed on us from a-bove Thine own bright ray ! Di - vine-ly
good thou art ; Thy sacred gifts impart To gladden each sad heart : O come to-day ! A- MEN.

185 FISK 7s.

CALVIN S. HARRINGTON

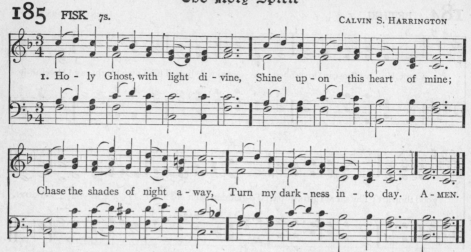

1. Ho - ly Ghost, with light di - vine, Shine up - on this heart of mine;

Chase the shades of night a - way, Turn my dark - ness in - to day. A - MEN.

2 Holy Ghost, with power divine,
   Cleanse this guilty heart of mine;
   Long hath sin, without control,
   Held dominion o'er my soul.

3 Holy Ghost, with joy divine,
   Cheer this saddened heart of mine;

Bid my many woes depart,
Heal my wounded, bleeding heart.

4 Holy Spirit, all divine,
   Dwell within this heart of mine;
   Cast down every idol-throne,
   Reign supreme, and reign alone.

ARTHUR REED

186 COOLING C. M.

ALONZO J. ABBEY

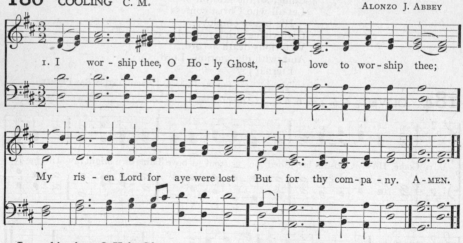

1. I wor - ship thee, O Ho - ly Ghost, I love to wor - ship thee;

My ris - en Lord for aye were lost But for thy com - pa - ny. A - MEN.

2 I worship thee, O Holy Ghost,
   I love to worship thee;
   I grieved thee long, alas! thou know'st
   It grieves me bitterly.

3 I worship thee, O Holy Ghost,
   I love to worship thee;

Thy patient love, at what a cost
At last it conquered me!

4 I worship thee, O Holy Ghost,
   I love to worship thee;
   With thee each day is Pentecost,
   Each night Nativity.

WILLIAM F. WARREN

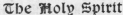

187 MELCOMBE L. M.

SAMUEL WEBBE

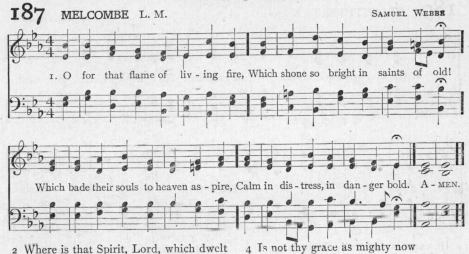

1. O for that flame of liv-ing fire, Which shone so bright in saints of old! Which bade their souls to heaven as-pire, Calm in dis-tress, in dan-ger bold. A-MEN.

2 Where is that Spirit, Lord, which dwelt
In Abraham's breast, and sealed him thine?
Which made Paul's heart with sorrow melt,
And glow with energy divine?

3 That Spirit which, from age to age,
Proclaimed thy love, and taught thy ways?
Brightened Isaiah's vivid page,
And breathed in David's hallowed lays?

4 Is not thy grace as mighty now
As when Elijah felt its power;
When glory beamed from Moses' brow,
Or Job endured the trying hour?

5 Remember, Lord, the ancient days;
Renew thy work; thy grace restore;
Warm our cold hearts to prayer and praise,
And teach us how to love thee more.

WILLIAM H. BATHURST

188 KEBLE L. M.

JOHN B. DYKES

1. O Spir-it of the liv-ing God! In all thy plen-i-tude of grace, Wher-e'er the foot of man hath trod, De-scend on our a-pos-tate race. A-MEN.

2 Give tongues of fire and hearts of love
To preach the reconciling word;
Give power and unction from above,
Whene'er the joyful sound is heard.

3 Be darkness, at thy coming, light;
Confusion, order, in thy path;

Souls without strength, inspire with might;
Bid mercy triumph over wrath.

4 Baptize the nations; far and nigh
The triumphs of the cross record;
The name of Jesus glorify,
Till every kindred call him Lord.

JAMES MONTGOMERY

The Holy Spirit

189 ST. CUTHBERT 8. 6. 8. 4.

JOHN B. DYKES

1. Our blest Re-deem-er, ere he breathed His ten-der last fare-well,

A Guide, a Com-fort-er be-queathed, With us to dwell A-MEN.

2 He came in tongues of living flame,
　To teach, convince, subdue;
　All-powerful as the wind he came,
　As viewless, too.

3 He comes, sweet influence to impart,
　A gracious, willing guest,
　While he can find one humble heart
　Wherein to rest.

4 And his that gentle voice we hear,
　Soft as the breath of even,　[fear,
　That checks each fault, that calms each
　And speaks of heaven.

5 Spirit of purity and grace,
　Our weakness, pitying, see;
　O make our hearts thy dwelling place,
　And worthier thee!

HARRIET AUBER

190 LAMBETH C. M.

Composer Unknown

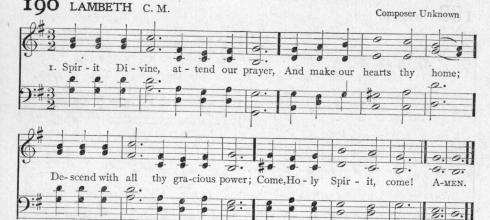

1. Spir-it Di-vine, at-tend our prayer, And make our hearts thy home;

De-scend with all thy gra-cious power; Come, Ho-ly Spir-it, come! A-MEN.

2 Come as the light: to us reveal
　Our sinfulness and woe;
　And lead us in those paths of life
　Where all the righteous go.

3 Come as the fire, and purge our hearts,
　Like sacrificial flame;
　Let our whole soul an offering be
　To our Redeemer's name.

4 Come as the wind, with rushing sound,
　With pentecostal grace;
　And make the great salvation known
　Wide as the human race.

5 Come as the dove, and spread thy wings,
　The wings of peaceful love;
　And let thy church on earth become
　Blest as thy church above.

ANDREW REED

191 BEALOTH S. M. D.   L. C. EVERETT

1. Spir - it of faith, come down, Re - veal the things of God;
And make to us the God - head known, And wit - ness with the blood.
'Tis thine the blood to ap - ply, And give us eyes to see,
Who did for ev - ery sin - ner die, Hath sure- ly died for me. A - MEN.

2 No man can truly say
  That Jesus is the Lord,
Unless thou take the veil away,
  And breathe the living word.
Then, only then, we feel
  Our interest in his blood,
And cry, with joy unspeakable,
  "Thou art my Lord, my God!"

3 O that the world might know
  The all-atoning Lamb!
Spirit of faith, descend, and show
  The virtue of his name.
The grace which all may find,
  The saving power, impart;
And testify to all mankind,
  And speak in every heart.

CHARLES WESLEY

192 LIGHT OF THE WORLD 8s. 7s. D.

FERDINAND H. HIMMEL

1. Ho - ly Ghost, dis - pel our sad - ness; Pierce the clouds of na - ture's night;

Come, thou Source of joy and glad - ness, Breathe thy life, and spread thy light:

From the height which knows no meas - ure, As a gra-cious shower de-scend,

Bring-ing down the rich - est treas-ure Man can wish, or God can send. A-MEN.

2 Author of the new creation,
   Come with unction and with power:
Make our hearts thy habitation;
   On our souls thy graces shower:
Hear, O hear our supplication,
   Blessèd Spirit, God of peace!
Rest upon this congregation,
   With the fullness of thy grace.

PAUL GERHARDT. Tr. by JOHN C. JACOBI. Alt.

193 HOLY SPIRIT, FAITHFUL GUIDE 7s. D.

MARCUS M. WELLS

1. Ho - ly Spir - it, faith - ful Guide, Ev - er near the Chris-tian's side;

Gen - tly lead us by the hand, Pil - grims in a des - ert land;

Wea - ry souls for - e'er re - joice, While they hear that sweet - est voice,

Whispering soft - ly, "Wan-derer, come! Fol - low me, I'll guide thee home." A - MEN.

2 Ever present, truest Friend,
Ever near thine aid to lend,
Leave us not to doubt and fear,
Groping on in darkness drear;
When the storms are raging sore,
Hearts grow faint, and hopes give o'er,
Whisper softly, "Wanderer, come!
Follow me, I'll guide thee home."

3 When our days of toil shall cease,
Waiting still for sweet release,
Nothing left but heaven and prayer,
Wondering if our names were there;
Wading deep the dismal flood,
Pleading naught but Jesus' blood,
Whisper softly, "Wanderer, come!
Follow me, I'll guide thee home."

MARCUS M. WELLS

194 ST. CATHERINE L. M. 6l.

Adapted by J. G. WALTON

1. Cre - a - tor, Spir - it! by whose aid The world's foun-da - tions first were laid,

Come, vis - it ev - ery pi - ous mind, Come, pour thy joys on hu - man-kind:

From sin and sor - row set us free, And make thy tem-ples wor - thy thee. A - MEN.

2 O Source of uncreated light,
The Father's promised Paraclete!
Thrice holy Fount, thrice holy Fire,
Our hearts with heavenly love inspire:
Come, and thy sacred unction bring,
To sanctify us while we sing.

3 Plenteous of grace, descend from high,
Rich in thy sevenfold energy!
Thou Strength of His almighty hand,
Whose power does heaven and earth com-
Refine and purge our earthly parts, [mand,
But O inflame and fire our hearts!

RABANUS MAURUS. Tr. by JOHN DRYDEN

195 PALGRAVE 7s. 6l.

H. DE LA HAYE BLACKITH

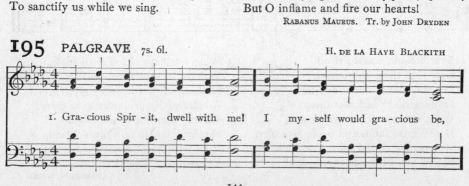

1. Gra - cious Spir - it, dwell with me! I my - self would gra - cious be,

The Holy Spirit

And, with words that help and heal, Would thy life in mine re - veal;

And with ac - tions bold and meek, Would for Christ my Sav-iour speak. A - MEN.

2 Truthful Spirit, dwell with me!
  I myself would truthful be;
  And, with wisdom kind and clear,
  Let thy life in mine appear;
  And, with actions brotherly,
  Speak my Lord's sincerity.

3 Tender Spirit, dwell with me!
  I myself would tender be;
  Shut my heart up like a flower
  In temptation's darksome hour,
  Open it when shines the sun,
  And his love by fragrance own.

4 Mighty Spirit, dwell with me!
  I myself would mighty be;
  Mighty so as to prevail,
  Where unaided man must fail;
  Ever, by a mighty hope,
  Pressing on and bearing up.

5 Holy Spirit, dwell with me!
  I myself would holy be:
  Separate from sin, I would
  Choose and cherish all things good;
  And whatever I can be
  Give to him who gave me thee.

THOMAS T. LYNCH

196 PURLEIGH S. M.

JOHN B. CALKIN

1. Breathe on me, Breath of God, Fill me with life a - new,

That I may love what thou dost love, And do what thou wouldst do. A - MEN.

2 Breathe on me, Breath of God,
  Until my heart is pure,
  Until with thee I will one will,
  To do or to endure.

3 Breathe on me, Breath of God,
  Till I am wholly thine,

Till all this earthly part of me
  Glows with thy fire divine.

4 Breathe on me, Breath of God,
  So shall I never die,
  But live with thee the perfect life
  Of thine eternity.

EDWIN HATCH

145

The Holy Spirit

197 EMILIE 10s.

JOHN W. BAUME

1. Spir-it of God! de-scend up-on my heart; Wean it from earth, through all its puls-es move; Stoop to my weak-ness, might-y as thou art, And make me love thee as I ought to love. A-MEN.

2 I ask no dream, no prophet ecstasies,
  No sudden rending of the veil of clay,
No angel visitant, no opening skies;
  But take the dimness of my soul away.

3 Hast thou not bid us love thee, God and King?
  All, all thine own, soul, heart and strength and mind;
I see thy cross; there teach my heart to cling:
  O let me seek thee, and O let me find!

4 Teach me to feel that thou art always nigh;
  Teach me the struggles of the soul to bear,
To check the rising doubt, the rebel sigh;
  Teach me the patience of unanswered prayer.

5 Teach me to love thee as thine angels love,
  One holy passion filling all my frame;
The kindling of the heaven-descended Dove,
  My heart an altar, and thy love the flame.

GEORGE CROLY

The Holy Scriptures

198 BURLINGTON C. M.

JOHN F. BURROWES

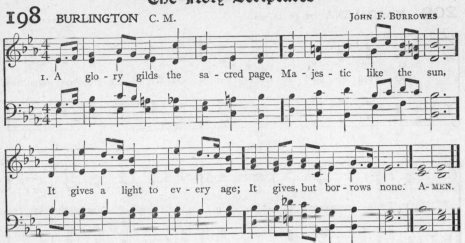

1. A glo - ry gilds the sa - cred page, Ma - jes - tic like the sun,

It gives a light to ev - ery age; It gives, but bor - rows none. A - MEN.

2 The hand that gave it still supplies
  The gracious light and heat;
His truths upon the nations rise:
  They rise, but never set.

3 Let everlasting thanks be thine
  For such a bright display,

As makes a world of darkness shine
  With beams of heavenly day.

4 My soul rejoices to pursue
  The steps of him I love,
Till glory breaks upon my view
  In brighter worlds above.

WILLIAM COWPER

199 HOLBORN HILL L. M.

St Alban's Tune Book

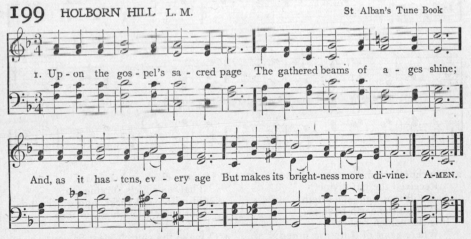

1. Up - on the gos - pel's sa - cred page The gathered beams of a - ges shine;

And, as it has - tens, ev - ery age But makes its bright-ness more di - vine. A - MEN.

2 On mightier wing, in loftier flight,
  From year to year does knowledge soar;
And, as it soars, the gospel light
  Becomes effulgent more and more.

3 More glorious still, as centuries roll,
  New regions blest, new powers unfurled,

Expanding with the expanding soul,
  Its radiance shall o'erflow the world,—

4 Flow to restore, but not destroy;
  As when the cloudless lamp of day
Pours out its floods of light and joy,
  And sweeps the lingering mists away.

JOHN BOWRING

200 MAGDALENA 7s. 6s. D.

JOHN STAINER

1. O Word of God in-car-nate, O Wis-dom from on high,
O Truth un-changed, un-chang-ing, O Light of our dark sky;
We praise thee for the ra-diance That from the hal-lowed page,
A lan-tern to our foot-steps, Shines on from age to age. A-MEN.

2 The church from thee, her Master,
　Received the gift divine,
And still that light she lifteth
　O'er all the earth to shine.
It is the golden casket
　Where gems of truth are stored;
It is the heaven-drawn picture
　Of thee, the living Word.

3 It floateth like a banner
　Before God's host unfurled;
It shineth like a beacon
　Above the darkling world;

It is the chart and compass,
　That, o'er life's surging sea,
'Mid mists, and rocks, and quicksands,
　Still guides, O Christ, to thee.

4 O make thy church, dear Saviour,
　A lamp of burnished gold,
To bear before the nations
　Thy true light, as of old;
O teach thy wandering pilgrims
　By this their path to trace,
Till, clouds and darkness ended,
　They see thee face to face.

WILLIAM W. HOW

201 BURLINGTON C. M.

JOHN F. BURROWES

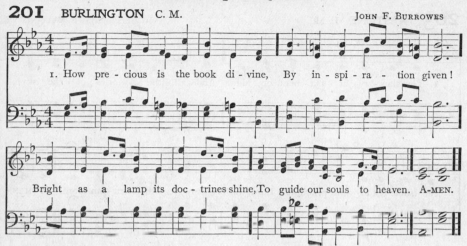

1. How pre - cious is the book di - vine, By in - spi - ra - tion given!
Bright as a lamp its doc - trines shine, To guide our souls to heaven. A-MEN.

2 It sweetly cheers our drooping hearts,
In this dark vale of tears;
Life, light, and joy it still imparts,
And quells our rising fears.

3 This lamp, through all the tedious night
Of life, shall guide our way,
Till we behold the clearer light
Of an eternal day.

JOHN FAWCETT

202 GILEAD L. M.

ETIENNE H. MEHUL

1. The heavens de-clare thy glo - ry, Lord; In ev - ery star thy wis - dom shines;
But when our eyes be-hold thy word, We read thy name in fair - er lines. A-MEN.

2 The rolling sun, the changing light,
And nights and days, thy power confess;
But the blest volume thou hast writ,
Reveals thy justice and thy grace.

3 Sun, moon, and stars convey thy praise
Round the whole earth, and never stand:
So, when thy truth began its race,
It touched and glanced on every land.

4 Nor shall thy spreading gospel rest,
Till through the world thy truth has run;
Till Christ has all the nations blessed
That see the light, or feel the sun.

5 Great Sun of righteousness, arise,
Bless the dark world with heavenly light;
Thy gospel makes the simple wise,
Thy laws are pure, thy judgments right.

6 Thy noblest wonders here we view,
In souls renewed, and sins forgiven;
Lord, cleanse my sins, my soul renew,
And make thy word my guide to heaven.

ISAAC WATTS

203 ALSTONE L. M.   CHRISTOPHER E. WILLING

1. The star-ry fir-ma-ment on high, And all the glo-ries of the sky,

Yet shine not to thy praise, O Lord, So bright-ly as thy writ-ten word. A-MEN.

2 The hopes that holy word supplies,
Its truths divine and precepts wise,
In each a heavenly beam I see,
And every beam conducts to thee.

3 Almighty Lord, the sun shall fail,
The moon forget her nightly tale,

And deepest silence hush on high
The radiant chorus of the sky;

4 But, fixed for everlasting years,
Unmoved amid the wreck of spheres,
Thy word shall shine in cloudless day,
When heaven and earth have passed away.

ROBERT GRANT

204 SALOME C. M.   LUDWIG VAN BEETHOVEN

1. How shall the young se-cure their hearts, And guard their lives from sin?

Thy word the choic-est rule im-parts, To keep the con-science clean. A-MEN.

2 When once it enters to the mind,
It spreads such light abroad,
The meanest souls instruction find,
And raise their thoughts to God.

3 'Tis like the sun, a heavenly light,
That guides us all the day;

And, through the dangers of the night,
A lamp to lead our way.

4 Thy word is everlasting truth;
How pure is every page!
That holy book shall guide our youth,
And well support our age.

ISAAC WATTS

205 BARTON C. M.

Composer Unknown

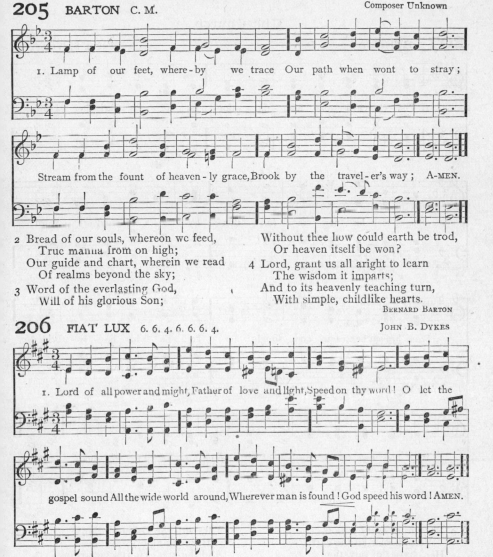

1. Lamp of our feet, where-by we trace Our path when wont to stray;

Stream from the fount of heaven-ly grace, Brook by the travel-er's way; A-MEN.

2 Bread of our souls, whereon we feed,
   True manna from on high;
   Our guide and chart, wherein we read
   Of realms beyond the sky;

3 Word of the everlasting God,
   Will of his glorious Son;

Without thee how could earth be trod,
   Or heaven itself be won?

4 Lord, grant us all aright to learn
   The wisdom it imparts;
   And to its heavenly teaching turn,
   With simple, childlike hearts.

BERNARD BARTON

206 FIAT LUX 6. 6. 4. 6. 6. 6. 4.

JOHN B. DYKES

1. Lord of all power and might, Father of love and light, Speed on thy word! O let the

gospel sound All the wide world around, Wherever man is found! God speed his word! AMEN.

2 Hail, blessèd Jubilee!
   Thine, Lord, the glory be;
       Hallelujah!
   Thine was the mighty plan;
   From thee the work began;
   Away with praise of man!
       Glory to God!

3 Lo, what embattled foes,
   Stern in their hate, oppose
       God's holy word!
   One for his truth we stand,

Strong in his own right hand,
   Firm as a martyr-band:
       God shield his word!

4 Onward shall be our course,
   Despite of fraud or force;
       God is before.
   His words erelong shall run
   Free as the noonday sun;
   His purpose must be done:
       God bless his word!

HUGH STOWELL

Institutions of Christianity

The Church

207 AURELIA 7s. 6s. D.

SAMUEL S. WESLEY

1. The church-'s one foun-da-tion Is Je-sus Christ her Lord;
She is his new cre-a-tion By wa-ter and the word:
From heaven he came and sought her To be his ho-ly bride;
With his own blood he bought her, And for her life he died. A-MEN.

2 Elect from every nation,
  Yet one o'er all the earth,
Her charter of salvation,
  One Lord, one faith, one birth;
One holy name she blesses,
  Partakes one holy food,
And to one hope she presses,
  With every grace endued.

3 'Mid toil and tribulation,
  And tumult of her war,
She waits the consummation
  Of peace for evermore;

Till, with the vision glorious,
  Her longing eyes are blest,
And the great church victorious
  Shall be the church at rest.

4 Yet she on earth hath union
  With God the Three in One,
And mystic sweet communion
  With those whose rest is won:
O happy ones and holy!
  Lord, give us grace that we,
Like them, the meek and lowly,
  On high may dwell with thee.

SAMUEL J. STONE

208 ST. THOMAS S. M.　　　　　　AARON WILLIAMS, Coll.

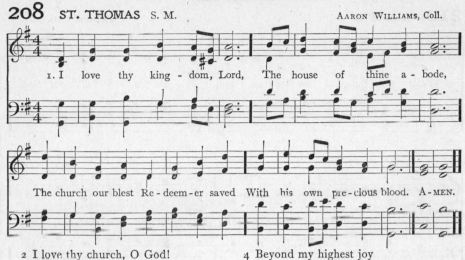

1. I love thy king-dom, Lord, The house of thine a-bode,

The church our blest Re-deem-er saved With his own pre-cious blood. A-MEN.

2 I love thy church, O God!
　Her walls before thee stand,
Dear as the apple of thine eye,
　And graven on thy hand.

3 For her my tears shall fall;
　For her my prayers ascend;
To her my cares and toils be given;
　Till toils and cares shall end.

4 Beyond my highest joy
　I prize her heavenly ways,
Her sweet communion, solemn vows,
　Her hymns of love and praise.

5 Sure as thy truth shall last,
　To Zion shall be given
The brightest glories earth can yield,
　And brighter bliss of heaven.
　　　　　　　TIMOTHY DWIGHT

209 BRACONDALE C. M.　　　　　　JOSIAH BOOTH

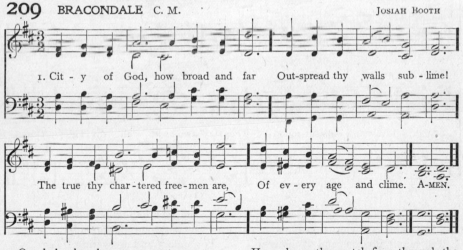

1. Cit-y of God, how broad and far Out-spread thy walls sub-lime!

The true thy char-tered free-men are, Of ev-ery age and clime. A-MEN.

2 One holy church, one army strong,
　One steadfast high intent,
One working band, one harvest song,
　One King omnipotent!

3 How purely hath thy speech come down
　From man's primeval youth!
How grandly hath thine empire grown
　Of freedom, love, and truth!

4 How gleam thy watch fires through the
　With never-fainting ray! [night,
How rise thy towers, serene and bright,
　To meet the dawning day!

5 In vain the surge's angry shock,
　In vain the drifting sands;
Unharmed upon the eternal Rock,
　The eternal city stands.
　　　　　　　SAMUEL JOHNSON

210 AUSTRIA 8s. 7s. D.

Francis J. Haydn

1. Glo - rious things of thee are spo - ken, Zi - on, cit - y of our God;

He, whose word can - not be bro - ken, Formed thee for his own a - bode;

On the Rock of A - ges found-ed, What can shake thy sure re - pose?

With sal - va-tion's walls sur-round-ed, Thou may'st smile at all thy foes. A-men.

2 See, the streams of living waters,
   Springing from eternal love,
Well supply thy sons and daughters,
   And all fear of want remove:
Who can faint, while such a river
   Ever flows their thirst to assuage?
Grace which, like the Lord, the giver,
   Never fails from age to age.

3 Round each habitation hovering,
   See the cloud and fire appear
For a glory and a covering,
   Showing that the Lord is near!
Glorious things of thee are spoken,
   Zion, city of our God;
He, whose word cannot be broken,
   Formed thee for his own abode.

John Newton

The Church

211 CRUCIFER 8s. 7s. D.

HENRY SMART

1. Hear what God the Lord hath spo-ken: O my peo-ple, faint and few,
Com-fort-less, af-flict-ed, bro-ken, Fair a-bodes I build for you;
Scenes of heart-felt trib-u-la-tion Shall no more per-plex your ways;
You shall name your walls "Sal-va-tion," And your gates shall all be "Praise." A-MEN.

2 There, like streams that feed the garden,
  Pleasures without end shall flow;
For the Lord, your faith rewarding,
  All his bounty shall bestow.
Still in undisturbed possession,
  Peace and righteousness shall reign;
Never shall you feel oppression,
  Hear the voice of war again.

3 Ye no more your suns descending,
  Waning moons no more shall see;
But, your griefs forever ending,
  Find eternal noon in me:
God shall rise, and, shining o'er you,
  Change to day the gloom of night;
He, the Lord, shall be your glory,
  God your everlasting light.

WILLIAM COWPER

212 ETON COLLEGE 8. 7. 8. 7. 4. 7.   JOSEPH BARNBY

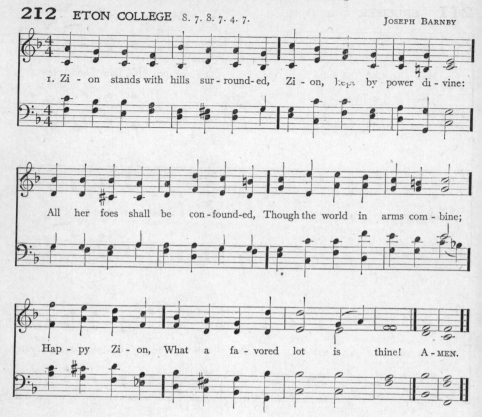

1. Zi - on stands with hills sur - round- ed, Zi - on, kept by power di - vine:

All her foes shall be con - found- ed, Though the world in arms com - bine;

Hap - py Zi - on, What a fa - vored lot is thine! A - MEN.

2 Every human tie may perish;
  Friend to friend unfaithful prove;
Mothers cease their own to cherish;
  Heaven and earth at last remove;
    But no changes
  Can attend Jehovah's love.

3 In the furnace God may prove thee,
  Thence to bring thee forth more bright,
But can never cease to love thee;
  Thou art precious in his sight:
    God is with thee,
  God, thine everlasting light.

THOMAS KELLY

213 PARK STREET L. M.   FREDERICK M. A. VENUA

1. Great God! at - tend, while Zi - on sings The joy that from thy

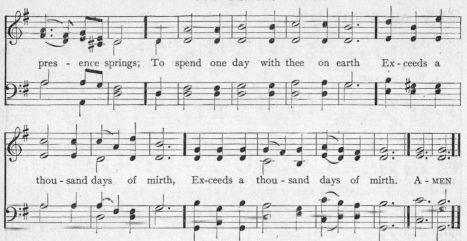

pres - ence springs; To spend one day with thee on earth Ex - ceeds a

thou - sand days of mirth, Ex-ceeds a thou - sand days of mirth. A - MEN.

2 Might I enjoy the meanest place
   Within thy house, O God of grace,
   Nor tents of ease, nor thrones of power,
   Should tempt my feet to leave thy door.

3 God is our sun, he makes our day:
   God is our shield, he guards our way

From all the assaults of hell and sin,
From foes without, and foes within.

4 O God, our King, whose sovereign sway
   The glorious hosts of heaven obey,
   And devils at thy presence flee;
   Blest is the man that trusts in thee.

ISAAC WATTS

214 ST. ANNE C. M.

WILLIAM CROFT

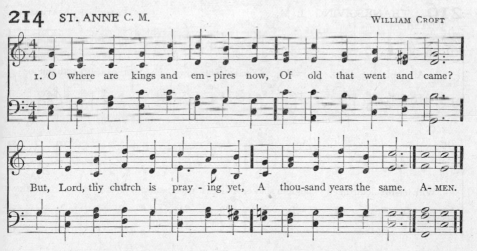

1. O where are kings and em - pires now, Of old that went and came?

But, Lord, thy church is pray - ing yet, A thou-sand years the same. A- MEN.

2 We mark her goodly battlements,
   And her foundations strong;
   We hear within the solemn voice
   Of her unending song.

3 For not like kingdoms of the world
   Thy holy church, O God!

Though earthquake shocks are threaten-
   And tempests are abroad;   [ing her,

4 Unshaken as eternal hills,
   Immovable she stands,
   A mountain that shall fill the earth,
   A house not made with hands.

A. CLEVELAND COXE

215 ALL SAINTS L. M.

WILLIAM KNAPP

1. How pleas-ant, how di-vine-ly fair, O Lord of hosts, thy dwell-ings are!

With strong de - sire my spir - it faints To meet th'as-sem-blies of thy saints. A-MEN.

2 Blest are the saints that sit on high,
Around thy throne of majesty;
Thy brightest glories shine above,
And all their work is praise and love.

3 Blest are the souls that find a place
Within the temple of thy grace:

Here they behold thy gentler rays,
And seek thy face, and learn thy praise.

4 Cheerful they walk with growing strength,
Till all shall meet in heaven at length,
Till all before thy face appear,
And join in nobler worship there.

ISAAC WATTS

216 THANKSGIVING L. M.

FRANCIS R. STATHAM

1. Arm of the Lord, a - wake, a - wake! Thine own im - mor - tal strength put on!

With ter-ror clothed, hell's kingdom shake, And cast thy foes with fu - ry down. A - MEN.

2 By death and hell pursued in vain,
To thee the ransomed seed shall come;
Shouting, their heavenly Zion gain,
And pass through death triumphant home.

3 The pain of life shall then be o'er,
The anguish and distracting care;

There sighing grief shall weep no more,
And sin shall never enter there.

4 Where pure, essential joy is found,
The Lord's redeemed their heads shall
With everlasting gladness crowned, [raise,
And filled with love, and lost in praise.

CHARLES WESLEY

The Church

217 LUTON L. M.

GEORGE BURDER

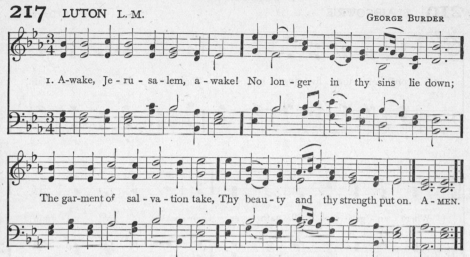

1. A-wake, Je-ru-sa-lem, a-wake! No lon-ger in thy sins lie down;

The gar-ment of sal-va-tion take, Thy beau-ty and thy strength put on. A - MEN.

2 Shake off the dust that blinds thy sight,
And hides the promise from thine eyes;
Arise, and struggle into light,
The great Deliverer calls, Arise!

3 Shake off the bands of sad despair;
Zion, assert thy liberty;

Look up, thy broken heart prepare,
And God shall set the captive free.

4 Vessels of mercy, sons of grace,
Be purged from every sinful stain,
Be like your Lord, his word embrace,
Nor bear his hallowed name in vain.

CHARLES WESLEY

218 WARD L. M.

Arr. by LOWELL MASON

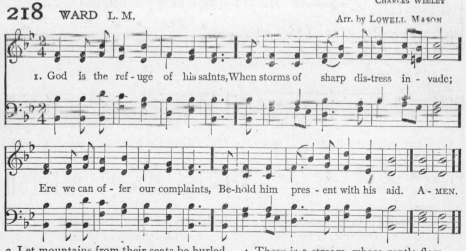

1. God is the ref-uge of his saints, When storms of sharp dis-tress in - vade;

Ere we can of-fer our complaints, Be-hold him pres - ent with his aid. A - MEN.

2 Let mountains from their seats be hurled
Down to the deep, and buried there,
Convulsions shake the solid world,
Our faith shall never yield to fear.

3 Loud may the troubled ocean roar;
In sacred peace our souls abide;
While every nation, every shore,
Trembles, and dreads the swelling tide.

4 There is a stream, whose gentle flow
Supplies the city of our God,
Life, love, and joy, still gliding through,
And watering our divine abode.

5 That sacred stream, thy holy word,
Our grief allays, our fear controls:
Sweet peace thy promises afford,
And give new strength to fainting souls.

ISAAC WATTS

219 BLAIRGOWRIE 7s. 6s. D.

JOHN B. DYKES

1. Lord of the liv - ing har - vest That whit - ens o'er the plain,
Where an - gels soon shall gath - er Their sheaves of gold - en grain;
Ac - cept these hands to la - bor, These hearts to trust and love,
And deign with them to hast - en Thy king - dom from a - bove. A - MEN.

2 As laborers in thy vineyard,
   Send us, O Christ, to be
Content to bear the burden
   Of weary days for thee;
We ask no other wages,
   When thou shalt call us home,
But to have shared the travail
   Which makes thy kingdom come.

3 Come down, thou Holy Spirit!
   And fill our souls with light,
Clothe us in spotless raiment,
   In linen clean and white;
Beside thy sacred altar
   Be with us, where we stand,
To sanctify thy people
   Through all this happy land.

JOHN S. B. MONSELL

220 TRURO L. M.
CHARLES BURNEY

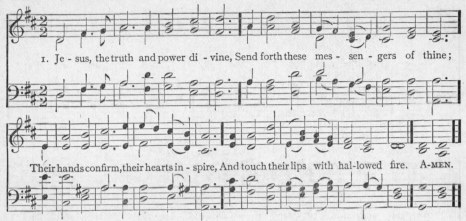

1. Je - sus, the truth and power di - vine, Send forth these mes - sen - gers of thine;

Their hands confirm, their hearts in - spire, And touch their lips with hal-lowed fire. A-MEN.

2 Be thou their mouth and wisdom, Lord;
Thou, by the hammer of thy word,
The rocky hearts in pieces break,
And bid the sons of thunder speak.

3 To those who would their Lord embrace,
Give them to preach the word of grace;

Sweetly their yielding bosoms move,
And melt them with the fire of love.

4 Let all with thankful hearts confess
Thy welcome messengers of peace;
Thy power in their report be found,
And let thy feet behind them sound.
CHARLES WESLEY

221 ST. VINCENT L. M.
JAMES UGLOW

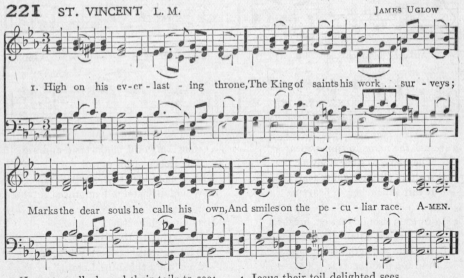

1. High on his ev-er - last - ing throne, The King of saints his work . . sur - veys;

Marks the dear souls he calls his own, And smiles on the pe - cu - liar race. A-MEN.

2 He rests well pleased their toils to see;
Beneath his easy yoke they move;
With all their heart and strength agree
In the sweet labor of his love.

3 See where the servants of their Lord,
A busy multitude, appear;
For Jesus day and night employed,
His heritage they toil to clear.

4 Jesus their toil delighted sees,
Their industry vouchsafes to crown;
He kindly gives the wished increase,
And sends the promised blessing down.

5 O multiply thy sower's seed,
And fruit we every hour shall bear;
Throughout the world thy gospel spread,
Thine everlasting truth declare!
161 AUGUSTUS G. SPANGENBERG. Tr. by JOHN WESLEY

7

222 CORONATION C. M.   OLIVER HOLDEN

1. Je - sus! the name high o - ver all, In hell, or earth, or sky;

An - gels and men be - fore it fall, And dev - ils fear and fly;

An - gels and men be - fore it fall, And dev - ils fear and fly. A - MEN.

2 Jesus! the name to sinners dear,
  The name to sinners given;
It scatters all their guilty fear;
It turns their hell to heaven.

3 Jesus the prisoner's fetters breaks,
  And bruises Satan's head;
Power into strengthless souls he speaks,
  And life into the dead.

4 O that the world might taste and see
  The riches of his grace!
The arms of love that compass me
  Would all mankind embrace.

5 His only righteousness I show,
  His saving truth proclaim;
'Tis all my business here below,
  To cry, "Behold the Lamb!"

6 Happy, if with my latest breath
  I may but gasp his name;
Preach him to all, and cry in death,
  "Behold, behold the Lamb!"

CHARLES WESLEY

223 CORNELL C. M.

JOHN H. CORNELL

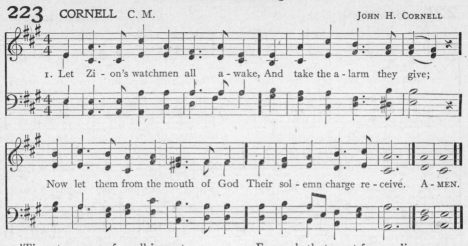

1. Let Zi - on's watchmen all a - wake, And take the a - larm they give;
Now let them from the mouth of God Their sol - emn charge re - ceive. A - MEN.

2 'Tis not a cause of small import
The pastor's care demands;
But what might fill an angel's heart,
And filled a Saviour's hands.

3 They watch for souls for whom the Lord
Did heavenly bliss forego;

For souls that must forever live
In raptures or in woe.

4 May they that Jesus, whom they preach,
Their own Redeemer see;
And watch thou daily o'er their souls,
That they may watch for thee.

PHILIP DODDRIDGE

224 ST. GABRIEL C. M.

HENRY W. GREATOREX

1. How rich thy boun - ty, King of kings! Thy fa - vors, how di - vine!
The bless-ings which thy gos - pel brings, How splen-did - ly they shine! A - MEN.

2 Gold is but dross, and gems but toys,
Should gold and gems compare,
How mean, when set against those joys
Thy poorest servants share!

3 Yet all these treasures of thy grace
Are lodged in urns of clay;
And the weak sons of mortal race
The immortal gifts convey.

4 Feebly they lisp thy glories forth,
Yet grace the victory gives;
Quickly they molder back to earth,
Yet still thy gospel lives.

5 Such wonders power divine effects;
Such trophies God can raise;
His hand, from crumbling dust, erects
His monuments of praise.

PHILIP DODDRIDGE

225 HAMBURG L. M.

LOWELL MASON

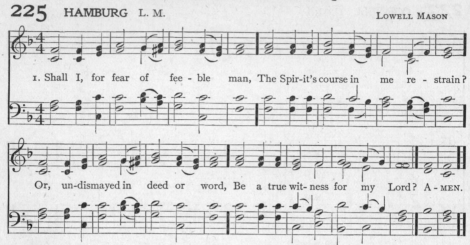

1. Shall I, for fear of fee-ble man, The Spir-it's course in me re-strain?

Or, un-dismayed in deed or word, Be a true wit-ness for my Lord? A-MEN.

2 Awed by a mortal's frown, shall I
Conceal the word of God most high?
How then before thee shall I dare
To stand, or how thine anger bear?

3 Shall I, to soothe the unholy throng,
Soften thy truth, and smooth my tongue,
To gain earth's gilded toys, or flee
The cross endured, my Lord, by thee?

4 What then is he whose scorn I dread,
Whose wrath or hate makes me afraid?
A man! an heir of death! a slave
To sin! a bubble on the wave!

5 Yea, let men rage, since thou wilt spread
Thy shadowing wings around my head:
Since in all pain thy tender love
Will still my sure refreshment prove.

JOHN J. WINKLER. Tr. by JOHN WESLEY

226 KEBLE L. M.

JOHN B. DYKES

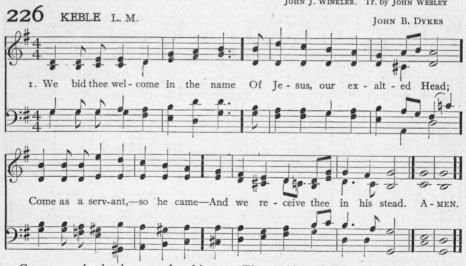

1. We bid thee wel-come in the name Of Je-sus, our ex-alt-ed Head;

Come as a serv-ant,—so he came—And we re-ceive thee in his stead. A-MEN.

2 Come as a shepherd; —guard and keep
This fold from hell, and earth, and sin;
Nourish the lambs, and feed the sheep,
The wounded heal, the lost bring in.

3 Come as an angel; — hence to guide
A band of pilgrims on their way,

That, softly walking at thy side,
We fail not, faint not, turn nor stray.

4 Come as a teacher — sent from God,
Charged his whole counsel to declare;
Lift o'er our ranks the prophet's rod,
While we uphold thy hands with prayer.

JAMES MONTGOMERY

227 OLMUTZ S. M.

GREGORIAN. Arr. by LOWELL MASON

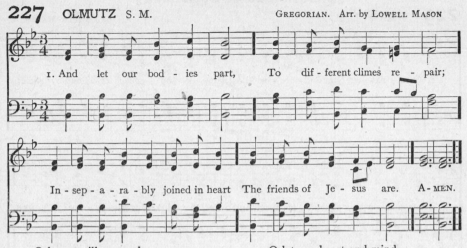

1. And let our bod-ies part, To dif-ferent climes re - pair;
In-sep-a-ra-bly joined in heart The friends of Je - sus are. A-MEN.

2 O let us still proceed
   In Jesus' work below;
And, following our triumphant Head,
   To further conquests go!

3 The vineyard of the Lord
   Before his laborers lies;
And lo! we see the vast reward
   Which waits us in the skies.

4 O let our heart and mind
   Continually ascend,
That haven of repose to find,
   Where all our labors end,

5 Where all our toils are o'er,
   Our suffering and our pain!
Who meet on that eternal shore
   Shall never part again.

CHARLES WESLEY

228 FAITH C. M.

JOHN B. DYKES

1. Blest be the dear u-nit-ing love That will not let us part;
Our bod-ies may far off re-move, We still are one in heart. A-MEN.

2 Joined in one spirit to our Head,
   Where he appoints we go;
And still in Jesus' footsteps tread,
   And do his work below.

3 O let us ever walk in him,
   And nothing know beside,
Nothing desire, nothing esteem,
   But Jesus crucified!

4 Partakers of the Saviour's grace,
   The same in mind and heart,
Nor joy, nor grief, nor time, nor place,
   Nor life, nor death, can part.

5 Then let us hasten to the day
   Which shall our flesh restore,
When death shall all be done away,
   And bodies part no more.

CHARLES WESLEY

229 WARD L. M.

Arr. by LOWELL MASON

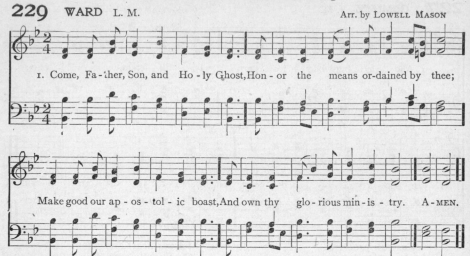

1. Come, Fa-ther, Son, and Ho-ly Ghost, Hon-or the means or-dained by thee;

Make good our ap-os-tol-ic boast, And own thy glo-rious min-is-try. A-MEN.

2 Father, in these reveal thy Son;
In these, for whom we seek thy face,
The hidden mystery make known,
The inward, pure, baptizing grace.

3 Jesus, with us thou always art;
Effectual make the sacred sign;

The gift unspeakable impart,
And bless the ordinance divine.

4 Eternal Spirit, from on high,
Baptizer of our spirits thou!
The sacramental seal apply,
And witness with the water now.

CHARLES WESLEY

230 SERENITY C. M.

WILLIAM V. WALLACE

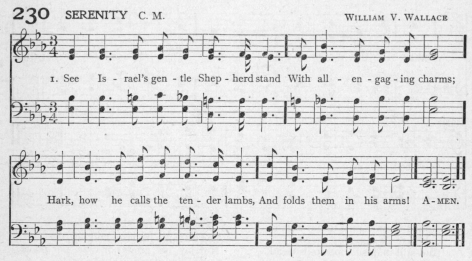

1. See Is-rael's gen-tle Shep-herd stand With all-en-gag-ing charms;

Hark, how he calls the ten-der lambs, And folds them in his arms! A-MEN.

2 "Permit them to approach," he cries,
"Nor scorn their humble name;
For 'twas to bless such souls as these
The Lord of angels came."

3 We bring them, Lord, in thankful hands,
And yield them up to thee;
Joyful that we ourselves are thine,
Thine let our offspring be.

PHILIP DODDRIDGE

Baptism

Baptism

231 BAPTISM L. M.

PETER C. LUTKIN

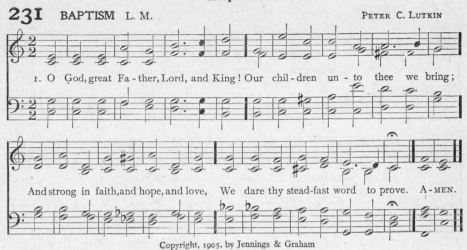

1. O God, great Fa-ther, Lord, and King! Our chil-dren un-to thee we bring;

And strong in faith, and hope, and love, We dare thy stead-fast word to prove. A-MEN.

Copyright, 1905, by Jennings & Graham

2 Thy covenant kindness did of old
Our fathers and their seed enfold;
That ancient promise standeth sure,
And shall while heaven and earth endure.

3 Look down upon us while we pray,
And visit us in grace to-day;
These little ones in mercy take
And make them thine for Jesus' sake.

4 While they the outward sign receive,
Wilt thou thy Holy Spirit give,
And keep and help them by thy power
In every hard and trying hour.

5 Guide thou their feet in holy ways:
Shine on them through the darkest days;
Uphold them till their life be past,
And bring them all to heaven at last.

E. EMBREE HOSS

232 MARYTON L. M.

H. PERCY SMITH

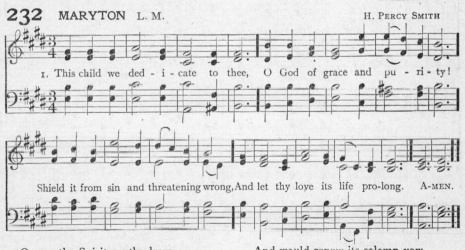

1. This child we ded-i-cate to thee, O God of grace and pu-ri-ty!

Shield it from sin and threatening wrong, And let thy love its life pro-long. A-MEN.

2 O may thy Spirit gently draw
Its willing soul to keep thy law;
May virtue, piety, and truth,
Dawn even with its dawning youth!

3 We, too, before thy gracious sight,
Once shared the blest baptismal rite,

And would renew its solemn vow
With love, and thanks, and praises, now.

4 Grant that, with true and faithful heart,
We still may act the Christian's part,
Cheered by each promise thou hast given,
And laboring for the prize in heaven.

From the German. Tr. by SAMUEL GILMAN

233 DUNDEE C. M.

Scotch Psalter

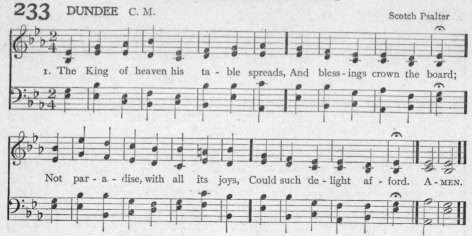

1. The King of heaven his ta - ble spreads, And bless-ings crown the board;

Not par - a - dise, with all its joys, Could such de - light af - ford. A - MEN.

2 Pardon and peace to dying men,
   And endless life are given,
Through the rich blood that Jesus shed
   To raise our souls to heaven.

3 Millions of souls, in glory now,
   Were fed and feasted here;

And millions more, still on the way,
   Around the board appear.

4 All things are ready, come away,
   Nor weak excuses frame;
Crowd to your places at the feast,
   And bless the Founder's name.

PHILIP DODDRIDGE

234 ST. JOHN'S, WESTMINSTER C. M.

JAMES TURLE

1. Ac - cord - ing to thy gra - cious word, In meek hu - mil - i - ty,

Slow

This will I do, my dy - ing Lord, I will re - mem - ber thee. A - MEN.

2 Thy body, broken for my sake,
   My bread from heaven shall be;
Thy testamental cup I take,
   And thus remember thee.

3 Gethsemane can I forget,
   Or there thy conflict see,
Thine agony and bloody sweat,
   And not remember thee?

4 When to the cross I turn mine eyes,
   And rest on Calvary,

O Lamb of God, my Sacrifice,
   I must remember thee!

5 Remember thee, and all thy pains,
   And all thy love to me;
Yea, while a breath, a pulse remains,
   Will I remember thee!

6 And when these failing lips grow dumb,
   And mind and memory flee,
When thou shalt in thy kingdom come,
   Then, Lord, remember me!

JAMES MONTGOMERY

235 AUTUMN 8s. 7s. D.

LOUIS VON ESCH

1. Je - sus spreads his ban-ner o'er us, Cheers our fam-ished souls with food;

He the ban-quet spreads be-fore us, Of his mys-tic flesh and blood.

Pre-cious ban-quet, bread of heav-en, Wine of glad-ness, flow-ing free;

May we taste it, kind-ly giv-en, In re-membrance, Lord, of thee. A-MEN.

2 In thy holy incarnation,
   When the angels sang thy birth;
In thy fasting and temptation,
   In thy labors on the earth,
In thy trial and rejection,
   In thy sufferings on the tree,
In thy glorious resurrection,
   May we, Lord, remember thee.

ROSWELL PARK

236 GERARD C. M. D. Traditional Air. Arr. by ARTHUR S. SULLIVAN

1. If hu-man kind-ness meets re-turn, And owns the grate-ful tie;

If ten-der thoughts with-in us burn To feel a friend is nigh;—

O shall not warm-er ac-cents tell The grat-i-tude we owe

To Him who died, our fears to quell, Our more than or-phan's woe! A-MEN.

2 While yet his anguished soul surveyed
Those pangs he would not flee,
What love his latest words displayed,—
"Meet and remember me!"
Remember thee! thy death, thy shame
Our sinful hearts to share!
O memory, leave no other name
But his recorded there!

GERARD T. NOEL

237 PENITENTIA 10s.

EDWARD DEARLE

1. Here, O my Lord, I see thee face to face; Here would I touch and
han - dle things un - seen; Here grasp with firm - er hand e - ter - nal grace,
And all my wea - ri - ness up - on thee lean. A - MEN.

2 Here would I feed upon the bread of God;
   Here drink with thee the royal wine of heaven;
   Here would I lay aside each earthly load,
   Here taste afresh the calm of sin forgiven.

3 Too soon we rise: the symbols disappear;
   The feast, though not the love, is passed and gone;
   The bread and wine remove: but thou art here,
   Nearer than ever, — still my shield and sun.

4 I have no help but thine, nor do I need
   Another arm save thine to lean upon;
   It is enough, my Lord, enough indeed:
   My strength is in thy might, — thy might alone.

5 I have no wisdom save in him who is
   My wisdom and my teacher both in one;
   No wisdom can I lack while thou art wise,
   No teaching do I crave save thine alone.

6 Feast after feast thus comes, and passes by;
   Yet, passing, points to the glad feast above.
   Giving sweet foretaste of the festal joy,
   The Lamb's great bridal feast of bliss and love.

HORATIUS BONAR

238 EUCHARISTIC HYMN 9s. 8s.

JOHN S. B. HODGES

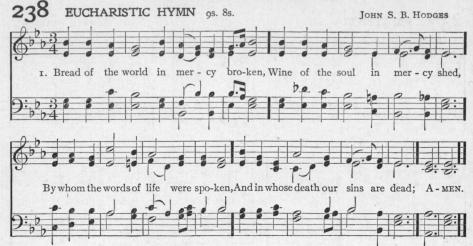

1. Bread of the world in mer - cy bro-ken, Wine of the soul in mer - cy shed,

By whom the words of life were spo-ken, And in whose death our sins are dead; A - MEN.

2 Look on the heart by sorrow broken,
Look on the tears by sinners shed;
And be thy feast to us the token
That by thy grace our souls are fed.

REGINALD HEBER

239 HANFORD 8. 8. 8. 4.

ARTHUR S. SULLIVAN

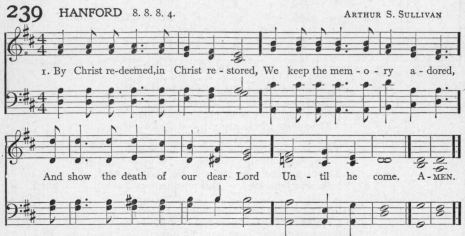

1. By Christ re-deemed, in Christ re - stored, We keep the mem - o - ry a - dored,

And show the death of our dear Lord Un - til he come. A - MEN.

2 His body, broken in our stead,
Is here, in this memorial bread;
And so our feeble love is fed
Until he come.

3 His fearful drops of agony,
His lifeblood shed for us we see:
The wine shall tell the mystery
Until he come.

4 And thus that dark betrayal night,
With the last advent we unite —
The shame, the glory, by this rite,
Until he come.

5 Until the trump of God be heard,
Until the ancient graves be stirred,
And with the great commanding word
The Lord shall come.

6 O blessed hope! with this elate
Let not our hearts be desolate,
But strong in faith, in patience wait
Until he come!

GEORGE RAWSON

The Lord's Supper

JOHANN ROSENMÜLLER

1. "Till He come," O let the words Linger on the trembling chords;
Let the "little while" between In their golden light be seen;
Let us think how heaven and home Lie beyond that, "Till he come." A-MEN.

2 When the weary ones we love
Enter on their rest above,
Seems the earth so poor and vast,
All our life-joy overcast?
Hush, be every murmur dumb;
It is only, "Till he come."

3 Clouds and conflicts round us press;
Would we have one sorrow less?
All the sharpness of the cross,
All that tells the world is lost,
Death and darkness, and the tomb,
Only whisper, "Till he come."

4 See, the feast of love is spread,
Drink the wine, and break the bread;
Sweet memorials, — till the Lord
Call us round his heavenly board;
Some from earth, from glory some,
Severed only, "Till he come."

EDWARD H. BICKERSTETH

The Gospel

The Need of Salvation

241 ST. PETER'S, OXFORD C. M.
ALEXANDER R. REINAGLE

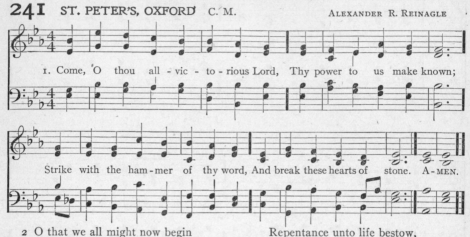

1. Come, O thou all - vic - to - rious Lord, Thy power to us make known;
Strike with the ham-mer of thy word, And break these hearts of stone. A-MEN.

2 O that we all might now begin
   Our foolishness to mourn;
And turn at once from every sin,
   And to the Saviour turn!

3 Give us ourselves and thee to know
   In this our gracious day;

Repentance unto life bestow,
   And take our sins away.

4 Convince us first of unbelief,
   And freely then release;
Fill every soul with sacred grief,
   And then with sacred peace.

CHARLES WESLEY

242 BALERMA C. M.
Arr. by ROBERT SIMPSON

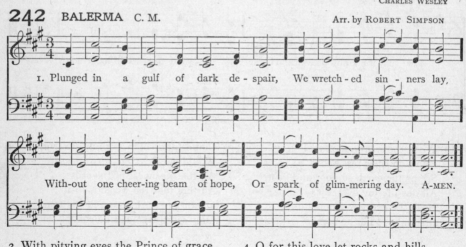

1. Plunged in a gulf of dark de - spair, We wretch - ed sin - ners lay,
With-out one cheer-ing beam of hope, Or spark of glim-mering day. A-MEN.

2 With pitying eyes the Prince of grace
   Beheld our helpless grief:
He saw, and, O amazing love!
   He ran to our relief.

3 Down from the shining seats above
   With joyful haste he sped,
Entered the grave in mortal flesh,
   And dwelt among the dead.

4 O for this love let rocks and hills
   Their lasting silence break;
And all harmonious human tongues,
   The Saviour's praises speak!

5 Angels, assist our mighty joys,
   Strike all your harps of gold;
But when you raise your highest notes,
   His love can ne'er be told.

ISAAC WATTS

The Need of Salvation

243 BURLINGTON C. M.

JOHN F. BURROWES

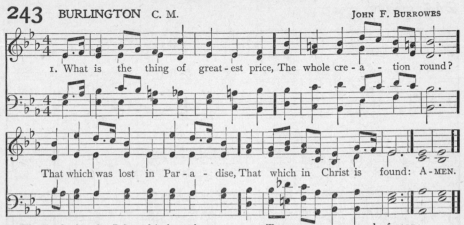

1. What is the thing of great-est price, The whole cre-a - tion round?

That which was lost in Par-a - dise, That which in Christ is found: A-MEN.

2 The soul of man, Jehovah's breath,
That keeps two worlds at strife;
Hell moves beneath to work its death,
Heaven stoops to give it life.

3 God, to reclaim it, did not spare
His well-belovèd Son;
Jesus, to save it, deigned to bear
The sins of all in one.

4 The Holy Spirit sealed the plan,
And pledged the blood divine,

To ransom every soul of man;
That price was paid for mine.

5 And is this treasure borne below,
In earthen vessels frail?
Can none its utmost value know,
Till flesh and spirit fail?

6 Then let us gather round the cross,
That knowledge to obtain;
Not by the soul's eternal loss,
But everlasting gain.

JAMES MONTGOMERY

244 RIVAULX L. M.

JOHN B. DYKES

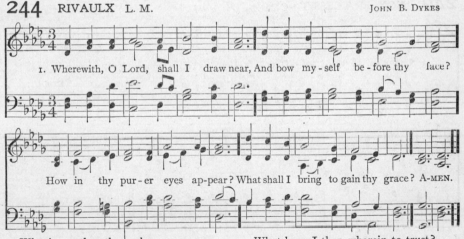

1. Wherewith, O Lord, shall I draw near, And bow my-self be-fore thy face?

How in thy pur-er eyes ap-pear? What shall I bring to gain thy grace? A-MEN.

2 Whoe'er to thee themselves approve
Must take the path thyself hast showed
Justice pursue, and mercy love,
And humbly walk by faith with God.

3 But though my life henceforth be thine,
Present for past can ne'er atone;
Though I to thee the whole resign,
I only give thee back thine own.

4 What have I then wherein to trust?
I nothing have, I nothing am;
Excluded is my every boast;
My glory swallowed up in shame.

5 Guilty I stand before thy face;
On me I feel thy wrath abide;
'Tis just the sentence should take place,
'Tis just — but O, thy Son hath died!

CHARLES WESLEY

The Gospel

245 JAZER C. M.

A. E. TOZER

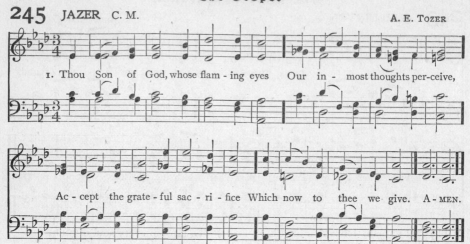

1. Thou Son of God, whose flam-ing eyes Our in-most thoughts per-ceive,

Ac-cept the grate-ful sac-ri-fice Which now to thee we give. A-MEN.

2 We bow before thy gracious throne,
  And think ourselves sincere;
  But show us, Lord, is every one
  Thy real worshiper?

3 Is here a soul that knows thee not,
  Nor feels his need of thee;
  A stranger to the blood which bought
  His pardon on the tree?

4 Convince him now of unbelief,
  His desperate state explain;
  And fill his heart with sacred grief,
  And penitential pain.

5 Speak with that voice that wakes the [dead,
  And bid the sleeper rise,
  And bid his guilty conscience dread
  The death that never dies.

CHARLES WESLEY

246 NOX PRÆCESSIT C. M.

JOHN B. CALKIN

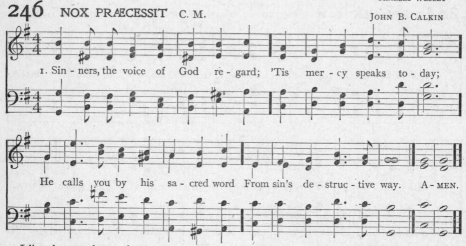

1. Sin-ners, the voice of God re-gard; 'Tis mer-cy speaks to-day;

He calls you by his sa-cred word From sin's de-struc-tive way. A-MEN.

2 Like the rough sea that cannot rest,
  You live devoid of peace;
  A thousand stings within your breast
  Deprive your souls of ease.

3 Why will you in the crooked ways
  Of sin and folly go?
  In pain you travel all your days,
  To reap eternal woe.

4 But he that turns to God shall live
  Through his abounding grace:
  His mercy will the guilt forgive
  Of those that seek his face.

5 Bow to the scepter of his word,
  Renouncing every sin;
  Submit to him, your sovereign Lord,
  And learn his will divine.

JOHN FAWCETT

247 HOLLINGSIDE 7s. D.

JOHN B. DYKES

1. Sin - ners, turn; why will ye die? God, your Ma - ker, asks you why;

God, who did your be - ing give, Made you with him - self to live;

He the fa - tal cause de - mands, Asks the work of his own hands:

Why, ye thank-less crea - tures, why Will ye cross his love, and die? A- MEN.

2 Sinners, turn; why will ye die?
God, your Saviour, asks you why;
God, who did your souls retrieve,
Died himself, that ye might live.
Will ye let him die in vain?
Crucify your Lord again?
Why, ye ransomed sinners, why
Will ye slight his grace, and die?

3 Sinners, turn; why will ye die?
God, the Spirit, asks you why;
He, who all your lives hath strove,
Wooed you to embrace his love;
Will ye not his grace receive?
Will ye still refuse to live?
Why, ye long-sought sinners, why
Will ye grieve your God, and die?

CHARLES WESLEY

248 PLEYEL'S HYMN 7s.

IGNACE J. PLEYEL

1. Hast-en, sin-ner, to be wise! Stay not for the mor-row's sun;

Wis-dom if thou still de-spise, Hard-er is it to be won. A-MEN.

2 Hasten, mercy to implore!
    Stay not for the morrow's sun,
  Lest thy season should be o'er
    Ere this evening's stage be run.

3 Hasten, sinner, to return!
    Stay not for the morrow's sun,

Lest thy lamp should cease to burn
  Ere salvation's work is done.

4 Hasten, sinner, to be blest!
    Stay not for the morrow's sun,
  Lest swift death should thee arrest
    Ere the morrow is begun.

THOMAS SCOTT

248 HORTON 7s. (*Second Tune*)

XAVIER SCHNEIDER

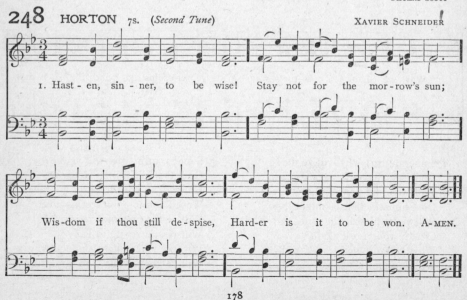

1. Hast-en, sin-ner, to be wise! Stay not for the mor-row's sun;

Wis-dom if thou still de-spise, Hard-er is it to be won. A-MEN.

249 BERA L. M.

JOHN E. GOULD

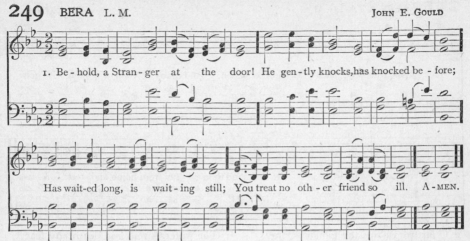

1. Be-hold, a Stran-ger at the door! He gen-tly knocks, has knocked be-fore;

Has wait-ed long, is wait-ing still; You treat no oth-er friend so ill. A-MEN.

2 O lovely attitude! he stands
With melting heart and laden hands:
O matchless kindness! and he shows
This matchless kindness to his foes.

3 But will he prove a friend indeed?
He will; the very friend you need:

The Friend of sinners — yes, 'tis he,
With garments dyed on Calvary.

4 Rise, touched with gratitude divine;
Turn out his enemy and thine,
That soul-destroying monster, sin,
And let the heavenly Stranger in.

JOSEPH GRIGG

250 FERNIEHURST S. M.

From the Church Hymnal

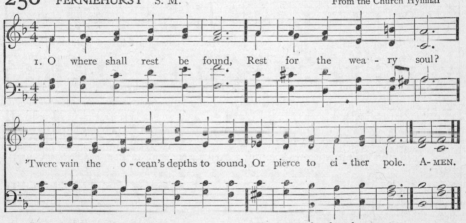

1. O where shall rest be found, Rest for the wea-ry soul?

'Twere vain the o-cean's depths to sound, Or pierce to ei-ther pole. A-MEN.

2 The world can never give
The bliss for which we sigh;
'Tis not the whole of life to live,
Nor all of death to die.

3 Beyond this vale of tears
There is a life above,
Unmeasured by the flight of years;
And all that life is love.

4 There is a death, whose pang
Outlasts the fleeting breath:
O what eternal horrors hang
Around the second death!

5 Lord God of truth and grace,
Teach us that death to shun;
Lest we be banished from thy face,
And evermore undone.

JAMES MONTGOMERY

251 CLOLATA L. M.

W. St. Clair Palmer

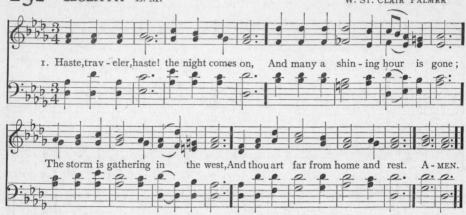

1. Haste, trav - eler, haste! the night comes on, And many a shin - ing hour is gone;

The storm is gathering in the west, And thou art far from home and rest. A - men.

2 O far from home thy footsteps stray;
Christ is the life, and Christ the way,
And Christ the light; thy setting sun
Sinks ere thy morning is begun.

3 The rising tempest sweeps the sky;
The rains descend, the winds are high;

The waters swell, and death and fear
Beset thy path, nor refuge near.

4 Then linger not in all the plain,
Flee for thy life, the mountain gain;
Look not behind, make no delay,
O speed thee, speed thee on thy way!

William B. Collyer

252 RIVAULX L. M.

John B. Dykes

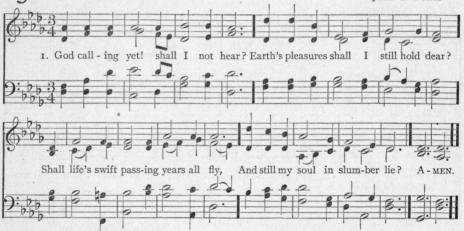

1. God call - ing yet! shall I not hear? Earth's pleasures shall I still hold dear?

Shall life's swift pass-ing years all fly, And still my soul in slum-ber lie? A - men.

2 God calling yet! shall I not rise?
Can I his loving voice despise,
And basely his kind care repay?
He calls me still; can I delay?

3 God calling yet! and shall he knock,
And I my heart the closer lock?
He still is waiting to receive,
And shall I dare his Spirit grieve?

4 God calling yet! and shall I give
No heed, but still in bondage live?
I wait, but he does not forsake;
He calls me still; my heart, awake!

5 God calling yet! I cannot stay;
My heart I yield without delay:
Vain world, farewell, from thee I part;
The voice of God hath reached my heart.

Gerhard Tersteegen. Tr. by Jane Borthwick

253 MORNINGTON S. M.   Earl of MORNINGTON

1. To - mor - row, Lord, is thine, Lodged in thy sov - ereign hand,

And if its sun a - rise and shine, It shines by thy com - mand. A-MEN.

2 The present moment flies,
    And bears our life away;
  O! make thy servants truly wise,
    That they may live to-day.

3 Since on this wingèd hour
    Eternity is hung,
  Waken, by thine almighty power,
    The agèd and the young.

4 One thing demands our care;
    O! be it still pursued,
  Lest, slighted once, the season fair
    Should never be renewed.

5 To Jesus may we fly,
    Swift as the morning light,
  Lest life's young golden beam should die
    In sudden, endless night.
                                    PHILIP DODDRIDGE

254 ST. CROSS L. M.   JOHN B. DYKES

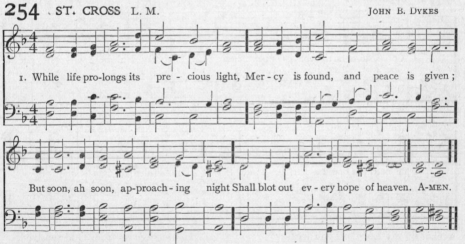

1. While life pro-longs its pre - cious light, Mer - cy is found, and peace is given;

But soon, ah soon, ap-proach - ing night Shall blot out ev - ery hope of heaven. A-MEN.

2 While God invites, how blest the day!
  How sweet the gospel's charming sound!
Come, sinners, haste, O haste away,
  While yet a pardoning God is found.

3 Soon, borne on time's most rapid wing,
  Shall death command you to the grave,

Before his bar your spirits bring,
  And none be found to hear or save.

4 In that lone land of deep despair
  No Sabbath's heavenly light shall rise,
No God regard your bitter prayer,
  No Saviour call you to the skies.
                                    TIMOTHY DWIGHT

The Gospel

255 WOODWORTH L. M.

WILLIAM B. BRADBURY

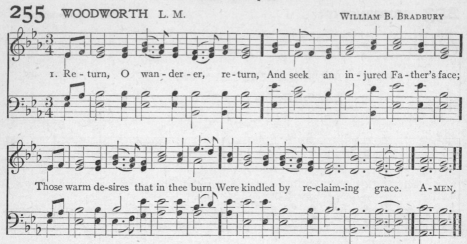

1. Re-turn, O wan-der-er, re-turn, And seek an in-jured Fa-ther's face;

Those warm de-sires that in thee burn Were kindled by re-claim-ing grace. A-MEN.

2 Return, O wanderer, return,
  And seek a Father's melting heart;
His pitying eyes thy grief discern,
  His hand shall heal thine inward smart.

3 Return, O wanderer, return;
  Thy Saviour bids thy spirit live;

Go to his bleeding feet, and learn
How freely Jesus can forgive.

4 Return, O wanderer, return,
  And wipe away the falling tear;
'Tis God who says, "No longer mourn;"
'Tis mercy's voice invites thee near.

WILLIAM B. COLLYER

256 UXBRIDGE L. M.

LOWELL MASON

1. Come, sin-ners, to the gos-pel feast; Let ev-ery soul be Je-sus' guest;

Ye need not one be left be-hind, For God hath bid-den all man-kind. A-MEN.

2 Sent by my Lord, on you I call;
  The invitation is to all:
Come all the world! come, sinner, thou!
All things in Christ are ready now.

3 Come, all ye souls by sin oppressed,
  Ye restless wanderers after rest;
Ye poor, and maimed, and halt, and blind,
In Christ a hearty welcome find.

4 My message as from God receive;
  Ye all may come to Christ and live:
O let his love your hearts constrain,
Nor suffer him to die in vain.

5 See him set forth before your eyes,
  That precious, bleeding sacrifice!
His offered benefits embrace,
And freely now be saved by grace.

CHARLES WESLEY

257 ST. BEES 7s.   JOHN B. DYKES

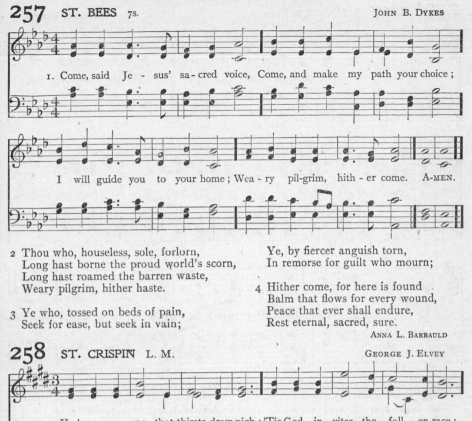

1. Come, said Je - sus' sa - cred voice, Come, and make my path your choice;

I will guide you to your home; Wea - ry pil-grim, hith - er come. A-MEN.

2 Thou who, houseless, sole, forlorn,
    Long hast borne the proud world's scorn,
    Long hast roamed the barren waste,
    Weary pilgrim, hither haste.

3 Ye who, tossed on beds of pain,
    Seek for ease, but seek in vain;

Ye, by fiercer anguish torn,
In remorse for guilt who mourn;

4 Hither come, for here is found
    Balm that flows for every wound,
    Peace that ever shall endure,
    Rest eternal, sacred, sure.

                              ANNA L. BARBAULD

258 ST. CRISPIN L. M.   GEORGE J. ELVEY

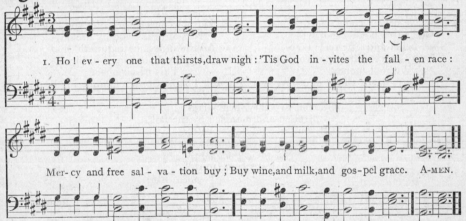

1. Ho! ev - ery one that thirsts, draw nigh : 'Tis God in - vites the fall - en race:

Mer-cy and free sal - va - tion buy ; Buy wine, and milk, and gos-pel grace. A-MEN.

2 Come to the living waters, come!
    Sinners, obey your Maker's call;
    Return, ye weary wanderers, home,
    And find my grace is free for all.

3 See from the rock a fountain rise!
    For you in healing streams it rolls;

Money ye need not bring, nor price,
Ye laboring, burdened, sin-sick souls.

4 Nothing ye in exchange shall give;
    Leave all you have and are behind;
    Frankly the gift of God receive;
    Pardon and peace in Jesus find.

                              CHARLES WESLEY

259 ETON 8. 7. 8. 7. 4. 7.

Joseph Barnby

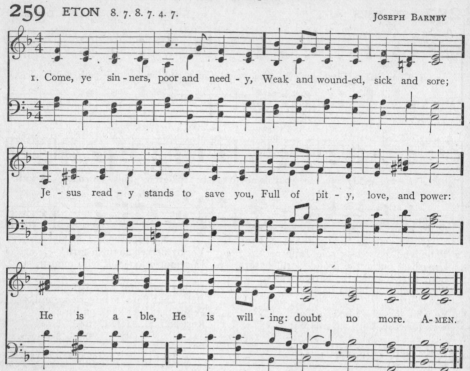

1. Come, ye sin-ners, poor and need-y, Weak and wound-ed, sick and sore;

Je - sus read - y stands to save you, Full of pit - y, love, and power:

He is a - ble, He is will - ing: doubt no more. A-MEN.

2 Now, ye needy, come and welcome;
  God's free bounty glorify;
  True belief and true repentance,
  Every grace that brings you nigh,
    Without money,
  Come to Jesus Christ and buy.

3 Let not conscience make you linger,
  Nor of fitness fondly dream;
  All the fitness he requireth
  Is to feel your need of him:
    This he gives you;
  'Tis the Spirit's glimmering beam.

4 Come, ye weary, heavy-laden,
  Bruised and mangled by the fall;
  If you tarry till you're better,
  You will never come at all;
    Not the righteous,—
  Sinners Jesus came to call.

Joseph Hart

259 GREENVILLE 8s. 7s. 6l. (*Second Tune*)

Jean J. Rousseau

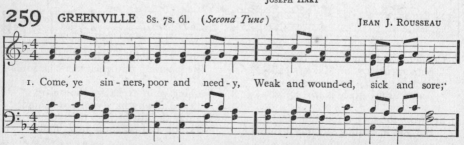

1. Come, ye sin-ners, poor and need-y, Weak and wound-ed, sick and sore;

Je - sus read - y stands to save you, Full of pit - y, love, and power:

He is a - ble, He is a - ble, He is will - ing: doubt no more. A - MEN.

260 BALERMA C. M.

Adapted by ROBERT SIMPSON

1. Come, hum - ble sin - ner, in whose breast A thou - sand thoughts re - volve,

Come, with your guilt and fear op-pressed, And make this last re - solve: A - MEN

2 I'll go to Jesus, though my sin
  Like mountains round me close;
I know his courts, I'll enter in,
  Whatever may oppose.

3 Prostrate I'll lie before his throne,
  And there my guilt confess;
I'll tell him, I'm a wretch undone
  Without his sovereign grace.

4 Perhaps he will admit my plea,
  Perhaps will hear my prayer;
But, if I perish, I will pray,
  And perish only there.

5 I can but perish if I go;
  I am resolved to try;
For if I stay away, I know
  I must forever die.

EDMUND JONES

261 STOCKTON 8s. 6s. *With Refrain* JOHN H. STOCKTON

1. Come, ev - ery soul by sin op-pressed, There's mer - cy with the Lord, And he will sure - ly give you rest, By trust - ing in his word.

REFRAIN

On - ly trust him, on - ly trust him, On - ly trust him now; He will save you, he will save you, He will save you now. A - MEN.

By permission

2 For Jesus shed his precious blood
Rich blessings to bestow;
Plunge now into the crimson flood
That washes white as snow.

3 Yes, Jesus is the Truth, the Way,
That leads you into rest;

Believe in him without delay,
And you are fully blest.

4 Come then, and join this holy band,
And on to glory go,
To dwell in that celestial land,
Where joys immortal flow.

JOHN H. STOCKTON

262 ROSEFIELD 7s. 6l. A. H. C. MALAN

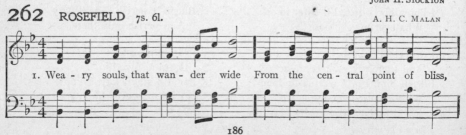

1. Wea - ry souls, that wan - der wide From the cen - tral point of bliss,

Warnings and Invitations

Turn to Je - sus cru - ci - fied, Fly to those dear wounds of his:

Sink in - to the pur - ple flood; Rise in - to the life of God. A - MEN.

2 Find in Christ the way of peace,
 Peace unspeakable, unknown;
By his pain he gives you ease,
 Life by his expiring groan:
Rise, exalted by his fall,
Find in Christ your all in all.

3 O believe the record true,
 God to you his Son hath given;
Ye may now be happy too,
 Find on earth the life of heaven:
Live the life of heaven above,
All the life of glorious love.

CHARLES WESLEY

263 PRESCOTT C. M.

PETER C. LUTKIN

1. Je - sus, thou all - re - deem - ing Lord, Thy bless - ing we im - plore;

O - pen the door to preach thy word, The great, ef - fec - tual door. A - MEN.

2 Gather the outcasts in, and save
 From sin and Satan's power;
And let them now acceptance have,
 And know their gracious hour.

3 Lover of souls! thou knowest to prize
 What thou hast bought so dear:
Come, then, and in thy people's eyes
 With all thy wounds appear.

4 The hardness of their hearts remove,
 Thou who for all hast died;
Show them the tokens of thy love,
 Thy feet, thy hands, thy side.

5 Ready thou art the blood to apply,
 And prove the record true;
And all thy wounds to sinners cry,
 "I suffered this for you!"

CHARLES WESLEY

264 GERAR S. M.

LOWELL MASON

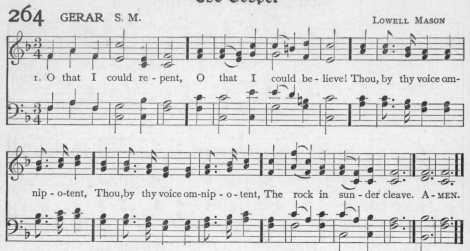

1. O that I could re-pent, O that I could be-lieve! Thou, by thy voice om-nip-o-tent, Thou, by thy voice om-nip-o-tent, The rock in sun-der cleave. A-MEN.

2 Thou, by thy two-edged sword,
  My soul and spirit part;
Strike with the hammer of thy word,
And break my stubborn heart.

3 Saviour, and Prince of Peace,
  The double grace bestow;

Unloose the bands of wickedness,
  And let the captive go:

4 Grant me my sins to feel,
  And then the load remove:
Wound, and pour in, my wounds to heal,
  The balm of pardoning love.

CHARLES WESLEY

265 SHAWMUT S. M.

LOWELL MASON

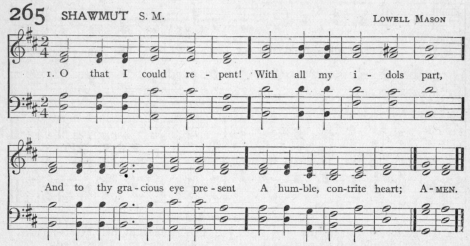

1. O that I could re-pent! With all my i-dols part, And to thy gra-cious eye pre-sent A hum-ble, con-trite heart; A-MEN.

2 A heart with grief oppressed
  For having grieved my God;
A troubled heart that cannot rest
Till sprinkled with thy blood.

3 Jesus, on me bestow
  The penitent desire;

With true sincerity of woe
  My aching breast inspire:

4 With softening pity look,
  And melt my hardness down;
Strike with thy love's resistless stroke,
  And break this heart of stone!

CHARLES WESLEY

266 LOUVAN L. M. VIRGIL C. TAYLOR

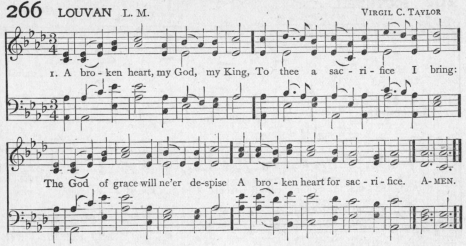

1. A bro - ken heart, my God, my King, To thee a sac - ri - fice I bring:

The God of grace will ne'er de-spise A bro - ken heart for sac - ri - fice. A-MEN.

2 My soul lies humbled in the dust,
And owns thy dreadful sentence just:
Look down, O Lord, with pitying eye,
And save the soul condemned to die.

3 Then will I teach the world thy ways;
Sinners shall learn thy sovereign grace;

I'll lead them to my Saviour's blood,
And they shall praise a pardoning God.

4 O may thy love inspire my tongue!
Salvation shall be all my song;
And all my powers shall join to bless
The Lord, my strength and righteousness.

ISAAC WATTS

267 SEYMOUR 7s. CARL M. VON WEBER

1. Depth of mer - cy! can there be Mer - cy still re - served for me?

Can my God his wrath for - bear,— Me, the chief of sin-ners, spare? A - MEN.

2 I have long withstood his grace;
Long provoked him to his face;
Would not hearken to his calls;
Grieved him by a thousand falls.

3 Now incline me to repent;
Let me now my sins lament;
Now my foul revolt deplore,
Weep, believe, and sin no more.

4 Kindled his relentings are;
Me he now delights to spare;
Cries, "How shall I give thee up?"
Lets the lifted thunder drop.

5 There for me the Saviour stands,
Shows his wounds and spreads his hands;
God is love! I know, I feel;
Jesus weeps and loves me still.

CHARLES WESLEY

268 SOUTHWELL C. M.

HERBERT S. IRONS

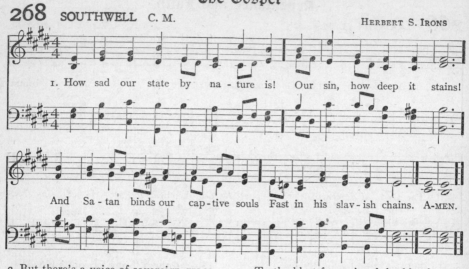

1. How sad our state by na - ture is! Our sin, how deep it stains!
And Sa - tan binds our cap - tive souls Fast in his slav - ish chains. A-MEN.

2 But there's a voice of sovereign grace
Sounds from the sacred word:
"Ho! ye despairing sinners, come,
And trust a faithful Lord."

3 My soul obeys the gracious call,
And runs to this relief:
I would believe thy promise, Lord,
O help my unbelief!

4 To the blest fountain of thy blood,
Incarnate God, I fly:
Here let me wash my spotted soul
From crimes of deepest dye.

5 A guilty, weak, and helpless worm,
Into thy arms I fall:
Be thou my strength and righteousness,
My Jesus and my all.

ISAAC WATTS

269 UXBRIDGE L. M.

LOWELL MASON

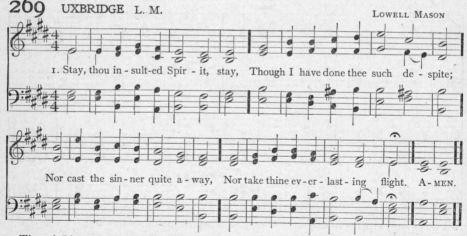

1. Stay, thou in - sult-ed Spir - it, stay, Though I have done thee such de - spite;
Nor cast the sin - ner quite a - way, Nor take thine ev - er - last - ing flight. A - MEN.

2 Though I have steeled my stubborn heart,
And shaken off my guilty fears;
And vexed, and urged thee to depart,
For many long rebellious years:

3 Though I have most unfaithful been,
Of all who e'er thy grace received;

Ten thousand times thy goodness seen;
Ten thousand times thy goodness grieved:

4 Yet, O, the chief of sinners spare,
In honor of my great High Priest;
Nor in thy righteous anger swear
To exclude me from thy people's rest.

CHARLES WESLEY

270 ST. CROSS L. M.

JOHN B. DYKES

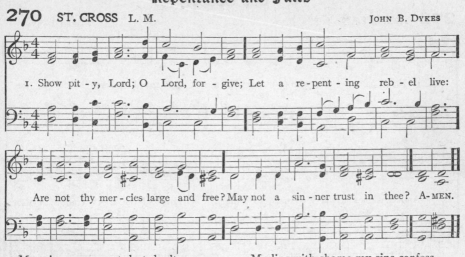

1. Show pit - y, Lord; O Lord, for - give; Let a re-pent - ing reb - el live:

Are not thy mer - cies large and free? May not a sin - ner trust in thee? A-MEN.

2 My crimes are great, but don't surpass
The power and glory of thy grace;
Great God! thy nature hath no bound,
So let thy pardoning love be found.

3 O wash my soul from every sin,
And make my guilty conscience clean!
Here on my heart the burden lies,
And past offenses pain my eyes.

4 My lips with shame my sins confess,
Against thy law, against thy grace;
Lord, should thy judgments grow severe,
I am condemned, but thou art clear.

5 Yet save a trembling sinner, Lord,
Whose hope, still hovering round thy word,
Would light on some sweet promise there,
Some sure support against despair.

ISAAC WATTS

271 FEDERAL STREET L. M.

HENRY K. OLIVER

1. Je - sus, the sin - ner's Friend, to thee, Lost and un-done, for aid I flee,

Wea - ry of earth, my - self, and sin; O-pen thine arms, and take me in. A-MEN.

2 Pity and heal my sin-sick soul;
'Tis thou alone canst make me whole;
Dark, till in me thine image shine,
And lost, I am, till thou art mine.

3 At last I own it cannot be
That I should fit myself for thee:

Here, then, to thee I all resign;
Thine is the work, and only thine.

4 What shall I say thy grace to move?
Lord, I am sin, but thou art love:
I give up every plea beside—
Lord, I am lost, but thou hast died.

CHARLES WESLEY

272 DUNSTAN 8. 8. 8. 6.

JOSEPH BARNBY

1. Just as I am, with-out one plea, But that thy blood was shed for me,

And that thou bidd'st me come to thee, O Lamb of God, I come! A-MEN.

2 Just as I am, and waiting not
To rid my soul of one dark blot,
To thee whose blood can cleanse each spot,
O Lamb of God, I come!

3 Just as I am, though tossed about
With many a conflict, many a doubt,
Fightings within, and fears without,
O Lamb of God, I come!

4 Just as I am, poor, wretched, blind;
Sight, riches, healing of the mind,

Yea, all I need, in thee to find,
O Lamb of God, I come!

5 Just as I am, thou wilt receive,
Wilt welcome, pardon, cleanse, relieve;
Because thy promise I believe,
O Lamb of God, I come!

6 Just as I am, thy love unknown
Hath broken every barrier down;
Now, to be thine, yea, thine alone,
O Lamb of God, I come!

CHARLOTTE ELLIOTT

272 WOODWORTH L. M. (*Second Tune*)

WILLIAM B. BRADBURY

1. Just as I am, with-out one plea, But that thy blood was shed for me,

And that thou bidd'st me come to thee, O Lamb of God, I come! I come! A-MEN.

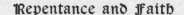

273 ELVEN L. M.

FELIX MENDELSSOHN–BARTHOLDY
Arr. by WM. DRESSLER

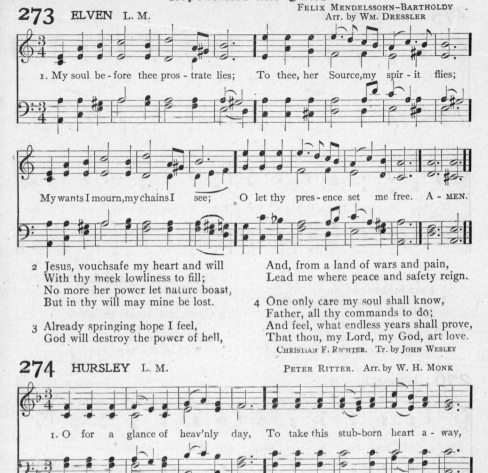

1. My soul be-fore thee pros-trate lies;
To thee, her Source, my spir-it flies;
My wants I mourn, my chains I see;
O let thy pres-ence set me free. A-MEN.

2 Jesus, vouchsafe my heart and will
With thy meek lowliness to fill;
No more her power let nature boast,
But in thy will may mine be lost.

3 Already springing hope I feel,
God will destroy the power of hell,

And, from a land of wars and pain,
Lead me where peace and safety reign.

4 One only care my soul shall know,
Father, all thy commands to do;
And feel, what endless years shall prove,
That thou, my Lord, my God, art love.

CHRISTIAN F. RICHTER. Tr. by JOHN WESLEY

274 HURSLEY L. M.

PETER RITTER. Arr. by W. H. MONK

1. O for a glance of heav'nly day, To take this stub-born heart a-way,
And thaw, with beams of love di-vine, This heart, this fro zen heart of mine! A-MEN.

2 The rocks can rend; the earth can quake;
The seas can roar; the mountains shake:
Of feeling, all things show some sign,
But this unfeeling heart of mine.

3 To hear the sorrows thou hast felt,
O Lord, an adamant would melt:

But I can read each moving line,
And nothing moves this heart of mine.

4 But power divine can do the deed;
And, Lord, that power I greatly need:
Thy Spirit can from dross refine,
And melt and change this heart of mine.

JOSEPH HART

8

275 BOYLSTON S. M.

LOWELL MASON

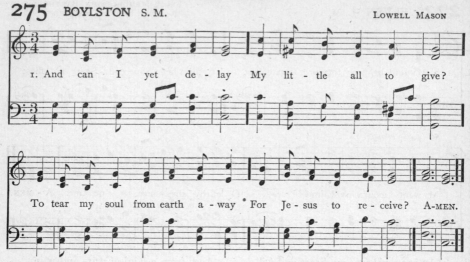

1. And can I yet de - lay My lit - tle all to give?

To tear my soul from earth a - way For Je - sus to re - ceive? A-MEN.

2 Nay, but I yield, I yield;
    I can hold out no more:
  I sink, by dying love compelled,
    And own thee conqueror.

3 Though late, I all forsake;
    My friends, my all, resign:

Gracious Redeemer, take, O take,
    And seal me ever thine!

4 Come, and possess me whole,
    Nor hence again remove;
  Settle and fix my wavering soul
    With all thy weight of love.

CHARLES WESLEY

276 MONSELL S. M.

JOSEPH BARNBY

1. Did Christ o'er sin - ners weep, And shall our cheeks be dry? Let

floods of pen - i - ten - tial grief Burst forth from ev - ery eye. A - MEN.

2 The Son of God in tears
    The wondering angels see!
  Be thou astonished, O my soul!
    He shed those tears for thee.

3 He wept that we might weep;
    Each sin demands a tear:
  In heaven alone no sin is found,
    And there's no weeping there.

BENJAMIN BEDDOME

Repentance and Faith

277 NAOMI C. M.

HANS G. NAEGELI

1. Fa-ther, I stretch my hands to thee; No oth-er help I know:
If thou with-draw thy-self from me, Ah! whith-er shall I go? A-MEN.

2 What did thine only Son endure,
Before I drew my breath!
What pain, what labor, to secure
My soul from endless death!

3 Surely thou canst not let me die;
O speak, and I shall live;

And here I will unwearied lie,
Till thou thy Spirit give.

4 Author of faith! to thee I lift
My weary, longing eyes:
O let me now receive that gift!
My soul without it dies.

CHARLES WESLEY

278 DALEHURST C. M.

ARTHUR COTTMAN

1. O for that ten-der-ness of heart Which bows be-fore the Lord,
Ac-knowl-edg-ing how just thou art, And trem-bling at thy word! A-MEN.

2 O for those humble, contrite tears,
Which from repentance flow;
That consciousness of guilt which fears
The long-suspended blow!

3 Saviour, to me in pity give
The sensible distress;
The pledge thou wilt, at last, receive,
And bid me die in peace.

CHARLES WESLEY

279 TOPLADY 7s. 6l.

THOMAS HASTINGS

1. Rock of A - ges, cleft for me, Let me hide my - self in thee;
Let the wa - ter and the blood, From thy wound - ed side which flowed,
Be of sin the dou - ble cure, Save from wrath and make me pure. A - MEN.

2 Could my tears forever flow,
Could my zeal no languor know,
These for sin could not atone;
Thou must save, and thou alone:
In my hand no price I bring;
Simply to thy cross I cling.

3 While I draw this fleeting breath,
When my eyes shall close in death,
When I rise to worlds unknown,
And behold thee on thy throne,
Rock of Ages, cleft for me,
Let me hide myself in thee.

AUGUSTUS M. TOPLADY. Alt.

280 GETHSEMANE 7s. 6l.

RICHARD REDHEAD

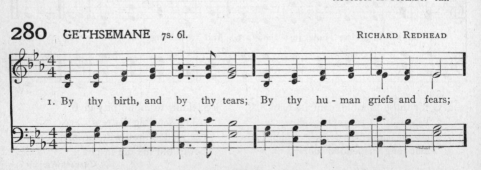

1. By thy birth, and by thy tears; By thy hu - man griefs and fears;

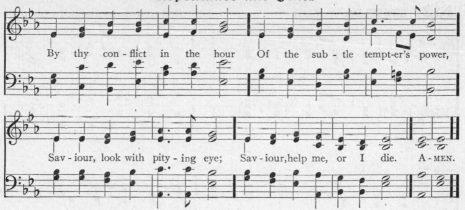

By thy con-flict in the hour Of the sub-tle tempt-er's power,

Sav-iour, look with pity-ing eye; Sav-iour, help me, or I die. A-MEN.

2 By the tenderness that wept
O'er the grave where Lazarus slept;
By the bitter tears that flowed
Over Salem's lost abode,
Saviour, look with pitying eye;
Saviour, help me, or I die.

3 By thy lonely hour of prayer;
By thy fearful conflict there;
By thy cross and dying cries;
By thy one great sacrifice,
Saviour, look with pitying eye;
Saviour, help me, or I die.

4 By thy triumph o'er the grave;
By thy power the lost to save;
By thy high, majestic throne;
By the empire all thine own,
Saviour, look with pitying eye;
Saviour, help me, or I die.

ROBERT GRANT. Alt.

281 SILOAM C. M.

ISAAC B. WOODBURY

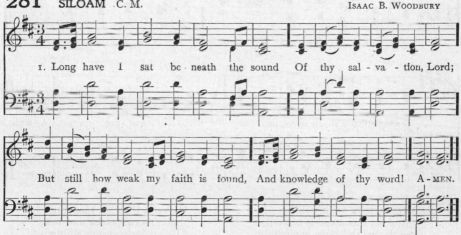

1. Long have I sat be-neath the sound Of thy sal-va-tion, Lord;

But still how weak my faith is found, And knowledge of thy word! A-MEN.

2 How cold and feeble is my love!
How negligent my fear!
How low my hopes of joys above!
How few affections there!

Write thy salvation on my heart,
And make me learn thy grace.

3 Great God! thy sovereign aid impart
To give thy word success;

4 Show my forgetful feet the way
That leads to joys on high,
Where knowledge grows without decay,
And love shall never die.

ISAAC WATTS

282 ST. HILDA 7s. 6s. D.   JUSTIN H. KNECHT and EDWARD HUSBAND

1. O Je - sus, thou art stand - ing Out - side the fast-closed door;
In low - ly pa - tience wait - ing To pass the thresh - old o'er:
Shame on us, Chris - tian breth - ren, His name and sign who bear:
O shame, thrice shame up - on us, To keep him stand - ing there! A - MEN.

2 O Jesus, thou art knocking:
   And lo! that hand is scarred,
And thorns thy brow encircle,
   And tears thy face have marred.
O love that passeth knowledge,
   So patiently to wait!
O sin that hath no equal,
   So fast to bar the gate!

3 O Jesus, thou art pleading
   In accents meek and low,
"I died for you, my children,
   And will ye treat me so?"
O Lord, with shame and sorrow
   We open now the door:
Dear Saviour, enter, enter,
   And leave us nevermore.

WILLIAM W. HOW

283 LEOMINSTER S. M. D.

Arr. by ARTHUR S. SULLIVAN

1. Ah! whith-er should I go, Bur-dened and sick and faint? To whom should I my trou-ble show, And pour out my com-plaint? My Sav-iour bids me come; Ah! why do I de-lay? He calls the wea-ry sin ner home, And yet from him I stay. A-MEN.

2 What is it keeps me back,
From which I cannot part,
Which will not let the Saviour take
Possession of my heart?
Searcher of hearts, in mine
Thy trying power display;
Into its darkest corners shine,
And take the veil away.

3 I now believe in thee,
Compassion reigns alone;
According to my faith, to me
O let it, Lord, be done!
In me is all the bar,
Which thou wouldst fain remove;
Remove it, and I shall declare
That God is only love.

CHARLES WESLEY

The Gospel

284 LANGRAN 10s.

JAMES LANGRAN

1. Wea-ry of earth, and la-den with my sin, I look at heaven and long to en-ter in; But there no e-vil thing may find a home, And yet I hear a voice that bids me "Come!" A-MEN.

2 So vile I am, how dare I hope to stand
In the pure glory of that holy land?
Before the whiteness of that throne appear?
Yet there are hands stretched out to draw me near.

3 The while I fain would tread the heavenly way,
Evil is ever with me day by day;
Yet on mine ears the gracious tidings fall,
"Repent, confess, thou shalt be loosed from all."

4 It is the voice of Jesus that I hear;
His are the hands stretched out to draw me near,
And his the blood that can for all atone,
And set me faultless there before the throne.

5 'Twas he who found me on the deathly wild,
And made me heir of heaven, the Father's child,
And day by day, whereby my soul doth live,
Gives me his grace of pardon, and will give.

6 O great Absolver, grant my soul may wear
The lowliest garb of penitence and prayer,
That in the Father's courts my glorious dress
May be the garment of thy righteousness!

7 Yea, thou wilt answer for me, righteous Lord;
Thine all the merits, mine the great reward;
Thine the sharp thorns, and mine the golden crown;
Mine the life won, and thine the life laid down.

SAMUEL J. STONE

285 SOHO C. M.

JOSEPH BARNBY

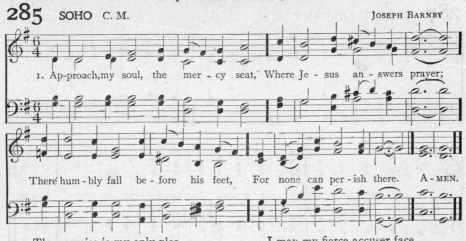

1. Ap-proach, my soul, the mer - cy seat, Where Je - sus an - swers prayer;

There humbly fall be - fore his feet, For none can per - ish there. A - MEN.

2 Thy promise is my only plea,
  With this I venture nigh;
Thou callest burdened souls to thee,
  And such, O Lord, am I.

3 Bowed down beneath a load of sin,
  By Satan sorely pressed,
By wars without, and fears within,
  I come to thee for rest.

4 Be thou my shield and hiding place,
  That, sheltered near thy side,

I may my fierce accuser face,
  And tell him, Thou hast died.

5 O wondrous love! to bleed and die,
  To bear the cross and shame,
That guilty sinners, such as I,
  Might plead thy gracious name!

6 "Poor tempest-tossèd soul, be still;
  My promised grace receive;"
'Tis Jesus speaks — I must, I will,
  I can, I do believe.

JOHN NEWTON

286 CONFIDENCE L. M.

Arr. from W. MOORE

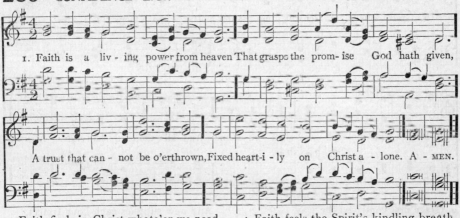

1. Faith is a liv - ing power from heaven That grasps the prom- ise God hath given,

A trust that can - not be o'erthrown, Fixed heart-i - ly on Christ a - lone. A - MEN.

2 Faith finds in Christ whate'er we need
  To save or strengthen us indeed,
Receives the grace he sends us down,
  And makes us share his cross and crown.

3 Faith in the conscience worketh peace,
  And bids the mourner's weeping cease;
By faith the children's place we claim,
  And give all honor to one name.

4 Faith feels the Spirit's kindling breath
  In love and hope that conquer death;
Faith worketh hourly joy in God,
  And trusts and blesses e'en the rod.

5 We thank thee then, O God of heaven
  That thou to us this faith hast given
In Jesus Christ thy Son, who is
  Our only fount and source of bliss.

PETRUS HERBERT. Tr. by CATHERINE WINKWORTH

201

287 MOUNT CALVARY C. M.

ROBERT P. STEWART

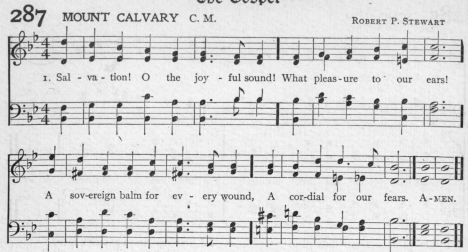

1. Sal - va - tion! O the joy - ful sound! What pleas - ure to our ears!

A sov-ereign balm for ev - ery wound, A cor-dial for our fears. A - MEN.

2 Salvation! let the echo fly
   The spacious earth around,
While all the armies of the sky
   Conspire to raise the sound.

3 Salvation! O thou bleeding Lamb!
   To thee the praise belongs:
Salvation shall inspire our hearts,
   And dwell upon our tongues.

ISAAC WATTS. Alt.

288 MONSELL S. M.

JOSEPH BARNBY

1. Grace! 'tis a charm - ing sound, Har - mo - nious to the ear;

Heaven with the ech - o shall re - sound, And all the earth shall hear. A - MEN.

2 Grace first contrived the way
   To save rebellious man;
And all the steps that grace display,
   Which drew the wondrous plan.

3 Grace taught my wandering feet
   To tread the heavenly road;

And new supplies each hour I meet,
   While pressing on to God.

4 Grace all the work shall crown
   Through everlasting days;
It lays in heaven the topmost stone,
   And well deserves our praise.

PHILIP DODDRIDGE

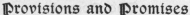

Provisions and Promises

289 ROCKINGHAM L. M.

LOWELL MASON

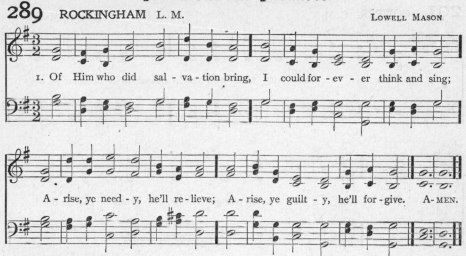

1. Of Him who did sal - va - tion bring, I could for - ev - er think and sing;
A - rise, ye need - y, he'll re - lieve; A - rise, ye guilt - y, he'll for - give. A - MEN.

2 Ask but his grace, and lo, 'tis given!
Ask, and he turns your hell to heaven:
Though sin and sorrow wound my soul,
Jesus, thy balm will make it whole.

3 To shame our sins he blushed in blood;
He closed his eyes to show us God:

Let all the world fall down and know
That none but God such love can show.

4 Insatiate to this spring I fly;
I drink, and yet am ever dry:
Ah! who against thy charms is proof?
Ah! who that loves, can love enough?

BERNARD of Clairvaux. Tr. by ANTHONY W. BOEHM

290 ST. BONIFACE L. M.

JOSEPH BARNBY

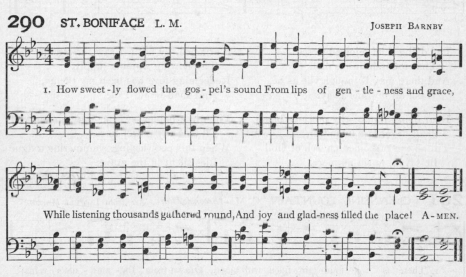

1. How sweet - ly flowed the gos - pel's sound From lips of gen - tle - ness and grace,
While listening thousands gathered round, And joy and glad-ness filled the place! A - MEN.

2 From heaven He came, of heaven he spoke,
To heaven he led his followers' way;
Dark clouds of gloomy night he broke,
Unveiling an immortal day.

3 "Come, wanderers, to my Father's home;
Come, all ye weary ones, and rest."
Yes, sacred Teacher, we will come,
Obey thee, love thee, and be blest.

JOHN BOWRING

291 COWPER C. M.

LOWELL MASON

1. There is a foun-tain filled with blood, Drawn from Im-man-uel's
veins; And sin-ners, plunged be-neath that flood,
Lose all their guilt-y stains, Lose all their guilt-y stains. A-MEN.

2 The dying thief rejoiced to see
   That fountain in his day;
   And there may I, though vile as he,
   Wash all my sins away.

3 Dear dying Lamb! thy precious blood
   Shall never lose its power,
   Till all the ransomed church of God
   Be saved, to sin no more.

4 E'er since, by faith, I saw the stream
   Thy flowing wounds supply,
   Redeeming love has been my theme,
   And shall be till I die.

5 Then in a nobler, sweeter song,
   I'll sing thy power to save,
   When this poor lisping, stammering tongue
   Lies silent in the grave.

WILLIAM COWPER

291 CLEANSING FOUNTAIN C. M. (*Second Tune*) Arr. from LOWELL MASON

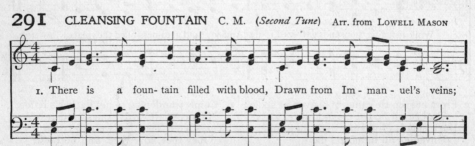

1. There is a foun-tain filled with blood, Drawn from Im-man-uel's veins;

Provisions and Promises

And sin-ners, plunged be-neath that flood, Lose all their guilt-y stains,

Lose all their guilt-y stains, Lose all their guilt-y stains; And

sin-ners, plunged be-neath that flood, Lose all their guilt-y stains. A-MEN.

292 HUMMEL C. M.

HEINRICH C. ZEUNER

1. O what a-maz-ing words of grace Are in the gos-pel found!

Suit-ed to ev-ery sin-ner's case, Who knows the joy-ful sound. A-MEN.

2 Poor, sinful, thirsty, fainting souls
  Are freely welcome here;
Salvation, like a river, rolls
  Abundant, free, and clear.

3 Come, then, with all your wants and wounds;
  Your every burden bring:
Here love, unchanging love, abounds,
  A deep, celestial spring.

SAMUEL MEDLEY. Alt.

The Gospel

293 STEPHANOS 8. 5. 8. 3.

HENRY W. BAKER

1. Art thou wea-ry, art thou lan-guid, Art thou sore dis-tressed?

"Come to me," saith One, "and, com-ing, Be at rest." A-MEN.

2 Hath he marks to lead me to him,
   If he be my guide?
"In his feet and hands are wound-prints,
   And his side."

3 Is there diadem, as monarch,
   That his brow adorns?
"Yea, a crown, in very surety,
   But of thorns."

4 If I find him, if I follow,
   What his guerdon here?
"Many a sorrow, many a labor,
   Many a tear."

5 If I still hold closely to him,
   What hath he at last?
"Sorrow vanquished, labor ended,
   Jordan passed."

6 If I ask him to receive me,
   Will he say me nay?
"Not till earth and not till heaven
   Pass away."

7 Finding, following, keeping, struggling,
   Is he sure to bless?
"Saints, apostles, prophets, martyrs,
   Answer, Yes."

JOHN M. NEALE

293 BULLINGER 8. 5. 8. 3. (Second Tune)

ETHELBERT W. BULLINGER

1. Art thou wea-ry, art thou lan-guid, Art thou sore dis-tressed?

"Come to me," saith One, "and, com-ing, Be .. at rest." A-MEN.

294 LENOX 6. 6. 6. 6. 8. 8.   LEWIS EDSON

1. Blow ye the trum-pet, blow! The glad-ly sol-emn sound Let all the na-tions know,

To earth's re - mot - est bound, The year of ju - bi - lee is come!

The year of ju - bi - lee is come! Re - turn, ye ransomed sin - ners, home. A-MEN.

2 Jesus, our great High Priest,
  Hath full atonement made;
  Ye weary spirits, rest;
  Ye mournful souls, be glad:
  The year of jubilee is come!
  Return, ye ransomed sinners, home.

3 Extol the Lamb of God,
  The all-atoning Lamb;
  Redemption through his blood
  Throughout the world proclaim:
  The year of jubilee is come!
  Return, ye ransomed sinners, home.

4 Ye slaves of sin and hell,
  Your liberty receive,
  And safe in Jesu dwell,
  And blest in Jesus live:
  The year of jubilee is come!
  Return, ye ransomed sinners, home.

5 Ye who have sold for naught
  Your heritage above,
  Receive it back unbought,
  The gift of Jesus' love:
  The year of jubilee is come!
  Return, ye ransomed sinners, home.

6 The gospel trumpet hear,
  The news of heavenly grace;
  And, saved from earth, appear
  Before your Saviour's face:
  The year of jubilee is come!
  Return, ye ransomed sinners, home.

CHARLES WESLEY

The Gospel

295 SAVOY CHAPEL 7s. 6s. D.

JOHN B. CALKIN

1. "Come un-to me, ye wea-ry, And I will give you rest." O bless-èd voice of Je - sus,
Which comes to hearts op - pressed! It tells of ben-e - dic-tion, Of par-don, grace, and peace,
Of joy that hath no end - ing, Of love which can - not' cease. A - MEN.

2 "Come unto me, dear children,
  And I will give you light."
O loving voice of Jesus,
  Which comes to cheer the night!
Our hearts were filled with sadness,
  And we had lost our way,
But morning brings us gladness,
  And songs the break of day.

3 "Come unto me, ye fainting,
  And I will give you life."
O cheering voice of Jesus,
  Which comes to aid our strife!

The foe is stern and eager,
  The fight is fierce and long;
But thou hast made us mighty,
  And stronger than the strong.

4 "And whosoever cometh,
  I will not cast him out."
O welcome voice of Jesus,
  Which drives away our doubt!
Which calls us, very sinners,
  Unworthy though we be
Of love so free and boundless,
  To come, dear Lord, to thee!

WILLIAM C. DIX

296 SELENA L. M. 6l.

ISAAC B. WOODBURY

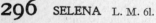

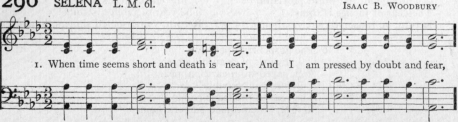

1. When time seems short and death is near, And I am pressed by doubt and fear,

Provisions and Promises

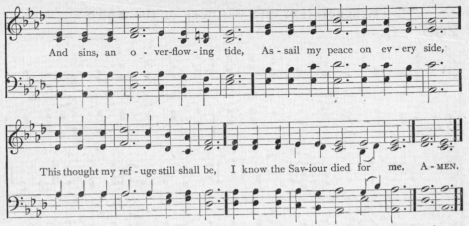

And sins, an o-ver-flow-ing tide, As-sail my peace on ev-ery side,

This thought my ref-uge still shall be, I know the Sav-iour died for me, A-MEN.

2 His name is Jesus, and he died,
For guilty sinners crucified;
Content to die that he might win
Their ransom from the death of sin:
No sinner worse than I can be,
Therefore I know he died for me.

3 If grace were bought, I could not buy;
If grace were coined, no wealth have I;
By grace alone I draw my breath,
Held up from everlasting death;
Yet, since I know his grace is free,
I know the Saviour died for me.
GEORGE W. BETHUNE

297 UPHAM C. M.

PETER C. LUTKIN

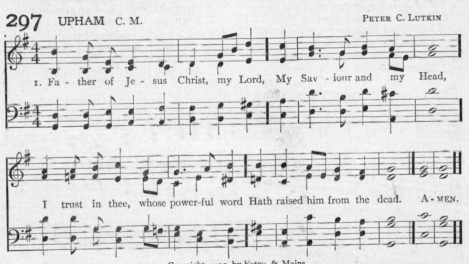

1. Fa-ther of Je-sus Christ, my Lord, My Sav-iour and my Head,

I trust in thee, whose power-ful word Hath raised him from the dead. A-MEN.

2 In hope, against all human hope,
Self-desperate, I believe;
Thy quickening word shall raise me up,
Thou shalt thy Spirit give.

3 Faith, mighty faith, the promise sees,
And looks to that alone;
Laughs at impossibilities,
And cries, "It shall be done!"

4 To thee the glory of thy power
And faithfulness I give;
I shall in Christ, at that glad hour,
And Christ in me shall live.

5 Obedient faith that waits on thee,
Thou never wilt reprove;
But thou wilt form thy Son in me,
And perfect me in love.
CHARLES WESLEY

The Christian Life

Regeneration and Witness of the Spirit

298 SAMSON L. M.

GEORGE F. HÄNDEL

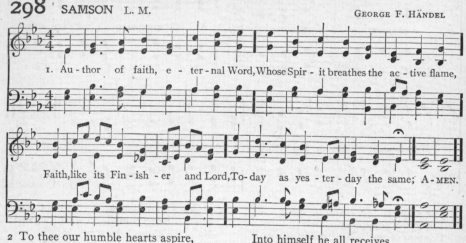

1. Au-thor of faith, e-ter-nal Word, Whose Spir-it breathes the ac-tive flame,

Faith, like its Fin-ish-er and Lord, To-day as yes-ter-day the same; A-MEN.

2 To thee our humble hearts aspire,
  And ask the gift unspeakable;
  Increase in us the kindled fire,
  In us the work of faith fulfill.

3 By faith we know thee strong to save;
  Save us, a present Saviour thou:
  Whate'er we hope, by faith we have;
  Future and past subsisting now.

4 To him that in thy name believes,
  Eternal life with thee is given;

  Into himself he all receives,
  Pardon, and holiness, and heaven.

5 The things unknown to feeble sense,
  Unseen by reason's glimmering ray,
  With strong, commanding evidence,
  Their heavenly origin display.

6 Faith lends its realizing light;
  The clouds disperse, the shadows fly;
  The Invisible appears in sight,
  And God is seen by mortal eye.

CHARLES WESLEY

299 HOLY TRINITY C. M.

JOSEPH BARNBY

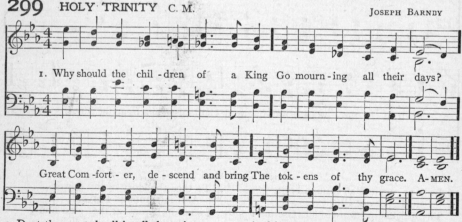

1. Why should the chil-dren of a King Go mourn-ing all their days?

Great Com-fort-er, de-scend and bring The tok-ens of thy grace. A-MEN.

2 Dost thou not dwell in all thy saints,
  And seal the heirs of heaven?
  When wilt thou banish my complaints,
  And show my sins forgiven?

3 Assure my conscience of her part
  In the Redeemer's blood;

  And bear thy witness with my heart,
  That I am born of God.

4 Thou art the earnest of his love,
  The pledge of joys to come;
  May thy blest wings, celestial Dove,
  Safely convey me home.

ISAAC WATTS

300 PASTOR BONUS S. M. D. · ALFRED J. CALDICOTT

1. I was a wan-dering sheep, I did not love the fold,
I did not love my Shep-herd's voice, I would not be con-trolled;
I was a way-ward child, I did not love my home,
I did not love my Fa-ther's voice, I loved a-far to roam. A-MEN.

2 The Shepherd sought his sheep,
   The Father sought his child;
He followed me o'er vale and hill,
   O'er deserts waste and wild;
He found me nigh to death,
   Famished, and faint, and lone;
He bound me with the bands of love,
   He saved the wandering one.

3 No more a wandering sheep,
   I love to be controlled,
I love my tender Shepherd's voice,
   I love the peaceful fold;
No more a wayward child,
   I seek no more to roam;
I love my heavenly Father's voice,
   I love, I love his home!

HORATIUS BONAR

301 LENOX 6. 6. 6. 6. 8. 8.

LEWIS EDSON

1. A - rise, my soul, a - rise; Shake off thy guilt-y fears; The bleed-ing Sac-ri - fice In my be - half ap - pears: Be - fore the throne my Sure - ty stands, Be - fore the throne my Sure-ty stands, My name is writ-ten on his hands. A-MEN.

2 He ever lives above,
For me to intercede;
His all-redeeming love,
His precious blood, to plead;
His blood atoned for all our race,
And sprinkles now the throne of grace.

3 Five bleeding wounds he bears,
Received on Calvary;
They pour effectual prayers,
They strongly plead for me:
"Forgive him, O forgive," they cry,
"Nor let that ransomed sinner die!"

4 The Father hears him pray,
His dear anointed One;
He cannot turn away
The presence of his Son;
His Spirit answers to the blood,
And tells me I am born of God.

5 My God is reconciled;
His pardoning voice I hear;
He owns me for his child,
I can no longer fear:
With confidence I now draw nigh,
And, "Father, Abba, Father," cry.

CHARLES WESLEY

302 ST. CHRYSOSTOM L. M. 6l.

JOSEPH BARNBY

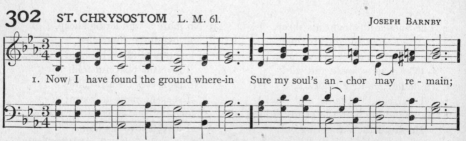

1. Now I have found the ground where-in Sure my soul's an - chor may re - main;

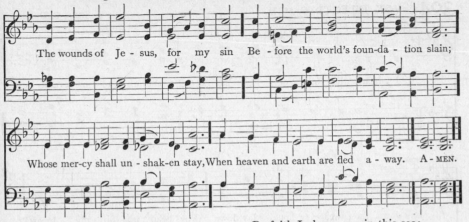

The wounds of Je-sus, for my sin Be-fore the world's foun-da-tion slain;

Whose mer-cy shall un-shak-en stay,When heaven and earth are fled a-way. A-MEN.

2 Father, thine everlasting grace
   Our scanty thought surpasses far:
 Thy heart still melts with tenderness;
   Thine arms of love still open are,
 Returning sinners to receive,
 That mercy they may taste, and live.

3 O love, thou bottomless abyss,
   My sins are swallowed up in thee!
 Covered is my unrighteousness,
   Nor spot of guilt remains on me,
 While Jesus' blood, through earth and skies,
 Mercy, free, boundless mercy, cries.

4 By faith I plunge me in this sea;
   Here is my hope, my joy, my rest;
 Hither, when hell assails, I flee;
   I look into my Saviour's breast:
 Away, sad doubt and anxious fear!
 Mercy is all that's written there.

5 Fixed on this ground will I remain,
   Though my heart fail, and flesh decay;
 This anchor shall my soul sustain,
   When earth's foundations melt away;
 Mercy's full power I then shall prove,
 Loved with an everlasting love.

JOHANN A. ROTHE. Tr. by JOHN WESLEY

303 RHODES S. M.   CHARLES W. JORDAN

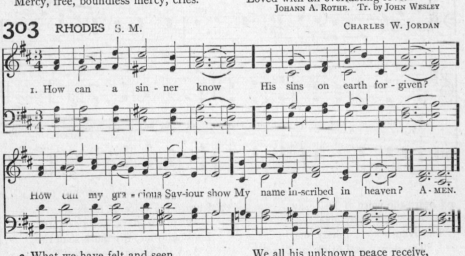

1. How can a sin-ner know His sins on earth for-given?

How can my gra-cious Sav-iour show My name in-scribed in heaven? A-MEN.

2 What we have felt and seen
   With confidence we tell;
 And publish to the sons of men
   The signs infallible.

3 We who in Christ believe
   That he for us hath died,

We all his unknown peace receive,
 And feel his blood applied.

4 Exults our rising soul,
   Disburdened of her load,
 And swells unutterably full
   Of glory and of God.

CHARLES WESLEY

304 VOX DILECTI C. M. D.

JOHN B. DYKES

1. I heard the voice of Je - sus say, "Come un - to me and rest;
Lay down, thou wea - ry one, lay down Thy head up - on my breast!"
I came to Je - sus as I was, Wea - ry and worn and sad;
I found in him a rest - ing place, And he has made me glad. A-MEN.

2 I heard the voice of Jesus say,
  "Behold, I freely give
The living water; thirsty one,
  Stoop down, and drink, and live!"
I came to Jesus, and I drank
  Of that life-giving stream;
My thirst was quenched, my soul revived,
  And now I live in him.

3 I heard the voice of Jesus say,
  "I am this dark world's light;
Look unto me, thy morn shall rise,
  And all thy day be bright!"
I looked to Jesus, and I found
  In him my star, my sun;
And in that light of life I'll walk,
  Till traveling days are done.

HORATIUS BONAR

304 TRUMAN C. M. D. (*Second Tune*)   JOSEPH P. HOLBROOK

1. I heard the voice of Je-sus say,"Come un-to me and rest; Lay down,thou wea-ry one, lay down Thy head up - on my breast!" I came to Je - sus as I was, Wea-ry and worn and sad; I found in him a rest-ing place,And he has made me glad. A-MEN.

305 CALM L. M.   Composer Unknown

1. In - to thy gra-cious hands I fall, And with the arms of faith em-brace; O King of glo-ry, hear my call! O raise me, heal me by thy grace! A-MEN.

2 Arm me with thy whole armor, Lord,
  Support my weakness with thy might;
Gird on my thigh thy conquering sword,
  And shield me in the threatening fight.

3 From faith to faith, from grace to grace,
  So in thy strength shall I go on,
Till heaven and earth flee from thy face,
  And glory end what grace begun.

WOLFGANG C. DESSLER. Tr. by JOHN WESLEY

306 DUANE STREET L. M. D.

GEORGE COLES

1. Je - sus, my all, to heaven is gone, He whom I fix my hopes up - on;

His track I see, and I'll pur - sue The nar-row way, till him I view.

The way the ho - ly proph-ets went, The road that leads from ban - ish - ment,

The King's highway of ho - li - ness, I'll go, for all his paths are peace. A-MEN.

2 This is the way I long have sought,
And mourned because I found it not;
My grief a burden long has been,
Because I was not saved from sin.
The more I strove against its power,
I felt its weight and guilt the more;
Till late I heard my Saviour say,
"Come hither, soul, I am the way."

3 Lo! glad I come; and thou, blest Lamb,
Shalt take me to thee, as I am;
Nothing but sin have I to give;
Nothing but love shall I receive.
Then will I tell to sinners round,
What a dear Saviour I have found;
I'll point to thy redeeming blood,
And say, "Behold the way to God."

JOHN CENNICK

Regeneration and Witness of the Spirit

307 SOLITUDE 7s.

LEWIS T. DOWNES

1. Hark, my soul! it is the Lord; 'Tis thy Sav-iour, hear his word;

Je-sus speaks, he speaks to thee: "Say, poor sin-ner, lov'st thou me? A-MEN.

2 "I delivered thee when bound,
And, when bleeding, healed thy wound;
Sought thee wandering, set thee right,
Turned thy darkness into light.

3 "Can a mother's tender care
Cease toward the child she bare?
Yes, she may forgetful be,
Yet will I remember thee.

4 "Mine is an unchanging love,
Higher than the heights above,

Deeper than the depths beneath,
Free and faithful, strong as death.

5 "Thou shalt see my glory soon,
When the work of faith is done;
Partner of my throne shalt be:
Say, poor sinner, lov'st thou me?"

6 Lord, it is my chief complaint
That my love is still so faint;
Yet I love thee and adore:
O for grace to love thee more!

WILLIAM COWPER

308 LUTON L. M.

GEORGE BURDER

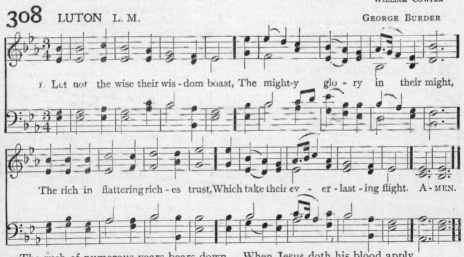

1. Let not the wise their wis-dom boast, The might-y glo-ry in their might,

The rich in flattering rich-es trust, Which take their ev-er-last-ing flight. A-MEN.

2 The rush of numerous years bears down
The most gigantic strength of man;
And where is all his wisdom gone,
When dust he turns to dust again?

3 One only gift can justify
The boasting soul that knows his God;

When Jesus doth his blood apply,
I glory in his sprinkled blood.

4 The Lord, my Righteousness, I praise,
I triumph in the love divine,
The wisdom, wealth, and strength of grace,
In Christ to endless ages mine.

CHARLES WESLEY

217

309 SIMPSON C. M.

From Louis Spohr

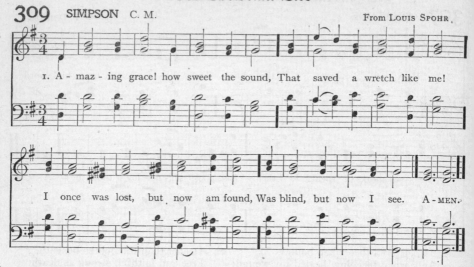

1. A-maz-ing grace! how sweet the sound, That saved a wretch like me! I once was lost, but now am found, Was blind, but now I see. A-MEN.

2 'Twas grace that taught my heart to fear,
And grace my fears relieved;
How precious did that grace appear
The hour I first believed!

3 Through many dangers, toils, and snares,
I have already come;
'Tis grace hath brought me safe thus far,
And grace will lead me home.

4 The Lord has promised good to me,
His word my hope secures;

He will my shield and portion be
As long as life endures.

5 Yes, when this flesh and heart shall fail,
And mortal life shall cease,
I shall possess, within the veil,
A life of joy and peace.

6 The earth shall soon dissolve like snow,
The sun forbear to shine;
But God, who called me here below,
Will be forever mine.

JOHN NEWTON

310 FILLMORE L. M. 6l.

JEREMIAH INGALLS

1. And can it be that I should gain An in-terest in the Saviour's blood? Died he for me, who caused his pain? For me, who him to death pur-sued?

Regeneration and Witness of the Spirit

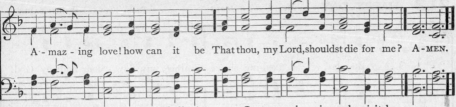

A - maz - ing love! how can it be That thou, my Lord, shouldst die for me? A-MEN.

2 'Tis mystery all! the Immortal dies!
  Who can explore his strange design?
In vain the firstborn seraph tries
  To sound the depths of love divine;
'Tis mercy all! let earth adore:
Let angel minds inquire no more.

3 He left his Father's throne above,
  So free, so infinite his grace!
Emptied himself of all but love,
  And bled for Adam's helpless race;
'Tis mercy all, immense and free,
For, O my God, it found out me!

4 Long my imprisoned spirit lay,
  Fast-bound in sin and nature's night;
Thine eye diffused a quickening ray,
  I woke, the dungeon flamed with light:
My chains fell off, my heart was free,
I rose, went forth, and followed thee.

5 No condemnation now I dread,
  Jesus, with all in him, is mine;
Alive in him, my living Head,
  And clothed in righteousness divine,
Bold I approach the eternal throne, [own.
And claim the crown, through Christ, my
                              CHARLES WESLEY

311 CITY ROAD 6. 6. 9. D.

JOHN JONES

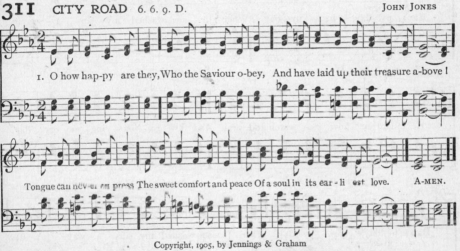

1. O how hap-py are they, Who the Saviour o-bey, And have laid up their treasure a-bove!

Tongue can nev-er ex press The sweet comfort and peace Of a soul in its ear-li est love. A-MEN.

2 That sweet comfort was mine,
  When the favor divine
I first found in the blood of the Lamb;
  When my heart first believed,
  What a joy I received,
What a heaven in Jesus's name!

3 'Twas a heaven below
  My Redeemer to know,
And the angels could do nothing more,
  Than to fall at his feet,
  And the story repeat,
And the Lover of sinners adore.

4 Jesus all the day long
  Was my joy and my song:
O that all his salvation might see!
  "He hath loved me," I cried,
  "He hath suffered and died,
To redeem a poor rebel like me."

5 O the rapturous height
  Of that holy delight
Which I felt in the life-giving blood!
  Of my Saviour possessed,
  I was perfectly blest,
As if filled with the fullness of God.
                              CHARLES WESLEY

312 HAPPY DAY L. M. *With Refrain* From EDWARD F. RIMBAULT

1. O hap-py day, that fixed my choice On thee, my Sav - iour and my God!

Well may this glow - ing heart re - joice, And tell its rap - tures all a - broad.

REFRAIN

Hap - py day, hap - py day, When Je - sus washed my sins a - way:

He taught me how to watch and pray, And live re - joic - ing ev - ery day.

Hap - py day, hap - py day, When Je - sus washed my sins a - way. A - MEN.

2 O happy bond, that seals my vows
   To him who merits all my love!
   Let cheerful anthems fill his house,
   While to that sacred shrine I move.

3 'Tis done: the great transaction's done!
   I am my Lord's, and he is mine;
   He drew me and I followed on,
   Charmed to confess the voice divine.

4 Now rest, my long-divided heart;
   Fixed on this blissful center, rest:
   With ashes who would grudge to part,
   When called on angels' bread to feast?

5 High heaven, that heard the solemn vow,
   That vow renewed shall daily hear,
   Till in life's latest hour I bow,
   And bless in death a bond so dear.

PHILIP DODDRIDGE

313 ANGELUS L. M.

Arr. from GEORG JOSEPHI

1. O Thou, who cam-est from a-bove, The pure ce-les-tial fire to im-part,

Kin-dle a flame of sa-cred love On the mean al-tar of my heart! A-MEN.

2 There let it for thy glory burn,
   With inextinguishable blaze,
   And trembling to its source return,
   In humble love and fervent praise.

3 Jesus, confirm my heart's desire,
   To work, and speak, and think, for thee;

Still let me guard the holy fire,
   And still stir up thy gift in me;

4 Ready for all thy perfect will,
   My acts of faith and love repeat,
   Till death thy endless mercies seal,
   And make the sacrifice complete.

CHARLES WESLEY

314 GREEN HILL C. M.

ALBERT L. PEACE

1. Re-li-gion is the chief con-cern Of mor-tals here be-low:

May I its great im-por-tance learn, Its sov-ereign vir-tue know! A-MEN.

2 O may my heart, by grace renewed,
   Be my Redeemer's throne;
   And be my stubborn will subdued,
   His government to own!

3 Let deep repentance, faith, and love
   Be joined with godly fear;

And all my conversation prove
   My heart to be sincere.

4 Let lively hope my soul inspire;
   Let warm affections rise;
   And may I wait with strong desire
   To mount above the skies!

JOHN FAWCETT

The Christian Life

ST. EDMUND 6. 4. 6. 4. 6. 6. 4. ARTHUR S. SULLIVAN

1. Near-er, my God, to thee, Near-er to thee! E'en though it be a cross That rais-eth me; Still all my song shall be, Near-er, my God, to thee, Near-er, my God, to thee, Near-er to thee! A-MEN.

2 Though like the wanderer,
  The sun gone down,
Darkness be over me,
  My rest a stone,
Yet in my dreams I'd be
Nearer, my God, to thee,
  Nearer to thee!

3 There let the way appear,
  Steps unto heaven;
All that thou sendest me,
  In mercy given;
Angels to beckon me
Nearer, my God, to thee,
  Nearer to thee!

4 Then, with my waking thoughts
  Bright with thy praise,
Out of my stony griefs
  Bethel I'll raise;
So by my woes to be
Nearer, my God, to thee,
  Nearer to thee!

5 Or if, on joyful wing
  Cleaving the sky,
Sun, moon, and stars forgot,
  Upward I fly,
Still all my song shall be,
Nearer, my God, to thee,
  Nearer to thee!

SARAH F. ADAMS

BETHANY 6. 4. 6. 4. 6. 6. 4. (Second Tune) LOWELL MASON

1. Near-er, my God, to thee, Near-er to thee! E'en though it be a cross

Aspiration and Hope

That rais-eth me; Still all my song shall be, Near-er, my God, to thee,

Near-er, my God, to thee, Near-er to thee! A-MEN.

316 SIMPSON C. M.

From LOUIS SPOHR

1. As pants the hart for cool-ing streams, When heat-ed in the chase,

So longs my soul, O God, for thee, And thy re fresh-ing grace. A-MEN.

2 For thee, my God, the living God,
    My thirsty soul doth pine;
  O when shall I behold thy face,
    Thou Majesty divine!

3 I sigh to think of happier days,
    When thou, O Lord, wast nigh;

When every heart was tuned to praise,
    And none more blest than I.

4 Why restless, why cast down, my soul?
    Hope still, and thou shalt sing
  The praise of him who is thy God,
    Thy Saviour, and thy King.

TATE and BRADY. Alt. by HENRY F. LYTE

223

The Christian Life

317 MORE LOVE TO THEE 6. 4. 6. 4. 6. 6. 4.

WILLIAM H. DOANE

1. More love to thee, O Christ, More love to thee! Hear thou the prayer I make,

On bend-ed knee; This is my ear-nest plea, More love, O Christ, to thee, More love to thee, More love to thee! A-MEN.

2 Once earthly joy I craved,
  Sought peace and rest;
Now thee alone I seek,
  Give what is best:
This all my prayer shall be,
More love, O Christ, to thee,
More love to thee!

3 Let sorrow do its work,
  Send grief and pain;
Sweet are thy messengers,
  Sweet their refrain,
When they can sing with me,
More love, O Christ, to thee,
More love to thee!

4 Then shall my latest breath
  Whisper thy praise;
This be the parting cry
  My heart shall raise,
This still its prayer shall be,
More love, O Christ, to thee,
More love to thee!

ELIZABETH P. PRENTISS

318 ARIEL 8. 8. 6. D.

Arr. by LOWELL MASON

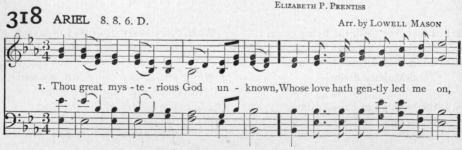

1. Thou great mys-te-rious God un-known, Whose love hath gen-tly led me on,

Aspiration and Hope

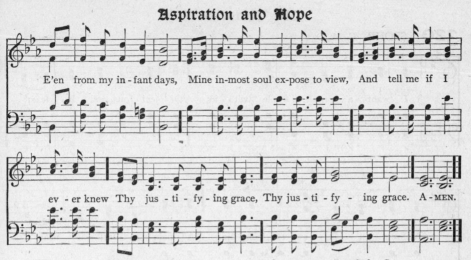

E'en from my in-fant days, Mine in-most soul ex-pose to view, And tell me if I ev-er knew Thy jus-ti-fy-ing grace, Thy jus-ti-fy-ing grace. A-MEN.

2 If I have only known thy fear,
  And followed, with a heart sincere,
    Thy drawings from above,
  Now, now the further grace bestow,
  And let my sprinkled conscience know
    Thy sweet forgiving love.

3 Father, in me reveal thy Son,
  And to my inmost soul make known
    How merciful thou art:
  The secret of thy love reveal,
  And by thy hallowing Spirit dwell
    Forever in my heart!

CHARLES WESLEY

319 SARDIS 8s. 7s.

LUDWIG VAN BEETHOVEN

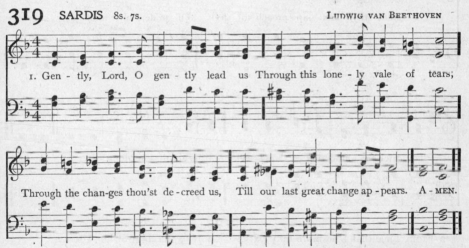

1. Gen-tly, Lord, O gen-tly lead us Through this lone-ly vale of tears; Through the chan-ges thou'st de-creed us, Till our last great change ap-pears. A-MEN.

2 When temptation's darts assail us,
    When in devious paths we stray,
  Let thy goodness never fail us,
    Lead us in thy perfect way.

3 In the hour of pain and anguish,
    In the hour when death draws near,

Suffer not our hearts to languish,
    Suffer not our souls to fear.

4 When this mortal life is ended,
    Bid us in thine arms to rest,
  Till, by angel-bands attended,
    We awake among the blest.

THOMAS HASTINGS

320 SPOHR C. M. D.

LOUIS SPOHR

1. I want a prin-ci-ple with-in, Of jeal-ous, god-ly fear;
A sen-si-bil-i-ty of sin, A pain to feel it near:
I want the first ap-proach to feel Of pride, or fond de-sire;
To catch the wan-dering of my will, And quench the kin-dling fire. A-MEN.

2 From Thee that I no more may part,
  No more thy goodness grieve,
The filial awe, the fleshly heart,
  The tender conscience, give,
Quick as the apple of an eye,
  O God, my conscience make!
Awake my soul when sin is nigh,
  And keep it still awake.

3 If to the right or left I stray,
  That moment, Lord, reprove;
And let me weep my life away
  For having grieved thy love.
O may the least omission pain
  My well-instructed soul,
And drive me to the blood again
  Which makes the wounded whole!

CHARLES WESLEY

321 NATIVITY C. M.

HENRY LAHEE

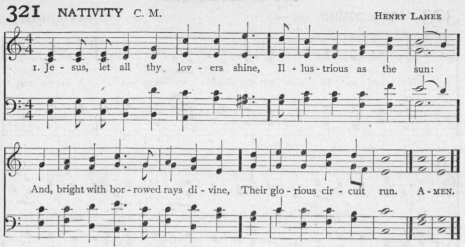

1. Je - sus, let all thy lov - ers shine, Il - lus - trious as the sun:

And, bright with bor - rowed rays di - vine, Their glo - rious cir - cuit run. A - MEN.

2 Beyond the reach of mortals, spread
  Their light where'er they go;
  And heavenly influences shed
    On all the world below.

3 As giants may they run their race,
  Exulting in their might;

As burning luminaries, chase
  The gloom of hellish night.

4 As the bright Sun of righteousness,
  Their healing wings display;
  And let their luster still increase
    Unto the perfect day.

CHARLES WESLEY

322 WELTON L. M.

A. H. C. MALAN

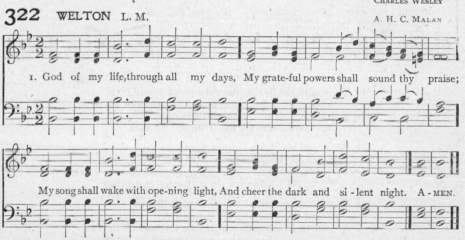

1. God of my life, through all my days, My grate-ful powers shall sound thy praise;

My song shall wake with ope-ning light, And cheer the dark and si - lent night. A - MEN.

2 When anxious cares would break my rest,
And griefs would tear my throbbing breast,
Thy tuneful praises raised on high
Shall check the murmur and the sigh.

3 When death o'er nature shall prevail,
And all the powers of language fail,
Joy through my swimming eyes shall break,
And mean the thanks I cannot speak.

4 But O, when that last conflict's o'er,
And I am chained to flesh no more,

With what glad accents shall I rise
To join the music of the skies!

5 Soon shall I learn the exalted strains
Which echo through the heavenly plains;
And emulate, with joy unknown,
The glowing seraphs round the throne.

6 The cheerful tribute will I give
Long as a deathless soul shall live:
A work so sweet, a theme so high,
Demands and crowns eternity.

PHILIP DODDRIDGE

323 VISIO DOMINI IIS. IOS.

JOHN B. DYKES

1. We would see Je - sus; for the shad - ows length - en A - cross this lit - tle land-scape of our life; We would see Je - sus, our weak faith to strength - en For the last wea - ri - ness, the fi - nal strife. A - MEN.

2 We would see Jesus, the great rock foundation
   Whereon our feet were set with sovereign grace:
   Nor life nor death, with all their agitation,
   Can thence remove us, if we see his face.

3 We would see Jesus: other lights are paling,
   Which for long years we have rejoiced to see;
   The blessings of our pilgrimage are failing:
   We would not mourn them, for we go to thee.

4 We would see Jesus: yet the spirit lingers
   Round the dear objects it has loved so long,
   And earth from earth can scarce unclasp its fingers;
   Our love to thee makes not this love less strong.

5 We would see Jesus: sense is all too binding,
   And heaven appears too dim, too far away;
   We would see thee, thyself our hearts reminding
   What thou hast suffered, our great debt to pay.

6 We would see Jesus: this is all we're needing;
   Strength, joy, and willingness come with the sight;
   We would see Jesus, dying, risen, pleading;
   Then welcome day, and farewell mortal night.

ANNA B. WARNER

Aspiration and Hope

324 SAVOY CHAPEL 7s. 6s. D.

JOHN B. CALKIN

1. To thee, O dear, dear Sav - iour! My spir - it turns for rest,
My peace is in thy fa - vor, My pil - low on thy breast;
Though all the world de - ceive me, I know that I am thine,
And thou wilt nev - er leave me, O bless - èd Sav - iour mine. A - MEN.

2 In thee my trust abideth,
  On thee my hope relies,
O thou whose love provideth
  For all beneath the skies;
O thou whose mercy found me,
  From bondage set me free,
And then forever bound me
  With threefold cords to thee.

3 My grief is in the dullness
  With which this sluggish heart
Doth open to the fullness
  Of all thou wouldst impart;
My joy is in thy beauty
  Of holiness divine,
My comfort in the duty
  That binds my life in thine.

4 Alas, that I should ever
  Have failed in love to thee,
The only one who never
  Forgot or slighted me!
O for a heart to love thee
  More truly as I ought,
And nothing place above thee
  In deed, or word, or thought.

5 O for that choicest blessing
  Of living in thy love,
And thus on earth possessing
  The peace of heaven above;
O for the bliss that by it
  The soul securely knows
The holy calm and quiet
  Of faith's serene repose!

JOHN S. B. MONSELL

325 BREAD OF LIFE 6s. 4s. D.

WILLIAM F. SHERWIN

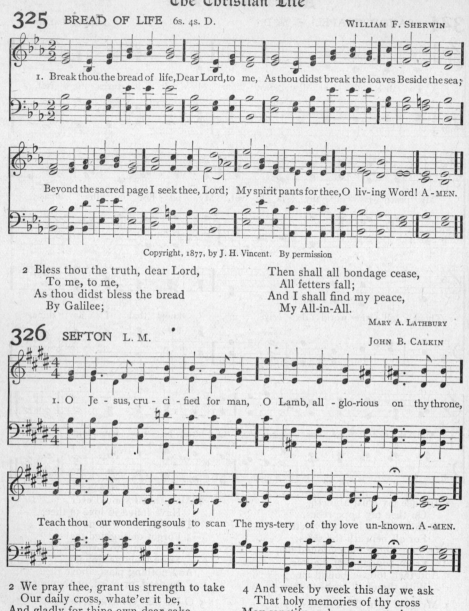

1. Break thou the bread of life, Dear Lord, to me, As thou didst break the loaves Beside the sea;

Beyond the sacred page I seek thee, Lord; My spirit pants for thee, O liv-ing Word! A-MEN.

Copyright, 1877, by J. H. Vincent. By permission

2 Bless thou the truth, dear Lord,
　To me, to me,
As thou didst bless the bread
　By Galilee;

Then shall all bondage cease,
　All fetters fall;
And I shall find my peace,
　My All-in-All.

MARY A. LATHBURY

326 SEFTON L. M.

JOHN B. CALKIN

1. O Je - sus, cru - ci - fied for man, O Lamb, all - glo-rious on thy throne,

Teach thou our wondering souls to scan The mys-tery of thy love un-known. A-MEN.

2 We pray thee, grant us strength to take
　Our daily cross, whate'er it be,
And gladly for thine own dear sake
　In paths of pain to follow thee.

3 As on our daily way we go,
　Through light or shade, in calm or strife,
O may we bear thy marks below
　In conquered sin and chastened life.

4 And week by week this day we ask
　That holy memories of thy cross
May sanctify each common task,
　And turn to gain each earthly loss.

5 Grant us, dear Lord, our cross to bear
　Till at thy feet we lay it down,
Win through thy blood our pardon there,
　And through the cross attain the crown.

WILLIAM W. HOW

327 HOLY TRINITY C. M.   JOSEPH BARNBY

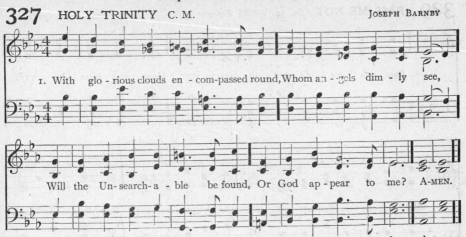

1. With glo - rious clouds en - com-passed round, Whom an - gels dim - ly see,

Will the Un-search-a - ble be found, Or God ap - pear to me? A-MEN.

2 Will he forsake his throne above,
   Himself to men impart?
Answer, thou Man of grief and love,
   And speak it to my heart.

3 Didst thou not in our flesh appear,
   And live and die below,
That I may now perceive thee near,
   And my Redeemer know?

4 Come then, and to my soul reveal
   The heights and depths of grace,
Those wounds which all my sorrows heal,
   Which all my sins efface.

5 Then shall I see in his own light,
   Whom angels dimly see;
And gaze, transported at the sight,
   To all eternity.

                  CHARLES WESLEY

328 RESIGNATION S. M.   MOSES S. CROSS

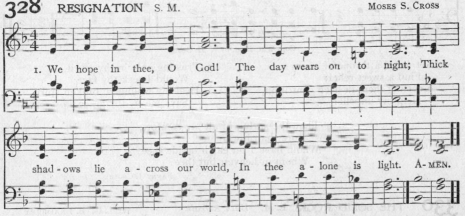

1. We hope in thee, O God! The day wears on to night; Thick

shad - ows lie a - cross our world, In thee a - lone is light. A - MEN.

2 We hope in thee, O God!
   The fading time is here,
But thou abidest strong and true
   Though all things disappear.

3 We hope in thee, O God!
   Our joys go one by one,
But lonely hearts can rest in thee,
   When all beside is gone.

4 We hope in thee, O God!
   Hope fails us otherwhere;
But since thou art in all that is,
   Peace takes the hand of care.

5 We hope in thee, O God!
   In whom none hope in vain;
We cling to thee in love and trust,
   And joy succeeds to pain.

                MARIANNE F. HEARN

329 PASS ME NOT 8s. 5s. *With Refrain*

WILLIAM H. DOANE

1. Pass me not, O gen-tle Sav-iour, Hear my hum-ble cry;
While on oth-ers thou art call-ing, Do not pass me by;

REFRAIN

Sav-iour, Sav-iour, hear my humble cry, While on oth-ers thou art call-ing, Do not pass me by. A-MEN.

Copyright, 1899, by W. H. Doane

2 Let me at a throne of mercy
   Find a sweet relief;
   Kneeling there in deep contrition,
   Help my unbelief.

3 Trusting only in thy merit,
   Would I seek thy face;
   Heal my wounded, broken spirit,
   Save me by thy grace.

4 Thou the spring of all my comfort,
   More than life for me;
   Whom have I on earth beside thee?
   Whom in heaven but thee?

FANNY J. CROSBY

330 THE SOLID ROCK L. M. *With Refrain*

WILLIAM B. BRADBURY

1. My hope is built on noth-ing less Than Je-sus' blood and right-eous-ness;

Aspiration and Hope

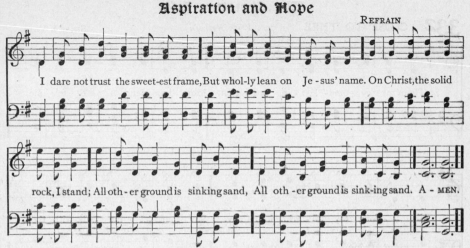

I dare not trust the sweet-est frame, But whol-ly lean on Je-sus' name. On Christ, the solid rock, I stand; All oth-er ground is sinking sand, All oth-er ground is sink-ing sand. A - MEN.

Used by permission of Biglow & Main Co.

2 When darkness veils his lovely face
  I rest on his unchanging grace;
  In every high and stormy gale,
  My anchor holds within the veil.

3 His oath, his covenant, his blood,
  Support me in the whelming flood;

When all around my soul gives way,
He then is all my hope and stay.

4 When he shall come with trumpet sound,
  O may I then in him be found;
  Dressed in his righteousness alone,
  Faultless to stand before the throne!

EDWARD MOTE

331 SPRING C. M.

L. C. EVERETT

1. Je-sus, the all - re - stor-ing word, My fall - en spir - it's hope,
Aft - er thy love - ly like - ness, Lord, Ah! when shall I wake up? A - MEN.

2 Thou, O my God, thou only art
  The life, the truth, the way;
  Quicken my soul, instruct my heart,
  My sinking footsteps stay.

3 Of all thou hast in earth below,
  In heaven above, to give,
  Give me thy only love to know,
  In thee to walk and live.

4 Fill me with all the life of love;
  In mystic union join
  Me to thyself, and let me prove
  The fellowship divine.

5 Open the intercourse between
  My longing soul and thee,
  Never to be broke off again
  To all eternity.

CHARLES WESLEY

332 CLOSE TO THEE 8s. 7s. *With Refrain* SILAS J. VAIL

1. Thou my ev - er - last - ing por - tion, More than friend or life to me,
All a - long my pil - grim jour - ney, Sav - iour, let me walk with thee.

REFRAIN
Close to thee, close to thee, Close to thee, close to thee; All a -
long my pil - grim jour - ney, Sav - iour, let me walk with thee. A - MEN.

2 Not for ease or worldly pleasure,
    Nor for fame my prayer shall be;
  Gladly will I toil and suffer,
    Only let me walk with thee.

REFRAIN
Close to thee, close to thee,
    Close to thee, close to thee;
  Gladly will I toil and suffer,
    Only let me walk with thee.

3 Lead me through the vale of shadows,
    Bear me o'er life's fitful sea;
  Then the gate of life eternal,
    May I enter, Lord, with thee.

REFRAIN
Close to thee, close to thee,
    Close to thee, close to thee;
  Then the gate of life eternal,
    May I enter, Lord, with thee.

FANNY J. CROSBY

333 YOAKLEY L. M. 6l.   WILLIAM YOAKLEY

1. Je - sus, thy boundless love to me   No thought can reach, no tongue de-clare;

O knit my thank-ful heart to thee,   And reign with-out a ri - val there!

Thine whol-ly, thine a - lone,—I am,   Be thou a - lone my con-stant flame. A - MEN.

2 O Love, how cheering is thy ray!
    All pain before thy presence flies;
Care, anguish, sorrow, melt away,
    Where'er thy healing beams arise:
O Jesus, nothing may I see,
Nothing desire, or seek, but thee!

3 Unwearied may I this pursue;
    Dauntless to the high prize aspire;
Hourly within my soul renew
    This holy flame, this heavenly fire:
And day and night, be all my care
To guard the sacred treasure there.

4 In suffering be thy love my peace;
    In weakness be thy love my power;
And when the storms of life shall cease,
    O Jesus, in that solemn hour,
In death as life be thou my guide,
And save me, who for me hast died.

PAUL GERHARDT. Tr. by JOHN WESLEY

334 BETHEL 6. 6. 4. 6. 6. 6. 4. JOHN H. CORNELL

1. My faith looks up to thee, Thou Lamb of Cal - va - ry,

Sav - iour di - vine! Now hear me while I pray, Take all my guilt a - way,

O let me from this day Be whol - ly thine! A - MEN.

2 May thy rich grace impart
Strength to my fainting heart,
   My zeal inspire;
As thou hast died for me,
O may my love to thee
Pure, warm, and changeless be,
   A living fire!

3 While life's dark maze I tread,
And griefs around me spread,
   Be thou my guide;
Bid darkness turn to day,
Wipe sorrow's tears away,
Nor let me ever stray
   From thee aside.

4 When ends life's transient dream,
When death's cold, sullen stream
   Shall o'er me roll;
Blest Saviour, then, in love,
Fear and distrust remove;
O bear me safe above,
   A ransomed soul!

RAY PALMER

334 OLIVET 6. 6. 4. 6. 6. 6. 4. (Second Tune) LOWELL MASON

1. My faith looks up to thee, Thou Lamb of Cal - va - ry,

Sav - iour di - vine! Now hear me while I pray, Take all my guilt a - way,

O let me from this day Be whol - ly thine! A - MEN.

335 BELOIT L. M.

CARL G. REISSIGER

1. I thirst, thou wounded Lamb of God, To wash me in thy cleansing blood;

To dwell with-in thy wounds,then pain Is sweet,and life or death is gain. A- MEN.

2 Take my poor heart, and let it be
Forever closed to all but thee;
Seal thou my breast, and let me wear
That pledge of love forever there.

3 How blest are they who still abide
Close sheltered in thy bleeding side,
Who thence their life and strength derive,
And by thee move, and in thee live!

4 How can it be, thou heavenly King,
That thou shouldst us to glory bring?
Make slaves the partners of thy throne,
Decked with a never-fading crown?

5 Hence our hearts melt, our eyes o'erflow,
Our words are lost, nor will we know,
Nor will we think of aught beside,
"My Lord, my Love is crucified."

From the German. Tr. by JOHN WESLEY

237

336 HOLBORN HILL L. M.

St. Alban's Tune Book

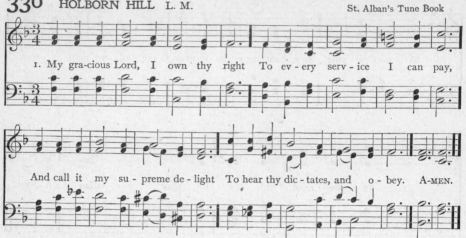

1. My gra-cious Lord, I own thy right To ev-ery serv-ice I can pay,

And call it my su - preme de - light To hear thy dic - tates, and o - bey. A-MEN.

2 What is my being but for thee,
Its sure support, its noblest end?
'Tis my delight thy face to see,
And serve the cause of such a Friend.

3 I would not sigh for worldly joy,
Or to increase my worldly good;
Nor future days nor powers employ
To spread a sounding name abroad.

4 'Tis to my Saviour I would live,
To him who for my ransom died;
Nor could all worldly honor give
Such bliss as crowns me at his side.

5 His work my hoary age shall bless,
When youthful vigor is no more;
And my last hour of life confess
His dying love, his saving power.

PHILIP DODDRIDGE

337 ALETTA 7s.

WILLIAM B. BRADBURY

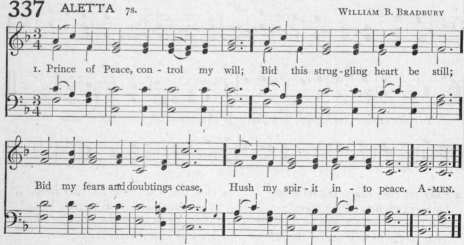

1. Prince of Peace, con - trol my will; Bid this strug-gling heart be still;

Bid my fears and doubtings cease, Hush my spir - it in - to peace. A-MEN.

2 Thou hast bought me with thy blood,
Opened wide the gate to God:
Peace I ask, but peace must be,
Lord, in being one with thee.

3 May thy will, not mine, be done;
May thy will and mine be one;

Chase these doubtings from my heart,
Now thy perfect peace impart.

4 Saviour, at thy feet I fall,
Thou my life, my God, my all!
Let thy happy servant be
One for evermore with thee!

MARY A. S. BARBER

338 HOWARD C. M.   ELIZABETH H. CUTHBERT

1. Do not I love thee, O my Lord? Then let me noth-ing love;
Dead be my heart to ev-ery joy, When Je-sus can-not move. A-MEN.

2 Is not thy name melodious still
   To mine attentive ear?
   Doth not each pulse with pleasure bound
   My Saviour's voice to hear?

3 Hast thou a lamb in all thy flock
   I would disdain to feed?
   Hast thou a foe, before whose face
   I fear thy cause to plead?

4 Would not mine ardent spirit vie
   With angels round the throne,
   To execute thy sacred will,
   And make thy glory known?

5 Thou know'st I love thee, dearest Lord,
   But O, I long to soar
   Far from the sphere of mortal joys,
   And learn to love thee more!
                               PHILIP DODDRIDGE

339 GERMANY L. M.   LUDWIG VAN BEETHOVEN

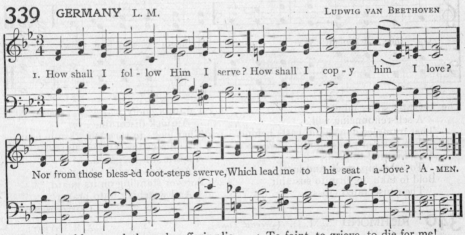

1. How shall I fol-low Him I serve? How shall I cop-y him I love?
Nor from those bless-èd foot-steps swerve, Which lead me to his seat a-bove? A-MEN.

2 Lord, should my path through suffering lie,
   Forbid it I should e'er repine;
   Still let me turn to Calvary,
   Nor heed my griefs, remembering thine.

3 O let me think how thou didst leave
   Untasted every pure delight,
   To fast, to faint, to watch, to grieve,
   The toilsome day, the homeless night: —

4 To faint, to grieve, to die for me!
   Thou camest not thyself to please:
   And, dear as earthly comforts be,
   Shall I not love thee more than these?

5 Yes! I would count them all but loss,
   To gain the notice of thine eye:
   Flesh shrinks and trembles at the cross,
   But thou canst give the victory.
                               JOSIAH CONDER

The Christian Life

340   CHALVEY S. M. D.

LEIGHTON G. HAYNE

1. Je - sus, my strength, my hope, On thee I cast my care,

With hum - ble con - fi - dence look up, And know thou hear'st my prayer.

Give me on thee to wait, Till I can all things do,

On thee, al - might - y to cre - ate, Al - might - y to re - new. A - MEN.

2 I want a sober mind,
   A self-renouncing will,
That tramples down, and casts behind
   The baits of pleasing ill:
A soul inured to pain,
   To hardship, grief, and loss;
Bold to take up, firm to sustain,
   The consecrated cross.

3 I want a godly fear,
   A quick discerning eye,
That looks to thee when sin is near,
   And sees the tempter fly:
A spirit still prepared,
   And armed with jealous care;
Forever standing on its guard,
   And watching unto prayer.

CHARLES WESLEY

340   RICHMOND S. M. D. (*Second Tune*)

A. B. EVERETT

1. Je - sus, my strength, my hope, On thee I cast my care,

Consecration and Growth in Grace

With hum - ble con - fi - dence look up, And know thou hear'st my prayer.

Give me on thee to wait, Till I can all things do,

On thee, al - might - y to cre - ate, Al - might - y to re - new. A - MEN.

341 MARYTON L. M.

H. PERCY SMITH

1. O Thou, who hast at thy com-mand The hearts of all men in thy hand,

Our wayward, err-ing hearts in - cline To have no oth - er will but thine. A - MEN.

2 Our wishes, our desires, control;
Mold every purpose of the soul;
O'er all may we victorious prove
That stands between us and thy love.

3 Thrice blest will all our blessings be,
When we can look through them to thee;

When each glad heart its tribute pays
Of love and gratitude and praise.

4 And while we to thy glory live,
May we to thee all glory give,
Until the final summons come,
That calls thy willing servants home.

JANE COTTERILL

The Christian Life

342 SESSIONS L. M.

LUTHER O. EMERSON

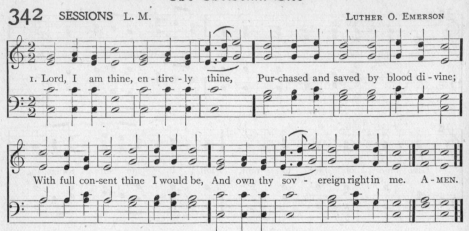

1. Lord, I am thine, en-tire-ly thine, Pur-chased and saved by blood di-vine;
With full con-sent thine I would be, And own thy sov - ereign right in me. A-MEN.

2 Grant one poor sinner more a place
Among the children of thy grace;
A wretched sinner, lost to God,
But ransomed by Immanuel's blood.

3 Thine would I live, thine would I die,
Be thine through all eternity;

The vow is past beyond repeal,
And now I set the solemn seal.

4 Here, at that cross where flows the blood
That bought my guilty soul for God,
Thee, my new Master, now I call,
And consecrate to thee my all.

SAMUEL DAVIES

343 FAITH C. M.

JOHN B. DYKES

1. Lord! when I all things would pos-sess, I crave but to be thine;
O low-ly is the loft - i - ness Of these de - sires di - vine. A-MEN.

2 Each gift but helps my soul to learn
How boundless is thy store;
I go from strength to strength, and yearn
For thee, my Helper, more.

3 How can my soul divinely soar,
How keep the shining way,
And not more tremblingly adore,
And not more humbly pray?

4 The more I triumph in thy gifts,
The more I wait on thee;
The grace that mightily uplifts
Most sweetly humbleth me.

5 The heaven where I would stand complete
My lowly love shall see,
And stronger grow the yearning sweet,
O holy One! for thee.

THOMAS H. GILL

Consecration and Growth in Grace

344 GODFREY 6s. 5s. D.

JOHN A. WEST

1. Sav-iour, bless-èd Sav-iour, Lis-ten while we sing; Hearts and voi-ces rais-ing Prais-es to our King; All we have to of-fer, All we hope to hope . . be; . . . Bod-y, soul, and spir-it, All we yield to thee. A-MEN.
to be;

2 Nearer, ever nearer,
   Christ, we draw to thee,
   Deep in adoration
   Bending low the knee:
   Thou for our redemption
   Cam'st on earth to die:
   Thou, that we might follow,
   Hast gone up on high.

3 Great, and ever greater
   Are thy mercies here,
   True and everlasting
   Are the glories there;
   Where no pain, or sorrow,
   Toil, or care, is known,
   Where the angel legions
   Circle round thy throne.

4 Clearer still, and clearer,
   Dawns the light from heaven
   In our sadness bringing
   News of sins forgiven;
   Life has lost its shadows;
   Pure the light within;
   Thou hast shed thy radiance
   On a world of sin.

5 Brighter still, and brighter,
   Glows the western sun,
   Shedding all its gladness
   O'er our work that's done;
   Time will soon be over,
   Toil and sorrow past,
   May we, blessèd Saviour,
   Find a rest at last!

6 Onward, ever onward,
   Journeying o'er the road
   Worn by saints before us,
   Journeying on to God!
   Leaving all behind us,
   May we hasten on,
   Backward never looking
   Till the prize is won.

7 Higher, then, and higher,
   Bear the ransomed soul,
   Earthly toils forgetting,
   Saviour, to its goal;
   Where in joys unthought of
   Saints with angels sing,
   Never weary, raising
   Praises to their King.

GODFREY THRING

345 ST. CHRYSOSTOM L. M. 6l.   JOSEPH BARNBY

1. Thou hid - den love of God, whose height, Whose depth un - fath-omed, no man knows,

I see from far thy beau-teous light, In - ly I sigh for thy re - pose:

My heart is pained, nor can it be At rest, till it finds rest in thee. A - MEN.

2 Is there a thing beneath the sun,
  That strives with thee my heart to share?
Ah, tear it thence, and reign alone,
  The Lord of every motion there!
Then shall my heart from earth be free,
When it hath found repose in thee.

3 O Love, thy sovereign aid impart,
  To save me from low-thoughted care;
Chase this self-will through all my heart,
  Through all its latent mazes there;
Make me thy duteous child, that I
Ceaseless may, "Abba, Father," cry.

4 Each moment draw from earth away
  My heart, that lowly waits thy call;
Speak to my inmost soul, and say,
  "I am thy Love, thy God, thy All!"
To feel thy power, to hear thy voice,
To taste thy love, be all my choice.

GERHARD TERSTEEGEN. Tr. by JOHN WESLEY

346 EVEN ME 8. 7. 8. 7. 3. *With Refrain*   WILLIAM B. BRADBURY

1. Lord, I hear of showers of bless - ing Thou art scat-tering full and free;

Consecration and Growth in Grace

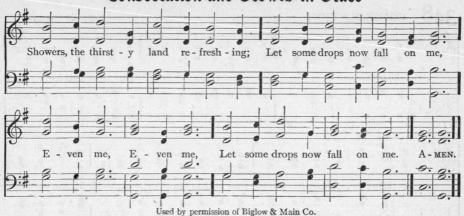

Showers, the thirst - y land re - fresh - ing; Let some drops now fall on me,

E - ven me, E - ven me, Let some drops now fall on me. A - MEN.

2 Pass me not, O gracious Father,
   Sinful though my heart may be;
   Thou mightst leave me, but the rather
   Let thy mercy light on me,
   Even me.

3 Pass me not, O tender Saviour,
   Let me love and cling to thee;
   1 am longing for thy favor;
   Whilst thou'rt calling, O call me,
   Even me.

4 Pass me not, O mighty Spirit,
   Thou canst make the blind to see;
   Witnesser of Jesus' merit,
   Speak the word of power to me,
   Even me.

5 Love of God, so pure and changeless,
   Blood of Christ, so rich, so free,
   Grace of God, so strong and boundless,
   Magnify them all in me,
   Even me.

ELIZABETH CODNER

347 BELLEVILLE L. M.

PETER C. LUTKIN

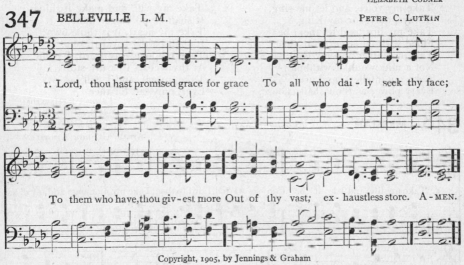

1. Lord, thou hast promised grace for grace To all who dai - ly seek thy face;

To them who have, thou giv - est more Out of thy vast; ex - haustless store. A - MEN.

2 Each step we take but gathers strength
   For further progress, till at length,
   With ease the highest steeps we gain,
   And count the mountain but a plain.

3 Who watch, and pray, and work each hour
   Receive new life and added power,

A power fresh victories to win
Over the world, and self, and sin.

4 Help us, O Lord, that we may grow
   In grace as thou dost grace bestow;
   And still thy richer gifts repeat
   Till grace in glory is complete.

SAMUEL K. COX

348 CONSECRATION 7s. D.

Composer Unknown

1. Take my life, and let it be Con-se-crated, Lord, to thee; Take my moments and my days;

Let them flow in cease-less praise; Take my hands, and let them move At the im-pulse

of thy love; Take my feet, and let them be Swift and beauti-ful for thee. A-MEN.

2 Take my voice, and let me sing,
Always, only, for my King.
Take my lips, and let them be
Filled with messages from thee.
Take my silver and my gold;
Not a mite would I withhold.
Take my intellect, and use
Every power as thou shalt choose.

3 Take my will, and make it thine;
It shall be no longer mine.
Take my heart, it is thine own;
It shall be thy royal throne.
Take my love; my Lord, I pour
At thy feet its treasure-store.
Take myself, and I will be
Ever, only, all for thee.

FRANCES R. HAVERGAL

348 MESSIAH 7s. D. (Second Tune)

LOUIS J. F. HERALD
Arr. by GEORGE KINGSLEY

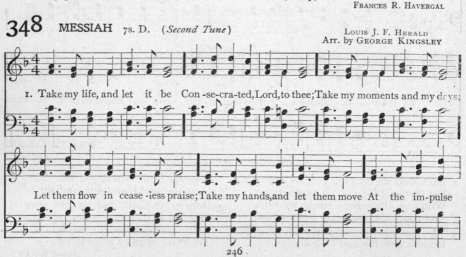

1. Take my life, and let it be Con-se-cra-ted, Lord, to thee; Take my moments and my days;

Let them flow in cease-less praise; Take my hands, and let them move At the im-pulse

Consecration and Growth in Grace

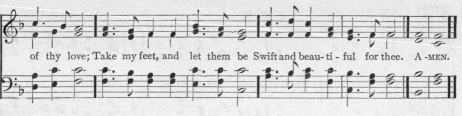

of thy love; Take my feet, and let them be Swift and beau-ti-ful for thee. A-MEN.

349   SOMETHING FOR JESUS   6. 4. 6. 4. 6. 6. 6. 4.   ROBERT LOWRY

1. Sav-iour, thy dy-ing love Thou gav-est me, Nor should I

aught with-hold, Dear Lord, from thee; In love my soul would bow, My heart ful-

fill its vow, Some of-fering bring thee now, Some-thing for thee. A-MEN.

2 At the blest mercy seat,
    Pleading for me,
My feeble faith looks up,
    Jesus, to thee;
Help me the cross to bear,
Thy wondrous love declare,
Some song to raise, or prayer,
    Something for thee.

3 Give me a faithful heart,
    Likeness to thee,
That each departing day
    Henceforth may see

Some work of love begun,
Some deed of kindness done,
Some wanderer sought and won,
    Something for thee.

4 All that I am and have,
    Thy gifts so free,
In joy, in grief, through life,
    Dear Lord, for thee!
And when thy face I see,
My ransomed soul shall be,
Through all eternity,
    Something for thee.

SYLVANUS D. PHELPS

The Christian Life

350 ANGEL'S STORY 7s. 6s. D.   ARTHUR H. MANN

1. O Je-sus, I have prom-ised To serve thee to the end; Be thou for-ev-er near me,

My Mas-ter and my Friend: I shall not fear the bat-tle If thou art by my side,

Nor wan-der from the path-way If thou wilt be my guide. A-MEN.

2 O let me feel thee near me;
  The world is ever near;
  I see the sights that dazzle,
  The tempting sounds I hear:
  My foes are ever near me,
  Around me and within;
  But, Jesus, draw thou nearer,
  And shield my soul from sin.

3 O Jesus, thou hast promised
  To all who follow thee,
  That where thou art in glory
  There shall thy servant be;
  And, Jesus, I have promised
  To serve thee to the end;
  O give me grace to follow,
  My Master and my Friend.

JOHN E. BODE

351 I AM COMING TO THE CROSS 7s. *With Refrain* WILLIAM G. FISCHER

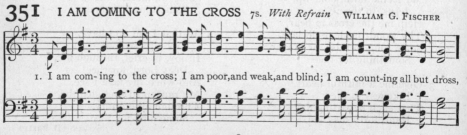

1. I am com-ing to the cross; I am poor, and weak, and blind; I am count-ing all but dross,

Consecration and Growth in Grace

REFRAIN

I shall full sal-va-tion find. I am trust-ing, Lord, in thee, Blest Lamb of Cal-va-ry;

Hum-bly at thy cross I bow, Save me, Je - sus, save me now. A - MEN.

2 Long my heart has sighed for thee,
   Long has evil reigned within;
   Jesus sweetly speaks to me,
   "I will cleanse you from all sin."

3 Here I give my all to thee,
   Friends, and time, and earthly store;
   Soul and body thine to be,
   Wholly thine for evermore.

4 In thy promises I trust,
   Now I feel the blood applied,
   I am prostrate in the dust,
   I with Christ am crucified.

5 Jesus comes! he fills my soul!
   Perfected in him I am;
   I am every whit made whole:
   Glory, glory to the Lamb!

WILLIAM McDONALD

352 GREENWOOD S. M.

JOSEPH E. SWEETSER

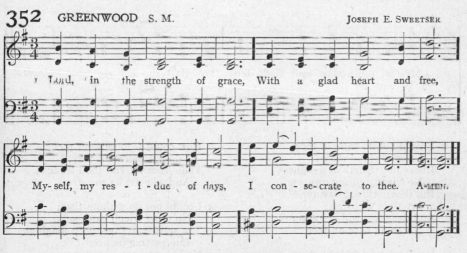

Lord, in the strength of grace, With a glad heart and free,

My-self, my res - i - due of days, I con - se-crate to thee. A-MEN.

2 Thy ransomed servant, I
   Restore to thee thine own;
   And, from this moment, live or die
   To serve my God alone.

CHARLES WESLEY

353 MAGDALENA 7s. 6s. D.   JOHN STAINER

1. I could not do with-out thee, O Sav-iour of the lost,
Whose pre-cious blood re-deemed me At such tre-men-dous cost:
Thy right-eous-ness, thy par-don, Thy pre-cious blood must be
My on-ly hope and com-fort, My glo-ry and my plea. A-MEN.

2 I could not do without thee,
  I cannot stand alone,
I have no strength or goodness,
  No wisdom of my own:
But thou, belovèd Saviour,
  Art all in all to me,
And weakness will be power
  If leaning hard on thee.

3 I could not do without thee,
  For O, the way is long,
And I am often weary,
  And sigh replaces song:

How could I do without thee?
  I do not know the way;
Thou knowest and thou leadest,
  And wilt not let me stray.

4 I could not do without thee;
  No other friend can read
The spirit's strange, deep longings,
  Interpreting its need:
No human heart could enter
  Each dim recess of mine,
And soothe and hush and calm it,
  O blessèd Lord, like thine.

FRANCES R. HAVERGAL

Entire Consecration and Perfect Love

354 SIMPSON C. M.

From Louis Spohr

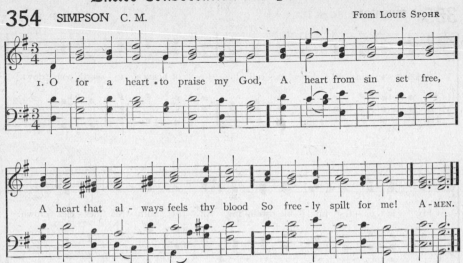

1. O for a heart to praise my God, A heart from sin set free,
A heart that al - ways feels thy blood So free - ly spilt for me! A - MEN.

2 A heart resigned, submissive, meek,
My great Redeemer's throne;
Where only Christ is heard to speak,
Where Jesus reigns alone;

3 A humble, lowly, contrite heart,
Believing, true, and clean,
Which neither life nor death can part
From him that dwells within;

4 A heart in every thought renewed,
And full of love divine;
Perfect, and right, and pure, and good,
A copy, Lord, of thine!

5 Thy nature, gracious Lord, impart;
Come quickly from above,
Write thy new name upon my heart,
Thy new, best name of Love.

CHARLES WESLEY

354 ARLINGTON C. M. (*Second Tune*)

THOMAS A. ARNE

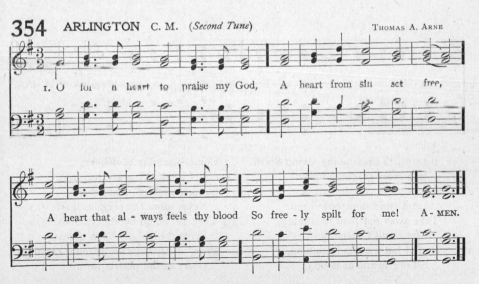

1. O for a heart to praise my God, A heart from sin set free,
A heart that al - ways feels thy blood So free - ly spilt for me! A - MEN.

251

355 WESTON 8s. 7s. D.

J. E. ROE

1. Love di - vine, all loves ex - cell - ing, Joy of heaven, to earth come down;

Fix in us thy hum - ble dwell - ing, All thy faith - ful mer - cies crown:

Je - sus, thou art all com-pas - sion, Pure, un-bound - ed love thou art;

Vis - it us with thy sal - va - tion, En - ter ev - ery trem-bling heart. A - MEN.

2 Breathe, O breathe thy loving Spirit
   Into every troubled breast!
Let us all in thee inherit,
   Let us find that second rest:
Take away our bent to sinning;
   Alpha and Omega be;
End of faith, as its beginning,
   Set our hearts at liberty.

3 Come, almighty to deliver,
   Let us all thy grace receive;
Suddenly return, and never,
   Never more thy temples leave:
Thee we would be always blessing,
   Serve thee as thy hosts above,
Pray, and praise thee without ceasing,
   Glory in thy perfect love.

Entire Consecration and Perfect Love

4 Finish then thy new creation,
   Pure and spotless let us be;
   Let us see thy great salvation,
   Perfectly restored in thee:

Changed from glory into glory,
   Till in heaven we take our place,
   Till we cast our crowns before thee,
   Lost in wonder, love, and praise.

CHARLES WESLEY

355 LOVE DIVINE 8s. 7s. D. (*Second Tune*)   JOHN ZUNDEL

1. Love di - vine, all loves ex - cell - ing, Joy of heaven, to earth come down;

Fix in us thy hum - ble dwell - ing, All thy faith - ful mer - cies crown:

Je - sus, thou art all com - pas - sion, Pure, un-bound - ed love thou art,

Vis - it us with thy sal - va - tion, En - ter ev - ery trem - bling heart. A - MEN.

356 EVAN C. M.

WILLIAM H. HAVERGAL

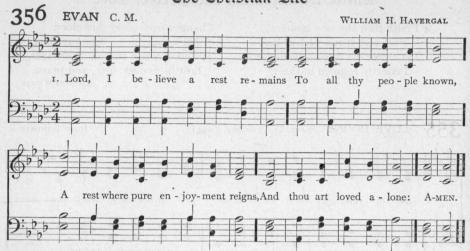

1. Lord, I be-lieve a rest re-mains To all thy peo-ple known,

A rest where pure en-joy-ment reigns, And thou art loved a-lone: A-MEN.

2 A rest where all our soul's desire
Is fixed on things above;
Where fear, and sin, and grief expire,
Cast out by perfect love.

3 O that I now the rest might know,
Believe, and enter in!

Now, Saviour, now the power bestow,
And let me cease from sin.

4 Remove this hardness from my heart,
This unbelief remove:
To me the rest of faith impart,
The Sabbath of thy love.

CHARLES WESLEY

357 AVON C. M.

HUGH WILSON

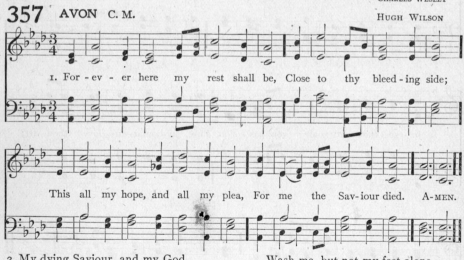

1. For-ev-er here my rest shall be, Close to thy bleed-ing side;

This all my hope, and all my plea, For me the Sav-iour died. A-MEN.

2 My dying Saviour, and my God,
Fountain for guilt and sin,
Sprinkle me ever with thy blood,
And cleanse and keep me clean.

3 Wash me, and make me thus thine own;
Wash me, and mine thou art;

Wash me, but not my feet alone,
My hands, my head, my heart.

4 The atonement of thy blood apply,
Till faith to sight improve,
Till hope in full fruition die,
And all my soul be love.

CHARLES WESLEY

358 LLANDAFF C. M.

EDWIN MOSS

1. What is our call-ing's glo-rious hope, But in-ward ho-li-ness?

For this to Je-sus I look up; I calm-ly wait for this. A-MEN.

2 I wait till he shall touch me clean,
　Shall life and power impart,
Give me the faith that casts out sin,
　And purifies the heart.

3 When Jesus makes my heart his home,
　My sin shall all depart;

And, lo! he saith, "I quickly come,
　To fill and rule thy heart."

4 Be it according to thy word;
　Redeem me from all sin;
My heart would now receive thee, Lord;
　Come in, my Lord, come in!

CHARLES WESLEY

359 BERA L. M.

JOHN E. GOULD

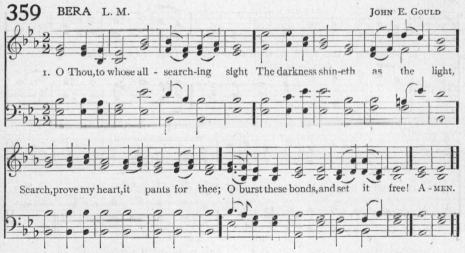

1. O Thou, to whose all-search-ing sight The darkness shin-eth as the light,

Search, prove my heart, it pants for thee; O burst these bonds, and set it free! A-MEN.

2 If in this darksome wild I stray,
　Be thou my Light, be thou my Way:
　No foes, no violence I fear,
　No fraud, while thou, my God, art near.

3 When rising floods my soul o'erflow,
　When sinks my heart in waves of woe,
　Jesus, thy timely aid impart,
　And raise my head, and cheer my heart.

4 Saviour, where'er thy steps I see,
　Dauntless, untired, I follow thee;
　O let thy hand support me still,
　And lead me to thy holy hill!

5 If rough and thorny be the way,
　My strength proportion to my day;
　Till toil, and grief, and pain shall cease,
　Where all is calm, and joy, and peace.

NICOLAUS L. ZINZENDORF. Tr. by JOHN WESLEY

The Christian Life

360 GREENWOOD S. M.

JOSEPH E. SWEETSER

1. Blest are the pure in heart, For they shall see our God; The se-cret of the Lord is theirs; Their soul is Christ's a-bode. A-MEN.

2 Still to the lowly soul
  He doth himself impart,
And for his temple and his throne
  Selects the pure in heart.

3 Lord, we thy presence seek,
  May ours this blessing be;
O give the pure and lowly heart,
  A temple meet for thee.

JOHN KEBLE

361 MANOAH C. M.

From GIOACHINO A. ROSSINI

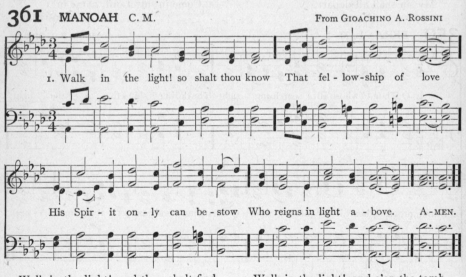

1. Walk in the light! so shalt thou know That fel-low-ship of love His Spir-it on-ly can be-stow Who reigns in light a-bove. A-MEN.

2 Walk in the light! and thou shalt find
  Thy heart made truly his
Who dwells in cloudless light enshrined,
  In whom no darkness is.

3 Walk in the light! and thou shalt own
  Thy darkness passed away,
Because that light hath on thee shone
  In which is perfect day.

4 Walk in the light! and e'en the tomb
  No fearful shade shall wear;
Glory shall chase away its gloom,
  For Christ hath conquered there.

5 Walk in the light! thy path snall be
  A path, though thorny, bright:
For God, by grace, shall dwell in thee,
  And God himself is light.

BERNARD BARTON

Entire Consecration and Perfect Love

362 **CARLISLE** S. M.

CHARLES LOCKHART

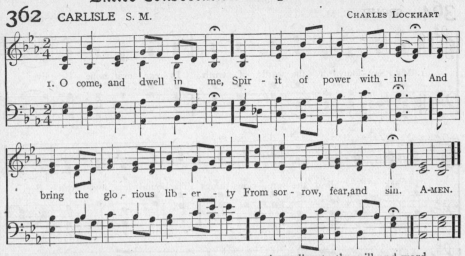

1. O come, and dwell in me, Spir-it of power with-in! And bring the glo-rious lib-er-ty From sor-row, fear, and sin. A-MEN.

2 Hasten the joyful day
  Which shall my sins consume;
  When old things shall be done away,
  And all things new become.

3 I want the witness, Lord,
  That all I do is right,

According to thy will and word,
  Well pleasing in thy sight.

4 I ask no higher state;
  Indulge me but in this,
  And soon or later then translate
  To my eternal bliss.

CHARLES WESLEY

363 **SAWLEY** C. M.

JAMES WALCH

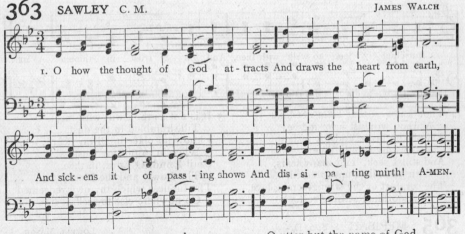

1. O how the thought of God at-tracts And draws the heart from earth, And sick-ens it of pass-ing shows And dis-si-pa-ting mirth! A-MEN.

2 'Tis not enough to save our souls,
  To shun the eternal fires;
  The thought of God will rouse the heart
  To more sublime desires.

3 God only is the creature's home,
  Though rough and strait the road;
  Yet nothing less can satisfy
  The love that longs for God.

4 O utter but the name of God
  Down in your heart of hearts,
  And see how from the world at once
  All tempting light departs!

5 A trusting heart, a yearning eye,
  Can win their way above;
  If mountains can be moved by faith,
  Is there less power in love?

FREDERICK W. FABER

10

364 SPOHR C. M. D.

LOUIS SPOHR

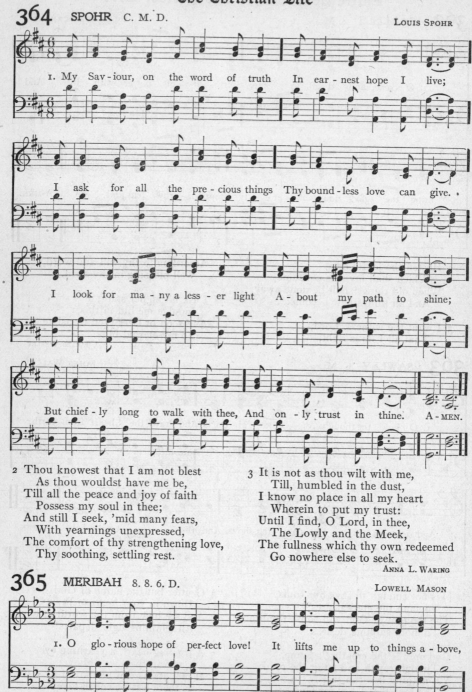

1. My Sav-iour, on the word of truth In ear-nest hope I live;

I ask for all the pre-cious things Thy bound-less love can give.

I look for ma-ny a less-er light A-bout my path to shine;

But chief-ly long to walk with thee, And on-ly trust in thine. A-MEN.

2 Thou knowest that I am not blest
    As thou wouldst have me be,
Till all the peace and joy of faith
    Possess my soul in thee;
And still I seek, 'mid many fears,
    With yearnings unexpressed,
The comfort of thy strengthening love,
    Thy soothing, settling rest.

3 It is not as thou wilt with me,
    Till, humbled in the dust,
I know no place in all my heart
    Wherein to put my trust:
Until I find, O Lord, in thee,
    The Lowly and the Meek,
The fullness which thy own redeemed
    Go nowhere else to seek.

ANNA L. WARING

365 MERIBAH 8. 8. 6. D.

LOWELL MASON

1. O glo-rious hope of per-fect love! It lifts me up to things a-bove,

It bears on ea-gles' wings; It gives my rav-ished soul a taste,

And makes me for some moments feast With Je-sus' priests and kings. A-MEN.

2 Rejoicing now in earnest hope,
  I stand, and from the mountain top
    See all the land below:
  Rivers of milk and honey rise,
  And all the fruits of paradise
    In endless plenty grow.

3 A land of corn, and wine, and oil,
  Favored with God's peculiar smile,
    With every blessing blest;
  There dwells the Lord our righteousness,
  And keeps his own in perfect peace,
    And everlasting rest.

CHARLES WESLEY

366   OVERBERG L. M.   JOHANN C. H. RINK

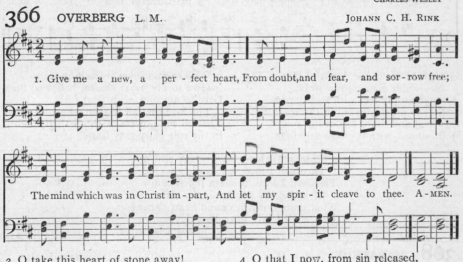

1. Give me a new, a per-fect heart, From doubt, and fear, and sor-row free;

The mind which was in Christ im-part, And let my spir-it cleave to thee. A-MEN.

2 O take this heart of stone away!
  Thy sway it doth not, cannot own;
  In me no longer let it stay;
  O take away this heart of stone!

3 Cause me to walk in Christ my Way;
  And I thy statutes shall fulfill,
  In every point thy law obey,
  And perfectly perform thy will.

4 O that I now, from sin released,
  Thy word may to the utmost prove!
  Enter into the promised rest,
  The Canaan of thy perfect love.

5 Now let me gain perfection's height;
  Now let me into nothing fall,
  Be less than nothing in thy sight,
  And feel that Christ is all in all.

CHARLES WESLEY

367 SILESIUS L. M. 6l.

ARTHUR H. MANN

1. I thank thee, un-cre-a-ted Sun, That thy bright beams on me have shined ; I
thank thee, who hast o-ver-thrown My foes, and healed my wound-ed mind; I
thank thee, whose en-liv-ening voice Bids my freed heart in thee re-joice. A-MEN.

2 Uphold me in the doubtful race,
  Nor suffer me again to stray;
Strengthen my feet with steady pace
  Still to press forward in thy way;
My soul and flesh, O Lord of might,
Fill, satiate, with thy heavenly light.

3 Give to mine eyes refreshing tears;
  Give to my heart chaste, hallowed fires;
Give to my soul, with filial fears,
  The love that all heaven's host inspires;
That all my powers, with all their might,
In thy sole glory may unite.

4 Thee will I love, my joy, my crown;
  Thee will I love, my Lord, my God;
Thee will I love, beneath thy frown
  Or smile, thy scepter or thy rod;
What though my flesh and heart decay?
Thee shall I love in endless day!

JOHANN A. SCHEFFLER. Tr. by JOHN WESLEY

368 HABAKKUK 8. 8. 6. D.

EDWARD HODGES

1. O Love di-vine, how sweet thou art! When shall I find my will-ing heart

260

Entire Consecration and Perfect Love

All tak-en up by thee? I thirst, I faint, I die to prove

The great-ness of re-deem-ing love, The love of Christ to me. A MEN.

2 Stronger his love than death or hell;
　Its riches are unsearchable;
　　The firstborn sons of light
　Desire in vain its depths to see;
　They cannot reach the mystery,
　　The length, the breadth, the height.

3 God only knows the love of God;
　O that it now were shed abroad
　　In this poor stony heart!
　For love I sigh, for love I pine;
　This only portion, Lord, be mine;
　　Be mine this better part!

4 O that I could forever sit
　With Mary at the Master's feet!
　　Be this my happy choice;
　My only care, delight, and bliss,
　My joy, my heaven on earth, be this,
　　To hear the Bridegroom's voice.

5 O that I could, with favored John,
　Recline my weary head upon
　　The dear Redeemer's breast!
　From care, and sin, and sorrow free,
　Give me, O Lord, to find in thee
　　My everlasting rest!

CHARLES WESLEY

369　ST. MARGUERITE C. M.

EDWARD C. WALKER

1. My God, ac-cept my heart this day, And make it al-ways thine;

That I from thee no more may stray, No more from thee de-cline. A MEN.

2 Before the cross of him who died,
　Behold, I prostrate fall;
　Let every sin be crucified,
　　Let Christ be All in All.

3 Let every thought, and work, and word,
　To thee be ever given;
　Then life shall be thy service, Lord,
　And death the gate of heaven.

MATTHEW BRIDGES

370 BRADFORD C.M.

From GEORGE F. HÄNDEL

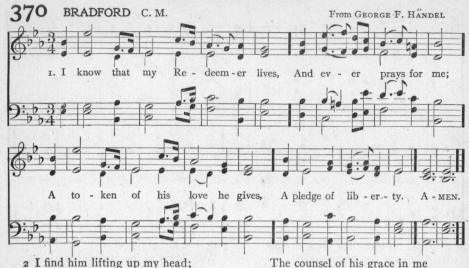

1. I know that my Re-deem-er lives, And ev-er prays for me;
A to-ken of his love he gives, A pledge of lib-er-ty. A-MEN.

2 I find him lifting up my head;
  He brings salvation near;
  His presence makes me free indeed,
  And he will soon appear.

3 He wills that I should holy be;
  What can withstand his will?

The counsel of his grace in me
He surely shall fulfill.

4 When God is mine, and I am his,
  Of paradise possessed,
  I taste unutterable bliss,
  And everlasting rest.

CHARLES WESLEY

371 LAUD C.M.

JOHN B. DYKES

1. O joy-ful sound of gos-pel grace! Christ shall in me ap-pear;
I, e-ven I, shall see his face, I shall be ho-ly here. A-MEN.

2 The glorious crown of righteousness
  To me reached out I view:
  Conqueror through him, I soon shall seize,
  And wear it as my due.

3 The promised land, from Pisgah's top,
  I now exult to see:
  My hope is full, O glorious hope!
  Of immortality.

4 With me, I know, I feel, thou art;
  But this cannot suffice,
  Unless thou plantest in my heart
  A constant paradise.

5 Come, O my God, thyself reveal,
  Fill all this mighty void:
  Thou only canst my spirit fill;
  Come, O my God, my God!

CHARLES WESLEY

Entire Consecration and Perfect Love

372 HESPERUS L. M.

HENRY W. BAKER

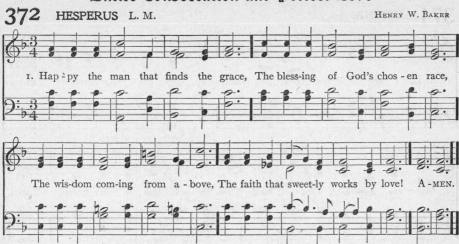

1. Hap-py the man that finds the grace, The bless-ing of God's chos-en race,

The wis-dom com-ing from a-bove, The faith that sweet-ly works by love! A-MEN.

2 Happy, beyond description, he
Who knows, "the Saviour died for me!"
The gift unspeakable obtains,
And heavenly understanding gains.

3 Wisdom divine! who tells the price
Of wisdom's costly merchandise?
Wisdom to silver we prefer,
And gold is dross compared to her.

4 Her hands are filled with length of days,
True riches and immortal praise,
Riches of Christ on all bestowed,
And honor that descends from God.

5 Happy the man who wisdom gains;
Thrice happy who his guest retains:
He owns, and shall forever own,
Wisdom, and Christ, and Heaven, are one.

CHARLES WESLEY

373 MOUNT CALVARY C. M.

ROBERT P. STEWART

1. Let Him to whom we now be-long His sov-ereign right as-sert,

And take up ev-ery thank-ful song, And ev-ery lov-ing heart. A-MEN.

2 He justly claims us for his own,
Who bought us with a price:
The Christian lives to Christ alone,
To Christ alone he dies.

3 Jesus, thine own at last receive,
Fulfill our heart's desire;

And let us to thy glory live,
And in thy cause expire.

4 Our souls and bodies we resign:
With joy we render thee
Our all, no longer ours, but thine,
To all eternity.

CHARLES WESLEY

374 VIENNA 7s.

JUSTIN H. KNECHT

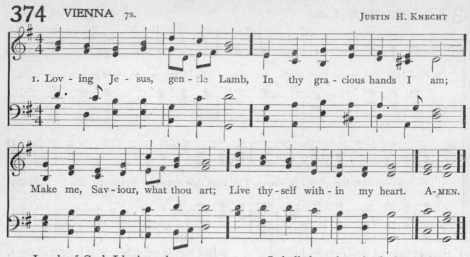

1. Lov - ing Je - sus, gen - tle Lamb, In thy gra - cious hands I am;

Make me, Sav - iour, what thou art; Live thy - self with - in my heart. A - MEN.

2 Lamb of God, I look to thee,
   Thou shalt my example be;
   Thou didst live to God alone,
   Thou didst never seek thine own.

3 I shall then show forth thy praise,
   Serve thee all my happy days;
   Then the world shall always see
   Christ, the holy Child, in me.

CHARLES WESLEY

375 AZMON C. M.

CARL G. GLASER. Arr. by LOWELL MASON

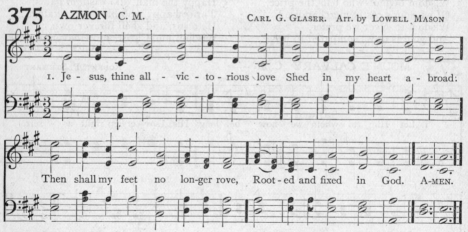

1. Je - sus, thine all - vic - to - rious love Shed in my heart a - broad:

Then shall my feet no lon-ger rove, Root - ed and fixed in God. A - MEN.

2 O that in me the sacred fire
   Might now begin to glow,
   Burn up the dross of base desire
   And make the mountains flow!

3 O that it now from heaven might fall,
   And all my sins consume!
   Come, Holy Ghost, for thee I call;
   Spirit of burning, come!

4 Refining fire, go through my heart;
   Illuminate my soul;

   Scatter thy life through every part,
   And sanctify the whole.

5 No longer then my heart shall mourn,
   While, purified by grace,
   I only for his glory burn,
   And always see his face.

6 My steadfast soul, from falling free,
   Shall then no longer move,
   While Christ is all the world to me,
   And all my heart is love.

CHARLES WESLEY

Entire Consecration and Perfect Love

376 GEER C. M.

HENRY W. GREATOREX

1. O for a heart of calm re - pose A - mid the world's loud roar,

A life that like a riv - er flows A - long a peace - ful shore! A - MEN.

2 Come, Holy Spirit! still my heart
  With gentleness divine;
Indwelling peace thou canst impart;
  O make that blessing mine!

3 Above these scenes of storm and strife
  There spreads a region fair;

Give me to live that higher life,
  And breathe that heavenly air.

4 Come, Holy Spirit! breathe that peace,
  That victory make me win;
Then shall my soul her conflict cease,
  And find a heaven within.

Author Unknown

377 SUTHERLAND L. M.

EMMA L. ASHFORD

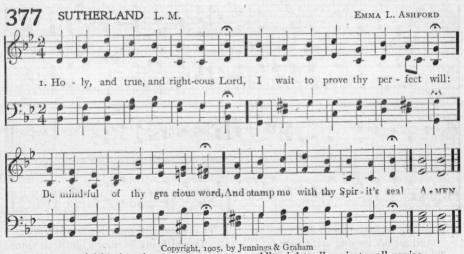

1. Ho - ly, and true, and right-eous Lord, I wait to prove thy per - fect will:

Be mind-ful of thy gra-cious word, And stamp me with thy Spir - it's seal A - MEN

Copyright, 1905, by Jennings & Graham

2 Open my faith's interior eye:
  Display thy glory from above;
And all I am shall sink and die,
  Lost in astonishment and love.

3 Confound, o'erpower me by thy grace;
  I would be by myself abhorred;

All might, all majesty, all praise,
  All glory, be to Christ my Lord.

4 Now let me gain perfection's height;
  Now let me into nothing fall,
As less than nothing in thy sight,
  And feel that Christ is all in all.

CHARLES WESLEY

378 JANES L. M.

JOHANN C. W. A. MOZART

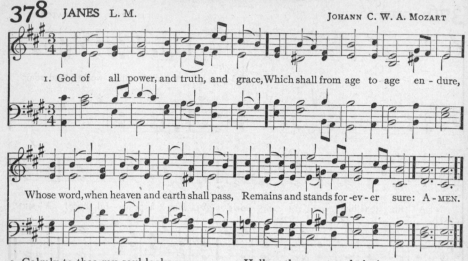

1. God of all power, and truth, and grace, Which shall from age to age en-dure,

Whose word, when heaven and earth shall pass, Remains and stands for-ev-er sure: A-MEN.

2 Calmly to thee my soul looks up,
    And waits thy promises to prove,
The object of my steadfast hope,
    The seal of thy eternal love.

3 That I thy mercy may proclaim,
    That all mankind thy truth may see,

Hallow thy great and glorious name,
    And perfect holiness in me.

4 Thy sanctifying Spirit pour,
    To quench my thirst, and make me clean;
Now, Father, let the gracious shower
    Descend, and make me pure from sin!
                                        CHARLES WESLEY

379 BARTHOLDY L. M.

FELIX MENDELSSOHN–BARTHOLDY

1. Come, Saviour, Je-sus, from a-bove! As-sist me with thy heavenly grace;

Emp-ty my heart of earth-ly love, And for thy-self pre-pare the place. A-MEN.

2 O let thy sacred presence fill,
    And set my longing spirit free!
Which pants to have no other will,
    But day and night to feast on thee.

3 While in this region here below,
    No other good will I pursue:
I'll bid this world of noise and show,
    With all its glittering snares, adieu!

4 That path with humble speed I'll seek,
    In which my Saviour's footsteps shine;
Nor will I hear, nor will I speak,
    Of any other love but thine.

5 Henceforth may no profane delight
    Divide this consecrated soul;
Possess it, thou who hast the right,
    As Lord and Master of the whole.

ANTOINETTE BOURIGNON. Tr. by JOHN WESLEY

Entire Consecration and Perfect Love

380 TETWORTH 8.7.8.8.7.

GEORGE M. GARRETT

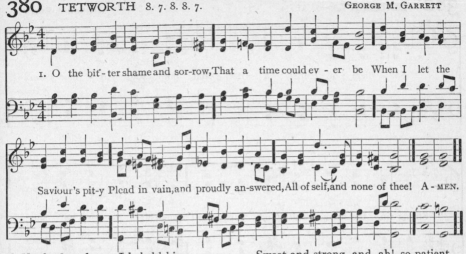

1. O the bit-ter shame and sor-row, That a time could ev - er be When I let the
Saviour's pit-y Plead in vain, and proudly an-swered, All of self, and none of thee! A - MEN.

2 Yet he found me; I beheld him
　Bleeding on the accursèd tree,
　Heard him pray, Forgive them, Father!
　And my wistful heart said faintly,
　　Some of self, and some of thee!

3 Day by day his tender mercy,
　Healing, helping, full and free,

Sweet and strong, and, ah! so patient,
Brought me lower, while I whispered,
　Less of self, and more of thee!

4 Higher than the highest heaven,
　Deeper than the deepest sea,
　Lord, thy love at last hath conquered;
　Grant me now my supplication,—
　　None of self, and all of thee!

THEODORE MONOD

381 HAMBURG L. M.

LOWELL MASON

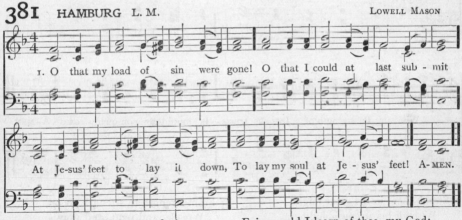

1. O that my load of sin were gone! O that I could at last sub - mit
At Je-sus' feet to lay it down, To lay my soul at Je - sus' feet! A - MEN.

2 Rest for my soul I long to find:
　Saviour of all, if mine thou art,
　Give me thy meek and lowly mind,
　And stamp thine image on my heart.

3 Break off the yoke of inbred sin,
　And fully set my spirit free:
　I cannot rest till pure within,
　Till I am wholly lost in thee.

4 Fain would I learn of thee, my God;
　Thy light and easy burden prove,
　The cross, all stained with hallowed blood,
　The labor of thy dying love.

5 I would, but thou must give the power;
　My heart from every sin release;
　Bring near, bring near the joyful hour,
　And fill me with thy perfect peace.

CHARLES WESLEY

382 DIADEMATA S. M. D.

GEORGE J. ELVEY

1. Sol - diers of Christ, a - rise, And put your ar - mor on,
Strong in the strength which God sup - plies Through his e - ter - nal Son;
Strong in the Lord of hosts, And in his might - y power,
Who in the strength of Je - sus trusts Is more than con-quer - or. A - MEN.

2 Stand, then, in his great might,
   With all his strength endued;
But take, to arm you for the fight,
   The panoply of God:
That, having all things done,
   And all your conflicts passed,
Ye may o'ercome through Christ alone,
   And stand entire at last.

3 From strength to strength go on,
   Wrestle, and fight, and pray;
Tread all the powers of darkness down,
   And win the well-fought day:
Still let the Spirit cry,
   In all his soldiers, "Come,"
Till Christ the Lord descend from high,
   And take the conquerors home.

CHARLES WESLEY

Activity and Zeal

ST. GERTRUDE 6s. 5s. D. *With Refrain*

ARTHUR S. SULLIVAN

1. Onward, Christian sol - diers! March-ing as to war, With the cross of Je - sus Go -ing on be - fore. Christ, the roy - al Mas - ter, Leads a -gainst the foe; For-ward in - to bat - tle, See, his ban-ners go! Onward, Christian sol - diers, Marching as to war, With the cross of Je - sus Go -ing on be - fore. A - MEN.

2 At the sign of triumph
    Satan's host doth flee;
On, then, Christian soldiers,
    On to victory!
Hell's foundations quiver
    At the shout of praise;
Brothers, lift your voices,
    Loud your anthems raise.

3 Like a mighty army
    Moves the church of God;
Brothers, we are treading
    Where the saints have trod;
We are not divided,
    All one body we,
One in hope and doctrine,
    One in charity.

4 Crowns and thrones may perish,
    Kingdoms rise and wane,
But the church of Jesus
    Constant will remain;
Gates of hell can never
    'Gainst that church prevail;
We have Christ's own promise,
    And that cannot fail.

5 Onward, then, ye people!
    Join our happy throng,
Blend with ours your voices
    In the triumph-song;
Glory, laud, and honor
    Unto Christ the King,
This through countless ages
    Men and angels sing.

SABINE BARING-GOULD

384 VEXILLUM 6s. 5s. 12l.

HENRY SMART

1. Forward! be our watch-word, Steps and voi-ces joined; Seek the things before us,

Not a look be-hind: Burns the fi-ery pil-lar At our ar-my's head;

Who shall dream of shrink-ing, By our Cap-tain led? Forward through the des-ert,

Through the toil and fight: Jor-dan flows be-fore us, Zi-on beams with light! A-MEN.

2 Forward! flock of Jesus,
  Salt of all the earth,
Till each yearning purpose
  Spring to glorious birth:
Sick, they ask for healing;
  Blind, they grope for day;
Pour upon the nations
  Wisdom's loving ray.
Forward, out of error,
  Leave behind the night;
Forward through the darkness,
  Forward into light!

3 Glories upon glories
  Hath our God prepared,
By the souls that love him
  One day to be shared:
Eye hath not beheld them,
  Ear hath never heard;

Nor of these hath uttered
  Thought or speech a word:
Forward, marching eastward
  Where the heaven is bright,
Till the veil be lifted,
  Till our faith be sight!

4 Far o'er yon horizon
  Rise the city towers,
Where our God abideth;
  That fair home is ours:
Flash the streets with jasper,
  Shine the gates with gold;
Flows the gladdening river
  Shedding joys untold;
Thither, onward thither,
  In the Spirit's might:
Pilgrims to your country,
  Forward into light!

HENRY ALFORD

Activity and Zeal

385   CALEDONIA   7. 7. 7. 6. D.   Old Scotch Melody

1. Sol-diers of the cross, a-rise! Lo! your Lead-er from the skies
Waves be-fore you glo-ry's prize, The prize of vic-to-ry.
Seize your ar-mor, gird it on; Now the bat-tle will be won;
See, the strife will soon be done; Then strug-gle man-ful-ly. A-MEN.

2 Jesus conquered when he fell,
Met and vanquished earth and hell;
Now he leads you on to swell
  The triumphs of his cross.
Though all earth and hell appear,
Who will doubt, or who can fear?
God, our strength and shield, is near;
  We cannot lose our cause.

3 Onward, then, ye hosts of God!
Jesus points the victor's rod;
Follow where your Leader trod;
  You soon shall see his face.
Soon, your enemies all slain,
Crowns of glory you shall gain,
Soon you'll join that glorious train
  Who shout their Saviour's praise.

JARED B. WATERBURY

386 WEBB 7s. 6s. D.

GEORGE J. WEBB

1. Stand up, stand up for Je - sus! Ye sol - diers of the cross;

Lift high his roy - al ban - ner, It must not suf - fer loss:

From vic - tory un - to vic - tory His ar - my shall he lead,

Till ev - ery foe is van - quished And Christ is Lord in - deed. A-MEN.

2 Stand up, stand up for Jesus!
  The trumpet call obey;
Forth to the mighty conflict,
  In this his glorious day:
Ye that are men, now serve him,
  Against unnumbered foes;
Your courage rise with danger,
  And strength to strength oppose.

3 Stand up, stand up for Jesus!
  Stand in his strength alone;
The arm of flesh will fail you;
  Ye dare not trust your own:

Put on the gospel armor,
  Each piece put on with prayer;
Where duty calls, or danger,
  Be never wanting there.

4 Stand up, stand up for Jesus!
  The strife will not be long;
This day the noise of battle,
  The next the victor's song:
To him that overcometh,
  A crown of life shall be;
He with the King of glory
  Shall reign eternally.

GEORGE DUFFIELD, Jr.

272

Activity and Zeal

387 LANCASHIRE 7s. 6s. D.

HENRY SMART

1. Go for - ward, Chris - tian sol - dier, Be - neath his ban - ner true:
The Lord him - self, thy Lead - er, Shall all thy foes sub - due.
His love fore - tells thy tri - als; He knows thine hour - ly need;
He can, with bread of heav - en, Thy faint - ing spir - it feed. A - MEN.

2 Go forward, Christian soldier,
  Fear not the secret foe;
Far more are o'er thee watching
  Than human eyes can know.
Trust only Christ, thy Captain,
  Cease not to watch and pray;
Heed not the treacherous voices,
  That lure thy soul astray.

3 Go forward, Christian soldier,
  Nor dream of peaceful rest,
Till Satan's host is vanquished,
  And heaven is all possessed;
Till Christ himself shall call thee
  To lay thine armor by,
And wear, in endless glory,
  The crown of victory.

LAURENCE TUTTIETT

388 BOYLSTON S. M.

LOWELL MASON

1. A charge to keep I have, A God to glo - ri - fy,

A nev - er - dy - ing soul to save, And fit it for the sky. A - MEN.

2 To serve the present age,
　My calling to fulfill;
O may it all my powers engage,
　To do my Master's will!

3 Arm me with jealous care,
　As in thy sight to live,

And O, thy servant, Lord, prepare,
　A strict account to give!

4 Help me to watch and pray,
　And on thyself rely,
Assured, if I my trust betray,
　I shall forever die.

CHARLES WESLEY

389 VENI S. M.

JOHN STAINER

1. Sow in the morn thy seed; At eve hold not thy hand; To

doubt and fear give thou no heed, Broad - cast it o'er the land. A - MEN.

2 Thou knowest not which shall thrive,
　The late or early sown;
Grace keeps the precious germ alive,
　When and wherever strown:

3 And duly shall appear,
　In verdure, beauty, strength,
The tender blade, the stalk, the ear,
　And the full corn at length.

4 Thou canst not toil in vain:
　Cold, heat, and moist, and dry,
Shall foster and mature the grain
　For garners in the sky.

5 Thence, when the glorious end,
　The day of God, shall come,
The angel reapers shall descend,
　And heaven shout, "Harvest-home!"

JAMES MONTGOMERY

Activity and Zeal

390 ST. GEORGE S. M.

HENRY J. GAUNTLETT

1. Make haste, O man, to live, For thou so soon must die; Time hur-ries past thee like the breeze; How swift its mo-ments fly! A-MEN.

2 Make haste, O man, to do
   Whatever must be done;
   Thou hast no time to lose in sloth,
   Thy day will soon be gone.

3 Up, then, with speed, and work;
   Fling ease and self away;

This is no time for thee to sleep,
   Up, watch, and work, and pray!

4 Make haste, O man, to live,
   Thy time is almost o'er;
   O sleep not, dream not, but arise,
   The Judge is at the door!

HORATIUS BONAR

391 VICTORY S. M.

H. A. WHITEHEAD

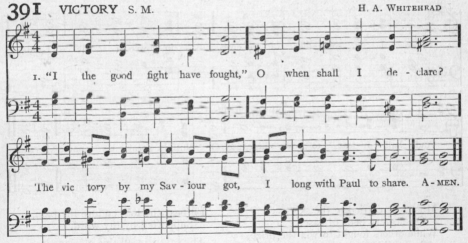

1. "I the good fight have fought," O when shall I de-clare? The vic-tory by my Sav-iour got, I long with Paul to share. A-MEN.

2 O may I triumph so,
   When all my warfare's past;
   And, dying, find my latest foe
   Under my feet at last!

3 This blessèd word be mine,
   Just as the port is gained,

"Kept by the power of grace divine,
   I have the faith maintained."

4 The apostles of my Lord,
   To whom it first was given,
   They could not speak a greater word,
   Nor all the saints in heaven.

CHARLES WESLEY

392 NATIVITY C. M.

HENRY LAHEE

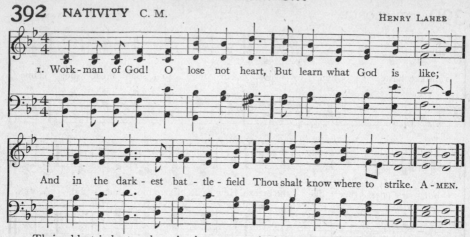

1. Work-man of God! O lose not heart, But learn what God is like; And in the dark-est bat-tle-field Thou shalt know where to strike. A-MEN.

2 Thrice blest is he to whom is given
  The instinct that can tell
That God is on the field, when he
  Is most invisible.

3 Blest too is he who can divine
  Where real right doth lie,

And dares to take the side that seems
  Wrong to man's blindfold eye.

4 Then learn to scorn the praise of men,
  And learn to lose with God;
For Jesus won the world through shame,
  And beckons thee his road.

FREDERICK W. FABER

393 ARLINGTON C. M.

THOMAS A. ARNE

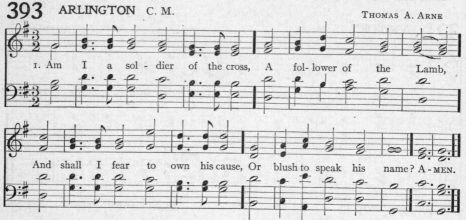

1. Am I a sol-dier of the cross, A fol-lower of the Lamb, And shall I fear to own his cause, Or blush to speak his name? A-MEN.

2 Must I be carried to the skies
  On flowery beds of ease,
While others fought to win the prize,
  And sailed through bloody seas?

3 Are there no foes for me to face?
  Must I not stem the flood?
Is this vile world a friend to grace,
  To help me on to God?

4 Sure I must fight, if I would reign;
  Increase my courage, Lord;

I'll bear the toil, endure the pain,
  Supported by thy word.

5 Thy saints in all this glorious war
  Shall conquer, though they die:
They see the triumph from afar,
  By faith they bring it nigh.

6 When that illustrious day shall rise,
  And all thy armies shine
In robes of victory through the skies,
  The glory shall be thine.

ISAAC WATTS

Activity and Zeal

394 ST. AGNES C. M.
JOHN B. DYKES

1. Be-hold us, Lord, a lit - tle space From dai - ly tasks set free,

And met with-in thy ho - ly place To rest a - while with thee. A - MEN.

2 Around us rolls the ceaseless tide
Of business, toil, and care,
And scarcely can we turn aside
For one brief hour of prayer.

3 Yet these are not the only walls
Wherein thou mayst be sought;
On homeliest work thy blessing falls
In truth and patience wrought.

4 Thine is the loom, the forge, the mart,
The wealth of land and sea;

The worlds of science and of art,
Revealed and ruled by thee.

5 Then let us prove our heavenly birth
In all we do and know,
And claim the kingdom of the earth
For thee, and not thy foe.

6 Work shall be prayer, if all be wrought
As thou wouldst have it done;
And prayer, by thee inspired and taught,
Itself with work be one.

JOHN ELLERTON

395 MOUNT CALVARY C. M.
ROBERT P. STEWART

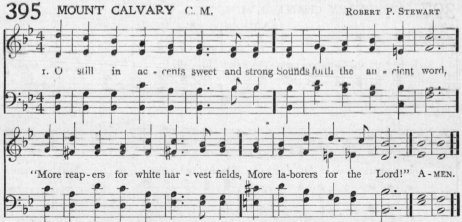

1. O still in ac - cents sweet and strong Sounds forth the an - cient word,

"More reap-ers for white har - vest fields, More la-borers for the Lord!" A - MEN.

2 We hear the call; in dreams no more
In selfish ease we lie,
But girded for our Father's work,
Go forth beneath his sky.

3 Where prophets' word, and martyrs' blood,
And prayers of saints were sown,

We, to their labors entering in,
Would reap where they have strown.

4 O Thou whose call our hearts has stirred,
To do thy will we come;
Thrust in our sickles at thy word,
And bear our harvest home.

SAMUEL LONGFELLOW

The Christian Life

396 CHRISTMAS C. M.

From GEORGE F. HÄNDEL

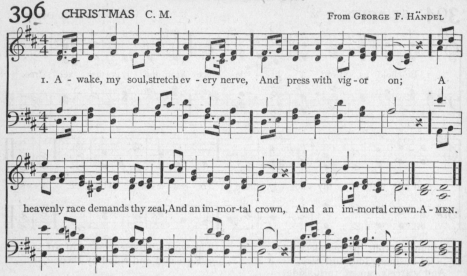

1. A - wake, my soul, stretch ev - ery nerve, And press with vig - or on; A heavenly race demands thy zeal, And an im-mor-tal crown, And an im-mortal crown. A - MEN.

2 A cloud of witnesses around
  Hold thee in full survey;
  Forget the steps already trod,
  And onward urge thy way.

3 'Tis God's all-animating voice
  That calls thee from on high;
  'Tis his own hand presents the prize
  To thine aspiring eye: —

4 That prize, with peerless glories bright,
  Which shall new luster boast,
  When victors' wreaths and monarchs' gems
  Shall blend in common dust.

5 Blest Saviour, introduced by thee,
  Have I my race begun;
  And, crowned with victory, at thy feet
  I'll lay my honors down.

PHILIP DODDRIDGE

397 MISSIONARY CHANT L. M.

HEINRICH C. ZEUNER

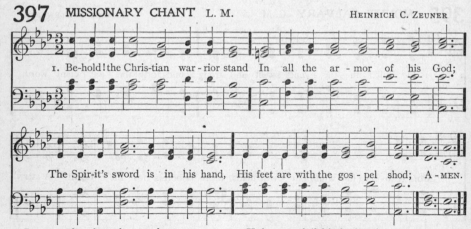

1. Be-hold! the Chris-tian war - rior stand In all the ar - mor of his God; The Spir-it's sword is in his hand, His feet are with the gos - pel shod; A - MEN.

2 In panoply of truth complete,
  Salvation's helmet on his head;
With righteousness a breastplate meet,
  And faith's broad shield before him spread.

3 Undaunted to the field he goes;
  Yet vain were skill and valor there,

Unless, to foil his legion foes,
  He takes the trustiest weapon, prayer.

4 Thus, strong in his Redeemer's strength,
  Sin, death, and hell, he tramples down;
Fights the good fight, and wins at length,
  Through mercy, an immortal crown.

JAMES MONTGOMERY

Activity and Zeal

398 ABENDS L. M.

HERBERT S. OAKELEY

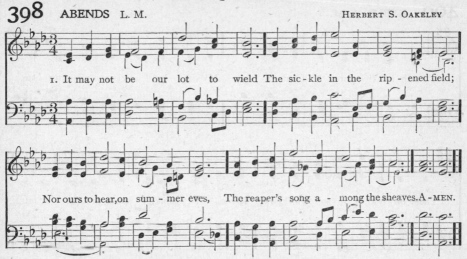

1. It may not be our lot to wield The sic-kle in the rip-ened field;

Nor ours to hear, on sum-mer eves, The reaper's song a-mong the sheaves. A-MEN.

2 Yet where our duty's task is wrought
In unison with God's great thought,
The near and future blend in one,
And whatso'er is willed, is done.

3 And ours the grateful service whence
Comes, day by day, the recompense;
The hope, the trust, the purpose stayed,
The fountain, and the noonday shade.

4 And were this life the utmost span,
The only end and aim of man,
Better the toil of fields like these
Than waking dream and slothful ease.

5 But life, though falling like our grain,
Like that revives and springs again;
And, early called, how blest are they
Who wait in heaven, their harvest day!

JOHN G. WHITTIER

399 ILLINOIS L. M.

JONATHAN SPILMAN, Arr. by THOMAS HASTINGS

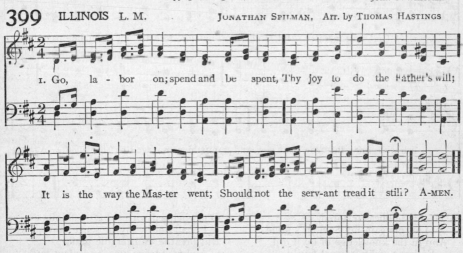

1. Go, la-bor on; spend and be spent, Thy joy to do the Father's will;

It is the way the Mas-ter went; Should not the serv-ant tread it still? A-MEN.

2 Go, labor on; 'tis not for naught;
Thine earthly loss is heavenly gain;
Men heed thee, love thee, praise thee not;
The Master praises, — what are men?

3 Go, labor on; your hands are weak;
Your knees are faint, your soul cast down;
Yet falter not; the prize you seek
Is near, — a kingdom and a crown!

HORATIUS BONAR

400 KEBLE L. M.

JOHN B. DYKES

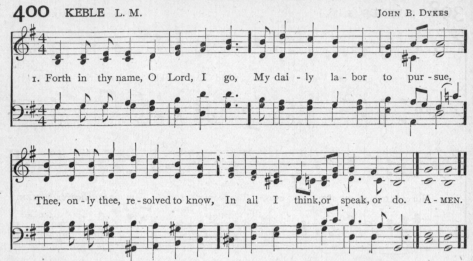

1. Forth in thy name, O Lord, I go, My dai - ly la - bor to pur - sue,

Thee, on - ly thee, re - solved to know, In all I think, or speak, or do. A - MEN.

2 The task thy wisdom hath assigned,
  O let me cheerfully fulfill;
In all my works thy presence find,
  And prove thy good and perfect will.

3 Give me to bear thy easy yoke,
  And every moment watch and pray;

And still to things eternal look,
  And hasten to thy glorious day:

4 For thee delightfully employ
  Whate'er thy bounteous grace hath given;
And run my course with even joy,
  And closely walk with thee to heaven.

CHARLES WESLEY

401 SEBASTIAN L. M.

SAMUEL S. WESLEY

1. O God, most mer - ci - ful and true, Thy na - ture to my soul im - part; 'Stab-

lish with me the cov-enant new, And stamp thine im - age on my heart. A - MEN.

2 To real holiness restored,
  O let me gain my Saviour's mind,
And in the knowledge of my Lord,
  Fullness of life eternal find!

3 Remember, Lord, my sins no more,
  That them I may no more forget;
But, sunk in guiltless shame, adore,
  With speechless wonder, at thy feet.

4 O'erwhelmed with thy stupendous grace,
  I shall not in thy presence move,
But breathe unutterable praise,
  And rapturous awe, and silent love.

5 Pardoned for all that I have done,
  My mouth as in the dust I hide
And glory give to God alone,
  My God forever pacified.

CHARLES WESLEY

Activity and Zeal

402 LUX EOI 8s. 7s. D. ARTHUR S. SULLIVAN

1. Hark, the voice of Je - sus call - ing, "Who will go and work to - day?
Fields are white, and har - vests wait - ing, Who will bear the sheaves a - way?"
Loud and long the Mas - ter call - eth, Rich re - ward he of - fers free;
Who will an - swer, glad - ly say - ing, "Here am I, send me, send me"? A men.

2 If you cannot cross the ocean,
    And the heathen lands explore,
You can find the heathen nearer,
    You can help them at your door:
If you cannot give your thousands,
    You can give the widow's mite;
And the least you give for Jesus
    Will be precious in his sight.

3 Let none hear you idly saying,
    "There is nothing I can do,"
While the souls of men are dying,
    And the Master calls for you:
Take the task he gives you gladly;
    Let his work your pleasure be;
Answer quickly when he calleth,
    "Here am I, send me, send me."

DANIEL MARCH

403 JOSHUA L. M. (*To be sung in Unison*)   PETER C. LUTKIN

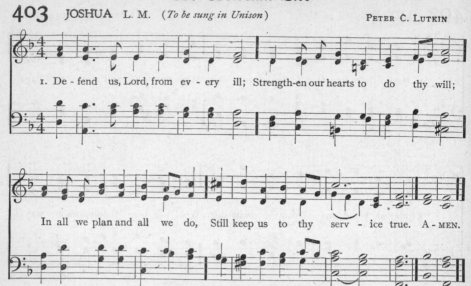

1. De - fend us, Lord, from ev - ery ill; Strength-en our hearts to do thy will;

In all we plan and all we do, Still keep us to thy serv - ice true. A - MEN.

Copyright, 1905, by Jennings & Graham

2 O let us hear the inspiring word
Which they of old at Horeb heard;
Breathe to our hearts the high command,
"Go onward and possess the land!"
Copyright, Houghton, Mifflin & Co.

3 Thou who art light, shine on each soul!
Thou who art truth, each mind control!
Open our eyes and make us see
The path which leads to heaven and thee!
JOHN HAY

403 GROSTETTE L. M. (*Second Tune*)   HENRY W. GREATOREX

1. De - fend us, Lord, from ev - ery ill; Strength-en our hearts to do thy will;

In all we plan and all we do, Still keep us to thy serv - ice true. A - MEN.

404 PETERBORO C. M.

RALPH HARRISON

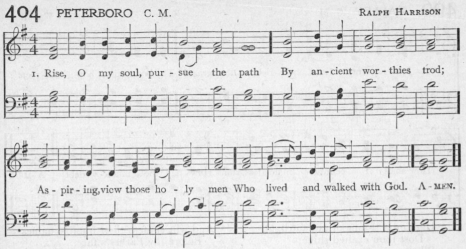

1. Rise, O my soul, pur-sue the path By an-cient wor-thies trod;
As-pir-ing, view those ho-ly men Who lived and walked with God. A-MEN.

2 Though dead, they speak in reason's ear,
  And in example live;
Their faith, and hope, and mighty deeds
  Still fresh instruction give.

3 'Twas through the Lamb's most precious
  They conquered every foe;   [blood

And to his power and matchless grace
  Their crowns of life they owe.

4 Lord, may I ever keep in view
  The patterns thou hast given,
And ne'er forsake the blessèd road
  That led them safe to heaven.
                        JOHN NEEDHAM

405 DOANE L. M.

JOHN B. CALKIN

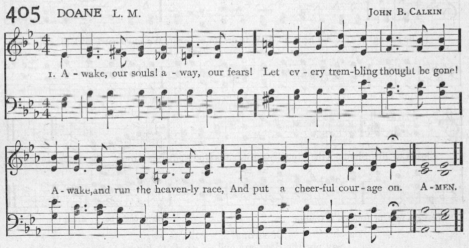

1. A-wake, our souls! a-way, our fears! Let ev-ery trem-bling thought be gone!
A-wake, and run the heaven-ly race, And put a cheer-ful cour-age on. A-MEN.

2 True, 'tis a strait and thorny road,
  And mortal spirits tire and faint;
But they forget the mighty God
  That feeds the strength of every saint.

3 From him, the overflowing spring,
  Our souls shall drink a fresh supply;

While such as trust their native strength,
  Shall melt away, and droop, and die.

4 Swift as the eagle cuts the air,
  We'll mount aloft to his abode;
On wings of love our souls shall fly,
  Nor tire amidst the heavenly road.
                        ISAAC WATTS

406 EAGLEY C. M.

JAMES WALCH

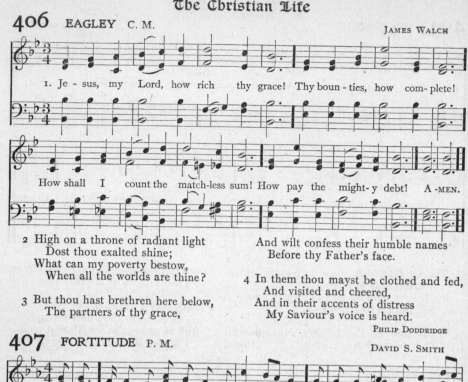

1. Je - sus, my Lord, how rich thy grace! Thy boun - ties, how com- plete!

How shall I count the match-less sum! How pay the might- y debt! A -MEN.

2 High on a throne of radiant light
  Dost thou exalted shine;
What can my poverty bestow,
  When all the worlds are thine?

3 But thou hast brethren here below,
  The partners of thy grace,

And wilt confess their humble names
Before thy Father's face.

4 In them thou mayst be clothed and fed,
  And visited and cheered,
And in their accents of distress
  My Saviour's voice is heard.

PHILIP DODDRIDGE

407 FORTITUDE P. M.

DAVID S. SMITH

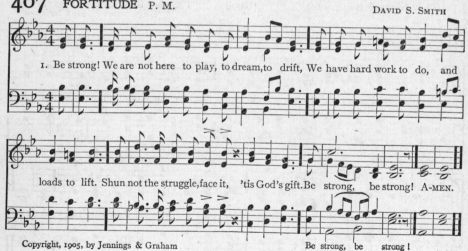

1. Be strong! We are not here to play, to dream, to drift, We have hard work to do, and

loads to lift. Shun not the struggle, face it, 'tis God's gift. Be strong, be strong! A-MEN.

Be strong, be strong!

2   Be strong!
Say not the days are evil — who's to blame?
And fold the hands and acquiesce — O shame!
Stand up, speak out, and bravely, in God's name.

3   Be strong!
It matters not how deep intrenched the wrong,
How hard the battle goes, the day, how long;
Faint not, fight on! To-morrow comes the song.

MALTBIE D. BABCOCK

408 LANCASHIRE 7s. 6s. D.

HENRY SMART

1. Lead on, O King E-ter-nal, The day of march has come;
Hence-forth in fields of con-quest Thy tents shall be our home.
Through days of prep-a-ra-tion Thy grace has made us strong,
And now, O King E-ter-nal, We lift our bat-tle song. A-MEN.

2 Lead on, O King Eternal,
   Till sin's fierce war shall cease,
And holiness shall whisper
   The sweet Amen of peace;
For not with swords loud clashing,
   Nor roll of stirring drums;
With deeds of love and mercy,
   The heavenly kingdom comes.

3 Lead on, O King Eternal,
   We follow, not with fears;
For gladness breaks like morning
   Where'er thy face appears;
Thy cross is lifted o'er us;
   We journey in its light:
The crown awaits the conquest;
   Lead on, O God of might.

ERNEST W. SHURTLEFF

409 PENTECOST L. M.

WILLIAM BOYD

1. Fight the good fight with all thy might, Christ is thy strength, and Christ thy right;

Lay hold on life, and it shall be Thy joy and crown e - ter - nal - ly. A - MEN.

2 Run the straight race through God's good
grace,
Lift up thine eyes, and seek his face;
Life with its way before us lies,
Christ is the path, and Christ the prize.

3 Cast care aside, lean on thy guide;
His boundless mercy will provide;

Trust, and thy trusting soul shall prove
Christ is its life, and Christ its love.

4 Faint not nor fear, his arms are near;
He changeth not, and thou art dear;
Only believe, and thou shalt see
That Christ is all in all to thee.

JOHN S. B. MONSELL

410 GRATITUDE L. M.

A. BOST

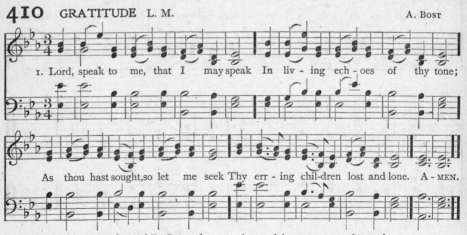

1. Lord, speak to me, that I may speak In liv - ing ech - oes of thy tone;

As thou hast sought, so let me seek Thy err - ing chil-dren lost and lone. A - MEN.

2 O strengthen me, that while I stand
Firm on the rock, and strong in thee,
I may stretch out a loving hand
To wrestlers with the troubled sea.

3 O teach me, Lord, that I may teach
The precious things thou dost impart;
And wing my words, that they may reach
The hidden depths of many a heart.

4 O give thine own sweet rest to me,
That I may speak with soothing power

A word in season, as from thee,
To weary ones in needful hour.

5 O fill me with thy fullness, Lord,
Until my very heart o'erflow
In kindling thought and glowing word,
Thy love to tell, thy praise to show.

6 O use me, Lord, use even me,
Just as thou wilt, and when, and where;
Until thy blessèd face I see,
Thy rest, thy joy, thy glory share.

FRANCES R. HAVERGAL

Activity and Zeal

411 CANONBURY L. M.

ROBERT SCHUMANN

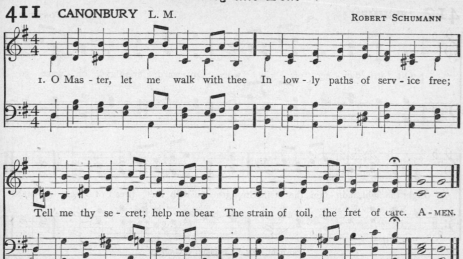

1. O Mas - ter, let me walk with thee In low - ly paths of serv - ice free;

Tell me thy se - cret; help me bear The strain of toil, the fret of care. A - MEN.

2 Help me the slow of heart to move
By some clear, winning word of love;
Teach me the wayward feet to stay,
And guide them in the homeward way.

3 Teach me thy patience; still with thee
In closer, dearer company,
In work that keeps faith sweet and strong,
In trust that triumphs over wrong.

4 In hope that sends a shining ray
Far down the future's broadening way;
In peace that only thou canst give,
With thee, O Master, let me live.

WASHINGTON GLADDEN

411 MARYTON L. M. (*Second Tune*)

H. PERCY SMITH

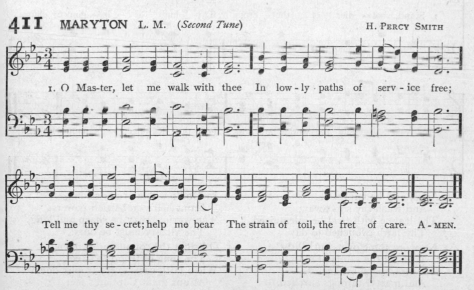

1. O Mas - ter, let me walk with thee In low - ly paths of serv - ice free;

Tell me thy se - cret; help me bear The strain of toil, the fret of care. A - MEN.

The Christian Life

412 EIGHMEY 7s.
WILLIAM H. PONTIUS

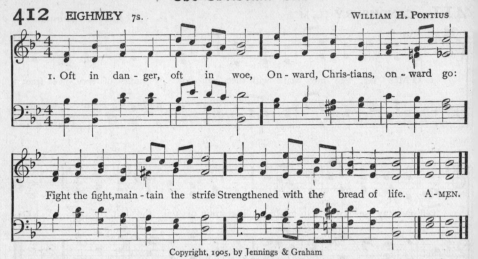

1. Oft in dan-ger, oft in woe, On-ward, Chris-tians, on-ward go:
Fight the fight, main-tain the strife Strengthened with the bread of life. A-MEN.

Copyright, 1905, by Jennings & Graham

2 Let your drooping hearts be glad:
  March in heavenly armor clad:
  Fight, nor think the battle long,
  Victory soon shall tune your song.

3 Let not sorrow dim your eye,
  Soon shall every tear be dry;

Let not fears your course impede,
Great your strength, if great your need.

4 Onward then in battle move,
  More than conquerors ye shall prove;
  Though opposed by many a foe,
  Christian soldiers, onward go.

H. KIRKE WHITE and FRANCES S. FULLER–MAITLAND

413 FESTAL SONG S. M.
WILLIAM H. WALTER

1. Stand, sol-dier of the cross, Thy high al-le-giance claim,
And vow to hold the world but loss For thy Re-deem-er's name. A-MEN.

2 Arise, and be baptized,
  And wash thy sins away;
  Thy league with God be solemnized,
  Thy faith avouched to-day.

3 No more thine own, but Christ's;
  With all the saints of old,
  Apostles, seers, evangelists,
  And martyr throngs enrolled.

4 In God's whole armor strong,
  Front hell's embattled powers:
  The warfare may be sharp and long,
  The victory must be ours.

5 O bright the conqueror's crown,
  The song of triumph sweet,
  When faith casts every trophy down
  At our great Captain's feet.

EDWARD H. BICKERSTETH

Activity and Zeal

414   SERVICE C. M. D.   LORIN WEBSTER

1. The toil of brain, or heart, or hand, Is man's ap-point-ed lot;
He who God's call can un-der-stand, Will work and mur-mur not.
Toil is no thorn-y crown of pain, Bound round man's brow for sin;
True souls, from it, all strength may gain, High man-li-ness may win. A-MEN.

2 O God! who workest hitherto,
     Working in all we see,
Fain would we be, and bear, and do,
     As best it pleaseth thee.
Where'er thou sendest we will go,
     Nor any question ask,
And what thou biddest we will do,
     Whatever be the task.

3 Our skill of hand, and strength of limb,
     Are not our own, but thine;
We link them to the work of Him
     Who made all life divine!
Our brother-friend, thy holy Son,
     Shared all our lot and strife;
And nobly will our work be done,
     If molded by his life.

THOMAS W. FRECKELTON

II

415 ST. CATHERINE L. M. 6l.

Adapted by J. G. WALTON

1. Faith of our fa-thers! liv-ing still In spite of dun-geon, fire, and sword:

O how our hearts beat high with joy When-e'er we hear that glo-rious word!

Faith of our fa-thers! ho-ly faith! We will be true to thee till death! A-MEN.

2 Our fathers, chained in prisons dark,
  Were still in heart and conscience free:
How sweet would be their children's fate,
  If they, like them, could die for thee!
Faith of our fathers! holy faith!
We will be true to thee till death!

3 Faith of our fathers! we will love
  Both friend and foe in all our strife:
And preach thee, too, as love knows how,
  By kindly words and virtuous life:
Faith of our fathers! holy faith!
We will be true to thee till death!

FREDERICK W. FABER

416 CUTLER C. M. D.

HENRY S. CUTLER

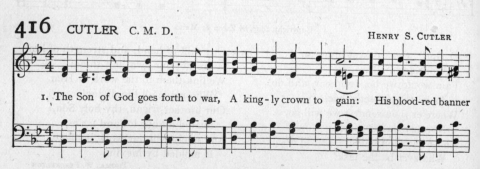

1. The Son of God goes forth to war, A king-ly crown to gain: His blood-red banner

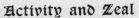

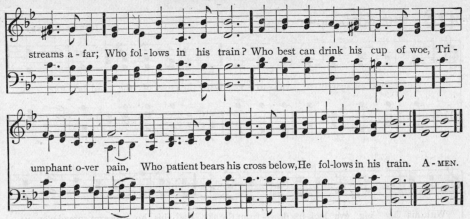

streams a-far; Who fol-lows in his train? Who best can drink his cup of woe, Tri-umphant o-ver pain, Who patient bears his cross below, He fol-lows in his train. A-MEN.

2 The martyr first, whose eagle eye
   Could pierce beyond the grave,
Who saw his Master in the sky,
   And called on him to save:
Like him, with pardon on his tongue,
   In midst of mortal pain,
He prayed for them that did the wrong:
   Who follows in his train?

3 A glorious band, the chosen few
   On whom the Spirit came,
Twelve valiant saints, their hope they knew,
   And mocked the cross and flame;
They climbed the steep ascent of heaven
   Through peril, toil, and pain:
O God, to us may grace be given
   To follow in their train.

REGINALD HEBER

417 MORNINGTON S. M. EARL OF MORNINGTON

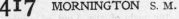

1. Teach me, my God and King, In all things thee to see,
And what I do in an-y-thing, To do it as for thee. A-MEN.

2 To scorn the senses' sway,
   While still to thee I tend;
In all I do be thou the way,
   In all be thou the end.

3 All may of thee partake;
   Nothing so small can be
But draws, when acted for thy sake,
   Greatness and worth from thee.

4 If done to obey thy laws,
   E'en servile labors shine;
Hallowed is toil, if this the cause,
   The meanest work, divine.

5 Thee, then, my God and King,
   In all things may I see;
And what I do, in anything,
   May it be done for thee!

GEORGE HERBERT. Alt.

418 THE GOOD FIGHT P. M.

JOSEPH BARNBY

We march, we march to vic - to - ry, With the cross of the Lord be - fore us,

With his lov - ing eye look-ing down from the sky, And his ho - ly arm spread o'er us,

His ho - ly arm spread o'er us. 1. We come in the might of the Lord of light,

His arm

A joy - ful host to meet him: And we put to flight the ar-mies of night,

That the sons of the day may greet him, The sons of the day may greet him.

Activity and Zeal

We march, we march to vic-to-ry, With the cross of the Lord be-fore us,

With his lov-ing eye look-ing down from the sky, And his ho-ly arm spread o'er us,

All verses except last | *Last verse only*

His ho-ly arm spread o'er us. 2. Our o'er.. us. A-men.

His arm spread o'er us.

2 Our sword is the Spirit of God on high,
   Our helmet is his salvation,
   Our banner, the cross of Calvary,
   Our watchword, the Incarnation.
   We march, we march, etc.

3 And the choir of angels with song awaits
   Our march to the golden Zion;
   For our Captain has broken the brazen gates,
   And burst the bars of iron.
   We march, we march, etc.

4 Then onward we march, our arms to prove,
   With the banner of Christ before us,
   With his eye of love looking down from above,
   And his holy arm spread o'er us.
   We march, we march to victory,
       With the cross of the Lord before us,
   With his loving eye looking down from the sky,
       And his holy arm spread o'er us.

GERARD MOULTRIE

419 ONE MORE DAY'S WORK P. M. *With Refrain* ROBERT LOWRY

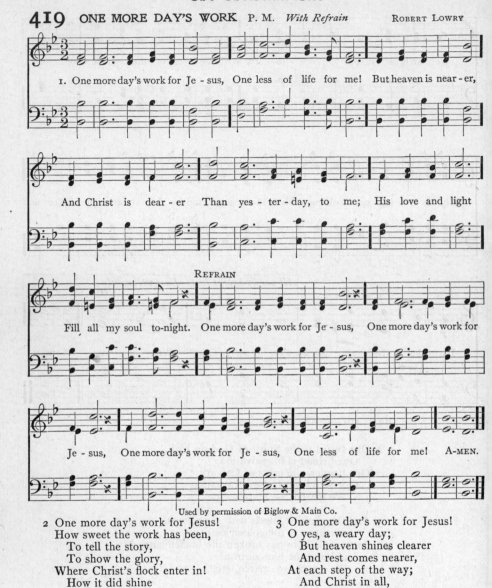

1. One more day's work for Je - sus, One less of life for me! But heaven is near - er,

And Christ is dear - er Than yes - ter - day, to me; His love and light

REFRAIN

Fill all my soul to-night. One more day's work for Je - sus, One more day's work for

Je - sus, One more day's work for Je - sus, One less of life for me! A-men.

2 One more day's work for Jesus!
How sweet the work has been,
To tell the story,
To show the glory,
Where Christ's flock enter in!
How it did shine
In this poor heart of mine!

3 One more day's work for Jesus!
O yes, a weary day;
But heaven shines clearer
And rest comes nearer,
At each step of the way;
And Christ in all,
Before his face I fall.

4 O blessèd work for Jesus!
O rest at Jesus' feet!
There toil seems pleasure,
My wants are treasure,
And pain for him is sweet.
Lord, if I may,
I'll serve another day!

ANNA B. WARNER

Activity and Zeal

TRUE-HEARTED, WHOLE-HEARTED 11s. 10s. *With Refrain*

GEORGE C. STEBBINS

1. True-heart-ed, whole-hearted, faith-ful and loy-al, King of our lives, by thy grace we will be; Un-der the stand-ard ex-alt-ed and roy-al, Strong in thy strength we will bat-tle for thee.

REFRAIN

Peal out the watch-word! si-lence it nev-er! Song of our spir-its, re-joic-ing and free; Peal out the watch-word! loy-al for-ev-er! King of our lives, by thy grace we will be. A-MEN.

Copyright, 1890, by Ira D. Sankey. By permission

2 True-hearted, whole-hearted, fullest alle-
    giance
  Yielding henceforth to our glorious King;
Valiant endeavor and loving obedience,
  Freely and joyously now would we bring.

3 True-hearted, whole-hearted, Saviour
    all-glorious!
  Take thy great power and reign there alone,
Over our wills and affections victorious,
  Freely surrendered and wholly thine own.

FRANCES R. HAVERGAL

The Christian Life

421 MARION S. M. *With Refrain*   ARTHUR H. MESSITER

1. Re-joice, ye pure in heart! Re-joice, give thanks and sing! Your glo-rious ban-ner wave on high, The cross of Christ your King!

REFRAIN

Re-joice, re-joice, Re-joice, give thanks and sing. A-MEN.
Re-joice, re-joice,

2 Bright youth, and snow-crowned age,
  Strong men and maidens meek:
  Raise high your free, exulting song!
  God's wondrous praises speak!

3 With all the angel choirs,
  With all the saints of earth,
  Pour out the strains of joy and bliss,
  True rapture, noblest mirth!

4 Your clear hosannas raise,
  And alleluias loud!
  Whilst answering echoes upward float,
  Like wreaths of incense cloud.

5 Yes, on through life's long path!
  Still chanting as ye go;
  From youth to age, by night and day,
  In gladness and in woe.

6 Still lift your standard high!
  Still march in firm array!
  As warriors through the darkness toil,
  Till dawns the golden day!

7 At last the march shall end;
  The wearied ones shall rest;
  The pilgrims find their Father's house,
  Jerusalem the blest.

8 Then on, ye pure in heart!
  Rejoice, give thanks, and sing!
  Your glorious banner wave on high,
  The cross of Christ your King!

EDWARD H. PLUMPTRE

422 WORK SONG 7s. 6s. D.   LOWELL MASON

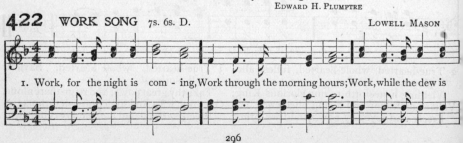

1. Work, for the night is com-ing, Work through the morning hours; Work, while the dew is

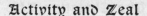

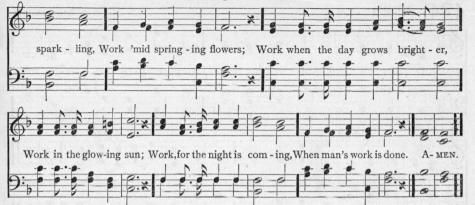

spark - ling, Work 'mid spring - ing flowers; Work when the day grows bright - er,

Work in the glow-ing sun; Work, for the night is com - ing, When man's work is done. A- MEN.

2 Work, for the night is coming,
    Work through the sunny noon;
Fill brightest hours with labor,
    Rest comes sure and soon.
Give every flying minute
    Something to keep in store:
Work, for the night is coming,
    When man works no more.

3 Work, for the night is coming,
    Under the sunset skies;
While their bright tints are glowing,
    Work, for daylight flies.
Work till the last beam fadeth,
    Fadeth to shine no more;
Work while the night is darkening,
    When man's work is o'er.

ANNIE L. WALKER

423 GERMANY L. M.

LUDWIG VAN BEETHOVEN

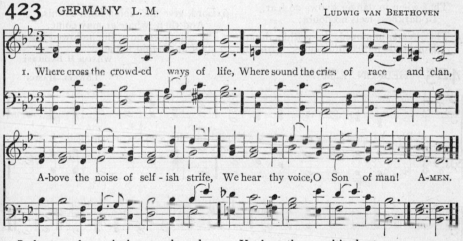

1. Where cross the crowd-ed ways of life, Where sound the cries of race and clan,

A-bove the noise of self - ish strife, We hear thy voice, O Son of man! A-MEN.

2 In haunts of wretchedness and need,
    On shadowed thresholds dark with fears,
From paths where hide the lures of greed,
    We catch the vision of thy tears.

3 From tender childhood's helplessness,
    From woman's grief, man's burdened toil,
From famished souls, from sorrow's stress,
    Thy heart has never known recoil.

4 The cup of water given for thee
    Still holds the freshness of thy grace;

Yet long these multitudes to see
    The sweet compassion of thy face.

5 O Master, from the mountain side,
    Make haste to heal these hearts of pain,
Among these restless throngs abide,
    O tread the city's streets again,

6 Till sons of men shall learn thy love
    And follow where thy feet have trod:
Till glorious from thy heaven above
    Shall come the city of our God.

F. MASON NORTH

424 HEBER C. M.

GEORGE KINGSLEY

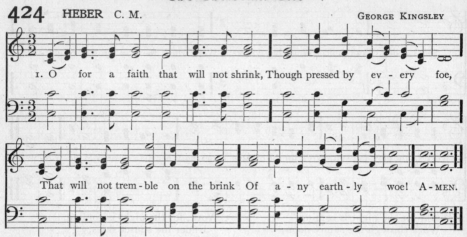

1. O for a faith that will not shrink, Though pressed by ev - ery foe,
That will not trem - ble on the brink Of a - ny earth - ly woe! A - MEN.

2 That will not murmur nor complain
Beneath the chastening rod,
But, in the hour of grief or pain,
Will lean upon its God;

3 A faith that shines more bright and clear
When tempests rage without;
That when in danger knows no fear,
In darkness feels no doubt;

4 That bears, unmoved, the world's dread
Nor heeds its scornful smile; [frown,

That seas of trouble cannot drown,
Nor Satan's arts beguile;

5 A faith that keeps the narrow way
Till life's last hour is fled,
And with a pure and heavenly ray
Lights up a dying bed.

6 Lord, give me such a faith as this,
And then, whate'er may come,
I'll taste, e'en now, the hallowed bliss
Of an eternal home.

WILLIAM H. BATHURST

425 HEBRON L. M.

LOWELL MASON

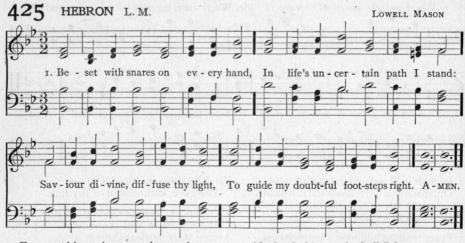

1. Be - set with snares on ev - ery hand, In life's un - cer - tain path I stand:
Sav - iour di - vine, dif - fuse thy light, To guide my doubt-ful foot-steps right. A - MEN.

2 Engage this roving, treacherous heart
To fix on Mary's better part,
To scorn the trifles of a day,
For joys that none can take away.

3 Then let the wildest storms arise;
Let tempests mingle earth and skies;

No fatal shipwreck shall I fear,
But all my treasures with me bear.

4 If thou, my Jesus, still be nigh,
Cheerful I live, and joyful die;
Secure, when mortal comforts flee,
To find ten thousand worlds in thee.

PHILIP DODDRIDGE

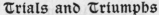

426 NOX PRÆCESSIT C. M.

JOHN B. CALKIN

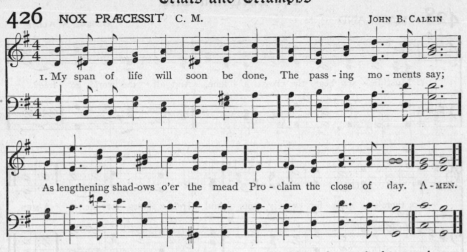

1. My span of life will soon be done, The pass-ing mo-ments say;

As lengthening shad-ows o'er the mead Pro-claim the close of day. A-MEN.

2 O that my heart might dwell aloof
From all created things,
And learn that wisdom from above
Whence true contentment springs!

3 Courage, my soul! thy bitter cross,
In every trial here,

Shall bear thee to thy heaven above,
But shall not enter there.

4 Courage, my soul, on God rely,
Deliverance soon will come:
A thousand ways has Providence
To bring believers home.

FRANCES M. COWPER

427 NAOMI C. M.

H. G. NAEGELI

1. Out of the depths to thee I cry, Whose faint-ing foot-steps trod

The paths of our hu-man-i-ty, In-car-nate Son of God! A-MEN.

2 Thou Man of grief, who once apart
Didst all our sorrows bear,—
The trembling hand, the fainting heart,
The agony, and prayer!

3 Is this the consecrated dower,
Thy chosen ones obtain,
To know thy resurrection power
Through fellowship of pain?

4 Then, O my soul, in silence wait;
Faint not, O faltering feet;
Press onward to that blest estate,
In righteousness complete.

5 Let faith transcend the passing hour,
The transient pain and strife,
Upraised by an immortal power,—
The power of endless life.

ELIZABETH E. MARCY

428 MAITLAND C. M.

GEORGE N. ALLEN

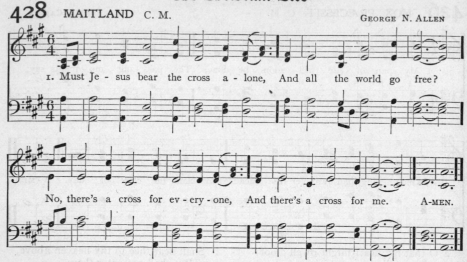

1. Must Je - sus bear the cross a - lone, And all the world go free?

No, there's a cross for ev - ery - one, And there's a cross for me. A-MEN.

2 How happy are the saints above,
Who once went sorrowing here!
But now they taste unmingled love,
And joy without a tear.

3 The consecrated cross I'll bear,
Till death shall set me free;
And then go home my crown to wear,
For there's a crown for me.

THOMAS SHEPHERD. Alt.

429 LABAN S. M.

LOWELL MASON

1. Ye . . serv - ants of the Lord, Each in his of - fice wait,

Ob - serv-ant of his heaven - ly word, And watch-ful at his gate. A-MEN.

2 Let all your lamps be bright,
And trim the golden flame;
Gird up your loins, as in his sight,
For awful is his name.

3 Watch, 'tis your Lord's command:
And while we speak he's near;

Mark the first signal of his hand,
And ready all appear.

4 O happy servant he
In such a posture found!
He shall his Lord with rapture see,
And be with honor crowned.

PHILIP DODDRIDGE

Trials and Triumphs

SARUM 10. 10. 10. *With Hallelujah*

JOSEPH BARNBY

1. For all the saints, who from their la - bors rest, Who thee by
faith be - fore the world con - fessed, Thy name, O Je - sus,
be for - ev - er blessed, Hal - le - lu - jah, Hal - le - lu - jah! A-men.

2 Thou wast their rock, their fortress, and their might;
Thou, Lord, their captain in the well-fought fight;
Thou, in the darkness drear, their one true light.

3 O may thy soldiers, faithful, true, and bold,
Fight as the saints who nobly fought of old,
And win with them the victor's crown of gold.

4 O blest communion, fellowship divine!
We feebly struggle, they in glory shine;
Yet all are one in thee, for all are thine.

5 And when the strife is fierce, the warfare long,
Steals on the ear the distant triumph song,
And hearts are brave again, and arms are strong.

6 The golden evening brightens in the west;
Soon, soon to faithful warriors comes thy rest;
Sweet is the calm of Paradise the blest.

7 But lo, there breaks a yet more glorious day;
The saints triumphant rise in bright array;
The King of glory passes on his way.

8 From earth's wide bounds, from ocean's farthest coast,
Through gates of pearl streams in the countless host,
Singing to Father, Son, and Holy Ghost,
　　"Hallelujah, Hallelujah!"

WILLIAM W. HOW

431 PENITENCE 6s. 5s. D. SPENCER LANE

1. In the hour of tri - al, Je - sus, plead for me; Lest by base de - ni - al,

I de-part from thee. When thou see'st me wav - er, With a look re - call,

rall.

Nor for fear or fa - vor Suf - fer me to fall. A - MEN.

2 With forbidden pleasures
  Would this vain world charm;
Or its sordid treasures
  Spread to work me harm;
Bring to my remembrance
  Sad Gethsemane,
Or, in darker semblance,
  Cross-crowned Calvary.

3 Should thy mercy send me
  Sorrow, toil, and woe;
Or should pain attend me
  On my path below;

Grant that I may never
  Fail thy hand to see;
Grant that I may ever
  Cast my care on thee.

4 When my last hour cometh,
  Fraught with strife and pain,
When my dust returneth
  To the dust again;
On thy truth relying,
  Through that mortal strife,
Jesus, take me, dying,
  To eternal life.

JAMES MONTGOMERY. Alt. by FRANCES A. HUTTON

432 HABAKKUK 8. 8. 6 D. EDWARD HODGES

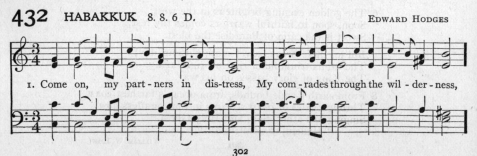

1. Come on, my part - ners in dis - tress, My com - rades through the wil - der - ness,

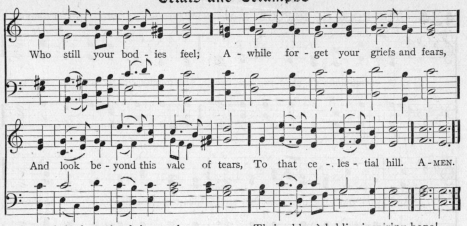

Who still your bod - ies feel; A - while for - get your griefs and fears,

And look be - yond this vale of tears, To that ce - les - tial hill. A - MEN.

2 Beyond the bounds of time and space,
  Look forward to that heavenly place,
    The saints' secure abode;
  On faith's strong eagle pinions rise,
  And force your passage to the skies,
    And scale the mount of God.

3 Who suffer with our Master here,
  We shall before his face appear
    And by his side sit down;
  To patient faith the prize is sure,
  And all that to the end endure
    The cross, shall wear the crown.

4 Thrice blessèd, bliss-inspiring hope!
  It lifts the fainting spirits up,
    It brings to life the dead:
  Our conflicts here shall soon be past,
  And you and I ascend at last,
    Triumphant with our head.

5 That great mysterious deity
  We soon with open face shall see;
    The beatific sight
  Shall fill the heavenly courts with praise,
  And wide diffuse the golden blaze
    Of everlasting light.

CHARLES WESLEY

433 GERMANY L. M.

From LUDWIG VAN BEETHOVEN

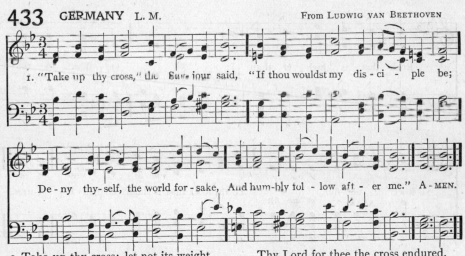

1. "Take up thy cross," the Sav - iour said, "If thou wouldst my dis - ci - ple be;

De - ny thy - self, the world for - sake, And hum - bly fol - low aft - er me." A - MEN.

2 Take up thy cross; let not its weight
  Fill thy weak spirit with alarm;
  His strength shall bear thy spirit up,
    And brace thy heart and nerve thine arm.

3 Take up thy cross, nor heed the shame;
  Nor let thy foolish pride rebel;

Thy Lord for thee the cross endured,
  To save thy soul from death and hell.

4 Take up thy cross, and follow Christ;
  Nor think till death to lay it down;
  For only he who bears the cross
    May hope to wear the glorious crown.

CHARLES W. EVEREST

434 THE ROCK OF REFUGE L. M *With Refrain* WILLIAM G. FISCHER

1. O some-times the shad-ows are deep, And rough seems the path to the goal,

And sor - rows, some-times how they sweep Like tem - pests down o - ver the soul!

REFRAIN

O then to the Rock let me fly, let me fly, To the

Rock that is high - er than I; is high - er than I; O then to the

Rock let me fly, let me fly, To the Rock that is high - er than I! A-MEN.

2 O sometimes how long seems the day,
  And sometimes how weary my feet;
  But toiling in life's dusty way,
  The Rock's blessèd shadow, how sweet!

3 O near to the Rock let me keep,
  If blessings or sorrows prevail;
  Or climbing the mountain way steep,
  Or walking the shadowy vale.

E. JOHNSON

Trust and Confidence

435 SCHUMANN S. M.　　　　　　　　ROBERT SCHUMANN

1. Com - mit thou all thy griefs And ways in - to His hands,

To his sure trust and ten - der care Who earth and neaven com-mands; A - MEN.

2 Who points the clouds their course,
　Whom winds and seas obey,
　He shall direct thy wandering feet,
　He shall prepare thy way.

3 Thou on the Lord rely,
　So, safe, shalt thou go on;
　Fix on his work thy steadfast eye,
　So shall thy work be done.

4 No profit canst thou gain
　By self-consuming care;

To him commend thy cause; his ear
Attends the softest prayer.

5 Thy everlasting truth,
　Father, thy ceaseless love,
　See all thy children's wants, and knows
　What best for each will prove.

6 Thou everywhere hast sway,
　And all things serve thy might;
　Thy every act pure blessing is,
　Thy path unsullied light.

PAUL GERHARDT. Tr. by JOHN WESLEY

436 CLOLATA L. M.　　　　　　　　W. ST. CLAIR PALMER

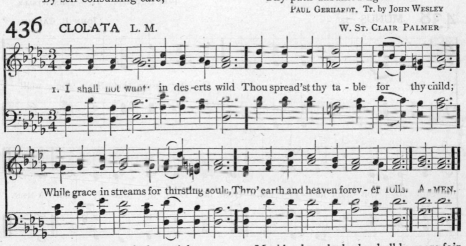

1. I shall not want in des-erts wild Thou spread'st thy ta - ble for thy child;

While grace in streams for thirsting souls, Thro' earth and heaven forev - er rolls. A - MEN.

2 I shall not want: my darkest night
　Thy loving smile shall fill with light;
　While promises around me bloom,
　And cheer me with divine perfume.

3 I shall not want: thy righteousness
　My soul shall clothe with glorious dress;

My blood-washed robe shall be more fair
Than garments kings or angels wear.

4 I shall not want: whate'er is good,
　Of daily bread or angels' food,
　Shall to my Father's child be sure,
　So long as earth and heaven endure.

CHARLES F. DEEMS

437 ST. GEORGE S. M.
HENRY J. GAUNTLETT

1. Give to the winds thy fears ; Hope, and be un - dis - mayed : God

hears thy sighs, and counts thy tears ; God shall lift up thy head. A - MEN.

2 Through waves, and clouds, and storms,
   He gently clears thy way;
   Wait thou his time, so shall this night
   Soon end in joyous day.

3 Still heavy is thy heart?
   Still sink thy spirits down?
   Cast off the weight, let fear depart,
   And every care be gone.

4 What though thou rulest not?
   Yet heaven, and earth, and hell

Proclaim, God sitteth on the throne,
And ruleth all things well.

5 Leave to his sovereign sway
   To choose and to command;
   So shalt thou, wondering, own his way,
   How wise, how strong his hand!

6 Far, far above thy thought
   His counsel shall appear,
   When fully he the work hath wrought
   That caused thy needless fear.

PAUL GERHARDT. Tr. by JOHN WESLEY

438 MUNUS 7s.
JOHN B. CALKIN

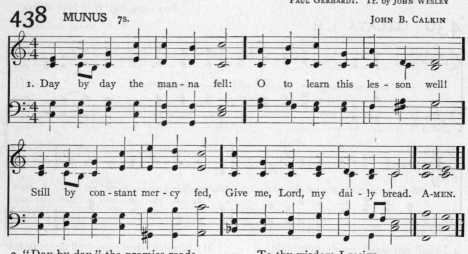

1. Day by day the man - na fell: O to learn this les - son well!

Still by con - stant mer - cy fed, Give me, Lord, my dai - ly bread. A - MEN.

2 "Day by day," the promise reads,
   Daily strength for daily needs:
   Cast foreboding fears away;
   Take the manna of to-day.

3 Lord! my times are in thy hand:
   All my sanguine hopes have planned,

To thy wisdom I resign,
And would make thy purpose mine.

4 Thou my daily task shalt give:
   Day by day to thee I live;
   So shall added years fulfill,
   Not my own, my Father's will.

JOSIAH CONDER

Trust and Confidence

439 WIMBORNE L. M.   JOHN WHITAKER

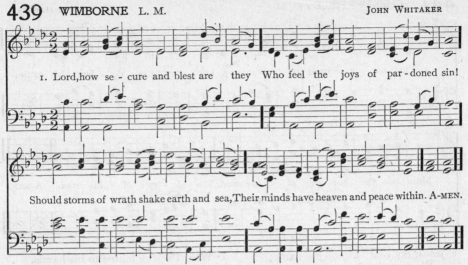

1. Lord, how se-cure and blest are they Who feel the joys of par-doned sin!

Should storms of wrath shake earth and sea, Their minds have heaven and peace within. A-MEN.

2 The day glides sweetly o'er their heads,
    Made up of innocence and love;
And soft and silent as the shades,
    Their nightly minutes gently move.

3 Quick as their thoughts their joys come on,
    But fly not half so swift away:
Their souls are ever bright as noon,
    And calm as summer evenings be.

4 How oft they look to the heavenly hills,
    Where groves of living pleasure grow;
And longing hopes, and cheerful smiles,
    Sit undisturbed upon their brow!

5 They scorn to seek earth's golden toys,
    But spend the day, and share the night,
In numbering o'er the richer joys
    That Heaven prepares for their delight.

ISAAC WATTS

440 ARLINGTON C. M.   THOMAS A. ARNE

1. When I can read my ti-tle clear To man-sions in the skies,

I bid fare-well to ev-ery fear, And wipe my weep-ing eyes. A-MEN.

2 Should earth against my soul engage,
    And fiery darts be hurled,
Then I can smile at Satan's rage,
    And face a frowning world.

3 Let cares like a wild deluge come,
    And storms of sorrow fall,

May I but safely reach my home,
    My God, my heaven, my all:

4 There I shall bathe my weary soul
    In seas of heavenly rest,
And not a wave of trouble roll
    Across my peaceful breast.

ISAAC WATTS

441 CHESTERFIELD C. M.

THOMAS HAWEIS

1. I'm not a-shamed to own my Lord, Or to de-fend his cause;

Main-tain the hon-or of his word, The glo-ry of his cross. A-MEN.

2 Jesus, my God! I know his name;
   His name is all my trust;
   Nor will he put my soul to shame,
   Nor let my hope be lost.

3 Firm as his throne his promise stands,
   And he can well secure

What I've committed to his hands,
Till the decisive hour.

4 Then will he own my worthless name
   Before his Father's face,
   And in the New Jerusalem
   Appoint my soul a place.

ISAAC WATTS

442 DALEHURST C. M.

ARTHUR COTTMAN

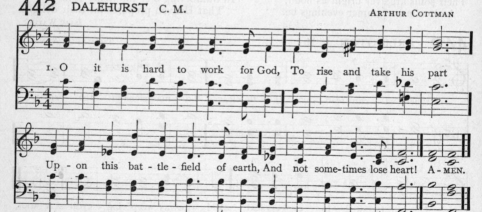

1. O it is hard to work for God, To rise and take his part

Up-on this bat-tle-field of earth, And not some-times lose heart! A-MEN.

2 He hides himself so wondrously,
   As though there were no God;
   He is least seen when all the powers
   Of ill are most abroad;

3 Or he deserts us in the hour
   The fight is all but lost;
   And seems to leave us to ourselves
   Just when we need him most.

4 It is not so, but so it looks;
   And we lose courage then;
   And doubts will come if God hath kept
   His promises to men.

5 But right is right, since God is God;
   And right the day must win;
   To doubt would be disloyalty,
   To falter would be sin!

FREDERICK W. FABER

Trust and Confidence

443 FEDERAL STREET L. M.　　　　　　　HENRY K. OLIVER

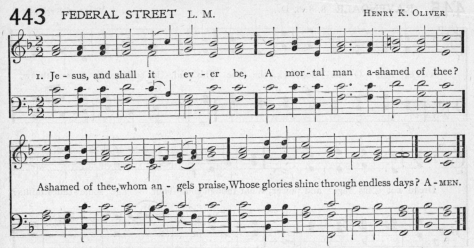

1. Je - sus, and shall it ev - er be, A mor - tal man a-shamed of thee?

Ashamed of thee, whom an - gels praise, Whose glories shine through endless days? A - MEN.

2 Ashamed of Jesus! sooner far
Let evening blush to own a star;
He sheds the beams of light divine
O'er this benighted soul of mine.

3 Ashamed of Jesus! just as soon
Let midnight be ashamed of noon;
'Tis midnight with my soul till he,
Bright Morning-Star, bid darkness flee.

4 Ashamed of Jesus! that dear friend
On whom my hopes of heaven depend!

No; when I blush, be this my shame,
That I no more revere his name.

5 Ashamed of Jesus! yes, I may,
When I've no guilt to wash away;
No tear to wipe, no good to crave,
No fears to quell, no soul to save.

6 Till then, nor is my boasting vain,
Till then I boast a Saviour slain;
And O, may this my glory be,
That Christ is not ashamed of me!

　　　　JOSEPH GRIGG. Alt. by BENJAMIN FRANCIS

444 WASHINGTON L. M.　　　　　　　CARL F. PRICE

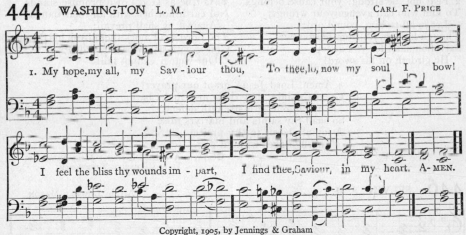

1. My hope, my all, my Sav - iour thou, To thee, lo, now my soul I bow!

I feel the bliss thy wounds im - part, I find thee, Saviour, in my heart. A - MEN.

2 Be thou my strength, be thou my way;
Protect me through my life's short day:
In all my acts may wisdom guide,
And keep me, Saviour, near thy side.

3 In fierce temptation's darkest hour,
Save me from sin and Satan's power;

Tear every idol from thy throne,
And reign, my Saviour, reign alone.

4 My suffering time shall soon be o'er;
Then shall I sigh and weep no more;
My ransomed soul shall soar away,
To sing thy praise in endless day.

　　　　　　　　　　Author Unknown

The Christian Life

445 RAVENDALE 8.8.6. D.
WALTER STOKES

1. Fear not, O lit-tle flock, the foe Who mad-ly seeks your o-ver-throw;
Dread not his rage and power; What though your cour - age some-times faints?
His seem-ing tri-umph o'er God's saints Lasts but a lit-tle hour. A-MEN.

2 Fear not, be strong! your cause belongs
To him who can avenge your wrongs;
    Leave all to him, your Lord:
Though hidden yet from mortal eyes,
Salvation shall for you arise;
    He girdeth on his sword!

3 As true as God's own promise stands,
Not earth nor hell with all their bands
    Against us shall prevail;
The Lord shall mock them from his throne;
God is with us; we are his own;
    Our victory cannot fail!

4 Amen, Lord Jesus, grant our prayer!
Great Captain, now thine arm make bare;
    Thy church with strength defend;
So shall thy saints and martyrs raise
A joyful chorus to thy praise,
    Through ages without end.

GUSTAVUS ADOLPHUS, in prose. JACOB FABRICIUS.
Tr. by CATHERINE WINKWORTH

446 SELVIN S. M.
Arr. by LOWELL MASON

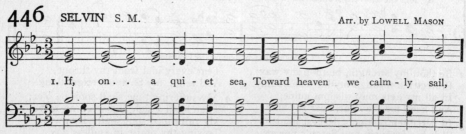

1. If, on . . a qui-et sea, Toward heaven we calm-ly sail,

Trust and Confidence

With grate-ful hearts, O God, to thee, We'll own the fav-oring gale,

With grate-ful hearts, O God, to thee, We'll own the fav-oring gale. A-MEN.

2 But should the surges rise,
And rest delay to come,
Blest be the tempest, kind the storm,
Which drives us nearer home.

3 Soon shall our doubts and fears
All yield to thy control;

Thy tender mercies shall illume
The midnight of the soul.

4 Teach us, in every state,
To make thy will our own;
And when the joys of sense depart,
To live by faith alone.

AUGUSTUS M. TOPLADY. Alt.

447 GOUDA C. M.
BERTHOLD TOURS

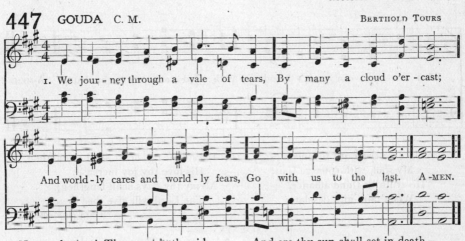

1. We jour-ney through a vale of tears, By many a cloud o'er-cast;

And world-ly cares and world-ly fears, Go with us to the last. A-MEN.

2 Not to the last! Thy word hath said,
Could we but read aright,
"Poor pilgrim, lift in hope thy head,
At eve it shall be light!"

3 Though earthborn shadows now may
Thy thorny path awhile,   [shroud
God's blessed word can part each cloud,
And bid the sunshine smile.

4 Only believe, in living faith,
His love and power divine;

And ere thy sun shall set in death,
His light shall round thee shine.

5 When tempest clouds are dark on high,
His bow of love and peace
Shines sweetly in the vaulted sky,
A pledge that storms shall cease.

6 Hold on thy way, with hope unchilled,
By faith and not by sight,
And thou shalt own his word fulfilled,
"At eve it shall be light."

BERNARD BARTON

311

448 JERUSALEM 7s. 6s. D.

JOHN STAINER

1. God is my strong sal-va-tion; What foe have I to fear? In dark-ness and temp-ta-tion, My light, my help, is near: Though hosts encamp around me, Firm in the fight I stand; What ter-ror can con-found me, With God at my right hand? A-MEN.

2 Place on the Lord reliance;
   My soul, with courage wait;
   His truth be thine affiance,
   When faint and desolate;

His might thy heart shall strengthen,
   His love thy joy increase;
   Mercy thy days shall lengthen;
   The Lord will give thee peace.

JAMES MONTGOMERY

448 AURELIA 7s. 6s. D. (*Second Tune*)

SAMUEL S. WESLEY

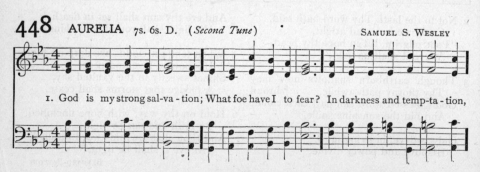

1. God is my strong sal-va-tion; What foe have I to fear? In darkness and temp-ta-tion,

My light, my help, is near: Though hosts encamp a-round me, Firm in the fight I stand;

What ter-ror can con-found me, With God at my right hand? A-MEN.

449 MONSELL S. M.   JOSEPH BARNBY

1. My times are in thy hand: My God, I wish them there;

My life, my friends, my soul, I leave En-tire-ly to thy care. A MEN.

2 My times are in thy hand,
  Whatever they may be;
Pleasing or painful, dark or bright,
  As best may seem to thee.

3 My times are in thy hand;
  Why should I doubt or fear?
My Father's hand will never cause
  His child a needless tear.

4 My times are in thy hand,
  Jesus, the crucified!
The hand my cruel sins had pierced
  Is now my guard and guide.

5 My times are in thy hand;
  I'll always trust in thee;
And, after death, at thy right hand
  I shall forever be.

WILLIAM F. LLOYD

The Christian Life

450   FELLOWSHIP   C. M.   ALFRED G. WATHALL

1. I lit-tle see, I lit-tle know, Yet can I fear no ill; .. He who hath guid-ed me till now Will be my lead-er still. A-MEN.

2 No burden yet was on me laid
   Of trouble or of care,
But he my trembling step hath stayed,
   And given me strength to bear.

3 I know not what beyond may lie,
   But look, in humble faith,
Into a larger life to die,
   And find new birth in death.

4 He will not leave my soul forlorn;
   I still must find him true,

Whose mercies have been new each morn
   And every evening new.

5 Upon his providence I lean,
   As lean in faith I must;
The lesson of my life hath been
   A heart of grateful trust.

6 And so my onward way I fare
   With happy heart and calm,
And mingle with my daily care
   The music of my psalm.
                      FREDERICK L. HOSMER

451   MIDDLETOWN   8s. 4s.   C. T. W.   Har. by KARL P. HARRINGTON

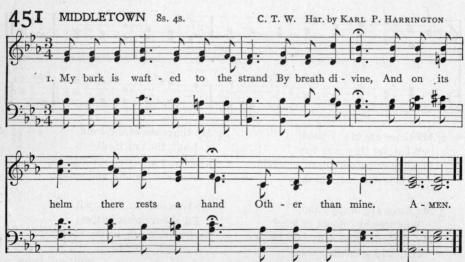

1. My bark is waft-ed to the strand By breath di-vine, And on its helm there rests a hand Oth-er than mine. A-MEN.

Trust and Confidence

2 One who was known in storms to sail
   I have on board;
Above the roaring of the gale
   I hear my Lord.

3 Safe to the land! safe to the land!
   The end is this,
And then with him go hand in hand,
   Far into bliss.

HENRY ALFORD

452 DAY OF REST 7s. 6s. D.

JAMES W. ELLIOTT

1. In heaven-ly love a-bid-ing, No change my heart shall fear;
And safe is such con-fid-ing, For noth-ing chan-ges here.
The storm may roar with-out me, My heart may low be laid,
But God is round a-bout me, And can I be dis-mayed? A-MEN.

2 Wherever he may guide me,
   No want shall turn me back;
My Shepherd is beside me,
   And nothing can I lack.
His wisdom ever waketh,
   His sight is never dim,
He knows the way he taketh,
   And I will walk with him.

3 Green pastures are before me,
   Which yet I have not seen;
Bright skies will soon be o'er me,
   Where darkest clouds have been.
My hope I cannot measure,
   My path to life is free,
My Saviour has my treasure,
   And he will walk with me.

ANNA L. WARING

The Christian Life

453 KEDRON 6. 4. 6. 4. 6. 6. 4.   A. B. SPRATT

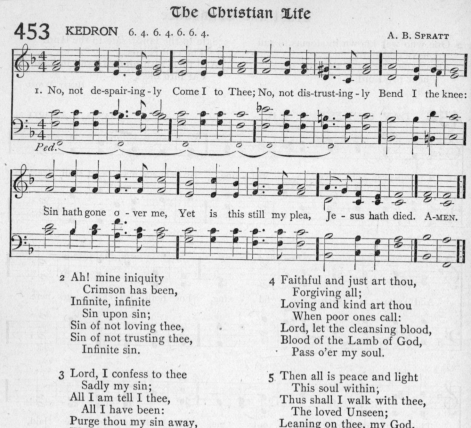

1. No, not de-spair-ing-ly Come I to Thee; No, not dis-trust-ing-ly Bend I the knee:

Sin hath gone o-ver me, Yet is this still my plea, Je-sus hath died. A-MEN.

2 Ah! mine iniquity
    Crimson has been,
  Infinite, infinite
    Sin upon sin;
  Sin of not loving thee,
  Sin of not trusting thee,
    Infinite sin.

3 Lord, I confess to thee
    Sadly my sin;
  All I am tell I thee,
    All I have been:
  Purge thou my sin away,
  Wash thou my soul this day;
    Lord, make me clean.

4 Faithful and just art thou,
    Forgiving all;
  Loving and kind art thou
    When poor ones call:
  Lord, let the cleansing blood,
  Blood of the Lamb of God,
    Pass o'er my soul.

5 Then all is peace and light
    This soul within;
  Thus shall I walk with thee,
    The loved Unseen;
  Leaning on thee, my God,
  Guided along the road,
    Nothing between.

HORATIUS BONAR

454 BENTLEY 7s. 6s. D.   JOHN HULLAH

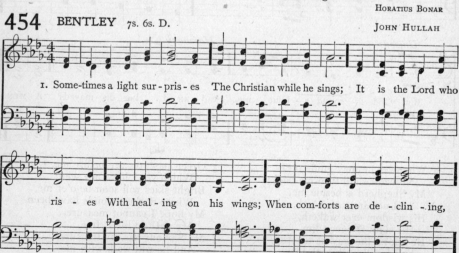

1. Some-times a light sur-pris-es The Christian while he sings; It is the Lord who

ris-es With heal-ing on his wings; When com-forts are de-clin-ing,

316

Trust and Confidence

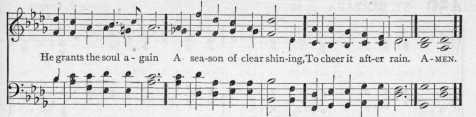

He grants the soul a - gain   A - sea-son of clear shin-ing, To cheer it aft-er rain.   A - MEN.

2 In holy contemplation,
　We sweetly then pursue
The theme of God's salvation,
　And find it ever new:
Set free from present sorrow,
　We cheerfully can say,
Let the unknown to-morrow
　Bring with it what it may.

3 It can bring with it nothing
　But he will bear us through;
Who gives the lilies clothing,
　Will clothe his people too;

Beneath the spreading heavens
　No creature but is fed;
And he who feeds the ravens
　Will give his children bread.

4 Though vine nor fig-tree neither
　Their wonted fruit should bear,
Though all the fields should wither,
　Nor flocks nor herds be there;
Yet God the same abiding,
　His praise shall tune my voice;
For while in him confiding,
　I cannot but rejoice.

WILLIAM COWPER

455   BEATITUDO C. M.

JOHN B. DYKES

1. When mus-ing sor - row weeps the past, And mourns the pres - ent pain,

'Tis sweet to think of peace at last, And feel that death is gain.   A - MEN.

2 'Tis not that murmuring thoughts arise,
　And dread a Father's will;
'Tis not that meek submission flies,
　And would not suffer still:

3 It is that heaven-born faith surveys
　The path that leads to light,
And longs her eagle plumes to raise,
　And lose herself in sight:

4 It is that hope with ardor glows,
　To see Him face to face,
Whose dying love no language knows
　Sufficient art to trace.

5 O let me wing my hallowed flight
　From earthborn woe and care,
And soar above these clouds of night,
　My Saviour's bliss to share!

GERARD T. NOEL

456 ST. BARBARA L. M.

PETER C. LUTKIN

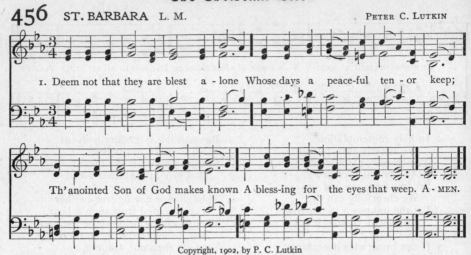

1. Deem not that they are blest a - lone Whose days a peace-ful ten - or keep;

Th' anointed Son of God makes known A bless-ing for the eyes that weep. A - MEN.

2 The light of smiles shall fill again
   The lids that overflow with tears;
And weary hours of woe and pain
   Are promises of happier years.

3 There is a day of sunny rest
   For every dark and troubled night;
And grief may bide an evening guest,
   But joy shall come with early light.

4 Nor let the good man's trust depart,
   Though life its common gifts deny,
Though with a pierced and broken heart,
   And spurned of men, he goes to die.

5 For God has marked each sorrowing day,
   And numbered every secret tear;
And heaven's long age of bliss shall pay
   For all his children suffer here.

WILLIAM C. BRYANT

457 ZEPHYR L. M.

WILLIAM B. BRADBURY

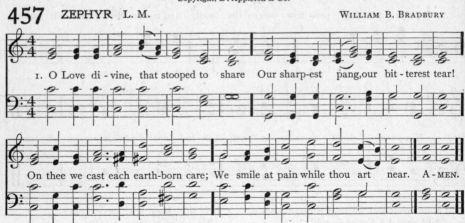

1. O Love di - vine, that stooped to share Our sharp-est pang, our bit - terest tear!

On thee we cast each earth-born care; We smile at pain while thou art near. A - MEN.

2 Though long the weary way we tread,
   And sorrow crown each lingering year,
No path we shun, no darkness dread,
   Our hearts still whispering, Thou art near!

3 When drooping pleasure turns to grief,
   And trembling faith is changed to fear,

The murmuring wind, the quivering leaf,
   Shall softly tell us, Thou art near!

4 On thee we fling our burdening woe,
   O Love divine, forever dear;
Content to suffer while we know,
   Living and lying, thou art near!

OLIVER W. HOLMES

318

Trust and Confidence

458 ELLESDIE 8s. 7s. D. From JOHANN C. W. A. MOZART

1. Je - sus, I my cross have tak - en, All to leave, and fol - low thee;
Des - ti - tute, de - spised, for - sak - en, Thou, from hence, my all shalt be:
Per - ish ev - ery fond am - bi - tion, All I've sought, and hoped, and known;
Yet how rich is my con - di - tion, God and heaven are still my own! A-MEN.

2 Let the world despise and leave me,
They have left my Saviour, too;
Human hearts and looks deceive me;
Thou art not, like man, untrue;
And, while thou shalt smile upon me,
God of wisdom, love, and might,
Foes may hate, and friends may shun me;
Show thy face, and all is bright.

3 Man may trouble and distress me,
'Twill but drive me to thy breast;
Life with trials hard may press me,
Heaven will bring me sweeter rest.

O 'tis not in grief to harm me,
While thy love is left to me;
O 'twere not in joy to charm me,
Were that joy unmixed with thee.

4 Haste thee on from grace to glory,
Armed by faith, and winged by prayer;
Heaven's eternal day's before thee,
God's own hand shall guide thee there.
Soon shall close thy earthly mission,
Swift shall pass thy pilgrim days,
Hope shall change to glad fruition,
Faith to sight, and prayer to praise.

HENRY F. LYTE

The Christian Life

459 MAGDALEN L. M. 6l.   JOHN STAINER

1. Lead - er of faith - ful souls, and Guide Of all that trav - el to the sky,

Come and with us, e'en us, a - bide, Who would on thee a - lone re - ly;

Voices in unison   *Harmony*

On thee a - lone our spir - its stay, While held in life's un - e - ven way. A-MEN.

2 Strangers and pilgrims here below,
    This earth, we know, is not our place;
  But hasten through the vale of woe,
    And, restless to behold thy face,
  Swift to our heavenly country move,
    Our everlasting home above.

3 We've no abiding city here,
    But seek a city out of sight;
  Thither our steady course we steer,
    Aspiring to the plains of light,
  Jerusalem, the saints' abode,
    Whose founder is the living God.

4 Patient the appointed race to run,
    This weary world we cast behind;
  From strength to strength we travel on,
    The new Jerusalem to find:
  Our labor this, our only aim,
    To find the new Jerusalem.

5 Through thee, who all our sins hast borne,
    Freely and graciously forgiven,
  With songs to Zion we return,
    Contending for our native heaven;
  That palace of our glorious King,
    We find it nearer while we sing.

6 Raised by the breath of love divine,
    We urge our way with strength renewed;
  The church of the firstborn to join,
    We travel to the mount of God;
  With joy upon our heads arise,
    And meet our Saviour in the skies.

CHARLES WESLEY

Trust and Confidence

460 LUX BENIGNA 10. 4. 10. 4. 10. 10. JOHN B. DYKES

1. Lead, kind-ly Light, a-mid th' en-cir-cling gloom, Lead thou me on!
The night is dark, and I am far from home; Lead thou me on!
Keep thou my feet; I do not ask to see . . .
The dis - tant scene; one step e - nough . for me. . A-MEN.

2 I was not ever thus, nor prayed that thou
    Shouldst lead me on;
I loved to choose and see my path; but now
    Lead thou me on!
I loved the garish day, and, spite of fears,
Pride ruled my will. Remember not past years!

3 So long thy power hath blest me, sure it still
    Will lead me on
O'er moor and fen, o'er crag and torrent, till
    The night is gone,
And with the morn those angel faces smile,
Which I have loved long since, and lost awhile!

JOHN H. NEWMAN

461 PORTUGUESE HYMN 11s.

Composer Unknown

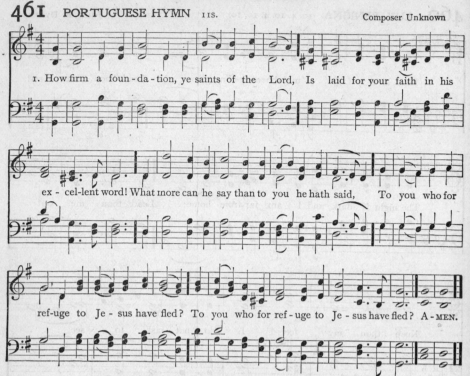

1. How firm a foun-da-tion, ye saints of the Lord, Is laid for your faith in his ex-cel-lent word! What more can he say than to you he hath said, To you who for ref-uge to Je-sus have fled? To you who for ref-uge to Je-sus have fled? A-MEN.

2 In every condition — in sickness, in health;
In poverty's vale, or abounding in wealth;
At home and abroad; on the land, on the sea —
"As thy days may demand, shall thy strength ever be.

3 "Fear not, I am with thee, O be not dismayed,
For I am thy God, and will still give thee aid;
I'll strengthen thee, help thee, and cause thee to stand,
Upheld by my righteous, omnipotent hand.

4 "When through the deep waters I call thee to go,
The rivers of woe shall not thee overflow;
For I will be with thee thy troubles to bless,
And sanctify to thee thy deepest distress.

5 "When through fiery trials thy pathway shall lie,
My grace, all-sufficient, shall be thy supply,
The flame shall not hurt thee; I only design
Thy dross to consume, and thy gold to refine.

6 "E'en down to old age all my people shall prove
My sovereign, eternal, unchangeable love;
And when hoary hairs shall their temples adorn,
Like lambs they shall still in my bosom be borne.

7 "The soul that on Jesus still leans for repose,
I will not, I will not desert to his foes;
That soul, though all hell should endeavor to shake,
I'll never, no never, no never forsake!"

GEORGE KEITH

461 FOUNDATION 11S. *(Second Tune)*   Composer Unknown

1. How firm a foun-da-tion, ye saints of the Lord, Is laid for your

faith in his ex-cel-lent word! What more can he say than to

you he hath said, To you who for ref-uge to Je-sus have fled? A-MEN.

462 HENLEY 11S. 10S.   LOWELL MASON

1. Come un-to Me, when shadows darkly gath-er, When the sad heart is weary and distressed,

Seeking for comfort from your heavenly Father, Come unto me, and I will give you rest. A-MEN.

2 Large are the mansions in thy Father's dwelling,
    Glad are the homes that sorrows never dim;
  Sweet are the harps in holy music swelling,
    Soft are the tones which raise the heavenly hymn.

3 There, like an Eden blossoming in gladness,
    Bloom the fair flowers the earth too rudely pressed·
  Come unto me, all ye who droop in sadness,
    Come unto me, and I will give you rest.

CATHERINE H. ESLING

463 HOLLINGSIDE 7s. D.   JOHN B. DYKES

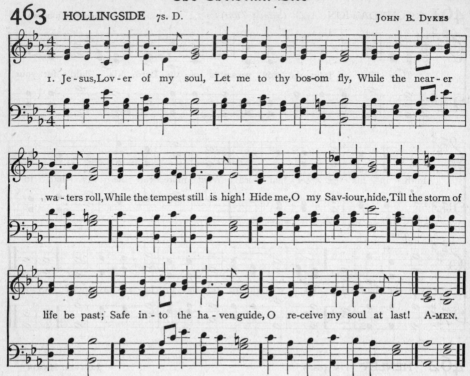

1. Je-sus, Lov-er of my soul, Let me to thy bos-om fly, While the near-er wa-ters roll, While the tempest still is high! Hide me, O my Sav-iour, hide, Till the storm of life be past; Safe in-to the ha-ven guide, O re-ceive my soul at last! A-MEN.

2 Other refuge have I none;
  Hangs my helpless soul on thee:
Leave, ah! leave me not alone,
  Still support and comfort me:
All my trust on thee is stayed,
  All my help from thee I bring;
Cover my defenseless head
  With the shadow of thy wing.

3 Thou, O Christ, art all I want;
  More than all in thee I find;
Raise the fallen, cheer the faint,
  Heal the sick, and lead the blind.

Just and holy is thy name,
  I am all unrighteousness;
False and full of sin I am,
  Thou art full of truth and grace.

4 Plenteous grace with thee is found,
  Grace to cover all my sin:
Let the healing streams abound;
  Make and keep me pure within.
Thou of life the fountain art,
  Freely let me take of thee:
Spring thou up within my heart,
  Rise to all eternity.

CHARLES WESLEY

463 ST. FABIAN 7s. D. (*Second Tune*)   JOSEPH BARNBY

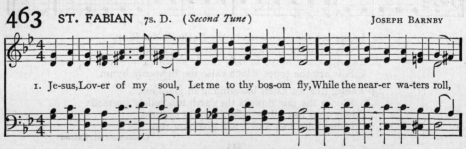

1. Je-sus, Lov-er of my soul, Let me to thy bos-om fly, While the near-er wa-ters roll,

Trust and Confidence

While the tempest still is high! Hide me, O my Saviour, hide, Till the storm of life be past;

Safe in - to the ha - ven guide, O re - ceive my soul at last! A - MEN.

463 MARTYN 7s. D. (Third Tune)

SIMEON B. MARSH

1. Je - sus, Lov - er of my soul, Let me to thy bos - om fly, While the near - er wa - ters roll,

While the tem - pest still is high! Hide me, O my Sav - iour, hide, Till the storm of

life be past; Safe in - to the ha - ven guide, O receive my soul at last! A - MEN.

The Christian Life

464 IMPLICIT TRUST 7s. 6s.

ALFRED G. WATHALL

Slowly

1. Slow - ly, slow - ly dark - 'ning The eve - ning hours roll on;

And soon be - hind the cloud - land Will sink my set - ting sun. A -MEN.

2 Around my path life's mysteries
    Their deepening shadows throw;
And as I gaze and ponder,
    They dark and darker grow.

3 But there's a voice above me
    Which says, "Wait, trust, and pray;
The night will soon be over,
    And light will come with day."

4 Father! the light and darkness
    Are both alike to thee;
Then to thy waiting servant,
    Alike they both shall be.

5 The great unending future,
    I cannot pierce its shroud;
Yet nothing doubt, nor tremble,
    God's bow is on the cloud.

6 To him I yield my spirit;
    On him I lay my load;
Fear ends with death; beyond it
    I nothing see but God.

7 Thus moving towards the darkness
    I calmly wait his call,
Now seeing, fearing — nothing;
    But hoping, trusting — all!

SAMUEL GREG

464 GLEASON 7s. 6s. (*Second Tune*)

PETER C. LUTKIN

1. Slow - ly, slow - ly dark - en - ing The eve - ning hours roll on;

And soon be - hind the cloud - land Will sink my set - ting sun. A -MEN.

326

Trust and Confidence

465 WARING C. M. 6l.   From Louis Spohr

1. Fa - ther, I know that all my life Is por - tioned out for me;

The chan - ges that are sure to come, I do not fear to see;

I ask thee for a pres - ent mind In - tent on pleas - ing thee. A - MEN.

2 I ask thee for a thoughtful love,
  Through constant watching wise,
To meet the glad with joyful smiles,
  And wipe the weeping eyes;
A heart at leisure from itself,
  To soothe and sympathize.

3 I would not have the restless will
  That hurries to and fro,
Seeking for some great thing to do,
  Or secret thing to know;
I would be treated as a child,
  And guided where I go.

4 Wherever in the world I am,
  In whatsoe'er estate,
I have a fellowship with hearts,
  To keep and cultivate;
A work of lowly love to do
  For Him on whom I wait.

5 I ask thee for the daily strength,
  To none that ask denied,
A mind to blend with outward life
  While keeping at thy side;
Content to fill a little space,
  If thou be glorified.

6 And if some things I do not ask
  Among my blessings be,
I'd have my spirit filled the more
  With grateful love to thee;
More careful, not to serve thee much,
  But please thee perfectly.

7 In service which thy love appoints
  There are no bonds for me;
My secret heart is taught the truth
  That makes thy children free:
A life of self-renouncing love
  Is one of liberty.

ANNA L. WARING. Alt.

327

466 PATER OMNIUM L. M. 6l.

H. J. E. HOLMES

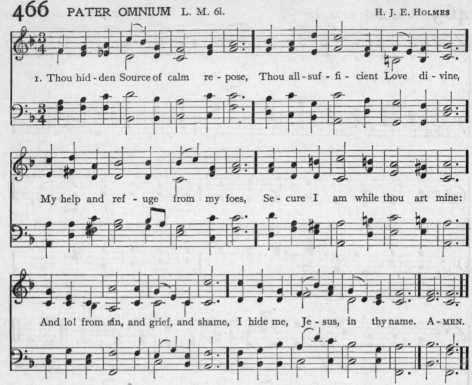

1. Thou hid-den Source of calm re-pose, Thou all-suf-fi-cient Love di-vine,

My help and ref-uge from my foes, Se-cure I am while thou art mine:

And lo! from sin, and grief, and shame, I hide me, Je-sus, in thy name. A-MEN.

2 Thy mighty name salvation is,
   And keeps my happy soul above.
Comfort it brings, and power, and peace,
   And joy, and everlasting love:
To me, with thy great name, are given
Pardon, and holiness, and heaven.

3 Jesus, my all in all thou art;
   My rest in toil, my ease in pain;
The medicine of my broken heart;
   In war my peace; in loss my gain;
My smile beneath the tyrant's frown;
In shame my glory and my crown:

4 In want my plentiful supply;
   In weakness my almighty power;
In bonds my perfect liberty;
   My light in Satan's darkest hour;
In grief my joy unspeakable;
My life in death,—my all in all.

CHARLES WESLEY

467 BENTLEY 7s. 6s. D.

JOHN HULLAH

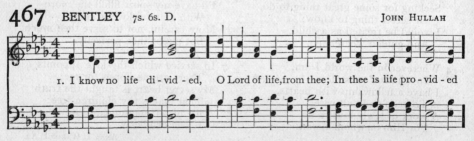

1. I know no life di-vid-ed, O Lord of life, from thee; In thee is life pro-vid-ed

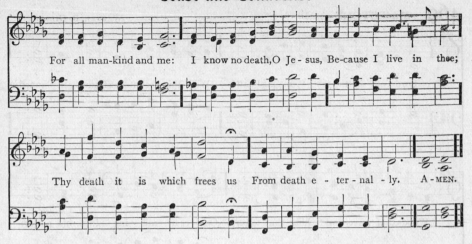

For all man-kind and me: I know no death, O Je - sus, Be-cause I live in thee;

Thy death it is which frees us From death e - ter - nal - ly. A - MEN.

2 I fear no tribulation,
  Since, whatsoe'er it be,
It makes no separation
  Between my Lord and me.
If thou, my God and teacher,
  Vouchsafe to be my own,
Though poor, I shall be richer
  Than monarch on his throne.

3 If, while on earth I wander,
  My heart is light and blest,
Ah, what shall I be yonder,
  In perfect peace and rest?
O blessèd thought! in dying
  We go to meet the Lord,
Where there shall be no sighing,
  A kingdom our reward.

CARL J. P. SPITTA. Tr. by RICHARD MASSIE

468 ST. BEES 7s.   JOHN B. DYKES

1. Cast thy bur - den on the Lord, On - ly lean up - on his word;

Thou shalt soon have cause to bless His e - ter - nal faith - ful - ness. A - MEN.

2 Ever in the raging storm
  Thou shalt see his cheering form,
Hear his pledge of coming aid:
  "It is I, be not afraid."

3 Cast thy burden at his feet;
  Linger at his mercy seat:

He will lead thee by the hand
Gently to the better land.

4 He will gird thee by his power,
  In thy weary, fainting hour:
Lean, then, loving, on his word;
  Cast thy burden on the Lord.

Author Unknown.

469 MAIDSTONE 7s. D.

WALTER B. GILBERT

1. Lord of earth, thy form-ing hand Well this beauteous frame hath planned—
Woods that wave, and hills that tower, O - cean roll - ing in his power:
Yet a - midst this scene so fair, Should I cease thy smile to share,
What were all its joys to me? Whom have I on earth but thee? A-MEN.

2 Lord of heaven, beyond our sight
Shines a world of purer light;
There in love's unclouded reign,
Severed friends shall meet again:
O that world is passing fair!
Yet, if thou wert absent there,
What were all its joys to me?
Whom have I in heaven but thee?

3 Lord of earth and heaven, my breast
Seeks in thee its only rest;
I was lost; thy accents mild
Homeward lured thy wandering child:
O if once thy smile divine
Ceased upon my soul to shine,
What were earth or heaven to me?
Whom have I in each but thee?

ROBERT GRANT

Trust and Confidence

470 ST. AGNES C. M.
JOHN B. DYKES

1. Lord, it be-longs not to my care Wheth-er I die or live;
To love and serve thee is my share, And this thy grace must give. A-MEN.

2 If life be long, I will be glad
That I may long obey;
If short, yet why should I be sad
To soar to endless day?

3 Christ leads me through no darker rooms
Than he went through before;
He that into God's kingdom comes
Must enter by this door.

4 Come, Lord, when grace hath made me
Thy blessèd face to see; [meet
For, if thy work on earth be sweet,
What will thy glory be?

5 My knowledge of that life is small;
The eye of faith is dim;
But 'tis enough that Christ knows all,
And I shall be with him.

RICHARD BAXTER

471 FERGUSON S. M.
GEORGE KINGSLEY

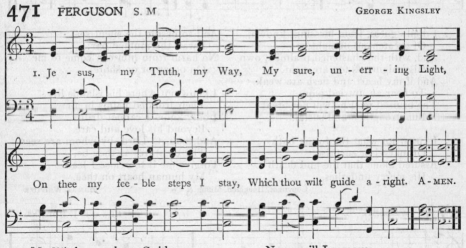

1. Je-sus, my Truth, my Way, My sure, un-err-ing Light,
On thee my fee-ble steps I stay, Which thou wilt guide a-right. A-MEN.

2 My Wisdom and my Guide,
My Counselor thou art;
O never let me leave thy side,
Or from thy paths depart!

3 I lift mine eyes to thee,
Thou gracious, bleeding Lamb,
That I may now enlightened be,
And never put to shame.

4 Never will I remove
Out of thy hands my cause;
But rest in thy redeeming love,
And hang upon thy cross.

5 Teach me the happy art
In all things to depend
On thee; O never, Lord, depart,
But love me to the end!

CHARLES WESLEY

472 ST. LEONARD C. M. D.

HENRY HILES

1. I bow my fore-head in the dust, I veil mine eyes for shame, And urge, in trembling

self-dis-trust, A prayer with-out a claim. No of-fering of mine own I have, Nor

works my faith to prove; I can but give the gifts He gave, And plead his love for love! A- MEN.

2 I dimly guess, from blessings known,
 Of greater out of sight;
And, with the chastened psalmist, own
 His judgments too are right.
And if my heart and flesh are weak
 To bear an untried pain,
The bruisèd reed he will not break,
 But strengthen and sustain.

3 I know not what the future hath
 Of marvel or surprise,
Assured alone that life and death
 His mercy underlies.

And so beside the silent sea
 I wait the muffled oar:
No harm from him can come to me
 On ocean or on shore.

4 I know not where his islands lift
 Their fronded palms in air;
I only know I cannot drift
 Beyond his love and care.
And thou, O Lord, by whom are seen
 Thy creatures as they be,
Forgive me if too close I lean
 My human heart on thee.

JOHN G. WHITTIER

473 WESSEX 8. 6. 8. 6. 8. 8.

EDWARD J. HOPKINS

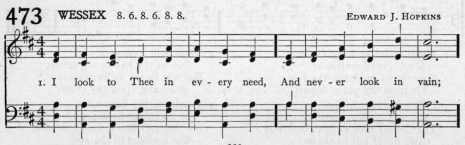

1. I look to Thee in ev - ery need, And nev - er look in vain;

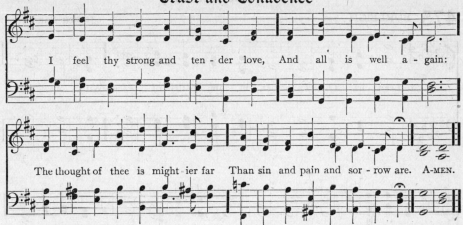

I feel thy strong and ten-der love, And all is well a-gain:

The thought of thee is might-ier far Than sin and pain and sor-row are. A-MEN.

2 Discouraged in the work of life,
   Disheartened by its load,
 Shamed by its failures or its fears,
   I sink beside the road:
 But let me only think of thee,
 And then new heart springs up in me.

3 Thy calmness bends serene above,
   My restlessness to still;
 Around me flows thy quickening life,
   To nerve my faltering will;
 Thy presence fills my solitude;
 Thy providence turns all to good.

4 Embosomed deep in thy dear love,
   Held in thy law, I stand;
 Thy hand in all things I behold,
   And all things in thy hand;
 Thou leadest me by unsought ways,
 And turn'st my mourning into praise.

Copyright, Houghton, Mifflin & Co.   SAMUEL LONGFELLOW

474 PLYMOUTH C. M.   ALFRED G. WATHALL

1. Our high-est joys suc-ceed our griefs, And peace is born of pain;

Smiles fol-low bit-ter blind-ing tears, As sun-shine fol-lows rain. A-MEN.

2 We gain our rest through weariness,
   From bitter draw the sweet: [fear,
 Strength comes from weakness, hope from
 And victory from defeat.

3 We reap where we have sown the seed;
   Gain is the fruit of loss;
 Life springs from death and, at the end,
   The crown succeeds the cross.

Author Unknown

The Christian Life

BURLEIGH 10s.

JOSEPH BARNBY

1. Lead us, O Fa - ther, in the paths of peace; With - out thy
guid-ing hand we go a - stray, And doubts ap - pall, and sor-rows still in-crease;
Lead us through Christ, the true and liv - ing Way. A-MEN.

2 Lead us, O Father, in the paths of truth
Unhelped by thee, in error's maze we grope,
While passion stains, and folly dims our youth,
And age comes on, uncheered by faith and hope.

3 Lead us, O Father, in the paths of right;
Blindly we stumble when we walk alone,
Involved in shadows of a darksome night,
Only with thee we journey safely on.

4 Lead us, O Father, to thy heavenly rest,
However rough and steep the path may be,
Through joy or sorrow, as thou deemest best,
Until our lives are perfected in thee.

WILLIAM H. BURLEIGH

476 BREMEN L. M. 6l.   GEORG NEUMARK

1. Leave God to or-der all thy ways, . And hope in him what-e'er be-tide;

Thou'lt find him, in the e-vil days, . Thine all-suf-fi-cient strength and guide.

Who trusts in God's un-chang-ing love Builds on the rock that naught can move! A-MEN.

2 Only thy restless heart keep still,
    And wait in cheerful hope, content
To take whate'er his gracious will,
    His all-discerning love hath sent;
Nor doubt our inmost wants are known
To him who chose us for his own.

3 He knows when joyful hours are best,
    He sends them as he sees it meet,
When thou hast borne the fiery test,
    And now art freed from all deceit,
He comes to thee all unaware,
And makes thee own his loving care.

4 Sing, pray, and swerve not from his ways;
    But do thine own part faithfully.
Trust his rich promises of grace,
    So shall they be fulfilled in thee.
God never yet forsook at need
The soul that trusted him indeed.

GEORG NEUMARK. Tr. by CATHERINE WINKWORTH

The Christian Life

477 INTERCESSION OLD L. M.

Old Latin Melody

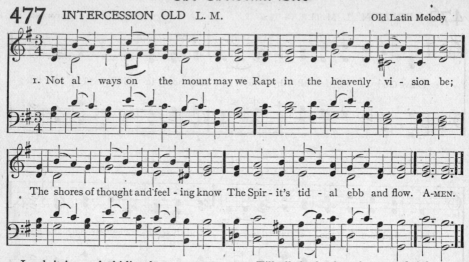

1. Not al - ways on the mount may we Rapt in the heavenly vi - sion be;

The shores of thought and feel - ing know The Spir - it's tid - al ebb and flow. A-MEN.

2 Lord, it is good abiding here.
We cry, the heavenly presence near;
The vision vanishes, our eyes
Are lifted into vacant skies!

3 Yet hath one such exalted hour,
Upon the soul redeeming power,
And in its strength through after days
We travel our appointed ways;

4 Till all the lowly vale grows bright,
Transfigured in remembered light,
And in untiring souls we bear
The freshness of the upper air.

5 The mount for vision, — but below
The paths of daily duty go,
And nobler life therein shall own
The pattern on the mountain shown.

FREDERICK L. HOSMER

478 FLEMMING 8. 8. 8. 6.

FRIEDRICH F. FLEMMING

1. O Ho - ly Sav - iour, Friend un - seen, Since on thine arm thou bidd'st me lean,

Help me, throughout life's chang-ing scene, By faith to cling to thee. A-MEN.

2 What though the world deceitful prove,
And earthly friends and hopes remove;
With patient, uncomplaining love,
Still would I cling to thee.

3 Though oft I seem to tread alone
Life's dreary waste, with thorns o'ergrown,

Thy voice of love, in gentlest tone,
Still whispers, "Cling to me!"

4 Though faith and hope are often tried,
I ask not, need not, aught beside;
So safe, so calm, so satisfied,
The soul that clings to thee.

CHARLOTTE ELLIOTT

Trust and Confidence

479 TRANSFIGURATION C. M.

PETER C. LUTKIN

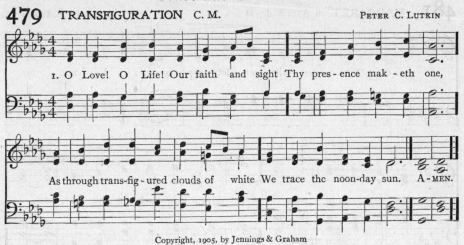

1. O Love! O Life! Our faith and sight Thy pres-ence mak-eth one,

As through trans-fig-ured clouds of white We trace the noon-day sun. A-MEN.

2 So, to our mortal eyes subdued,
Flesh-veiled, but not concealed,
We know in thee the fatherhood
And heart of God revealed.

3 We faintly hear, we dimly see,
In differing phrase we pray;
But, dim or clear, we own in thee
The Light, the Truth, the Way!

4 Our Friend, our Brother, and our Lord,
What may thy service be? —
Nor name, nor form, nor ritual word,
But simply following thee.

5 Thy litanies, sweet offices
Of love and gratitude;
Thy sacramental liturgies,
The joy of doing good.

JOHN G. WHITTIER

480 HOLY TRINITY C. M.

JOSEPH BARNBY

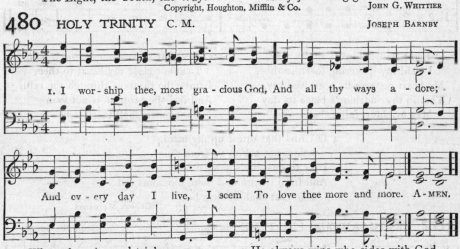

1. I wor-ship thee, most gra-cious God, And all thy ways a-dore;

And ev-ery day I live, I seem To love thee more and more. A-MEN.

2 When obstacles and trials seem
Like prison-walls to be,
I do the little I can do,
And leave the rest to thee.

3 I have no cares, O blessèd Will,
For all my cares are thine;
I live in triumph, Lord, for thou
Hast made thy triumphs mine.

4 He always wins who sides with God,
To him no chance is lost;
God's will is sweetest to him when
It triumphs at his cost.

5 Ill that he blesses is our good,
And unblest good is ill;
And all is right that seems most wrong,
If it be his sweet will.

FREDERICK W. FABER

481 MARGARET 8. 8. 8. 8. 6. ALBERT L. PEACE

1. O Love that wilt not let me go, ... I rest my
wea - ry soul in thee; I give thee back the life I owe,
That in thine o-cean depths its flow May rich - er, full - er be. A - MEN.

2 O Light that followest all my way,
   I yield my flickering torch to thee,
My heart restores its borrowed ray,
That in thy sunshine's blaze its day
   May brighter, fairer, be.

3 O Joy that seekest me through pain,
   I cannot close my heart to thee;
I trace the rainbow through the rain,
And feel the promise is not vain
   That morn shall tearless be.

4 O Cross that liftest up my head,
   I dare not ask to fly from thee;
I lay in dust life's glory dead,
And from the ground there blossoms red
   Life that shall endless be.

GEORGE MATHESON

482 JESUS, SAVIOUR, PILOT ME 7s. 6l. JOHN E. GOULD

1. Je - sus, Sav - iour, pi - lot me O - ver life's tem - pes - tuous sea;

338

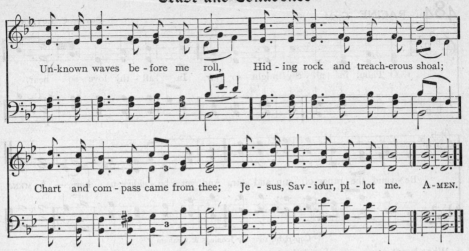

Un-known waves be-fore me roll, Hid-ing rock and treach-erous shoal;

Chart and com-pass came from thee; Je - sus, Sav - iour, pi - lot me. A-MEN.

2 As a mother stills her child,
   Thou canst hush the ocean wild;
   Boisterous waves obey thy will
   When thou sayest to them "Be still!"
   Wondrous Sovereign of the sea,
   Jesus, Saviour, pilot me.

3 When at last I near the shore,
   And the fearful breakers roar
   'Twixt me and the peaceful rest,
   Then, while leaning on thy breast,
   May I hear thee say to me,
   "Fear not, I will pilot thee."
   EDWARD HOPPER

483 ST. BERNARD C. M.

JOHN RICHARDSON

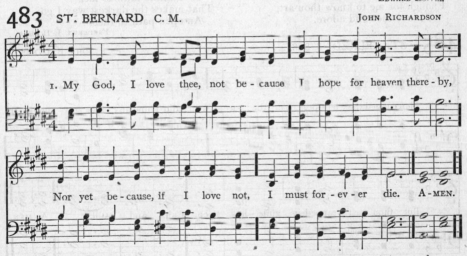

1. My God, I love thee, not be - cause I hope for heaven there - by,

Nor yet be - cause, if I love not, I must for - ev - er die. A-MEN.

2 Thou, O my Jesus, thou didst me
   Upon the cross embrace:
   For me didst bear the nails, and spear,
   And manifold disgrace.

3 Then why, O blessèd Jesus Christ,
   Should I not love thee well?
   Not for the hope of winning heaven,
   Nor of escaping hell;

4 Not with the hope of gaining aught,
   Not seeking a reward;
   But as thyself hast lovèd me,
   O ever-loving Lord!

5 So would I love thee, dearest Lord,
   And in thy praise will sing;
   Solely because thou art my God,
   And my eternal King.
   FRANCIS XAVIER. Tr. by EDWARD CASWALL

The Christian Life

484 RACINE C. M.

PETER C. LUTKIN

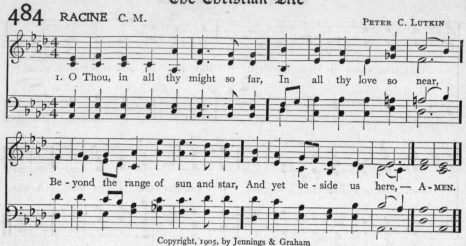

1. O Thou, in all thy might so far, In all thy love so near,

Be - yond the range of sun and star, And yet be - side us here, — A - MEN.

Copyright, 1905, by Jennings & Graham

2 What heart can comprehend thy name,
Or, searching, find thee out,
Who art within, a quickening flame,
A presence round about?

3 Yet though I know thee but in part,
I ask not, Lord, for more:
Enough for me to know thou art,
To love thee and adore.

4 O sweeter than aught else besides,
The tender mystery
That like a veil of shadow hides
The light I may not see!

5 And dearer than all things I know
Is childlike faith to me,
That makes the darkest way I go
An open path to thee.

FREDERICK L. HOSMER

485 ST. AELRED 8. 8. 8. 4.

JOHN B. DYKES

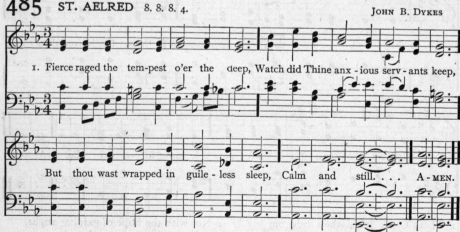

1. Fierce raged the tem-pest o'er the deep, Watch did Thine anx - ious serv - ants keep,

But thou wast wrapped in guile - less sleep, Calm and still. . . . A - MEN.

2 "Save, Lord, we perish," was their cry,
"O save us in our agony!"
Thy word above the storm rose high,
"Peace, be still."

3 The wild winds hushed; the angry deep
Sank, like a little child, to sleep;

The sullen billows ceased to leap,
At thy will.

4 So, when our life is clouded o'er,
And storm-winds drift us from the shore,
Say, lest we sink to rise no more,
"Peace, be still."

GODFREY THRING

Trust and Confidence

486 DIADEMA 11. 10. 11. 6.   JOSEPH BARNBY

1. Still will we trust, though earth seem dark and drear-y, And the heart
faint be-neath his chas-tening rod; Though rough and steep our
path-way, worn and wea-ry, Still will we trust in God! A-MEN.

2 Our eyes see dimly till by faith anointed,
   And our blind choosing brings us grief and pain;
   Through him alone who hath our way appointed,
     We find our peace again.

3 Choose for us, God! nor let our weak preferring
   Cheat our poor souls of good thou hast designed:
   Choose for us, God! thy wisdom is unerring,
     And we are fools and blind.

4 Let us press on, in patient self-denial,
   Accept the hardship, shrink not from the loss;
   Our portion lies beyond the hour of trial,
     Our crown beyond the cross.

WILLIAM H. BURLEIGH

487 RODIGAST P. M.

WALTER B. GILBERT

1. Whate'er my God or-dains is right; His will is ev - er just; How-e'er he
or-ders now my cause, I will be still and trust. He is my God; Though dark my road,
He holds me that I shall not fall, Where-fore to him I leave it all. A - MEN.

2 Whate'er my God ordains is right;
    He never will deceive;
    He leads me by the proper path,
      And so to him I cleave,
        And take content
        What he hath sent;
    His hand can turn my griefs away,
    And patiently I wait his day.

3 Whate'er my God ordains is right;
    Though I the cup must drink
    That bitter seems to my faint heart,
      I will not fear nor shrink;
        Tears pass away
        With dawn of day;
Sweet comfort yet shall fill my heart,
And pain and sorrow all depart.

4 Whate'er my God ordains is right;
    My light, my life is he,
    Who cannot will me aught but good;
      I trust him utterly;
        For well I know,
        In joy or woe,
We soon shall see, as sunlight clear,
How faithful was our guardian here.

5 Whate'er my God ordains is right;
    Here will I take my stand,
Though sorrow, need, or death make earth
    For me a desert land.
      My Father's care
      Is round me there,
He holds me that I shall not fall;
And so to him I leave it all.

SAMUEL RODIGAST. Tr. by CATHERINE WINKWORTH

Trust and Confidence

488 ST. HILDA 7s. 6s. D.   JUSTIN H. KNECHT and EDWARD HUSBAND

1. I lay my sins on Je - sus, The spot - less Lamb of God;
He bears them all and frees us From the ac - curs - èd load:
I bring my guilt to Je - sus, To wash my crim - son stains
White in his blood most pre - cious, Till not a stain re - mains. A - MEN.

2 I lay my wants on Jesus;
  All fullness dwells in him;
He healeth my diseases,
  He doth my soul redeem:
I lay my griefs on Jesus,
  My burdens and my cares;
He from them all releases,
  He all my sorrows shares.

3 I long to be like Jesus,
  Meek, loving, lowly, mild;
I long to be like Jesus,
  The Father's holy child:
I long to be with Jesus
  Amid the heavenly throng,
To sing with saints his praises,
  And learn the angels' song.

HORATIUS BONAR

489 HE LEADETH ME L. M. *With Refrain*

WILLIAM B. BRADBURY

1. He lead - eth me! O bless - èd thought! O words with heavenly com - fort fraught!

What-e'er I do, wher-e'er I be, Still 'tis God's hand that lead - eth me.

REFRAIN

He lead-eth me, he lead - eth me, By his own hand he lead - eth me:

His faith -ful fol-lower I would be, For by his hand he lead - eth me. A - MEN.

Used by permission of Biglow & Main Co.

2 Sometimes 'mid scenes of deepest gloom,
Sometimes where Eden's bowers bloom,
By waters still, o'er troubled sea,—
Still 'tis his hand that leadeth me!

3 Lord, I would clasp thy hand in mine,
Nor ever murmur nor repine,

Content, whatever lot I see,
Since 'tis my God that leadeth me!

4 And when my task on earth is done,
When, by thy grace, the victory's won,
E'en death's cold wave I will not flee,
Since God through Jordan leadeth me.

JOSEPH H. GILMORE

Trust and Confidence

490 EVERY DAY AND HOUR 7s. 9s. *With Refrain* WILLIAM H. DOANE

1. Sav-iour, more than life to me, I am cling-ing, cling-ing close to thee;
Let thy pre-cious blood ap-plied, Keep me ev-er, ev-er near thy side.

REFRAIN

Ev-ery day, ev-ery hour, Let me feel thy cleans-ing
Ev-ery day and hour, ev-ery day and hour,

power; May thy ten-der love to me Bind me clos-er, clos-er, Lord, to thee. A-MEN.

2 Through this changing world below,
  Lead me gently, gently as I go;
  Trusting thee, I cannot stray,
  I can never, never lose my way.

3 Let me love thee more and more,
  Till this fleeting, fleeting life is o'er;
  Till my soul is lost in love,
  In a brighter, brighter world above.

FANNY J. CROSBY

491 CONTRITION P. M.

WILLIAM H. OAKLEY

1. Je - sus, let thy pit - ying eye Call back a wan-dering sheep;

False to thee, like Pe - ter, I Would fain, like Pe - ter, weep.

Let me be by grace re-stored; On me be all long - suf- fering shown;

Turn, and look up - on me, Lord, And break my heart of stone. A - MEN.

2 Saviour, Prince, enthroned above,
    Repentance to impart,
  Give me, through thy dying love,
    The humble, contrite heart;
  Give what I have long implored,
    A portion of thy grief unknown;
  Turn, and look upon me, Lord,
  And break my heart of stone.

3 See me, Saviour, from above,
    Nor suffer me to die;
  Life, and happiness, and love
    Drop from thy gracious eye;

  Speak the reconciling word,
    And let thy mercy melt me down;
  Turn, and look upon me, Lord,
    And break my heart of stone.

4 Look, as when thy languid eye
    Was closed that we might live;
  "Father," at the point to die
    My Saviour prayed, "forgive!"
  Surely, with that dying word,   [done!"
    He turns, and looks, and cries. "'Tis
  O my bleeding, loving Lord,
    Thou break'st my heart of stone!

CHARLES WESLEY

346

492 RUTH C. M.

LORIN WEBSTER

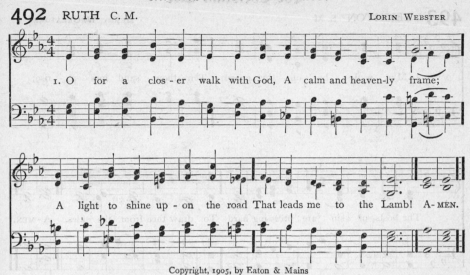

1. O for a clos-er walk with God, A calm and heaven-ly frame;

A light to shine up-on the road That leads me to the Lamb! A-MEN.

Copyright, 1905, by Eaton & Mains

2 Where is the blessedness I knew,
When first I saw the Lord?
Where is the soul-refreshing view
Of Jesus and his word?

3 What peaceful hours I once enjoyed!
How sweet their memory still!
But they have left an aching void
The world can never fill.

4 Return, O holy Dove, return,
Sweet messenger of rest!

I hate the sins that made thee mourn,
And drove thee from my breast.

5 The dearest idol I have known,
Whate'er that idol be,
Help me to tear it from thy throne,
And worship only thee.

6 So shall my walk be close with God,
Calm and serene my frame;
So purer light shall mark the road
That leads me to the Lamb.

WILLIAM COWPER

492 NAOMI C. M. *(Second Tune)*

HANS G. NAEGELI

1. O for a clos-er walk with God, A calm and heaven-ly frame;

A light to shine up-on the road That leads me to the Lamb! A-MEN.

493 LEIGHTON S. M.

HENRY W. GREATOREX

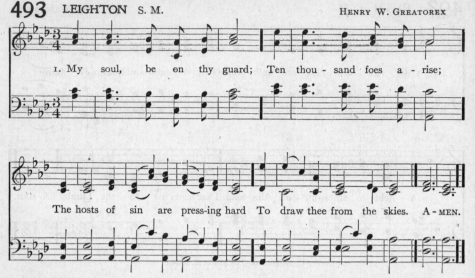

1. My soul, be on thy guard; Ten thou - sand foes a - rise; The hosts of sin are press-ing hard To draw thee from the skies. A - MEN.

2 O watch, and fight, and pray;
The battle ne'er give o'er;
Renew it boldly every day,
And help divine implore.

3 Ne'er think the victory won,
Nor lay thine armor down;

The work of faith will not be done,
Till thou obtain the crown.

4 Fight on, my soul, till death
Shall bring thee to thy God;
He'll take thee, at thy parting breath,
To his divine abode.

GEORGE HEATH

493 LABAN S. M. (*Second Tune*)

LOWELL MASON

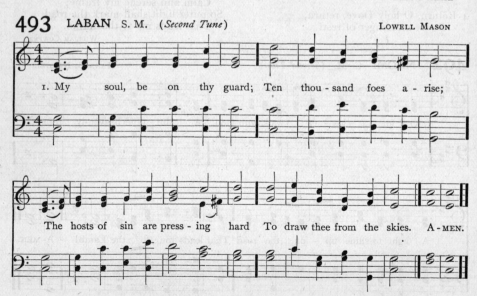

1. My soul, be on thy guard; Ten thou - sand foes a - rise; The hosts of sin are press - ing hard To draw thee from the skies. A - MEN.

Watchfulness and Prayer

494 VIGILATE 7. 7. 7. 3.

WILLIAM H. MONK

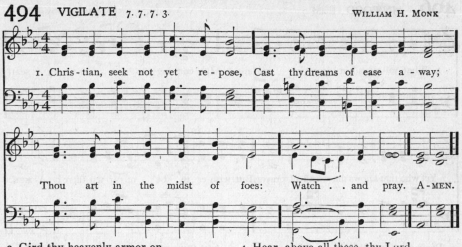

1. Chris - tian, seek not yet re - pose, Cast thy dreams of ease a - way;

Thou art in the midst of foes: Watch . . and pray. A - MEN.

2 Gird thy heavenly armor on,
  Wear it ever night and day;
  Near thee lurks the evil one;
  Watch and pray.

3 Hear the victors who o'ercame;
  Still they watch each warrior's way;
  All with one deep voice exclaim,
  Watch and pray.

4 Hear, above all these, thy Lord,
  Him thou lovest to obey;
  Hide within thy heart his word,
  Watch and pray.

5 Watch, as if on that alone
  Hung the issue of the day;
  Pray that help may be sent down;
  Watch and pray.

CHARLOTTE ELLIOTT

495 RETREAT L. M.

THOMAS HASTINGS

1. From ev - ery storm - y wind that blows, From ev - ery swell - ing tide of woes,

There is a calm, a sure re-treat: 'Tis found be - neath the mer - cy seat. A - MEN.

2 There is a place where Jesus sheds
The oil of gladness on our heads;
A place than all besides more sweet:
It is the blood-bought mercy seat.

3 There is a scene where spirits blend,
Where friend holds fellowship with friend;
Though sundered far, by faith they meet
Around one common mercy seat.

4 Ah! whither could we flee for aid,
When tempted, desolate, dismayed;
Or how the hosts of hell defeat,
Had suffering saints no mercy seat?

5 There, there on eagle wings we soar,
And sin and sense molest no more;
And heaven comes down our souls to greet,
While glory crowns the mercy seat.

HUGH STOWELL

496 LINWOOD L. M.

GIOACHINO A. ROSSINI

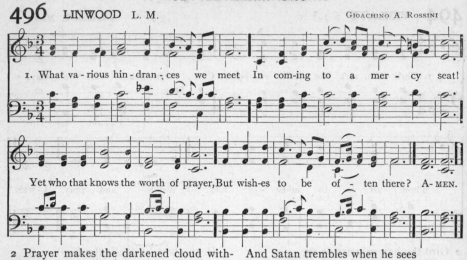

1. What va-rious hin-dran-ces we meet In com-ing to a mer-cy seat!

Yet who that knows the worth of prayer, But wish-es to be of-ten there? A-MEN.

2 Prayer makes the darkened cloud with-
Prayer climbs the ladder Jacob saw; [draw;
Gives exercise to faith and love;
Brings every blessing from above.

3 Restraining prayer, we cease to fight;
Prayer keeps the Christian's armor bright;

And Satan trembles when he sees
The weakest saint upon his knees.

4 Were half the breath that's vainly spent,
To heaven in supplication sent,
Our cheerful song would oftener be,
"Hear what the Lord has done for me."
WILLIAM COWPER

497 LAMBETH C. M.

Composer Unknown

1. Prayer is the soul's sin-cere de-sire, Ut-tered or un-ex-pressed;

The mo-tion of a hid-den fire That trem-bles in the breast. A-MEN.

2 Prayer is the burden of a sigh,
  The falling of a tear,
The upward glancing of an eye,
  When none but God is near.

3 Prayer is the simplest form of speech
  That infant lips can try;
Prayer the sublimest strains that reach
  The Majesty on high.

4 Prayer is the contrite sinner's voice,
  Returning from his ways;

While angels in their songs rejoice
  And cry, "Behold, he prays!"

5 Prayer is the Christian's vital breath,
  The Christian's native air,
His watchword at the gates of death;
  He enters heaven with prayer.

6 O Thou, by whom we come to God,
  The Life, the Truth, the Way;
The path of prayer thyself hast trod:
  Lord, teach us how to pray!
IAMES MONTGOMERY

498 WOODSTOCK C. M.

DEODATUS DUTTON, Jr.

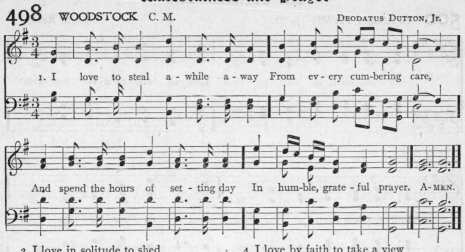

1. I love to steal a-while a-way From ev-ery cum-bering care,

And spend the hours of set-ting day In hum-ble, grate-ful prayer. A-MEN.

2 I love in solitude to shed
   The penitential tear,
   And all his promises to plead
   Where none but God can hear.

3 I love to think on mercies past,
   And future good implore,
   And all my cares and sorrows cast
   On him whom I adore.

4 I love by faith to take a view
   Of brighter scenes in heaven;
   The prospect doth my strength renew,
   While here by tempests driven.

5 Thus, when life's toilsome day is o'er,
   May its departing ray
   Be calm at this impressive hour,
   And lead to endless day.

PHŒBE H. BROWN

499 SOHO C. M.

JOSEPH BARNBY

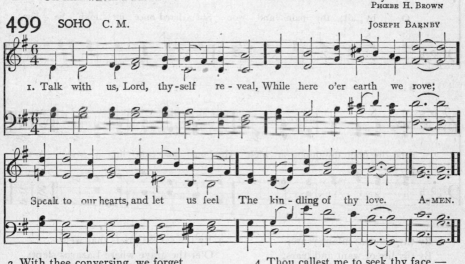

1. Talk with us, Lord, thy-self re-veal, While here o'er earth we rove;

Speak to our hearts, and let us feel The kin-dling of thy love. A-MEN.

2 With thee conversing, we forget
   All time, and toil, and care;
   Labor is rest, and pain is sweet,
   If thou, my God, art here.

3 Here, then, my God, vouchsafe to stay,
   And bid my heart rejoice;
   My bounding heart shall own thy sway,
   And echo to thy voice.

4 Thou callest me to seek thy face,—
   'Tis all I wish to seek;
   To attend the whispers of thy grace,
   And hear thee inly speak.

5 Let this my every hour employ,
   Till I thy glory see;
   Enter into my Master's joy,
   And find my heaven in thee.

CHARLES WESLEY

500 SPANISH HYMN 7s. D.   Spanish Melody

1. Sav - iour, when, in dust, to thee Low we bend th'a - dor - ing knee;
When, re - pent - ant, to the skies Scarce we lift our weep - ing eyes;
O by all thy pains and woe Suf - fered once for man be - low,
Bend - ing from thy throne on high, Hear our sol - emn lit - a - ny! A - MEN.

2 By thy helpless infant years;
By thy life of want and tears;
By thy days of sore distress,
In the savage wilderness;
By the dread mysterious hour
Of the insulting tempter's power;
Turn, O turn a favoring eye,
Hear our solemn litany!

3 By the sacred griefs that wept
O'er the grave where Lazarus slept;
By the boding tears that flowed
Over Salem's loved abode;
By the anguished sigh that told
Treachery lurked within thy fold;
From thy seat above the sky,
Hear our solemn litany!

Watchfulness and Prayer

4 By thine hour of dire despair;
By thine agony of prayer;
By the cross, the nail, the thorn,
Piercing spear, and torturing scorn;
By the gloom that veiled the skies
O'er the dreadful sacrifice;
Listen to our humble cry,
Hear our solemn litany!

5 By thy deep, expiring groan;
By the sad sepulchral stone;
By the vault whose dark abode
Held in vain the rising God;
O from earth to heaven restored,
Mighty, reascended Lord,
Listen, listen to the cry
Of our solemn litany!

ROBERT GRANT

500 BLUMENTHAL 7s. D. (*Second Tune*) JACOB BLUMENTHAL

1. Sav-iour, when, in dust, to thee Low we bend th'a-dor-ing knee;
When, re-pent-ant, to the skies Scarce we lift our weep-ing eyes;
O by all thy pains and woe Suf-fered once for man be-low,
Bend-ing from thy throne on high, Hear our sol-emn lit-a-ny! A-MEN.

353

13

The Christian Life

501 ALMSGIVING 8. 8. 8. 4.   JOHN B. DYKES

1. My God, is an - y hour so sweet, From blush of morn to eve - ning star,
As that which calls me to thy feet, The hour of prayer? A - MEN.

2 Blest is that tranquil hour of morn,
  And blest that solemn hour of eve,
When, on the wings of prayer upborne,
  The world I leave.

3 Then is my strength by thee renewed;
  Then are my sins by thee forgiven;
Then dost thou cheer my solitude
  With hopes of heaven.

4 No words can tell what sweet relief
  Here for my every want I find;

What strength for warfare, balm for grief,
  What peace of mind.

5 Hushed is each doubt, gone every fear;
  My spirit seems in heaven to stay;
And e'en the penitential tear
  Is wiped away.

6 Lord, till I reach that blissful shore,
  No privilege so dear shall be,
As thus my inmost soul to pour
  In prayer to thee.

CHARLOTTE ELLIOTT

502 UXBRIDGE L. M.   LOWELL MASON

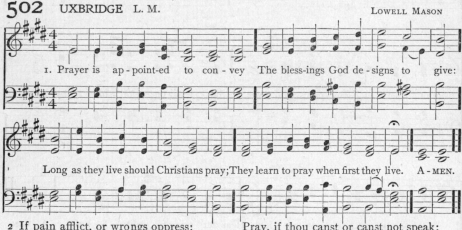

1. Prayer is ap - point-ed to con - vey The bless-ings God de - signs to give:
Long as they live should Christians pray; They learn to pray when first they live. A - MEN.

2 If pain afflict, or wrongs oppress;
  If cares distract, or fears dismay;
If guilt deject; if sin distress;
  In every case, still watch and pray.

3 'Tis prayer supports the soul that's weak;
  Though thought be broken, language lame,

Pray, if thou canst or canst not speak;
  But pray with faith in Jesus' name.

4 Depend on him; thou canst not fail;
  Make all thy wants and wishes known;
Fear not; his merits must prevail:
  Ask but in faith, it shall be done.

JOSEPH HART

Watchfulness and Prayer

503 LOUVAN L. M.

VIRGIL C. TAYLOR

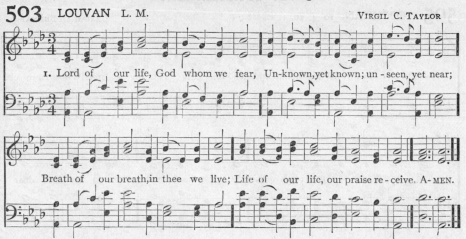

1. Lord of our life, God whom we fear, Un-known, yet known; un-seen, yet near;

Breath of our breath, in thee we live; Life of our life, our praise re-ceive. A-MEN.

2 Thine eye detects the sparrow's fall;
Thy heart of love expands for all;
Our throbbing life is full of thee,
Throned in thy vast infinity.

3 Shine in our darkness, Light of Light,
Our minds illume, disperse our night;

Make us responsive to thy will,
Our souls with all thy fullness fill.

4 We love thy name, we heed thy rod,
Thy word, our law; O gracious God!
We wait thy will; on thee we call;
Our light, our life, our love, our all.

SAMUEL F. SMITH

504 ABIDING GRACE C. M.

JOHN S. CAMP

1. Since with-out Thee we do no good, And with thee do no ill,

A-bide with us in weal and woe, In ac-tion and in will; A-MEN.

2 In weal, that while our lips confess
The Lord who gives, we may
Remember with an humble thought
The Lord who takes away;

3 In woe, that while to drowning tears
Our hearts their joys resign,
We may remember who can turn
Such water into wine;

4 By hours of day, that when our feet
O'er hill and valley run,

We still may think the light of truth
More welcome than the sun;

5 By hours of night, that when the air
Its dew and shadow yields,
We still may hear the voice of God
In silence of the fields.

6 Abide with us, abide with us,
While flesh and soul agree;
And when our flesh is only dust,
Abide our souls with thee.

ELIZABETH B. BROWNING

505 COCHRAN 10. 4. 10. 4. 10. 10.

UZZIAH C. BURNAP

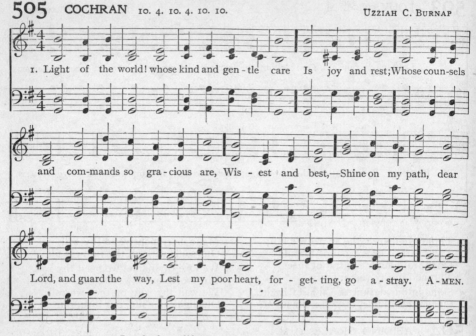

1. Light of the world! whose kind and gen-tle care Is joy and rest; Whose coun-sels and com-mands so gra-cious are, Wis-est and best,—Shine on my path, dear Lord, and guard the way, Lest my poor heart, for-get-ting, go a-stray. A-MEN.

2 Lord of my life! my soul's most pure desire,
　　Its hope and peace;
　Let not the faith thy loving words inspire
　　Falter, or cease;
　But be to me, true Friend, my chief delight,
　And safely guide, that every step be right.

3 My blessèd Lord! what bliss to feel thee near,
　　Faithful and true;
　To trust in thee, without one doubt or fear,
　　Thy will to do;
　And all the while to know that thou, our Friend,
　Art blessing us, and wilt bless to the end.

4 And then, O then! when sorrow's night is o'er,
　　Life's daylight come,
　And we are safe within heaven's golden door,
　　At home! at home!
　How full of glad rejoicing will we raise,
　Saviour, to thee our everlasting praise.

HENRY BATEMAN

506 I NEED THEE EVERY HOUR 6s. 4s. *With Refrain* ROBERT LOWRY

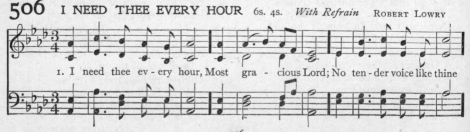

1. I need thee ev-ery hour, Most gra-cious Lord; No ten-der voice like thine

Watchfulness and Prayer

REFRAIN

Can peace af - ford. I need thee, O I need thee; Ev - ery hour I

need thee; O bless me now, my Sav - iour, I come to thee! A - MEN.

2 I need thee every hour;
  Stay thou near by;
  Temptations lose their power
  When thou art nigh.

3 I need thee every hour,
  In joy or pain;
  Come quickly and abide,
  Or life is vain.

4 I need thee every hour;
  Teach me thy will;
  And thy rich promises
  In me fulfill.

5 I need thee every hour,
  Most Holy One;
  O make me thine indeed,
  Thou blessèd Son!

ANNIE S. HAWKS

507 HENDON 7s.

A. H. C. MALAN.

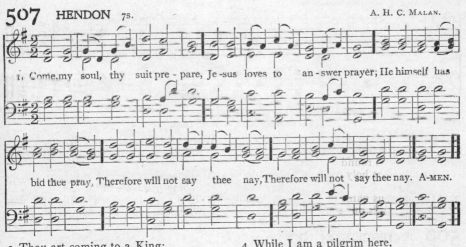

1. Come, my soul, thy suit pre - pare, Je - sus loves to an - swer prayer; He himself has

bid thee pray, Therefore will not say thee nay, Therefore will not say thee nay. A - MEN.

2 Thou art coming to a King;
  Large petitions with thee bring;
  For his grace and power are such,
  None can ever ask too much.

3 Lord, I come to thee for rest;
  Take possession of my breast;
  There thy blood-bought right maintain,
  And without a rival reign.

4 While I am a pilgrim here,
  Let thy love my spirit cheer;
  As my guide, my guard, my friend,
  Lead me to my journey's end.

5 Show me what I have to do;
  Every hour my strength renew;
  Let me live a life of faith,
  Let me die thy people's death.

JOHN NEWTON

The Christian Life

508 PRECIOUS NAME 8s. 7s. *With Refrain*

WILLIAM H. DOANE

1. Take the name of Je-sus with you, Child of sor-row and of woe;
It will joy and com-fort give you; Take it, then, wher-e'er you go.

REFRAIN

Pre-cious name, O how sweet! Hope of earth and joy of heaven;
Pre-cious name, O how sweet!
Pre-cious name, O how sweet! Hope of earth and joy of heaven. A - MEN.
Pre-cious name, O how sweet, how sweet!

Copyright, 1899, by W. H. Doane

2 Take the name of Jesus ever,
  As a shield from every snare;
If temptations round you gather,
  Breathe that holy name in prayer.

3 O the precious name of Jesus!
  How it thrills our souls with joy,

When his loving arms receive us,
  And his songs our tongues employ!

4 At the name of Jesus bowing,
  Falling prostrate at his feet,
King of kings in heaven we'll crown him,
  When our journey is complete.

LYDIA BAXTER

509 INTERCESSION NEW P. M.

WILLIAM H. CALLCOTT

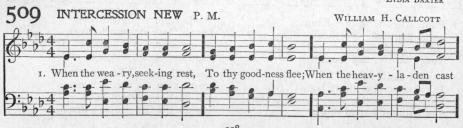

1. When the wea-ry, seek-ing rest, To thy good-ness flee; When the heav-y - la-den cast

Watchfulness and Prayer

All their load on thee; When the troubled, seek-ing peace, On thy name shall call;

When the sin-ner, seek-ing life, At thy feet shall fall: . . . Hear then in

love, O Lord, the cry In heaven, thy dwell-ing place on high. A - MEN.

*From Mendelssohn

2 When the worldling, sick at heart,
　Lifts his soul above;
When the prodigal looks back
　To his Father's love;
When the proud man, in his pride,
　Stoops to seek thy face;
When the burdened brings his guilt
　To thy throne of grace:
Hear then in love, O Lord, the cry
In heaven, thy dwelling place on high.

3 When the stranger asks a home,
　All his toils to end;
When the hungry craveth food,
　And the poor a friend;
When the sailor on the wave
　Bows the fervent knee;
When the soldier on the field
　Lifts his heart to thee:
Hear then in love, O Lord, the cry
In heaven, thy dwelling place on high.

4 When the man of toil and care
　In the city crowd;
When the shepherd on the moor
　Names the name of God:
When the learnèd and the high,
　Tired of earthly fame,
Upon higher joys intent,
　Name the blessèd name:
Hear then in love, O Lord, the cry
In heaven, thy dwelling place on high.

5 When the child, with grave fresh lip,
　Youth or maiden fair;
When the aged, weak and gray,
　Seek thy face in prayer;
When the widow weeps to thee,
　Sad and lone and low;
When the orphan brings to thee
　All his orphan-woe;
Hear then in love, O Lord, the cry
In heaven, thy dwelling place on high.

HORATIUS BONAR

510 VINCENT 8s. 4s. D.

HORATIO R. PALMER

1. Lord, for to-mor-row and its needs I do not pray; Keep me, my God, from stain of sin Just for to-day. Help me to la-bor ear-nest-ly, And du-ly pray; Let me be kind in word and deed, Fa-ther, to-day. A-MEN.

Copyright, 1887, by H. R. Palmer

2 Let me no wrong or idle word
Unthinking say;
Set thou a seal upon my lips
Through all to-day.
Let me in season, Lord, be grave,
In season gay;
Let me be faithful to thy grace,
Dear Lord, to-day.

3 And if, to-day, this life of mine
Should ebb away,
Give me thy sacrament divine,
Father, to-day.
So for to-morrow and its needs
I do not pray;
Still keep me, guide me, love me, Lord,
Through each to-day.

ERNEST R. WILBERFORCE

511 ST. CATHERINE L. M. 6l.

Adapted by J. G. WALTON

1. Come, O thou Trav-el-er un-known, Whom still I hold, but can-not see; My com-pa-ny be-fore is gone, And I am left a-lone with thee:

Watchfulness and Prayer

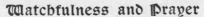

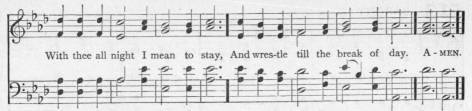

With thee all night I mean to stay, And wres-tle till the break of day. A - MEN.

2 I need not tell thee who I am,
My sin and misery declare;
Thyself hast called me by my name,
Look on thy hands, and read it there:
But who, I ask thee, who art thou?
Tell me thy name, and tell me now.

3 In vain thou strugglest to get free,
I never will unloose my hold:
Art thou the Man that died for me?
The secret of thy love unfold:
Wrestling, I will not let thee go,
Till I thy name, thy nature know.

4 Wilt thou not yet to me reveal
Thy new, unutterable name?
Tell me, I still beseech thee, tell;
To know it now resolved I am:
Wrestling, I will not let thee go,
Till I thy name, thy nature know.

5 Yield to me now, for I am weak,
But confident in self-despair;
Speak to my heart, in blessing speak,
Be conquered by my instant prayer:
Speak, or thou never hence shalt move,
And tell me if thy name be Love.

6 'Tis Love! 'tis Love! thou diedst for me!
I hear thy whisper in my heart;
The morning breaks, the shadows flee;
Pure, universal love thou art:
To me, to all, thy mercies move;
Thy nature and thy name is Love.

7 I know thee, Saviour, who thou art,
Jesus, the feeble sinner's Friend;
Nor wilt thou with the night depart,
But stay and love me to the end:
Thy mercies never shall remove;
Thy nature and thy name is Love.

CHARLES WESLEY

512 SHIRLAND S. M.

SAMUEL STANLEY

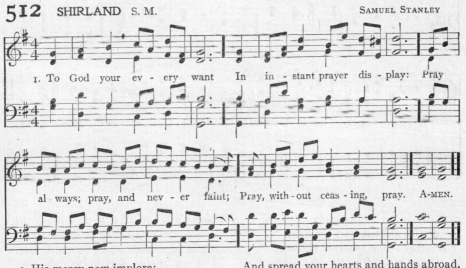

1. To God your ev - er - y want In in - stant prayer dis - play: Pray al - ways; pray, and nev - er faint; Pray, with - out ceas - ing, pray. A-MEN.

2 His mercy now implore;
And now show forth his praise;
In shouts, or silent awe, adore
His miracles of grace.

3 Pour out your souls to God,
And bow them with your knees;
And spread your hearts and hands abroad,
And pray for Zion's peace.

4 Your guides and brethren bear
Forever on your mind;
Extend the arms of mighty prayer
In grasping all mankind.

CHARLES WESLEY

513 BARONY 8s. 7s. D.

ARTHUR S. SULLIVAN

1. Cour-age, broth-er! do not stum-ble, Though thy path be dark as night;

There's a star to guide the hum - ble, Trust in God, and do the right.

Though the road be long and drear-y, And the end be out of sight, Tread it brave-ly,

strong or wea - ry, Trust in God, trust in God, trust in God, and do the right. A - MEN.

2 Perish policy and cunning,
  Perish all that fears the light,
Whether losing, whether winning,
  Trust in God, and do the right.
Shun all forms of guilty passion,
  Fiends can look like angels bright;
Heed no custom, school, or fashion,
  Trust in God, and do the right.

3 Some will hate thee, some will love thee,
  Some will flatter, some will slight;
Cease from man, and look above thee,
  Trust in God, and do the right.
Simple rule and safest guiding,
  Inward peace and shining light,
Star upon our path abiding,
  Trust in God, and do the right.

NORMAN MACLEOD

Watchfulness and Prayer

514 SEYMOUR 7s.

CARL M. VON WEBER

1. Lord, I can-not let thee go, Till a bless-ing thou be-stow:
Do not turn a-way thy face, Mine's an ur-gent, press-ing case. A-MEN.

2 Dost thou ask me who I am?
Ah! my Lord, thou know'st my name;
Yet the question gives a plea
To support my suit with thee.

3 Thou didst once a wretch behold,
In rebellion blindly bold,
Scorn thy grace, thy power defy:
That poor rebel, Lord, was I.

4 Once a sinner, near despair,
Sought thy mercy seat by prayer;
Mercy heard, and set him free:
Lord, that mercy came to me.

5 Many days have passed since then,
Many changes I have seen;
Yet have been upheld till now;
Who could hold me up but thou?

6 Thou hast helped in every need;
This emboldens me to plead:
After so much mercy past,
Canst thou let me sink at last?

7 No; I must maintain my hold;
'Tis thy goodness makes me bold;
I can no denial take,
When I plead for Jesus' sake.

JOHN NEWTON

515 EVELYN 7s.

EMMA L. ASHFORD

1. They who seek the throne of grace, Find that throne in ev-ery place;
If we live a life of prayer, God is pres-ent ev-ery-where. A-MEN.

Copyright, 1905, by Jennings & Graham

2 In our sickness or our health,
In our want or in our wealth,
If we look to God in prayer,
God is present everywhere.

3 When our earthly comforts fail,
When the foes of life prevail,

'Tis the time for earnest prayer;
God is present everywhere.

4 Then, my soul, in every strait
To thy Father come and wait;
He will answer every prayer;
God is present everywhere.

OLIVER HOLDEN. Alt.

516 SWEET HOUR OF PRAYER 8s. D.

WILLIAM B. BRADBURY

1. Sweet hour of prayer, sweet hour of prayer, That calls me from a world of care,

And bids me, at my Fa-ther's throne, Make all my wants and wish-es known!

In sea-sons of dis-tress and grief, My soul has oft-en found re-lief,

And oft es-caped the tempt-er's snare, By thy re-turn, sweet hour of prayer. A-MEN.

2 Sweet hour of prayer, sweet hour of prayer,
Thy wings shall my petition bear
To Him, whose truth and faithfulness
Engage the waiting soul to bless:
And since he bids me seek his face,
Believe his word, and trust his grace,
I'll cast on him my every care,
And wait for thee, sweet hour of prayer.

3 Sweet hour of prayer, sweet hour of
May I thy consolation share,   [prayer,
Till, from Mount Pisgah's lofty height,
I view my home, and take my flight:
This robe of flesh I'll drop, and rise,
To seize the everlasting prize;
And shout, while passing through the air,
Farewell, farewell, sweet hour of prayer!

WILLIAM W. WALFORD

Resignation and Consolation

517 SIMPSON C. M.

From LOUIS SPOHR

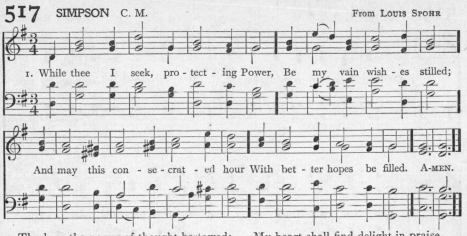

1. While thee I seek, pro-tect-ing Power, Be my vain wish-es stilled;
And may this con-se-crat-ed hour With bet-ter hopes be filled. A-MEN.

2 Thy love the power of thought bestowed;
  To thee my thoughts would soar:
Thy mercy o'er my life has flowed;
  That mercy I adore.

3 In each event of life, how clear
  Thy ruling hand I see!
Each blessing to my soul more dear,
  Because conferred by thee.

4 In every joy that crowns my days,
  In every pain I bear,

My heart shall find delight in praise,
  Or seek relief in prayer.

5 When gladness wings my favored hour,
  Thy love my thoughts shall fill;
Resigned, when storms of sorrow lower,
  My soul shall meet thy will.

6 My lifted eye, without a tear,
  The gathering storm shall see:
My steadfast heart shall know no fear;
  That heart will rest on thee.

HELEN M. WILLIAMS

518 ALSACE L. M.

From LUDWIG VAN BEETHOVEN

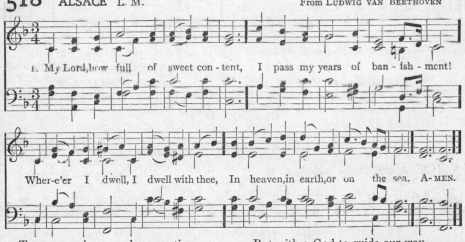

1. My Lord, how full of sweet con-tent, I pass my years of ban-ish-ment!
Wher-e'er I dwell, I dwell with thee, In heaven, in earth, or on the sea. A-MEN.

2 To me remains nor place nor time;
My country is in every clime:
I can be calm and free from care
On any shore, since God is there.

3 While place we seek, or place we shun
The soul finds happiness in none;

But with a God to guide our way,
'Tis equal joy, to go or stay.

4 Could I be cast where thou art not,
That were indeed a dreadful lot;
But regions none remote I call,
Secure of finding God in all.

Madame GUYON. Tr. by WILLIAM COWPER

519 MERIBAH 8. 8. 6. D.

LOWELL MASON

1. O Lord! how hap-py should we be, If we could leave our cares to thee,

If we from self could rest; And feel at heart that one a-bove,

In per-fect wis-dom, per-fect love, Is work-ing for the best. A-MEN.

2 For when we kneel and cast our care
  Upon our God in humble prayer,
    With strengthened souls we rise,
  Sure that our Father who is nigh,
  To hear the ravens when they cry,
    Will hear his children's cries.

3 O may these anxious hearts of ours
  The lesson learn from birds and flowers,
    And learn from self to cease,
  Leave all things to our Father's will,
  And in his mercy trusting still,
    Find in each trial peace!

JOSEPH ANSTICE

520 ASCENDING SONG C. M.

ALFRED G. WATHALL

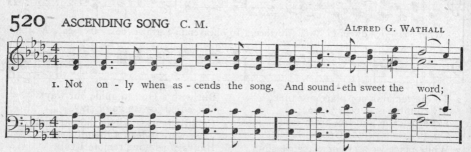

1. Not on-ly when as-cends the song, And sound-eth sweet the word;

Resignation and Consolation

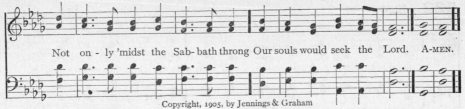

Not on-ly 'midst the Sab-bath throng Our souls would seek the Lord. A-MEN.

2 We mingle with another throng,
And other words we speak;
To other business we belong,
But still our Lord we seek.

3 We would not to our daily task
Without our God repair;
But in the world thy presence ask,
And seek thy glory there.

4 Would we against some wrong be bold,
And break some yoke abhorred?

Amidst the strife and stir behold
The seekers of the Lord!

5 When on thy glorious works we gaze,
There thee we fain would see;
Our gladness in their beauty raise,
O God, to joy in thee!

6 O everywhere, O every day,
Thy grace is still outpoured;
We work, we watch, we strive, we pray;
Behold thy seekers, Lord!

THOMAS H. GILL

521 HANFORD 8, 8, 8. 4.   ARTHUR S. SULLIVAN

1 My God, my Fa-ther, while I stray Far from my home, on life's rough way,
O teach me from my heart to say, "Thy will be done!" A-MEN.

2 Though dark my path, and sad my lot,
Let me be still and murmur not,
Or breathe the prayer divinely taught,
"Thy will be done!"

3 What though in lonely grief I sigh
For friends beloved no longer nigh:
Submissive still would I reply,
"Thy will be done!"

4 If thou shouldst call me to resign
What most I prize, — it ne'er was mine:
I only yield thee what is thine;
"Thy will be done!"

5 Let but my fainting heart be blest
With thy sweet Spirit for its guest,
My God, to thee I leave the rest;
"Thy will be done!"

6 Renew my will from day to day;
Blend it with thine, and take away
All that now makes it hard to say,
"Thy will be done!"

7 Then, when on earth I breathe no more
The prayer oft mixed with tears before,
I'll sing upon a happier shore,
"Thy will be done!"

CHARLOTTE ELLIOTT

The Christian Life

522 ELM C. M.

J. VARLEY ROBERTS

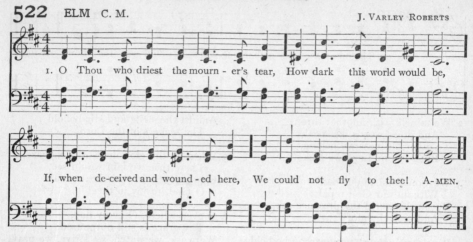

1. O Thou who driest the mourn - er's tear, How dark this world would be,

If, when de-ceived and wound - ed here, We could not fly to thee! A-MEN.

2 The friends who in our sunshine live,
  When winter comes are flown;
And he who has but tears to give,
  Must weep those tears alone.

3 But thou wilt heal that broken heart,
  Which, like the plants that throw
Their fragrance from the wounded part,
  Breathes sweetness out of woe.

4 When joy no longer soothes or cheers,
  And e'en the hope that threw

A moment's sparkle o'er our tears,
  Is dimmed and vanished too, —

5 O who could bear life's stormy doom,
  Did not thy wing of love
Come brightly wafting through the gloom
  Our peace-branch from above?

6 Then sorrow, touched by thee, grows
  With more than rapture's ray; [bright,
As darkness shows us worlds of light
  We never saw by day.

THOMAS MOORE

523 NAOMI C. M.

HANS G. NAEGELI

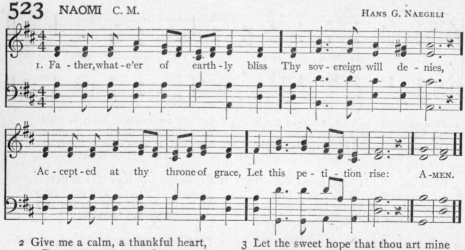

1. Fa - ther, what - e'er of earth - ly bliss Thy sov - ereign will de - nies,

Ac - cept - ed at thy throne of grace, Let this pe - ti - tion rise: A-MEN.

2 Give me a calm, a thankful heart,
  From every murmur free;
The blessings of thy grace impart,
  And make me live to thee.

3 Let the sweet hope that thou art mine
  My life and death attend;
Thy presence through my journey shine,
  And crown my journey's end.

ANNE STEELE

368

524 JEWETT 6s. D. From CARL M. VON WEBER

1. My Je - sus, as thou wilt: O may thy will be mine!

In - to thy hand of love I would my all re - sign.

Through sor - row or through joy, Con - duct me as thine own,

And help me still to say, "My Lord, thy will be done." A - MEN.

2 My Jesus, as thou wilt:
    If needy here and poor,
  Give me thy people's bread,
    Their portion rich and sure:
  The manna of thy Word
    Let my soul feed upon;
  And if all else should fail,
    My Lord, thy will be done.

3 My Jesus, as thou wilt:
    Though seen through many a tear,
  Let not my star of hope
    Grow dim or disappear.

Since thou on earth hast wept
    And sorrowed oft alone,
  If I must weep with thee,
    My Lord, thy will be done.

4 My Jesus, as thou wilt:
    All shall be well for me;
  Each changing future scene
    I gladly trust with thee.
  Straight to my home above,
    I travel calmly on,
  And sing in life or death,
    "My Lord, thy will be done."

BENJAMIN SCHMOLKE. Tr. by JANE BORTHWICK

369

525 RHODES S. M.

CHARLES W. JORDAN

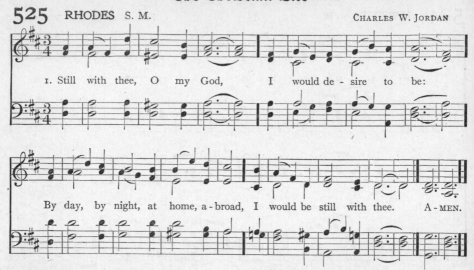

1. Still with thee, O my God, I would de - sire to be:

By day, by night, at home, a - broad, I would be still with thee. A - MEN.

2 With thee when dawn comes in
  And calls me back to care,
Each day returning to begin
  With thee, my God, in prayer.

3 With thee amid the crowd
  That throngs the busy mart,
To hear thy voice, when time's is loud,
  Speak softly to my heart.

4 With thee when day is done,
  And evening calms the mind;

The setting as the rising sun
  With thee my heart would find.

5 With thee when darkness brings
  The signal of repose,
Calm in the shadow of thy wings,
  Mine eyelids I would close.

6 With thee, in thee, by faith
  Abiding, I would be;
By day, by night, in life, in death,
  I would be still with thee.

JAMES D. BURNS

526 COME, YE DISCONSOLATE 11S. 10S.

SAMUEL WEBBE

1. Come, ye dis - con - so - late, wher-e'er ye lan - guish; Come to the

mer - cy seat, fer - vent - ly kneel; Here bring your wound - ed hearts,

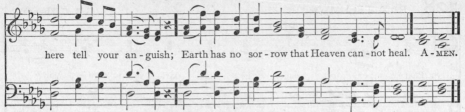

here tell your an-guish; Earth has no sor-row that Heaven can-not heal. A - MEN.

2 Joy of the desolate, light of the straying,
  Hope of the penitent, fadeless and pure,
  Here speaks the Comforter, tenderly saying,
  "Earth has no sorrow that Heaven cannot cure."

3 Here see the bread of life; see waters flowing
  Forth from the throne of God, pure from above;
  Come to the feast of love; come, ever knowing
  Earth has no sorrow but Heaven can remove.

THOMAS MOORE and THOMAS HASTINGS

527 **BLESSED HOME** 6s. D.   JOHN STAINER

1. Thy way, not mine, O Lord, How-ev-er dark it be! Lead me by thine own hand;

Choose thou the path for me. I dare not choose my lot; I would not if I might;

Choose thou for me, my God, So shall I walk a-right. A - MEN.

2 The kingdom that I seek
  Is thine; so let the way
  That leads to it be thine,
  Else I must surely stray.
  Take thou my cup, and it
  With joy or sorrow fill,
  As best to thee may seem;
  Choose thou my good and ill.

3 Choose thou for me my friends,
  My sickness or my health;
  Choose thou my cares for me,
  My poverty or wealth.
  Not mine, not mine the choice,
  In things or great or small;
  Be thou my guide, my strength,
  My wisdom, and my all.

HORATIUS BONAR

528 PAX TECUM 10s.

G. T. CALDBECK

1. Peace, per - fect peace, in this dark world of sin?
The blood of Je - sus whis - pers peace with - in. A-MEN.

2 Peace, perfect peace, by thronging duties pressed?
To do the will of Jesus, — this is rest.

3 Peace, perfect peace, with sorrows surging round?
On Jesus' bosom naught but calm is found.

4 Peace, perfect peace, with loved ones far away?
In Jesus' keeping we are safe, and they.

5 Peace, perfect peace, our future all unknown?
Jesus we know, and he is on the throne.

6 Peace, perfect peace, death shadowing us and ours?
Jesus has vanquished death and all its powers.

7 It is enough: earth's struggles soon shall cease,
And Jesus call us to heaven's perfect peace.

EDWARD H. BICKERSTETH

529 LUNDIE 6. 4. 6. 4. 6. 6. 6. 4.

THEODORE E. PERKINS

1. Fade, fade, each earth - ly joy; Je - sus is mine. Break ev - ery

ten - der tie; Je - sus is mine. Dark is the wil - der - ness,

Peace, Joy, and Praise

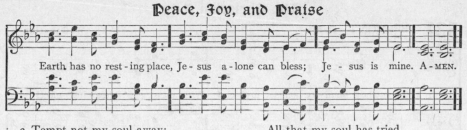

Earth has no rest-ing place, Je-sus a-lone can bless; Je-sus is mine. A-MEN.

2 Tempt not my soul away;
   Jesus is mine.
   Here would I ever stay;
   Jesus is mine.
   Perishing things of clay,
   Born but for one brief day,
   Pass from my heart away;
   Jesus is mine.

3 Farewell, ye dreams of night;
   Jesus is mine.
   Lost in this dawning bright,
   Jesus is mine.

All that my soul has tried
Left but a dismal void;
Jesus has satisfied;
Jesus is mine.

4 Farewell, mortality;
   Jesus is mine.
   Welcome, eternity;
   Jesus is mine.
   Welcome, O loved and blest,
   Welcome, sweet scenes of rest,
   Welcome, my Saviour's breast;
   Jesus is mine.

JANE C. BONAR

530 MEDITATION 11s. 8s.

FREEMAN LEWIS. Arr. by HUBERT P. MAIN

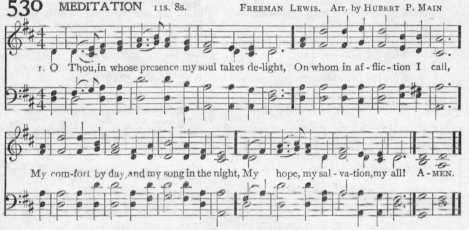

1. O Thou, in whose presence my soul takes de-light, On whom in af-flic-tion I call,

My com-fort by day, and my song in the night, My hope, my sal-va-tion, my all! A-MEN.

2 Where dost thou, dear Shepherd, resort with thy sheep,
   To feed them in pastures of love?
   Say, why in the valley of death should I weep,
   Or alone in this wilderness rove?

3 O why should I wander an alien from thee,
   Or cry in the desert for bread?
   Thy foes will rejoice when my sorrows they see,
   And smile at the tears I have shed.

4 Restore, my dear Saviour, the light of thy face;
   Thy soul-cheering comfort impart;
   And let the sweet tokens of pardoning grace
   Bring joy to my desolate heart.

5 He looks! and ten thousands of angels rejoice,
   And myriads wait for his word;
   He speaks! and eternity, filled with his voice,
   Re-echoes the praise of the Lord.

JOSEPH SWAIN

The Christian Life

531 BELMONT C. M.

W. GARBLINE

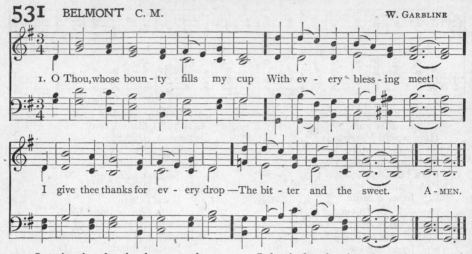

1. O Thou, whose boun-ty fills my cup With ev - ery bless - ing meet!
I give thee thanks for ev - ery drop —The bit - ter and the sweet. A - MEN.

2 I praise thee for the desert road,
   And for the riverside;
   For all thy goodness hath bestowed,
   And all thy grace denied.

3 I thank thee for both smile and frown,
   And for the gain and loss;
   I praise thee for the future crown,
   And for the present cross.

4 I thank thee for the wing of love,
   Which stirred my worldly nest;
   And for the stormy clouds which drove
   Me, trembling, to thy breast.

5 I bless thee for the glad increase,
   And for the waning joy;
   And for this strange, this settled peace,
   Which nothing can destroy.

JANE CREWDSON

532 EMMONS C. M.

Arr. from FRIEDRICH BURGMÜLLER

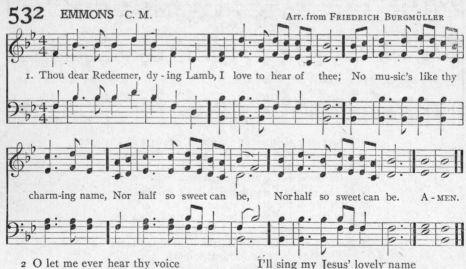

1. Thou dear Redeemer, dy - ing Lamb, I love to hear of thee; No mu-sic's like thy charm-ing name, Nor half so sweet can be, Nor half so sweet can be. A - MEN.

2 O let me ever hear thy voice
   In mercy to me speak!
   In thee, my Priest, will I rejoice,
   And thy salvation seek.

3 My Jesus shall be still my theme,
   While in this world I stay;

I'll sing my Jesus' lovely name
   When all things else decay.

4 When I appear in yonder cloud,
   With all thy favored throng,
   Then will I sing more sweet, more loud,
   And Christ shall be my song.

JOHN CENNICK

Peace, Joy, and Praise

533   SAWLEY C. M.   JAMES WALCH

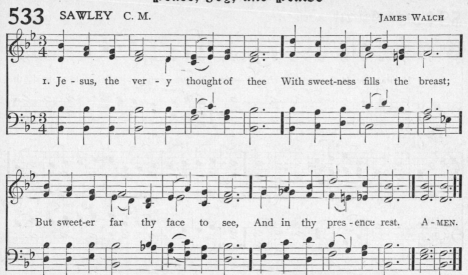

1. Je - sus, the ver - y thought of thee With sweet-ness fills the breast;

But sweet-er far thy face to see, And in thy pres - ence rest. A - MEN.

2 Nor voice can sing, nor heart can frame,
   Nor can the memory find
A sweeter sound than thy blest name,
   O Saviour of mankind!

3 O Hope of every contrite heart,
   O Joy of all the meek,
To those who ask, how kind thou art!
   How good to those who seek!

4 But what to those who find? Ah, this
   Nor tongue nor pen can show:
The love of Jesus, what it is,
   None but his loved ones know.

5 Jesus, our only joy be thou,
   As thou our prize wilt be;
In thee be all our glory now,
   And through eternity.

BERNARD of Clairvaux. Tr. by EDWARD CASWALL

533   HOLY CROSS C. M. *(Second Tune)*   Arranged by JAMES C. WADE

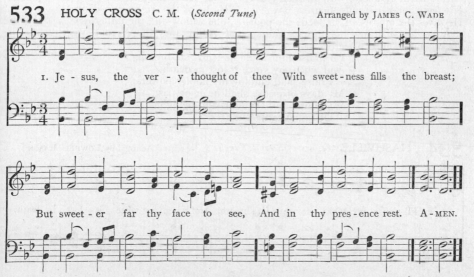

1. Je - sus, the ver - y thought of thee With sweet - ness fills the breast;

But sweet - er far thy face to see, And in thy pres - ence rest. A - MEN.

The Christian Life

534 MONMOUTH 8s. 6l.

G. DAVIS

1. I'll praise my Mak-er while I've breath, And when my voice is lost in death,

Praise shall em - ploy my no-bler powers; My days of praise shall ne'er be past,

While life, and thought, and be - ing last, Or im - mor-tal - i - ty en-dures. A-MEN.

2 Happy the man whose hopes rely
On Israel's God; he made the sky,
   And earth and seas, with all their train;
His truth forever stands secure;
He saves the oppressed, he feeds the poor,
   And none shall find his promise vain.

3 The Lord pours eyesight on the blind;
The Lord supports the fainting mind;
   He sends the laboring conscience peace;
He helps the stranger in distress,
The widow and the fatherless,
   And grants the prisoner sweet release.

4 I'll praise him while he lends me breath,
   And when my voice is lost in death,
      Praise shall employ my nobler powers;
   My days of praise shall ne'er be past,
   While life, and thought, and being last,
      Or immortality endures.

ISAAC WATTS

534 NASHVILLE 8s. 6l. (*Second Tune*)

Adapted by LOWELL MASON

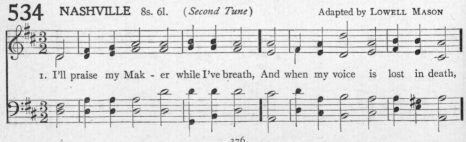

1. I'll praise my Mak - er while I've breath, And when my voice is lost in death,

Peace, Joy, and Praise

Praise shall em - ploy my no - bler powers; My days of praise shall ne'er be past,

While life, and thought, and be - ing last, Or im - mor - tal - i - ty en - dures. A - MEN.

535 CHESTERFIELD C. M.

THOMAS HAWEIS

1. My God, the spring of all my joys, The life of my de - lights, The

glo - ry of my bright - est days, And com - fort of my nights! A - MEN.

2 In darkest shades, if thou appear,
    My dawning is begun;
  Thou art my soul's bright morning-star,
    And thou my rising sun.

3 The opening heavens around me shine
    With beams of sacred bliss,
  If Jesus shows his mercy mine,
    And whispers I am his.

4 My soul would leave this heavy clay
    At that transporting word,
  Run up with joy the shining way,
    To see and praise my Lord.

5 Fearless of hell and ghastly death,
    I'd break through every foe;
  The wings of love and arms of faith
    Would bear me conqueror through.

ISAAC WATTS

377

The Christian Life

536 WESTCOTT L. M.

JOSEPH BARNBY

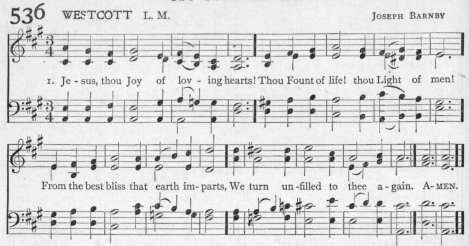

1. Je - sus, thou Joy of lov - ing hearts! Thou Fount of life! thou Light of men! From the best bliss that earth im- parts, We turn un -filled to thee a - gain. A - MEN.

2 Thy truth unchanged hath ever stood;
  Thou savest those that on thee call;
To them that seek thee, thou art good,
  To them that find thee, all in all.

3 We taste thee, O thou Living Bread,
  And long to feast upon thee still;
We drink of thee, the Fountain Head,
  And thirst our souls from thee to fill!

4 Our restless spirits yearn for thee,
  Where'er our changeful lot is cast;
Glad, when thy gracious smile we see,
  Blest, when our faith can hold thee fast.

5 O Jesus, ever with us stay;
  Make all our moments calm and bright;
Chase the dark night of sin away,
  Shed o'er the world thy holy light!

BERNARD of Clairvaux. Tr. by RAY PALMER

537 RADIANCE C. M.

JOSEPH SMITH

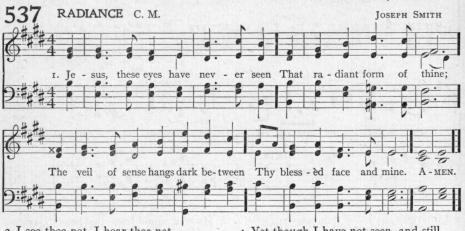

1. Je - sus, these eyes have nev - er seen That ra - diant form of thine; The veil of sense hangs dark be - tween Thy bless - èd face and mine. A - MEN.

2 I see thee not, I hear thee not,
  Yet art thou oft with me;
And earth hath ne'er so dear a spot
  As where I meet with thee.

3 Like some bright dream that comes un-
  When slumbers o'er me roll,   [sought
Thine image ever fills my thought,
  And charms my ravished soul.

4 Yet though I have not seen, and still
  Must rest in faith alone,
I love thee, dearest Lord, and will,
  Unseen, but not unknown.

5 When death these mortal eyes shall seal,
  And still this throbbing heart,
The rending veil shall thee reveal,
  All-glorious as thou art.

RAY PALMER

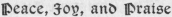

Peace, Joy, and Praise

538 CONTRAST 8s. D.

German

1. How te-dious and taste-less the hours When Je-sus no lon-ger I see;

Sweet pros-pects, sweet birds, and sweet flowers, Have all lost their sweetness to me;

The mid-sum-mer sun shines but dim, The fields strive in vain to look gay,

But when I am hap-py in him, De-cem-ber's as pleas-ant as May. A-MEN.

2 His name yields the richest perfume,
And sweeter than music his voice;
His presence disperses my gloom,
And makes all within me rejoice;
I should, were he always thus nigh,
Have nothing to wish or to fear;
No mortal so happy as I,
My summer would last all the year.

3 Content with beholding his face,
My all to his pleasure resigned,
No changes of season or place
Would make any change in my mind:

While blest with a sense of his love,
A palace a toy would appear,
And prisons would palaces prove,
If Jesus would dwell with me there.

4 Dear Lord, if indeed I am thine,
If thou art my sun and my song,
Say, why do I languish and pine?
And why are my winters so long?
O drive these dark clouds from my sky,
Thy soul-cheering presence restore;
Or take me to thee up on high,
Where winter and clouds are no more.

JOHN NEWTON

The Christian Life

539 ALL SAINTS L. M.

WILLIAM KNAPP

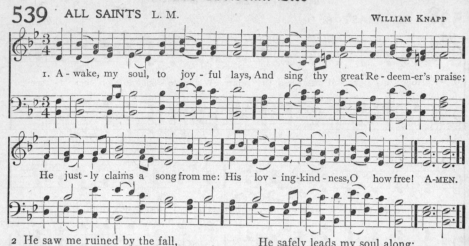

1. A - wake, my soul, to joy - ful lays, And sing thy great Re - deem-er's praise;
He just - ly claims a song from me: His lov - ing-kind - ness, O how free! A-MEN.

2 He saw me ruined by the fall,
Yet loved me, notwithstanding all;
He saved me from my lost estate:
His loving-kindness, O how great!

3 Though numerous hosts of mighty foes,
Though earth and hell my way oppose,

He safely leads my soul along:
His loving-kindness, O how strong!

4 When trouble, like a gloomy cloud,
Has gathered thick and thundered loud,
He near my soul has always stood:
His loving-kindness, O how good!

SAMUEL MEDLEY

539 LOVING-KINDNESS L. M. (*Second Tune*)

WILLIAM CALDWELL

1. A - wake, my soul, to joy - ful lays, And sing thy great Re-deem-er's praise;
He just - ly claims a song from me: His lov - ing-kind-ness, O how free!
Lov - ing-kind-ness, lov - ing-kind-ness, His lov - ing-kind- ness, O how free! A-MEN.

540 ARIEL 8. 8. 6. D.

Arr. by LOWELL MASON

1. O could I speak the match-less worth, O could I sound the glo-ries forth, Which in my Sav-iour shine, I'd soar and touch the heavenly strings, And vie with Ga-briel while he sings In notes al-most di-vine, In notes al-most di-vine. A-MEN.

2 I'd sing the precious blood he spilt,
My ransom from the dreadful guilt
Of sin, and wrath divine;
I'd sing his glorious righteousness,
In which all-perfect, heavenly dress
My soul shall ever shine.

3 I'd sing the characters he bears,
And all the forms of love he wears,
Exalted on his throne;
In loftiest songs of sweetest praise,
I would to everlasting days
Make all his glories known.

4 Well, the delightful day will come
When my dear Lord will bring me home,
And I shall see his face;
Then with my Saviour, Brother, Friend,
A blest eternity I'll spend,
Triumphant in his grace.

SAMUEL MEDLEY

541 PATER OMNIUM L. M. 6l. H. J. E. HOLMES

1. Of all the thoughts of God that are Borne in-ward in - to souls a - far,

A - long the psalm - ist's mu - sic deep, Now tell me if that a - ny is,

For gift or grace sur-pass - ing this: "He giv - eth his be - lov - èd sleep"? A - MEN.

2 What would we give to our beloved,—
The hero's heart to be unmoved,
  The poet's star-tuned harp, to sweep,
The patriot's voice, to teach and rouse,
The monarch's crown, to light the brows?
  He giveth his belovèd sleep.

3 "Sleep soft, beloved!" we sometimes say,
Who have no tune to charm away [creep;
  Sad dreams that through the eyelids
But never doleful dream again
Shall break the happy slumber when
  He giveth his belovèd sleep.

4 His dews drop mutely on the hill,
His cloud above it saileth still,
  Though on its slope men sow and reap;
More softly than the dew is shed,
Or cloud is floated overhead,
  He giveth his belovèd sleep.

ELIZABETH B. BROWNING

542 ORONO 10s. 4s. KARL P. HARRINGTON

1. I do not ask, O Lord, that life may be A pleas - ant road;

Peace, Joy, and Praise

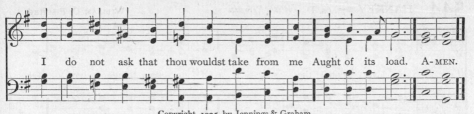

I do not ask that thou wouldst take from me Aught of its load. A-MEN.

2 I do not ask that flowers should always
Beneath my feet; [spring
I know too well the poison and the sting
Of things too sweet.

3 For one thing only, Lord, dear Lord, I
Lead me aright, [plead:
Though strength should falter and
though heart should bleed,
Through peace to light.

4 I do not ask, O Lord, that thou shouldst
Full radiance here; [shed
Give but a ray of peace, that I may tread
Without a fear.

5 I do not ask my cross to understand,
My way to see;
Better in darkness just to feel thy hand,
And follow thee.

6 Joy is like restless day; but peace divine
Like quiet night:
Lead me, O Lord, till perfect day shall shine,
Through peace to light.

ADELAIDE A. PROCTER

543 ELTON 8. 6. 8. 8. 6.

FREDERICK C. MAKER

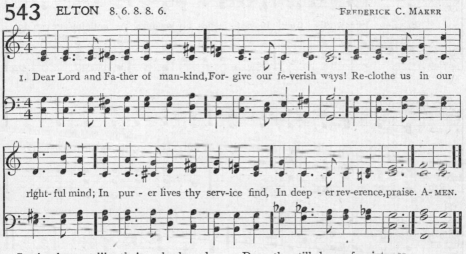

1. Dear Lord and Fa-ther of man-kind, For- give our fe-verish ways! Re-clothe us in our right-ful mind; In pur - er lives thy serv-ice find, In deep - er rev-erence, praise. A-MEN.

2 In simple trust like theirs who heard,
Beside the Syrian sea
The gracious calling of the Lord,
Let us, like them, without a word,
Rise up and follow thee.

3 O Sabbath rest by Galilee!
O calm of hills above,
Where Jesus knelt to share with thee
The silence of eternity,
Interpreted by love!

4 Drop thy still dews of quietness,
Till all our strivings cease;
Take from our souls the strain and stress,
And let our ordered lives confess
The beauty of thy peace.

5 Breathe through the heats of our desire
Thy coolness and thy balm;
Let sense be dumb, let flesh retire: [fire,
Speak through the earthquake, wind, and
O still small voice of calm!

JOHN G. WHITTIER

544 HANKEY 7s. 6s. D. *With Refrain*

WILLIAM G. FISCHER

1. I love to tell the sto - ry, Of un - seen things a - bove, Of

Je - sus and his glo - ry, Of Je - sus and his love. I love to tell the sto - ry,

Be-cause I know 'tis true; It sat - is -fies my longings, As noth-ing else can do.

REFRAIN

I love to tell the sto - ry, 'Twill be my theme in glo - ry,

To tell the old, old sto - ry Of Je - sus and his love. A -MEN.

2 I love to tell the story;
  More wonderful it seems
Than all the golden fancies
  Of all our golden dreams.

I love to tell the story,
  It did so much for me;
And that is just the reason
  I tell it now to thee.

3 I love to tell the story;
    'Tis pleasant to repeat
What seems, each time I tell it,
    More wonderfully sweet.
I love to tell the story;
    For some have never heard
The message of salvation
    From God's own holy word.

4 I love to tell the story;
    For those who know it best
Seem hungering and thirsting
    To hear it like the rest.
And when, in scenes of glory,
    I sing the new, new song,
'Twill be the old, old story
    That I have loved so long.

KATHERINE HANKEY

545 JUDE 8s. 7s.   WILLIAM H. JUDE

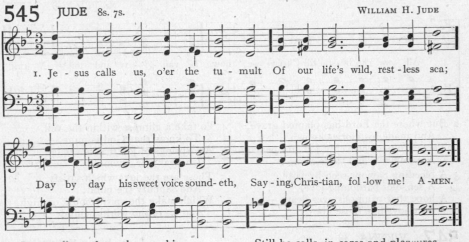

1. Je - sus calls us, o'er the tu - mult Of our life's wild, rest - less sea;

Day by day his sweet voice sound-eth, Say-ing, Chris-tian, fol -low me! A -MEN.

2 Jesus calls us from the worship
    Of the vain world's golden store;
From each idol that would keep us,
    Saying, Christian, love me more!

3 In our joys and in our sorrows,
    Days of toil and hours of ease,

Still he calls, in cares and pleasures,
    Christian, love me more than these!

4 Jesus calls us! by thy mercies,
    Saviour, may we hear thy call;
Give our hearts to thy obedience,
    Serve and love thee best of all!

CECIL F. ALEXANDER

545 WILMOT 8s. 7s. (*Second Tune*)   CARL M. VON WEBER

1. Je - sus calls us, o'er the tu - mult Of our life's wild, rest - less sea;

Day by day his sweet voice soundeth, Say-ing, Chris-tian, fol - low me! A - MEN.

546 ELIZABETHTOWN C. M.

GEORGE KINGSLEY

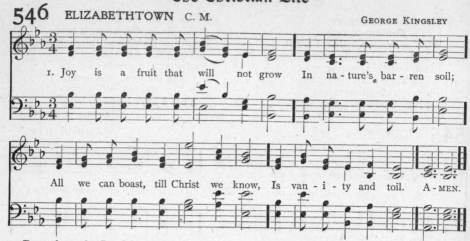

1. Joy is a fruit that will not grow In na-ture's bar-ren soil;

All we can boast, till Christ we know, Is van-i-ty and toil. A-MEN.

2 But where the Lord has planted grace,
And made his glories known,
There fruits of heavenly joy and peace
Are found — and there alone.

3 A bleeding Saviour seen by faith,
A sense of pardoning love,
A hope that triumphs over death —
Give joys like those above.

4 To take a glimpse within the veil,
To know that God is mine —
Are springs of joy that never fail,
Unspeakable, divine!

5 These are the joys which satisfy,
And sanctify the mind;
Which make the spirit mount on high,
And leave the world behind.

JOHN NEWTON

547 VIENNA 7s.

JUSTIN H. KNECHT

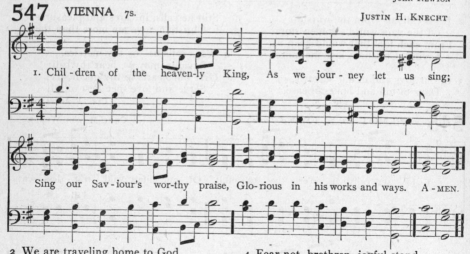

1. Chil-dren of the heaven-ly King, As we jour-ney let us sing;

Sing our Sav-iour's wor-thy praise, Glo-rious in his works and ways. A-MEN.

2 We are traveling home to God,
In the way our fathers trod;
They are happy now, and we
Soon their happiness shall see.

3 O ye banished seed, be glad;
Christ our Advocate is made:
Us to save our flesh assumes,
Brother to our souls becomes.

4 Fear not, brethren, joyful stand
On the borders of our land;
Jesus Christ, our Father's Son,
Bids us undismayed go on.

5 Lord, obediently we'll go,
Gladly leaving all below:
Only thou our Leader be,
And we still will follow thee.

JOHN CENNICK

Peace, Joy, and Praise

548 BLESSED ASSURANCE 9s. *With Refrain*   Mrs. Joseph F. Knapp

1. Bless-èd as-sur-ance, Je-sus is mine! O what a fore-taste of glo-ry di-vine! Heir of sal-va-tion, pur-chase of God, Born of his Spir-it, washed in his blood.

REFRAIN

This is my sto-ry, this is my song, Prais-ing my Sav-iour all the day long; This is my sto-ry, this is my song, Prais-ing my Sav-iour all the day long. A - MEN.

2 Perfect submission, perfect delight,
  Visions of rapture burst on my sight,
  Angels descending, bring from above,
  Echoes of mercy, whispers of love.

3 Perfect submission, all is at rest,
  I in my Saviour am happy and blest,
  Watching and waiting, looking above,
  Filled with his goodness, lost in his love.

  Fanny J. Crosby

549 WARATAH L. M.

MOSES S. CROSS

1. Je - sus, the calm that fills my breast, No oth - er heart than thine can give;

This peace unstirred, this joy of rest, None but thy loved ones can re - ceive. A-MEN.

Copyright, 1905, by Jennings & Graham

2 My weary soul has found a charm
That turns to blessedness my woe;
Within the shelter of thine arm,
I rest secure from storm and foe.

3 In desert wastes I feel no dread,
Fearless I walk the trackless sea;
I care not where my way is led,
Since all my life is life with thee.

4 O Christ, through changeless years my
My Comforter in sorrow's night,   [Guide,
My Friend, when friendless — still abide,
My Lord, my Counselor, my Light.

5 My time, my powers, I give to thee;
My inmost soul 'tis thine to move;
I wait for thy eternity,
I wait, in peace, in praise, in love.

F. MASON NORTH

550 ST. JOHN'S, WESTMINSTER C. M.

JAMES TURLE

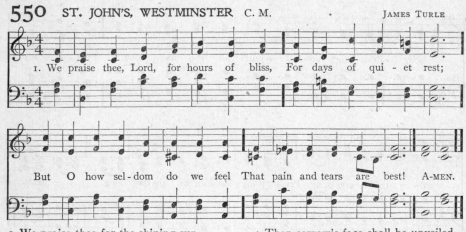

1. We praise thee, Lord, for hours of bliss, For days of qui - et rest;

But O how sel - dom do we feel That pain and tears are best! A-MEN.

2 We praise thee for the shining sun,
For kind and gladsome ways:
When shall we learn, O Lord, to sing
Through weary nights and days!

3 Teach thou our weak and wandering hearts
Aright to read thy way;
That thou with loving hand dost trace
Our path from day to day.

4 Then sorrow's face shall be unveiled,
And we at last shall see
Her eyes are eyes of tenderness,
Her speech but echoes thee!

5 Then every thorny crown of care
Worn well in patience now,
Shall prove a glorious diadem
Upon the faithful brow.

JOHN P. HOPPS

551 CONVERSE 8s. 7s. D.

CHARLES C. CONVERSE

1. What a Friend we have in Je - sus, All our sins and griefs to bear!

What a priv - i - lege to car - ry Ev - ery - thing to God in prayer!

O what peace we oft - en for - feit, O what need - less pain we bear,

All be - cause we do not car - ry Ev - ery - thing to God in prayer! A - MEN.

2 Have we trials and temptations?
　Is there trouble anywhere?
We should never be discouraged,
　Take it to the Lord in prayer.
Can we find a friend so faithful
　Who will all our sorrows share?
Jesus knows our every weakness,
　Take it to the Lord in prayer.

3 Are we weak and heavy laden,
　Cumbered with a load of care? —
Precious Saviour, still our refuge, —
　Take it to the Lord in prayer.
Do thy friends despise, forsake thee?
　Take it to the Lord in prayer;
In his arms he'll take and shield thee,
　Thou wilt find a solace there.

JOSEPH SCRIVEN

The Christian Life

552 CORNELL C. M.

JOHN H. CORNELL

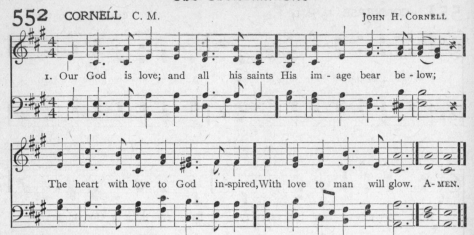

1. Our God is love; and all his saints His im-age bear be-low;
The heart with love to God in-spired, With love to man will glow. A-MEN.

2 Teach us to love each other, Lord,
As we are loved by thee;
None who are truly born of God
Can live in enmity.

3 Heirs of the same immortal bliss,
Our hopes and fears the same,

With bonds of love our hearts unite,
With mutual love inflame.

4 So may the unbelieving world
See how true Christians love;
And glorify our Saviour's grace,
And seek that grace to prove.

THOMAS COTTERILL

553 ARMENIA C. M.

SYLVANUS B. POND

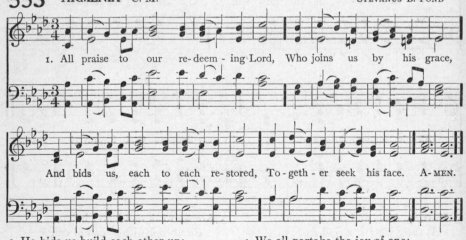

1. All praise to our re-deem-ing Lord, Who joins us by his grace,
And bids us, each to each re-stored, To-geth-er seek his face. A-MEN.

2 He bids us build each other up;
And, gathered into one,
To our high calling's glorious hope,
We hand in hand go on.

3 The gift which he on one bestows,
We all delight to prove;
The grace through every vessel flows,
In purest streams of love.

4 We all partake the joy of one;
The common peace we feel;
A peace to worldly minds unknown,
A joy unspeakable.

5 And if our fellowship below
In Jesus be so sweet,
What height of rapture shall we know
When round his throne we meet!

CHARLES WESLEY

Love and Fellowship

554 MOUNT CALVARY C. M.
ROBERT P. STEWART

1. How sweet, how heaven-ly is the sight, When those who love the Lord

In one an-oth-er's peace de-light, And so ful-fill his word! A-MEN.

2 When each can feel his brother's sigh,
And with him bear a part!
When sorrow flows from eye to eye,
And joy from heart to heart!

3 When, free from envy, scorn, and pride,
Our wishes all above,
Each can his brother's failings hide,
And show a brother's love!

4 Let love, in one delightful stream,
Through every bosom flow,
And union sweet, and dear esteem,
In every action glow.

5 Love is the golden chain that binds
The happy souls above;
And he's an heir of heaven who finds
His bosom glow with love.
JOSEPH SWAIN

555 BEATITUDO C. M.
JOHN B. DYKES

1. Try us, O God, and search the ground Of ev-ery sin-ful heart;

What-e'er of sin in us is found, O bid it all de-part! A-MEN.

2 When to the right or left we stray,
Leave us not comfortless;
But guide our feet into the way
Of everlasting peace.

3 Help us to help each other, Lord,
Each other's cross to bear;

Let each his friendly aid afford,
And feel his brother's care.

4 Help us to build each other up,
Our little stock improve;
Increase our faith, confirm our hope,
And perfect us in love.
CHARLES WESLEY

556 DENNIS S. M.

Hans G. Naegeli

1. Blest be the tie that binds Our hearts in Chris-tian love;
The fel - low-ship of kin - dred minds Is like to that a - bove. A-MEN.

2 Before our Father's throne,
  We pour our ardent prayers;
  Our fears, our hopes, our aims are one,
  Our comforts and our cares.

3 We share our mutual woes,
  Our mutual burdens bear;
  And often for each other flows
  The sympathizing tear.

4 When we asunder part,
  It gives us inward pain;

But we shall still be joined in heart,
  And hope to meet again.

5 This glorious hope revives
  Our courage by the way;
  While each in expectation lives,
  And longs to see the day.

6 From sorrow, toil, and pain,
  And sin we shall be free;
  And perfect love and friendship reign
  Through all eternity.

John Fawcett

557 MAITLAND C. M.

George N. Allen

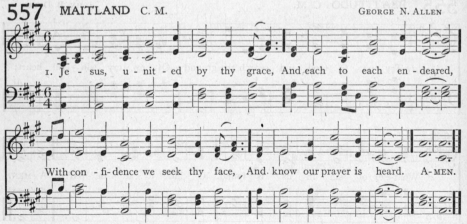

1. Je - sus, u - nit - ed by thy grace, And each to each en - deared,
With con - fi-dence we seek thy face, And know our prayer is heard. A-MEN.

2 Still let us own our common Lord,
  And bear thine easy yoke;
  A band of love, a threefold cord,
  Which never can be broke.

3 Make us into one spirit drink;
  Baptize into thy name;
  And let us always kindly think,
  And sweetly speak, the same.

4 Touched by the loadstone of thy love,
  Let all our hearts agree,
  And ever toward each other move,
  And ever move toward thee.

5 Yet when the fullest joy is given,
  The same delight we prove;
  In earth, in paradise, in heaven,
  Our all in all is love.

Charles Wesley

Love and Fellowship

558 HUMMEL C. M.

HEINRICH C. ZEUNER

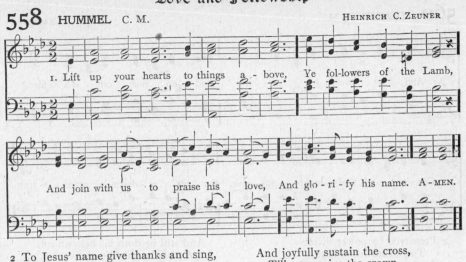

1. Lift up your hearts to things a - bove, Ye fol-lowers of the Lamb, And join with us to praise his love, And glo - ri - fy his name. A - MEN.

2 To Jesus' name give thanks and sing,
  Whose mercies never end:
Rejoice! rejoice! the Lord is King;
  The King is now our friend!

3 We for his sake count all things loss;
  On earthly good look down;

And joyfully sustain the cross,
  Till we receive the crown.

4 O let us stir each other up,
  Our faith by works to approve,
By holy, purifying hope,
  And the sweet task of love.

CHARLES WESLEY

559 SAMUEL 6. 6. 6. 6. 8. 8.

ARTHUR S. SULLIVAN

1. One sole bap - tis - mal sign, One Lord be - low, a - bove, One faith, one hope di - vine, One on - ly watch - word, love; From dif-ferent tem-ples though it rise, One song as-cend-eth to the skies. A - MEN.

2 Our Sacrifice is one;
  Our Priest before the throne,
  The slain, the risen Son,

Redeemer, Lord alone;
Thou who didst raise him from the dead,
Unite thy people in their Head.

GEORGE ROBINSON

560 DENNIS S. M.

HANS G. NAEGELI

1. And are we yet a - live, And see each oth - er's face?

Glo - ry and praise to Je - sus give, For his re - deem- ing grace. A- MEN.

2 Preserved by power divine
   To full salvation here,
   Again in Jesus' praise we join,
   And in his sight appear.

3 What troubles have we seen,
   What conflicts have we passed,
   Fightings without, and fears within,
   Since we assembled last!

4 But out of all the Lord
   Hath brought us by his love;

   And still he doth his help afford,
   And hides our life above.

5 Then let us make our boast
   Of his redeeming power,
   Which saves us to the uttermost,
   Till we can sin no more:

6 Let us take up the cross,
   Till we the crown obtain;
   And gladly reckon all things loss,
   So we may Jesus gain.

CHARLES WESLEY

561 LOUVAN L. M.

VIRGIL C. TAYLOR

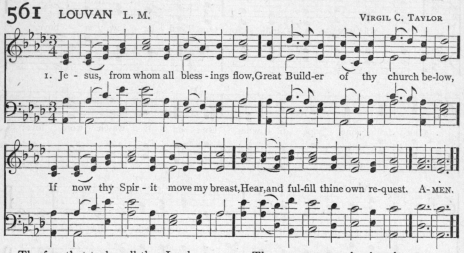

1. Je - sus, from whom all bless - ings flow, Great Build-er of thy church be-low,

If now thy Spir - it move my breast, Hear, and ful-fill thine own re-quest. A- MEN.

2 The few that truly call thee Lord,
   And wait thy sanctifying word,
   And thee their utmost Saviour own,
   Unite and perfect them in one.

3 O let them all thy mind express,
   Stand forth thy chosen witnesses,

   Thy power unto salvation show,
   And perfect holiness below!

4 In them let all mankind behold
   How Christians lived in days of old;
   Mighty their envious foes to move,
   A proverb of reproach — and love.

CHARLES WESLEY

562 MERCY 7s.   LOUIS GOTTSCHALK. Arr. by EDWIN P. PARKER

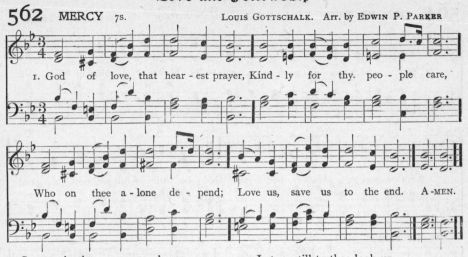

1. God of love, that hear-est prayer, Kind-ly for thy. peo-ple care,

Who on thee a-lone de-pend; Love us, save us to the end. A-MEN.

2 Save us in the prosperous hour,
  From the flattering tempter's power;
  From his unsuspected wiles,
  From the world's pernicious smiles.

3 Never let the world break in,
  Fix a mighty gulf between,
  Keep us humble and unknown,
  Prized and loved by God alone.

4 Let us still to thee look up,
  Thee, thy Israel's strength and hope;
  Nothing know or seek beside
  Jesus, and him crucified.

5 Far above created things
  Look we down on earthly kings;
  Taste our glorious liberty,
  Find our happy all in thee.
          CHARLES WESLEY

563 HAMPSTEAD C. M.   E. F. HORNER

1. Giv-er of con-cord, Prince of Peace, Meek, lamb-like Son of God,

Bid our un-ru-ly pas-sions cease, By thine a-ton-ing blood. A-MEN.

2 Us into closest union draw,
  And in our inward parts
  Let kindness sweetly write her law,
  And love command our hearts.

3 Saviour, look down with pitying eyes,
  Our jarring wills control;

Let cordial, kind affections rise,
  And harmonize the soul.

4 O let us find the ancient way,
  Our wondering foes to move,
  And force the heathen world to say,
  "See how these Christians love!"
          CHARLES WESLEY

564 GOD BE WITH YOU 9. 8. 8. 9. *With Refrain* WILLIAM G. TOMER

1. God be with you till we meet a-gain! By his coun-sels guide, up-hold you,

With his sheep se-cure-ly fold you; God be with you till we meet a-gain!

REFRAIN

Till we meet! . . . Till we meet! Till we meet at Je-sus' feet;
Till we meet! Till we meet a-gain!
Till we meet!

Till we meet! . . . Till we meet! God be with you till we meet a-gain! A-MEN.
Till we meet! Till we meet a-gain!

By permission of J. E. Rankin

2 God be with you till we meet again!
'Neath his wings securely hide you,
Daily manna still provide you;
God be with you till we meet again!

3 God be with you till we meet again!
When life's perils thick confound you,

Put his arms unfailing round you;
God be with you till we meet again!

4 God be with you till we meet again!
Keep love's banner floating o'er you,
Smite death's threatening wave before you;
God be with you till we meet again!

JEREMIAH E. RANKIN

565 LISCHER 6. 6. 6. 6. 8. 8. FRIEDRICH SCHNEIDER

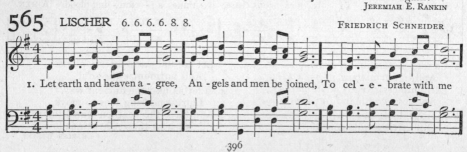

1. Let earth and heaven a-gree, An-gels and men be joined, To cel-e-brate with me

Love and Fellowship

The Sav-iour of man-kind; T' a-dore the all - a - ton - ing Lamb, And bless the sound of
Je - sus' name, And bless . . the sound of Je - sus'. . name. A-MEN.
And bless the sound

2 O unexampled love!
    O all-redeeming grace!
How swiftly didst thou move
    To save a fallen race!
What shall I do to make it known
What thou for all mankind hast done?

3 O for a trumpet voice,
    On all the world to call!
To bid their hearts rejoice
    In him who died for all!
For all my Lord was crucified;
For all, for all my Saviour died.
                              CHARLES WESLEY

566 RADIANT MORN 8. 8. 8. 4.   CHARLES F. GOUNOD

1. Fa - ther of all, from land and sea The na - tions sing, "Thine, Lord, are we,
Count-less in num - ber, but in thee May we be one." A-MEN.

2 O Son of God, whose love so free
For men did make thee man to be,
United to our God in thee
    May we be one.

3 Thou, Lord, didst once for all atone:
Thee may both Jew and Gentile own
Of their two walls the Corner Stone,
    Making them one.

4 Join high and low, join young and old,
In love that never waxes cold;

Under one Shepherd, in one fold,
    Make us all one.

5 O Spirit blest, who from above
Cam'st gently gliding like a dove,
Calm all our strife, give faith and love;
    O make us one!

6 So, when the world shall pass away,
May we awake with joy and say,
"Now in the bliss of endless day
    We all are one."
                        CHRISTOPHER WORDSWORTH

567 LUX EOI 8s. 7s. D.   ARTHUR S. SULLIVAN

1. Through the night of doubt and sor-row On-ward goes the pil-grim band,
Sing-ing songs of ex-pec-ta-tion, March-ing to the prom-ised land.
Clear be-fore us through the dark-ness Gleams and burns the guid-ing light:
Broth-er clasps the hand of broth-er, Step-ping fear-less through the night. A-MEN.

2 One, the light of God's own presence,
  O'er his ransomed people shed,
Chasing far the gloom and terror,
  Brightening all the path we tread:
One, the object of our journey,
  One, the faith which never tires,
One, the earnest looking forward,
  One, the hope our God inspires.

3 One, the strain that lips of thousands
  Lift as from the heart of one;
One the conflict, one the peril,
  One, the march in God begun:

One, the gladness of rejoicing
  On the far eternal shore,
Where the one Almighty Father
  Reigns in love for evermore.

4 Onward therefore, pilgrim brothers,
  Onward, with the cross our aid!
Bear its shame, and fight its battle,
  Till we rest beneath its shade!
Soon shall come the great awaking;
  Soon the rending of the tomb;
Then, the scattering of all shadows,
  And the end of toil and gloom.

BERNHARDT S. INGEMANN. Tr. by SABINE BARING-GOULD

Time and Eternity

Watch-Night and New Year

568 LUCAS P. M.

JAMES LUCAS

1. Come, let us a-new our jour-ney pur-sue, Roll round with the year, And nev-er stand still till the Mas-ter ap-pear. His a-dor-a-ble will let us glad-ly ful-fill, And our tal-ents im-prove, By the pa-tience of hope, and the la-bor of love, By the pa-tience of hope, and the la-bor of love. A-MEN.

2 Our life is a dream; our time, as a stream,
    Glides swiftly away,
And the fugitive moment refuses to stay.
The arrow is flown, the moment is gone;
    The millennial year
Rushes on to our view, and eternity's here.

3 O that each in the day of his coming may say,
    "I have fought my way through;
I have finished the work thou didst give me to do!"
O that each from his Lord may receive the glad word,
    "Well and faithfully done!
Enter into my joy, and sit down on my throne!"

CHARLES WESLEY

569 ST. MARTIN'S C. M.

WILLIAM TANSUR

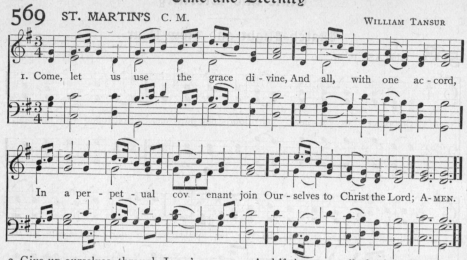

1. Come, let us use the grace di-vine, And all, with one ac-cord, In a per-pet-ual cov-enant join Our-selves to Christ the Lord; A-MEN.

2 Give up ourselves, through Jesus' power,
His name to glorify;
And promise, in this sacred hour,
For God to live and die.

3 The covenant we this moment make
Be ever kept in mind;
We will no more our God forsake,
Or cast his words behind.

4 We never will throw off his fear
Who hears our solemn vow;

And if thou art well pleased to hear,
Come down, and meet us now.

5 Thee, Father, Son, and Holy Ghost,
Let all our hearts receive;
Present with the celestial host,
The peaceful answer give.

6 To each the covenant blood apply,
Which takes our sins away;
And register our names on high,
And keep us to that day.

CHARLES WESLEY

570 GREEN HILL C. M.

ALBERT L. PEACE

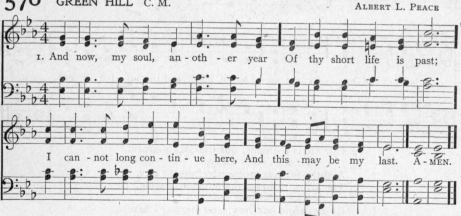

1. And now, my soul, an-oth-er year Of thy short life is past; I can-not long con-tin-ue here, And this may be my last. A-MEN.

2 Awake, my soul! with utmost care
Thy true condition learn:
What are thy hopes? how sure? how fair?
What is thy great concern?

3 Behold, another year begins!
Set out afresh for heaven;

Seek pardon for thy former sins,
In Christ so freely given.

4 Devoutly yield thyself to God,
And on his grace depend;
With zeal pursue the heavenly road,
Nor doubt a happy end.

SIMON BROWNE

571 **SYLVESTER** 7s. 6s.

JOHN S. CAMP

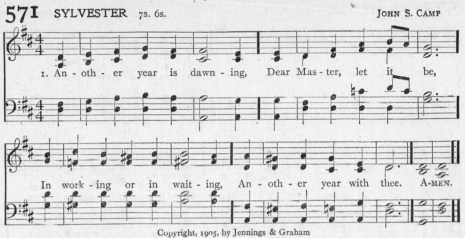

1. An-oth-er year is dawn-ing, Dear Mas-ter, let it be,

In work-ing or in wait-ing, An-oth-er year with thee. A-MEN.

2 Another year of mercies,
  Of faithfulness and grace;
  Another year of gladness
  In the shining of thy face.

3 Another year of progress,
  Another year of praise,
  Another year of proving
  Thy presence all the days.

4 Another year of service,
  Of witness for thy love;
  Another year of training
  For holier work above.

5 Another year is dawning,
  Dear Master, let it be,
  On earth, or else in heaven
  Another year for thee!

FRANCES R. HAVERGAL

572 **GREETING** C. M.

ALFRED G. WATHALL

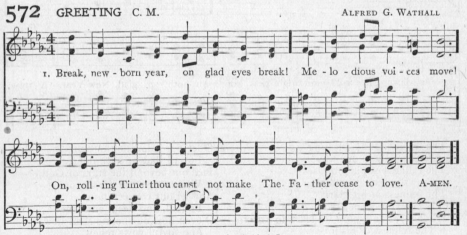

1. Break, new-born year, on glad eyes break! Me-lo-dious voi-ces move!

On, roll-ing Time! thou canst not make The Fa-ther cease to love. A-MEN.

2 The parted year had wingèd feet;
  The Saviour still doth stay:
  The New Year comes; but, Spirit sweet,
  Thou goest not away.

3 Our hearts in tears may oft run o'er;
  But, Lord, thy smile still beams;
  Our sins are swelling evermore;
  But pardoning grace still streams.

4 Lord! from this year more service win,
  More glory, more delight!
  O make its hours less sad with sin,
  Its days with thee more bright!

5 Then we may bless its precious things
  If earthly cheer should come,
  Or gladsome mount on angel wings
  If thou shouldst take us home.

THOMAS H. GILL

573 ST. COLOMB 7. 6. 8. 6. D.

WILLIAM S. HOYTE

1. From glo - ry un - to glo - ry! Be this our joy - ous song;
As on the King's own high - way, We brave - ly march a - long.
From glo - ry un - to glo - ry! O word of stir - ring cheer,
As dawns the sol - emn bright-ness of An - oth - er glad New Year. A - MEN.

2 The fullness of his blessing
  Encompasseth our way;
The fullness of his promises
  Crowns every brightening day;
The fullness of his glory,
  Is beaming from above,
While more and more we learn to know
  The fullness of his love.

3 And closer yet and closer
  The golden bonds shall be,
Uniting all who love our Lord
  In pure sincerity;
And wider yet and wider
  Shall the circling glory glow,
As more and more are taught of God
  That mighty love to know.

4 O let our adoration
  For all that he hath done,
Peal out beyond the stars of God,
  While voice and life are one;
And let our consecration
  Be real, and deep, and true:
O even now our hearts shall bow,
  And joyful vows renew.

5 Now onward, ever onward,
  From strength to strength we go,
While grace for grace abundantly
  Shall from his fullness flow,
To glory's full fruition,
  From glory's foretaste here,
Until his very presence crown
  Our happiest New Year.

FRANCES R. HAVERGAL

574 BENEVENTO 7s. D.   SAMUEL WEBBE

1. While, with ceaseless course, the sun Hasted through the former year,
Many souls their race have run, Nevermore to meet us here:
Fixed in an eternal state, They have done with all below;
We a little longer wait, But how little, none can know. A-MEN.

2 As the wingèd arrow flies
   Speedily the mark to find;
As the lightning from the skies
   Darts, and leaves no trace behind;
Swiftly thus our fleeting days
   Bear us down life's rapid stream;
·Upward, Lord, our spirits raise;
   All below is but a dream.

3 Thanks for mercies past receive;
   Pardon of our sins renew;
Teach us henceforth how to live
   With eternity in view:
Bless thy word to young and old;
   Fill us with a Saviour's love;
And when life's short tale is told,
   May we dwell with thee above.

JOHN NEWTON

575 GOULD C. M.

JOHN E. GOULD

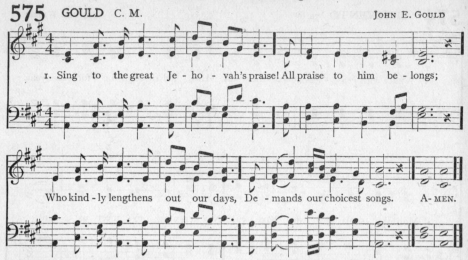

1. Sing to the great Je-ho-vah's praise! All praise to him be-longs;
Who kind-ly lengthens out our days, De-mands our choicest songs. A-MEN.

2 His providence hath brought us through
   Another various year;
   We all, with vows and anthems new,
   Before our God appear.

3 Father, thy mercies past we own,
   Thy still continued care;
   To thee presenting, through thy Son,
   Whate'er we have or are.

4 Our lips and lives shall gladly show
   The wonders of thy love,

While on in Jesus steps we go
To see thy face above.

5 Our residue of days or hours
   Thine, wholly thine, shall be;
   And all our consecrated powers
   A sacrifice to thee:

6 Till Jesus in the clouds appear
   To saints on earth forgiven,
   And bring the grand sabbatic year,
   The jubilee of heaven.

CHARLES WESLEY

576 WINCHESTER OLD C. M.

G. KIRBYE

1. Join, all ye ran-somed sons of grace, The ho-ly joy pro-long,
And shout to the Re-deem-er's praise A sol-emn mid-night song. A-MEN.

2 Blessing and thanks and love and might,
   Be to our Jesus given,
Who turns our darkness into light,
   Who turns our hell to heaven.

3 Thither our faithful souls he leads;
   Thither he bids us rise,
With crowns of joy upon our heads,
   To meet him in the skies.

CHARLES WESLEY

Brevity and Uncertainty of Life

577 ST. ANNE C. M. WILLIAM CROFT

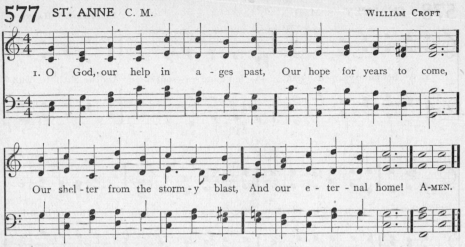

1. O God, our help in a-ges past, Our hope for years to come,
Our shel-ter from the storm-y blast, And our e-ter-nal home! A-MEN.

2 Under the shadow of thy throne
   Still may we dwell secure;
   Sufficient is thine arm alone,
   And our defense is sure.

3 Before the hills in order stood,
   Or earth received her frame,
   From everlasting thou art God,
   To endless years the same.

4 A thousand ages, in thy sight,
   Are like an evening gone;
   Short as the watch that ends the night,
   Before the rising sun.

5 The busy tribes of flesh and blood,
   With all their cares and fears,
   Are carried downward by the flood,
   And lost in following years.

6 Time, like an ever-rolling stream,
   Bears all its sons away;
   They fly, forgotten, as a dream
   Dies at the opening day.

7 O God, our help in ages past,
   Our hope for years to come;
   Be thou our guide while life shall last,
   And our eternal home!

ISAAC WATTS

577 MEAR C. M. (*Second Tune*) Composer Unknown

1. O God, our help in a-ges past, Our hope for years to come,
Our shel-ter from the storm-y blast, And our e-ter-nal home! A-MEN.

578 CHALVEY S. M. D.

LEIGHTON G. HAYNE

1. A few more years shall roll, A few more sea-sons come; And we shall be with those that rest, Asleep with-in the tomb. Then, O my Lord, pre-pare My soul for that blest day; O wash me in thy pre-cious blood, And take my sins a-way! A-MEN.

2 A few more storms shall beat
   On this wild, rocky shore,
And we shall be where tempests cease
   And surges swell no more.
Then, O my Lord, prepare
   My soul for that blest day;
O wash me in thy precious blood,
   And take my sins away!

3 A few more struggles here,
   A few more partings o'er,
A few more toils, a few more tears,
   And we shall weep no more.
Then, O my Lord, prepare
   My soul for that blest day;
O wash me in thy precious blood,
   And take my sins away!

HORATIUS BONAR

579 MERIBAH 8. 8. 6. D.

LOWELL MASON

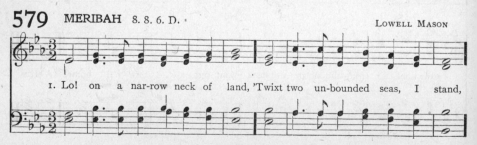

1. Lo! on a nar-row neck of land, 'Twixt two un-bounded seas, I stand,

Brevity and Uncertainty of Life

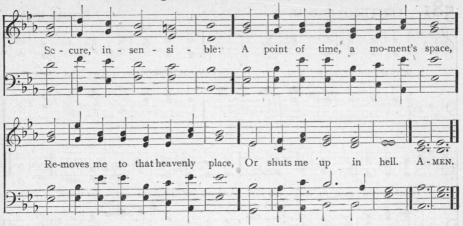

Se - cure, in - sen - si - ble: A point of time, a mo-ment's space,

Re-moves me to that heavenly place, Or shuts me up in hell. A - MEN.

2 O God, mine inmost soul convert,
  And deeply in my thoughtful heart
    Eternal things impress:
  Give me to feel their solemn weight,
  And tremble on the brink of fate,
    And wake to righteousness.

3 Be this my one great business here,
  With serious industry and fear
    Eternal bliss to insure;

Thine utmost counsel to fulfill,
  And suffer all thy righteous will,
    And to the end endure.

4 Then, Saviour, then my soul receive,
  Transported from this vale, to live
    And reign with thee above,
  Where faith is sweetly lost in sight,
  And hope in full, supreme delight,
    And everlasting love.

CHARLES WESLEY

580 ABER S. M

WILLIAM H. MONK

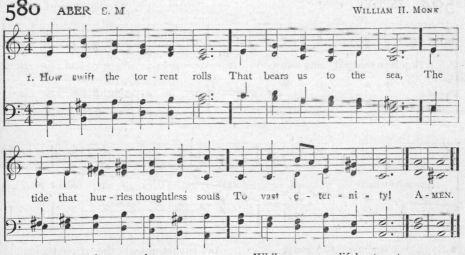

1. How swift the tor - rent rolls That bears us to the sea, The

tide that hur - ries thoughtless souls To vast e - ter - ni - ty! A - MEN.

2 Our fathers, where are they,
  With all they called their own?
Their joys and griefs, and hopes and cares,
  And wealth and honor gone.

3 God of our fathers, hear,
  Thou everlasting Friend!

While we, as on life's utmost verge,
  Our souls to thee commend.

4 Of all the pious dead
  ' May we the footsteps trace,
Till with them, in the land of light,
  We dwell before thy face.

PHILIP DODDRIDGE

581 PENTECOST L. M.

WILLIAM BOYD

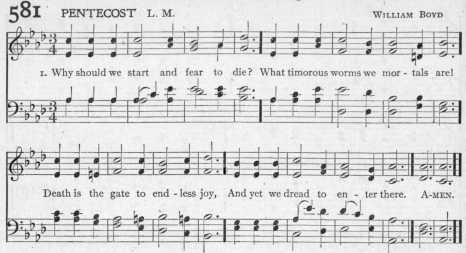

1. Why should we start and fear to die? What timorous worms we mor - tals are!

Death is the gate to end - less joy, And yet we dread to en - ter there. A-MEN.

2 The pains, the groans, the dying strife,
   Fright our approaching souls away;
   And we shrink back again to life,
   Fond of our prison and our clay.

3 O if my Lord would come and meet,
   My soul would stretch her wings in haste,

Fly fearless through death's iron gate,
Nor feel the terrors as she passed!

4 Jesus can make a dying-bed
   Feel soft as downy pillows are,
   While on his breast I lean my head,
   And breathe my life out sweetly there.

ISAAC WATTS

582 ZEPHYR L. M.

WILLIAM B. BRADBURY

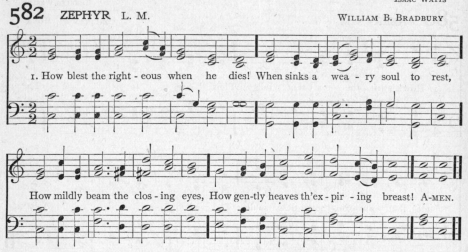

1. How blest the right - eous when he dies! When sinks a wea - ry soul to rest,

How mildly beam the clos - ing eyes, How gen-tly heaves th'ex - pir - ing breast! A-MEN.

2 So fades a summer cloud away;
   So sinks the gale when storms are o'er;
So gently shuts the eye of day;
   So dies a wave along the shore.

3 A holy quiet reigns around,
   A calm which life nor death destroys;

And naught disturbs that peace profound
Which his unfettered soul enjoys.

4 Life's labor done, as sinks the clay,
   Light from its load the spirit flies,
   While heaven and earth combine to say,
   "How blest the righteous when he dies!"

ANNA L. BARBAULD. Alt.

Death and the Resurrection

583 CARYL L. M.

PETER C. LUTKIN

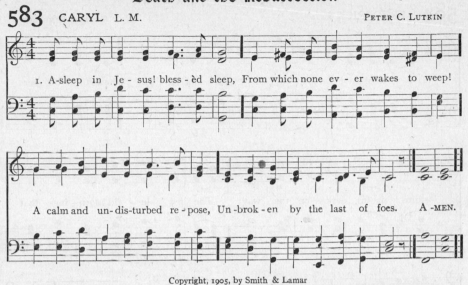

1. A-sleep in Je - sus! bless - èd sleep, From which none ev - er wakes to weep!

A calm and un-dis-turbed re - pose, Un-brok-en by the last of foes. A -MEN.

Copyright, 1905, by Smith & Lamar

2 Asleep in Jesus! O how sweet
To be for such a slumber meet!
With holy confidence to sing,
That death hath lost his venomed sting.

3 Asleep in Jesus! peaceful rest,
Whose waking is supremely blest!
No fear, no woe, shall dim that hour
That manifests the Saviour's power.

4 Asleep in Jesus! O for me
May such a blissful refuge be!
Securely shall my ashes lie,
Waiting the summons from on high.

5 Asleep in Jesus! far from thee
Thy kindred and their graves may be;
But thine is still a blessèd sleep,
From which none ever wakes to weep.

MARGARET MACKAY

583 REST L. M. (Second Tune)

WILLIAM B. BRADBURY

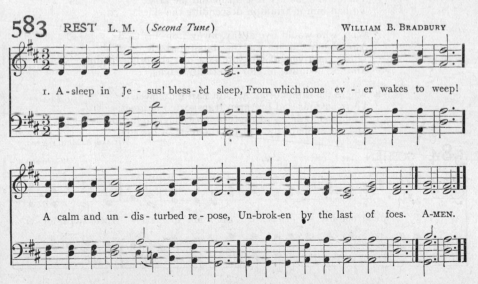

1. A-sleep in Je - sus! bless - èd sleep, From which none ev - er wakes to weep!

A calm and un - dis - turbed re - pose, Un-brok-en by the last of foes. A-MEN.

584 FREDERICK 11S.

GEORGE KINGSLEY

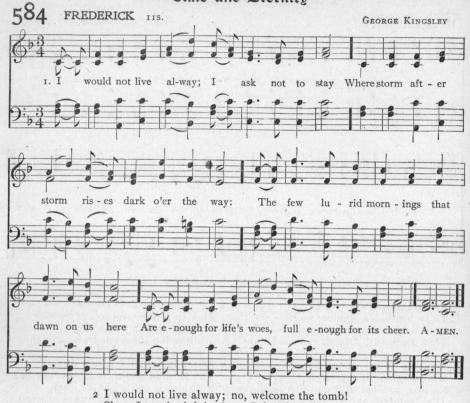

1. I would not live al-way; I ask not to stay Where storm aft - er storm ris - es dark o'er the way: The few lu - rid morn - ings that dawn on us here Are e -nough for life's woes, full e -nough for its cheer. A - MEN.

2 I would not live alway; no, welcome the tomb!
Since Jesus hath lain there, I dread not its gloom;
There sweet be my rest till he bid me arise,
To hail him in triumph descending the skies.

3 Who, who would live alway, away from his God?
Away from yon heaven, that blissful abode,
Where the rivers of pleasure flow o'er the bright plains,
And the noontide of glory eternally reigns;

4 Where the saints of all ages in harmony meet,
Their Saviour and brethren transported to greet;
While the anthems of rapture unceasingly roll,
And the smile of the Lord is the feast of the soul.

WILLIAM A. MUHLENBERG

584 GOSHEN 11S. *(Second Tune)*

German

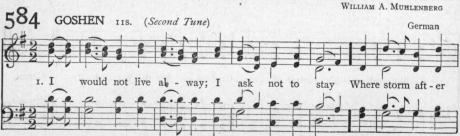

1. I would not live al - way; I ask not to stay Where storm aft - er

Death and the Resurrection

storm ris - es dark o'er the way: The few lu - rid morn-ings that
dawn on us here Are e-nough for life's woes, full e - nough for its cheer. A-MEN.

585 GREENWOOD S. M. JOSEPH E. SWEETSER

1. It is not death to die, To leave this wea - ry road,
And midst the broth - er - hood on high To be at home with God. A-MEN.

2 It is not death to close
  The eye long dimmed by tears,
And wake, in glorious repose
  To spend eternal years.

3 It is not death to fling
  Aside this sinful dust,

And rise, on strong exulting wing,
  To live among the just.

4 Jesus, thou Prince of life,
  Thy chosen cannot die!
Like thee, they conquer in the strife,
  To reign with thee on high.

ABRAHAM H. C. MALAN. Tr. by GEORGE W. BETHUNE

411

Time and Eternity

586 DIRGE L. M. 4 or 6l.

Arr. from GEORGE F. HÄNDEL

1. Un-veil thy bos-om, faith-ful tomb, Take this new treas-ure to thy trust, And give these sa-cred rel-ics room To slum-ber in the si - lent dust, And give these sa-cred rel - ics room To slumber in the si - lent dust. A - MEN.

2 Nor pain, nor grief, nor anxious fear
Invades thy bounds; no mortal woes
Can reach the peaceful sleeper here,
While angels watch the soft repose.

3 So Jesus slept: God's dying Son [bed:
Passed through the grave, and blessed the

Rest here, blest saint, till from his throne
The morning break and pierce the shade.

4 Break from his throne, illustrious morn!
Attend, O earth! his sovereign word:
Restore thy trust: a glorious form
Shall then ascend to meet the Lord!

ISAAC WATTS

587 BATH 6. 6. 8. 6. 8. 8.

W. H. COOKE

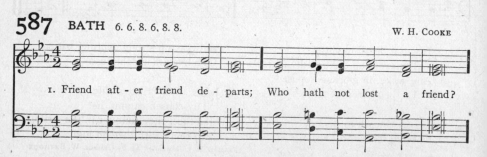

1. Friend aft - er friend de - parts; Who hath not lost a friend?

Death and the Resurrection

There is no un-ion here of hearts, That finds not here an end:
Were this frail world our fi-nal rest, Liv-ing or dy-ing, none were blest. A-MEN.

2 Beyond the flight of time,
   Beyond this vale of death,
There surely is some blessèd clime
   Where life is not a breath,
Nor life's affections, transient fire,
Whose sparks fly upward and expire.

3 There is a world above,
   Where parting is unknown,
A long eternity of love,
   Formed for the good alone;
And faith beholds the dying here
Translated to that happier sphere.

4 Thus star by star declines,
   Till all are passed away,
As morning high and higher shines
   To pure and perfect day;
Nor sink those stars in empty night,
But hide themselves in heaven's own light.

JAMES MONTGOMERY

588   SABBATA C. M.

HENRY F. HEMY

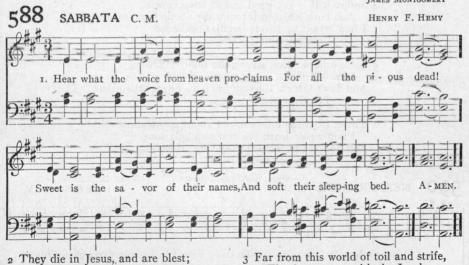

1. Hear what the voice from heaven pro-claims For all the pi-ous dead!
Sweet is the sa-vor of their names, And soft their sleep-ing bed. A-MEN.

2 They die in Jesus, and are blest;
   How kind their slumbers are!
From sufferings and from sins released,
   And freed from every snare.

3 Far from this world of toil and strife,
   They're present with the Lord:
The labors of their mortal life
   End in a large reward.

ISAAC WATTS

Time and Eternity

589 DIADEMA 11. 10. 11. 6.

JOSEPH BARNBY

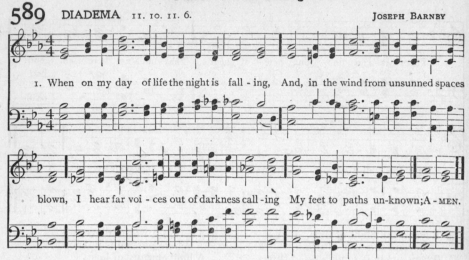

1. When on my day of life the night is fall-ing, And, in the wind from unsunned spaces blown, I hear far voi-ces out of darkness call-ing My feet to paths un-known; A-MEN.

2 Thou, who hast made my home of life so pleasant,
Leave not its tenant when its walls decay;
O Love Divine, O Helper ever present,
Be thou my strength and stay.

3 I have but thee, my Father! let thy Spirit
Be with me then to comfort and uphold;
No gate of pearl, no branch of palm I merit,
Nor street of shining gold.

4 Suffice it if — my good and ill unreckoned,
And both forgiven through thy abounding grace —
I find myself by hands familiar beckoned
Unto my fitting place, —

5 Some humble door among thy many mansions,
Some sheltering shade where sin and striving cease,
And flows forever through heaven's green expansions
The river of thy peace.

6 There, from the music round about me stealing,
I fain would learn the new and holy song,
And find at last, beneath thy trees of healing,
The life for which I long.

JOHN G. WHITTIER

590 NEARER HOME S. M. D.

ISAAC B. WOODBURY
Arr. by ARTHUR S. SULLIVAN

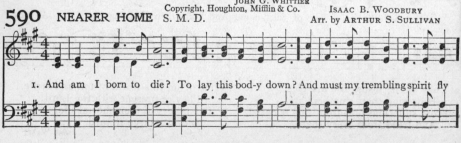

1. And am I born to die? To lay this bod-y down? And must my trembling spirit fly

Death and the Resurrection

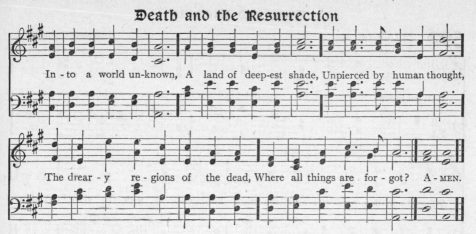

In-to a world un-known, A land of deep-est shade, Unpierced by human thought,

The drear-y re-gions of the dead, Where all things are for-got? A-MEN.

2 Soon as from earth I go,
   What will become of me?
   Eternal happiness or woe
   Must then my portion be:
   Waked by the trumpet's sound,
   I from my grave shall rise,
   And see the Judge, with glory crowned,
   And see the flaming skies!

3 Who can resolve the doubt
   That tears my anxious breast?
   Shall I be with the damned cast out,
   Or numbered with the blest?

I must from God be driven,
   Or with my Saviour dwell;
   Must come at his command to heaven,
   Or else — depart to hell!

4 O Thou who wouldst not have
   One wretched sinner die;
   Who diedst thyself my soul to save
   From endless misery;
   Show me the way to shun
   Thy dreadful wrath severe,
   That when thou comest on thy throne
   I may with joy appear.

CHARLES WESLEY

591 GREEN HILL C.M.

ALBERT L. PEACE

1. Why should our tears in sor-row flow When God re-calls his own,

And bids them leave a world of woe For an im-mor-tal crown? A-MEN.

2 Is not e'en death a gain to those
   Whose life to God was given?
   Gladly to earth their eyes they close,
   To open them in heaven.

3 Their toils are past, their work is done,
   And they are fully blest;

They fought the fight, the victory won,
   And entered into rest.

4 Then let our sorrows cease to flow;
   God has recalled his own;
   But let our hearts, in every woe,
   Still say, "Thy will be done."

WILLIAM H. BATHURST

415

592 MEAR C. M.   Composer Unknown

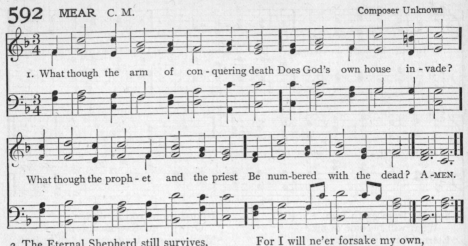

1. What though the arm of con-quering death Does God's own house in-vade?
What though the proph-et and the priest Be num-bered with the dead? A-MEN.

2 The Eternal Shepherd still survives,
   New comfort to impart;
   His eye still guides us, and his voice
   Still animates our heart.

3 "Lo! I am with you," saith the Lord,
   "My church shall safe abide;

For I will ne'er forsake my own,
Whose souls in me confide."

4 Through every scene of life and death,
   This promise is our trust;
   And this shall be our children's song,
   When we are cold in dust.

PHILIP DODDRIDGE

593 VICTORY S. M.   H. A. WHITEHEAD

1. Serv-ant of God, well done! Thy glo-rious war-fare's past;
The bat-tle's fought, the race is won, And thou art crowned at last; A-MEN.

2 Of all thy heart's desire
   Triumphantly possessed;
   Lodged by the ministerial choir
   In thy Redeemer's breast.

3 In condescending love,
   Thy ceaseless prayer he heard;
   And bade thee suddenly remove
   To thy complete reward.

4 With saints enthroned on high,
   Thou dost thy Lord proclaim,

And still to God salvation cry,
Salvation to the Lamb!

5 O happy, happy soul!
   In ecstasies of praise,
   Long as eternal ages roll,
   Thou seest thy Saviour's face.

6 Redeemed from earth and pain,
   Ah! when shall we ascend,
   And all in Jesus' presence reign
   With our translated friend?

CHARLES WESLEY

Death and the Resurrection

594 ST. CYPRIAN 8s. D. JOHN GOSS

1. Weep not for a broth-er de-ceased, Our loss is his in-fi-nite gain;
A soul out of pris-on re-leased, And freed from its bod-i-ly chain;
With songs let us fol-low his flight, And mount with his spir-it a-bove,
Es-caped to the mansions of light, And lodged in the E-den of love. A-MEN.

2 Our brother the haven hath gained,
    Outflying the tempest and wind;
His rest he hath sooner obtained,
    And left his companions behind,
Still tossed on a sea of distress,
    Hard toiling to make the blest shore,
Where all is assurance and peace,
    And sorrow and sin are no more.

3 There all the ship's company meet,
    Who sailed with the Saviour beneath;
With shouting each other they greet,
    And triumph o'er sorrow and death:
The voyage of life's at an end;
    The mortal affliction is past;
The age that in heaven they spend,
    Forever and ever shall last.

CHARLES WESLEY

15   417

595 CLAUDIUS C. M.

ARTHUR H. MANN

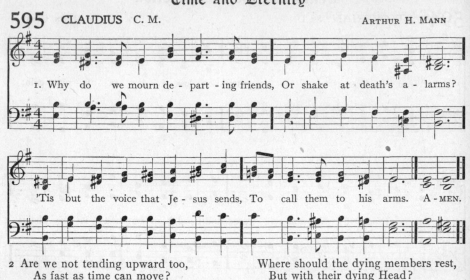

1. Why do we mourn de - part - ing friends, Or shake at death's a - larms?

'Tis but the voice that Je - sus sends, To call them to his arms. A - MEN.

2 Are we not tending upward too,
As fast as time can move?
Nor should we wish the hours more slow
To keep us from our Love.

3 The graves of all his saints he blest,
And softened every bed:

Where should the dying members rest,
But with their dying Head?

4 Then let the last loud trumpet sound,
And bid our kindred rise:
Awake, ye nations under ground;
Ye saints, ascend the skies!

ISAAC WATTS

596 ROSEDALE L. M.

GEORGE F. ROOT

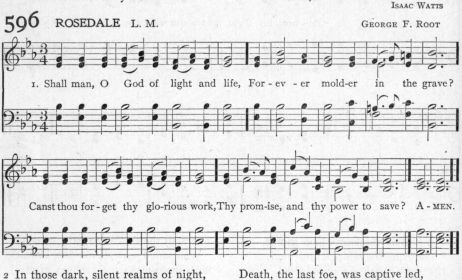

1. Shall man, O God of light and life, For - ev - er mold-er in the grave?

Canst thou for - get thy glo-rious work, Thy prom-ise, and thy power to save? A - MEN.

2 In those dark, silent realms of night,
Shall peace and hope no more arise?
No future morning light the tomb,
Nor day-star gild the darksome skies?

3 Cease, cease, ye vain, desponding fears:
When Christ, our Lord, from darkness sprang,

Death, the last foe, was captive led,
And heaven with praise and wonder rang.

4 Faith sees the bright, eternal doors
Unfold, to make his children way;
They shall be clothed with endless life,
And shine in everlasting day.

TIMOTHY DWIGHT

Death and the Resurrection

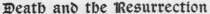

597 NEARER HOME S. M. D.

ISAAC B. WOODBURY
Arr. by ARTHUR S. SULLIVAN

1. "Serv-ant of God, well done! Rest from thy loved em-ploy;
The bat-tle fought, the vic-tory won, En-ter thy Mas-ter's joy."
The voice at mid-night came; He start-ed up to hear;
A mor-tal ar-row pierced his frame: He fell; but felt no fear. A-MEN.

2 Tranquil amid alarms,
　It found him on the field,
A veteran, slumbering on his arms,
　Beneath his red-cross shield.
His sword was in his hand,
　Still warm with recent fight,
Ready that moment, at command,
　Through rock and steel to smite.

3 The pains of death are past,
　Labor and sorrow cease;
And, life's long warfare closed at last,
　His soul is found in peace.
Soldier of Christ, well done!
　Praise be thy new employ;
And while eternal ages run,
　Rest in thy Saviour's joy.

JAMES MONTGOMERY

598 FALKIRK P. M.

From THOMAS A. ARNE

1. Stand the om-nip - o - tent de - cree! Je - ho - vah's will be done!

Na - ture's end we wait to see, And hear her fi - nal groan.

Let this earth dis - solve, and blend In death the wick - ed and the just;

Let those pon-derous orbs de - scend, And grind us in - to dust: — A -MEN.

2 Rests secure the righteous man;
    At his Redeemer's beck,
· Sure to emerge and rise again,
    And mount above the wreck:
Lo! the heavenly spirit towers,
    Like flames o'er nature's funeral pyre,
Triumphs in immortal powers,
    And claps his wings of fire!

3 Nothing hath the just to lose,
    By worlds on worlds destroyed:
Far beneath his feet he views,
    With smiles, the flaming void;
Sees the universe renewed,
    The grand millennial reign begun;
Shouts, with all the sons of God,
    Around the eternal throne.

CHARLES WESLEY

599 REYNOLDSTONE 7s. 6l.

TIMOTHY R. MATTHEWS

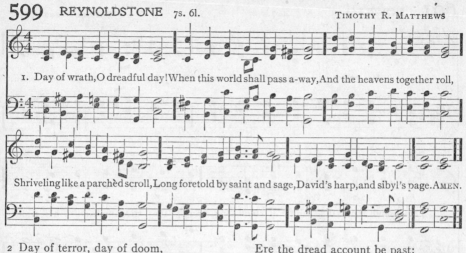

1. Day of wrath, O dreadful day! When this world shall pass a-way, And the heavens together roll,

Shriveling like a parchèd scroll, Long foretold by saint and sage, David's harp, and sibyl's page. AMEN.

2 Day of terror, day of doom,
   When the Judge at last shall come!
   Through the deep and silent gloom,
   Shrouding every human tomb,
   Shall the archangel's trumpet tone
   Summon all before the throne.

3 O just Judge, to whom belongs
   Vengeance for all earthly wrongs,
   Grant forgiveness, Lord, at last,

Ere the dread account be past:
Lo, my sighs, my guilt, my shame!
Spare me for thine own great name.

4 Thou, who bad'st the sinner cease
   From her tears and go in peace,—
   Thou, who to the dying thief
   Spakest pardon and relief,—
   Thou, O Lord, to me hast given,
   E'en to me, the hope of heaven.

THOMAS of Celano. Tr by ARTHUR P. STANLEY

600 SINAI C. M.

JOSEPH BARNBY

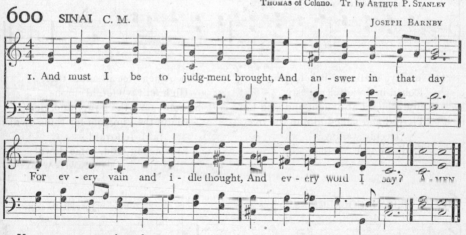

1. And must I be to judg-ment brought, And an-swer in that day

For ev-ery vain and i-dle thought, And ev-ery word I say? A-MEN

2 Yes, every secret of my heart
   Shall shortly be made known,
   And I receive my just desert
   For all that I have done.

3 How careful, then, ought I to live,
   With what religious fear!
   Who such a strict account must give
   For my behavior here.

4 Thou awful Judge of quick and dead,
   The watchful power bestow;
   So shall I to my ways take heed,
   To all I speak or do.

5 If now thou standest at the door,
   O let me feel thee near;
   And make my peace with God, before
   I at thy bar appear.

CHARLES WESLEY

Time and Eternity

601 NOVELLO 8. 7. 8. 7. 4. 7.   SAMUEL WEBBE (?)

1. Lo! He comes, with clouds de-scend-ing, Once for fa-vored sin-ners slain;

Thou-sand thou-sand saints at-tend-ing, Swell the tri-umph of his train:

Hal-le-lu-jah! Hal-le-lu-jah! God ap-pears on earth to reign. A-MEN.

2 Every eye shall now behold him
  Robed in dreadful majesty;
Those who set at naught and sold him,
  Pierced and nailed him to the tree,
    Deeply wailing,
  Shall the true Messiah see.

3 Yea, Amen! let all adore thee,
  High on thy eternal throne;
Saviour, take the power and glory;
  Claim the kingdom for thine own:
    Jah! Jehovah!
  Everlasting God, come down!

CHARLES WESLEY

602 ETON COLLEGE 8. 7. 8. 7. 4. 7.   JOSEPH BARNBY

1. Christ is com-ing! let cre-a-tion Bid her groans and trav-ail cease;

Let the glo-rious proc-la-ma-tion Hope re-store and faith in-crease; Christ is com-.ng! Come, thou bless-èd Prince of Peace! A-MEN.

2 Long thy exiles have been pining,
　Far from rest, and home, and thee;
But, in heavenly vesture shining,
　Soon they shall thy glory see;
　　Christ is coming!
　Haste the joyous jubilee.

3 With that blessèd hope before us,
　Let no harp remain unstrung;
Let the mighty advent chorus
　Onward roll from tongue to tongue;
　　Christ is coming!
　Come, Lord Jesus, quickly come!
　　　　　JOHN R. MACDUFF

603 IRAE L. M.　　　　　　　　　　JOSEPH BARNBY

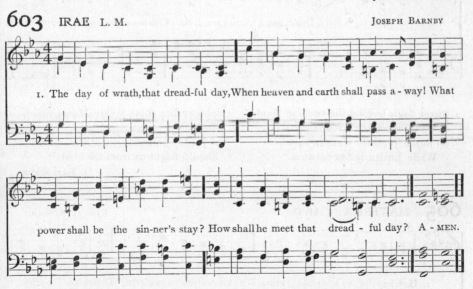

1. The day of wrath, that dread-ful day, When heaven and earth shall pass a-way! What power shall be the sin-ner's stay? How shall he meet that dread-ful day? A-MEN.

2 When, shriveling like a parchèd scroll,
The flaming heavens together roll;
And louder yet, and yet more dread,
Swells the high trump that wakes the dead:

3 O on that day, that wrathful day,
When man to judgment wakes from clay,
Be thou, O Christ, the sinner's stay,
Though heaven and earth shall pass away!
　　　　　WALTER SCOTT

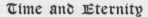

604 VARINA C. M. D.

GEORGE F. ROOT

1. There is a land of pure de-light, Where saints immortal reign; In-fi-nite day ex-cludes the night, And pleas-ures ban-ish pain. There ev-er-last-ing spring a-bides, And never-withering flowers; Death, like a narrow sea, divides This heavenly land from ours. AMEN.

2 Sweet fields beyond the swelling flood
   Stand dressed in living green;
   So to the Jews old Canaan stood,
   While Jordan rolled between.

Could we but climb where Moses stood,
   And view the landscape o'er,
   Not Jordan's stream, nor death's cold flood,
   Should fright us from the shore.

ISAAC WATTS

605 MATERNA C. M. D.

SAMUEL A. WARD

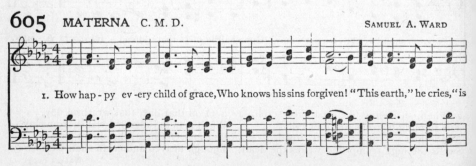

1. How hap-py ev-ery child of grace, Who knows his sins forgiven! "This earth," he cries, "is

not my place, I seek my place in heaven,— A coun-try far from mor-tal sight,

Which yet by faith I see, The land of rest, the saints' delight, The heaven prepared for me." AMEN.

2 O what a blessèd hope is ours!
  While here on earth we stay;
We more than taste the heavenly powers,
  And antedate that day.
We feel the resurrection near,
  Our life in Christ concealed,
And with his glorious presence here
  Our earthen vessels filled.

3 O would he more of heaven bestow,
  And let the vessels break,
And let our ransomed spirits go
  To grasp the God we seek;
In rapturous awe on him to gaze,
  Who bought the sight for me;
And shout and wonder at his grace
  Through all eternity!

CHARLES WESLEY

606   NEWBOLD C. M.

GEORGE KINGSLEY

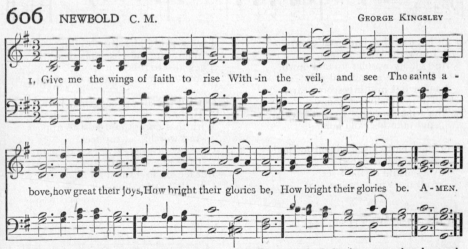

1, Give me the wings of faith to rise With-in the veil, and see The saints a-

bove, how great their joys, How bright their glories be, How bright their glories be. A-MEN.

2 Once they were mourners here below,
  And poured out cries and tears;
They wrestled hard, as we do now,
  With sins, and doubts, and fears.

3 I ask them whence their victory came:
  They, with united breath,
Ascribe their conquest to the Lamb,
  Their triumph to his death.

4 They marked the footsteps that he trod;
  His zeal inspired their breast;
And, following their incarnate God,
  Possess the promised rest.

5 Our glorious Leader claims our praise
  For his own pattern given;
While the long cloud of witnesses
  Show the same path to heaven.

ISAAC WATTS

Time and Eternity

607 REX REGUM C. M. D.

JOHN STAINER

1. And let this fee-ble bod-y fail, And let it droop and die; My soul shall quit the mourn-ful vale, And soar to worlds on high; Shall join the dis-em-bod-ied saints, And find its long-sought rest, That on-ly bliss for which it pants, In my Redeemer's breast. A-MEN.

2 In hope of that immortal crown
   I now the cross sustain,
And gladly wander up and down,
   And smile at toil and pain:
I suffer out my threescore years,
   Till my Deliverer come,
And wipe away his servant's tears,
   And take his exile home.

3 O what hath Jesus bought for me!
   Before my ravished eyes
Rivers of life divine I see,
   And trees of paradise:

I see a world of spirits bright,
   Who taste the pleasures there;
They all are robed in spotless white,
   And conquering palms they bear.

4 O what are all my sufferings here,
   If, Lord, thou count me meet
With that enraptured host to appear,
   And worship at thy feet!
Give joy or grief, give ease or pain,
   Take life or friends away,
But let me find them all again
   In that eternal day.

CHARLES WESLEY

608 LAMBETH C. M.

Composer Unknown

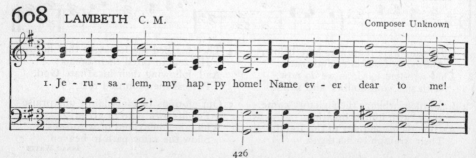

1. Je-ru-sa-lem, my hap-py home! Name ev-er dear to me!

426

Heaven

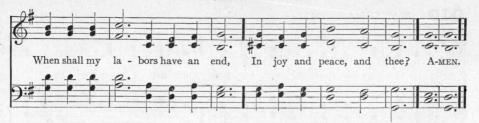

When shall my la - bors have an end, In joy and peace, and thee? A-MEN.

2 When shall these eyes thy heaven-built
And pearly gates behold? [walls
Thy bulwarks with salvation strong,
And streets of shining gold?

3 O when, thou city of my God,
Shall I thy courts ascend,
Where congregations ne'er break up,
And sabbaths have no end?

4 There happier bowers than Eden's bloom,
Nor sin nor sorrow know:

Blest seats! through rude and stormy scenes
I onward press to you.

5 Apostles, martyrs, prophets, there
Around my Saviour stand;
And soon my friends in Christ below
Will join the glorious band.

6 Jerusalem, my happy home!
My soul still pants for thee;
Then shall my labors have an end,
When I thy joys shall see.

Author Unknown

609 WOODLAND 8. 6. 8. 8. 6.
NATHANAEL D. GOULD

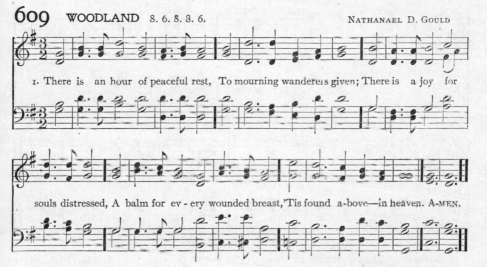

1. There is an hour of peaceful rest, To mourning wanderers given; There is a joy for souls distressed, A balm for ev - ery wounded breast,'Tis found a-bove—in heaven. A-MEN.

2 There is a home for weary souls
By sin and sorrow driven,
When tossed on life's tempestuous shoals,
Where storms arise and ocean rolls,
And all is drear — 'tis heaven.

3 There faith lifts up the tearless eye
To brighter prospects given;
And views the tempest passing by,
The evening shadows quickly fly,
And all serene — in heaven.

4 There fragrant flowers immortal bloom,
And joys supreme are given;
There rays divine disperse the gloom:
Beyond the confines of the tomb
Appears the dawn — of heaven.

WILLIAM B. TAPPAN

427

610 MATERNA C. M. D.　　　　　　　　　　　SAMUEL A. WARD

1. O moth-er dear, Je-ru-sa-lem! When shall I come to thee?

When shall my sor-rows have an end? Thy joys when shall I see? . . .

O hap-py har-bor of God's saints! O sweet and pleas-ant soil! . . .

In thee no sor-row may be found, No grief, no care, no toil. A-MEN.

Copyright. Used by permission

2 No murky cloud o'ershadows thee,
　　Nor gloom, nor darksome night;
But every soul shines as the sun;
　　For God himself gives light.
O my sweet home, Jerusalem,
　　Thy joys when shall I see?
The King that sitteth on thy throne
　　In his felicity?

3 Thy gardens and thy goodly walks
　　Continually are green,
Where grow such sweet and pleasant flowers
　　As nowhere else are seen.

Right through thy streets, with silver
　　The living waters flow,　　　[sound,
And on the banks, on either side,
　　The trees of life do grow.

4 Those trees for evermore bear fruit,
　　And evermore do spring:
There evermore the angels are,
　　And evermore do sing.
Jerusalem, my happy home,
　　Would God I were in thee!
Would God my woes were at an end,
　　Thy joys that I might see!

Author Unknown

Heaven

611 HOLMFIRTH C. M. D.   BENJAMIN GILL

1. Come, let us join our friends a - bove That have ob - tained the prize,
And on the ea - gle wings of love To joys ce - les - tial rise:
Let all the saints ter - res - trial sing, With those to glo - ry gone;
For all the serv - ants of our King, In earth and heaven, are one. A-MEN.

2 One family we dwell in him,
   One church, above, beneath,
Though now divided by the stream,
   The narrow stream, of death:
One army of the living God,
   To his command we bow;
Part of his host have crossed the flood,
   And part are crossing now.

3 Ten thousand to their endless home
   This solemn moment fly;
And we are to the margin come,
   And we expect to die:
His militant embodied host,
   With wishful looks we stand,
And long to see that happy coast,
   And reach the heavenly land.

4 Our old companions in distress
   We haste again to see,
And eager long for our release,
   And full felicity:
E'en now by faith we join our hands
   With those that went before;
And greet the blood-besprinkled bands
   On the eternal shore.

5 Our spirits, too, shall quickly join,
   Like theirs with glory crowned,
And shout to see our Captain's sign,
   To hear his trumpet sound:
O that we now might grasp our Guide!
   O that the word were given!
Come, Lord of hosts, the waves divide,
   And land us all in heaven!

CHARLES WESLEY

429

Time and Eternity

612 EWING 7s. 6s. D.

ALEXANDER EWING

1. Je - ru - sa - lem the gold - en, With milk and hon - ey blest,

Be - neath thy con - tem - pla - tion Sink heart and voice op - pressed:

'I know not, O I know not What so - cial joys are there;

What ra - dian - cy of glo - ry, What light be - yond com - pare. A-MEN.

2 They stand, those halls of Zion,
　All jubilant with song,
And bright with many an angel,
　And all the martyr throng;
The Prince is ever in them,
　The daylight is serene;
The pastures of the blessèd
　Are decked in glorious sheen.

3 There is the throne of David;
　And there, from care released,
The song of them that triumph,
　The shout of them that feast;

And they who with their Leader,
　Have conquered in the fight,
Forever and forever
　Are clad in robes of white.

4 O sweet and blessèd country,
　The home of God's elect!
O sweet and blessèd country
　That eager hearts expect!
Jesus, in mercy bring us
　To that dear land of rest;
Who art, with God the Father,
　And Spirit, ever blest.

BERNARD of Cluny. Tr. by JOHN M. NEALE

Heaven

613 CARLTON 8s. 7s. D.

1. Hark! the sound of ho-ly voi-ces, Chant-ing at the crys-tal sea,
Al-le-lu-ia! Al-le-lu-ia! Al-le-lu-ia! Lord, to thee!
Mul-ti-tude which none can num-ber, Like the stars in glo-ry stands,
Clothed in white ap-par-el, hold-ing Palms of vic-tory in their hands. A-MEN.

JOSEPH BARNBY

2 Patriarch, and holy prophet
  Who prepared the way for Christ,
King, apostle, saint, confessor,
  Martyr, and evangelist;
Saintly maiden, godly matron,
  Widows who have watched to prayer,
Joined in holy concert, singing
  To the Lord of all, are there.

3 Marching with thy cross, their banner,
  They have triumphed, following
Thee, the Captain of salvation,
  Thee, their Saviour and their King.

Gladly, Lord, with thee they suffered;
  Gladly, Lord, with thee they died;
And by death to life immortal
  They were born and glorified.

4 Now they reign in heavenly glory,
  Now they walk in golden light,
Now they drink, as from a river,
  Holy bliss and infinite:
Love and peace they taste forever,
  And all truth and knowledge see
In the beatific vision
  Of the blessèd Trinity.

CHRISTOPHER WORDSWORTH

431

614 RUTHERFORD 7s. 6s. D.

CRÉTIEN D'URHAN
Arr. by EDWARD F. RIMBAULT

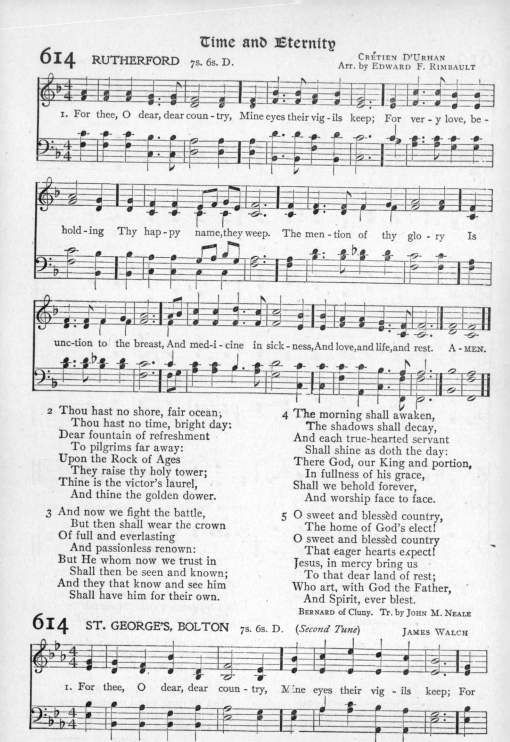

1. For thee, O dear, dear coun-try, Mine eyes their vig-ils keep; For ver-y love, be-hold-ing Thy hap-py name, they weep. The men-tion of thy glo-ry Is unc-tion to the breast, And med-i-cine in sick-ness, And love, and life, and rest. A-MEN.

2 Thou hast no shore, fair ocean;
  Thou hast no time, bright day:
Dear fountain of refreshment
  To pilgrims far away:
Upon the Rock of Ages
  They raise thy holy tower;
Thine is the victor's laurel,
  And thine the golden dower.

3 And now we fight the battle,
  But then shall wear the crown
Of full and everlasting
  And passionless renown:
But He whom now we trust in
  Shall then be seen and known;
And they that know and see him
  Shall have him for their own.

4 The morning shall awaken,
  The shadows shall decay,
And each true-hearted servant
  Shall shine as doth the day:
There God, our King and portion,
  In fullness of his grace,
Shall we behold forever,
  And worship face to face.

5 O sweet and blessèd country,
  The home of God's elect!
O sweet and blessèd country
  That eager hearts expect!
Jesus, in mercy bring us
  To that dear land of rest;
Who art, with God the Father,
  And Spirit, ever blest.

BERNARD of Cluny. Tr. by JOHN M. NEALE

614 ST. GEORGE'S, BOLTON 7s. 6s. D. (*Second Tune*)

JAMES WALCH

1. For thee, O dear, dear coun-try, Mine eyes their vig-ils keep; For

432

ver - y love, be-hold - ing Thy hap-py name, they w ep. The mention of thy glo - ry

Is unc-tion to the breast, And med-i-cine in sickness, And love, and life, and rest. A - MEN.

615 HOMELAND 7s. 6s. D. ARTHUR S. SULLIVAN

1. The Homeland! O the Homeland! The land of souls freeborn! No gloomy night is known there,

But aye the fade-less morn: I'm sigh-ing for that coun - try, My heart is ach-ing here;

There is no pain in the Home-land To which I'm draw-ing near. A - MEN.

2 My Lord is in the Homeland,
   With angels bright and fair;
No sinful thing nor evil,
   Can ever enter there;
The music of the ransomed
   Is ringing in my ears,
And when I think of the Homeland,
   My eyes are wet with tears.

3 For loved ones in the Homeland
   Are waiting me to come
Where neither death nor sorrow
   Invades their holy home:
O dear, dear native country!
   O rest and peace above!
Christ bring us all to the Homeland
   Of his eternal love.

HUGH R. HAWEIS

616 ST. ANDREW OF CRETE 6s. 5s. D.

JOHN B. DYKES

1. Chris-tian! dost thou see them On the ho-ly ground, How the powers of dark-ness Rage thy steps a-round? Chris-tian! up and smite them, Count-ing gain but loss; In the strength that com-eth By the ho-ly cross. A-MEN.

2 Christian! dost thou feel them,
  How they work within,
Striving, tempting, luring,
  Goading into sin?
Christian! never tremble;
  Never be downcast;
Gird thee for the battle,
  Watch, and pray, and fast!

3 Christian! dost thou hear them,
  How they speak thee fair?
"Always fast and vigil?
  Always watch and prayer?"

Christian! answer boldly:
  "While I breathe I pray!"
Peace shall follow battle,
  Night shall end in day.

4 "Well I know thy trouble,
  O my servant true;
Thou art very weary,
  I was weary too;
But that toil shall make thee
  Some day all mine own,
And the end of sorrow
  Shall be near my throne."

ANDREW of Crete. Tr. by JOHN M. NEALE

616 GREEK HYMN 6s. 5s. D. (Second Tune)

JOSEPH P. HOLBROOK

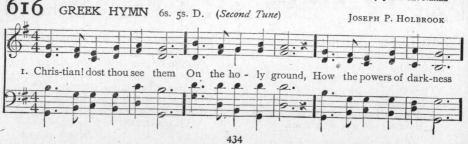

1. Chris-tian! dost thou see them On the ho-ly ground, How the powers of dark-ness

Rage thy steps a-round? Chris-tian! up and smite them, Count-ing gain but loss;

In the strength that com - eth By the ho - ly cross. A-MEN.

617 BEATITUDO C. M.   JOHN B. DYKES

1. On Jor-dan's storm - y banks I stand, And cast a wish - ful eye

To Ca-naan's fair and hap - py land, Where my pos - ses - sions lie. A-MEN.

2 O the transporting, rapturous scene,
  That rises to my sight;
Sweet fields arrayed in living green,
  And rivers of delight!

3 O'er all those wide-extended plains
  Shines one eternal day;
There God the Son forever reigns,
  And scatters night away.

4 No chilling winds, or poisonous breath,
  Can reach that healthful shore;

Sickness and sorrow, pain and death,
  Are felt and feared no more.

5 When shall I reach that happy place,
  And be forever blest?
When shall I see my Father's face,
  And in his bosom rest?

6 Filled with delight, my raptured soul
  Would here no longer stay:
Though Jordan's waves around me roll,
  Fearless I'd launch away.

SAMUEL STENNETT

435

618 ALFORD 7. 6. 8. 6. D.

JOHN B. DYKES

1. Ten thou-sand times ten thou-sand, In spark-ling rai-ment bright, The ar-mies of the ransomed saints Throng up the steeps of light: 'Tis fin-ished, all is fin-ished, Their fight with death and sin: Fling o-pen wide the golden gates, And let the victors in! A-MEN.

2 What rush of hallelujahs
    Fills all the earth and sky!
What ringing of a thousand harps
    Bespeaks the triumph nigh!
O day, for which creation
    And all its tribes were made!
O joy, for all its former woes
    A thousandfold repaid!

3 O then what raptured greetings
    On Canaan's happy shore,
What knitting severed friendships up,
    Where partings are no more!
Then eyes with joy shall sparkle,
    That brimmed with tears of late,
Orphans no longer fatherless,
    Nor widows desolate.

HENRY ALFORD

619 LEYDEN 7s. D.

LOUIS SPOHR. Arr. by SAMUEL S. WESLEY

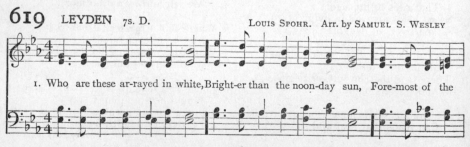

1. Who are these ar-rayed in white, Bright-er than the noon-day sun, Fore-most of the

Heaven

sons of light, Nearest the e -ternal throne? These are they that bore the cross, Nobly for their Mas -ter stood; Suf-ferers in his righteous cause, Followers of the dy-ing God. A - MEN.

2 Out of great distress they came,
    Washed their robes by faith below,
In the blood of yonder Lamb,
    Blood that washes white as snow;
Therefore are they next the throne,
    Serve their Maker day and night;
God resides among his own,
    God doth in his saints delight.

3 More than conquerors at last,
    Here they find their trials o'er;
They have all their sufferings passed,
    Hunger now and thirst no more.
He that on the throne doth reign,
    Them the Lamb shall always feed,
With the tree of life sustain,
    To the living fountains lead.

CHARLES WESLEY

620 CARY P. M.   EBEN TOURJÉE. Arr. by L. FRANKLIN SNOW.

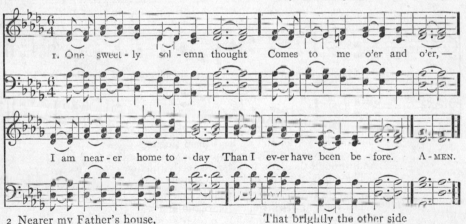

1. One sweet - ly sol - emn thought Comes to me o'er and o'er, —
I am near - er home to - day Than I ev-er have been be - fore. A - MEN.

2 Nearer my Father's house,
    Where the many mansions be;
Nearer the great white throne;
    Nearer the crystal sea;

3 Nearer the bound of life,
    Where we lay our burdens down;
Nearer leaving the cross;
    Nearer gaining the crown.

4 But the waves of that silent sea
    Roll dark before my sight,

That brightly the other side
    Break on a shore of light.

5 O if my mortal feet
    Have almost gained the brink,
If it be I am nearer home
    Even to-day than I think,

6 Father, perfect my trust;
    Let my spirit feel in death
That her feet are firmly set
    On the rock of a living faith.

PHŒBE CARY

621 PILGRIMS 11S. 10S. *With Refrain*

HENRY SMART

1. Hark, hark, my soul! an - gel - ic songs are swell - ing O'er earth's green fields and o - cean's wave-beat shore; How sweet the truth those bless-èd strains are tell - ing Of that new life when sin shall be no more! An - gels of Je - sus, an - gels of light, Sing - ing to wel - come the pil-grims of the night! A-MEN.

REFRAIN

2 Onward we go, for still we hear them singing,
  "Come, weary souls, for Jesus bids you come;"
And through the dark, its echoes sweetly ringing,
  The music of the gospel leads us home.

3 Far, far away, like bells at evening pealing,
  The voice of Jesus sounds o'er land and sea,
And laden souls by thousands, meekly stealing,
  Kind Shepherd, turn their weary steps to thee.

4 Rest comes at length, though life be long and dreary;
  The day must dawn, and darksome night be past;
All journeys end in welcome to the weary,
  And heaven, the heart's true home, will come at last.

5 Angels, sing on! your faithful watches keeping;
  Sing us sweet fragments of the songs above;
Till morning's joy shall end the night of weeping,
  And life's long shadows break in cloudless love.

FREDERICK W. FABER

621 ANGELS' SONG ITS. IOS. *With Refrain* *(Second Tune)* JOHN B. DYKES

1. Hark, hark, my soul! an - gel - ic songs are swell - ing. O'er earth's green fields and o-cean's wave-beat shore; How sweet the truth those bless - èd strains are tell - ing Of that new life when sin shall be no more! An - gels of Je - sus, an - gels of light, Sing - ing to wel - come the pil - grims of the night! Sing - ing to wel - come the pil - grims, the pil - grims of the night! A - MEN.

Time and Eternity

JOHN B. DYKES

1. O Par-a-dise! O Par-a-dise! Who doth not crave for rest?

Who would not seek the hap-py land Where they that loved are blest;

REFRAIN

Where loy-al hearts and true
hearts .... and true
Stand ev-er in the light,

All rap-ture through and through, In God's most ho-ly sight? A-MEN.

2 O Paradise! O Paradise!
　The world is growing old;
Who would not be at rest and free
Where love is never cold;

3 O Paradise! O Paradise!
　I want to sin no more,
I want to be as pure on earth
As on thy spotless shore;

4 O Paradise! O Paradise!
　I greatly long to see
The special place my dearest Lord
In love prepares for me;

5 Lord Jesus, King of Paradise,
　O keep me in thy love,
And guide me to that happy land
Of perfect rest above.

FREDERICK W. FABER

622 PARADISE (No. 2) 8s. 6s. *With Refrain* JOSEPH BARNBY
(*Second Tune*)

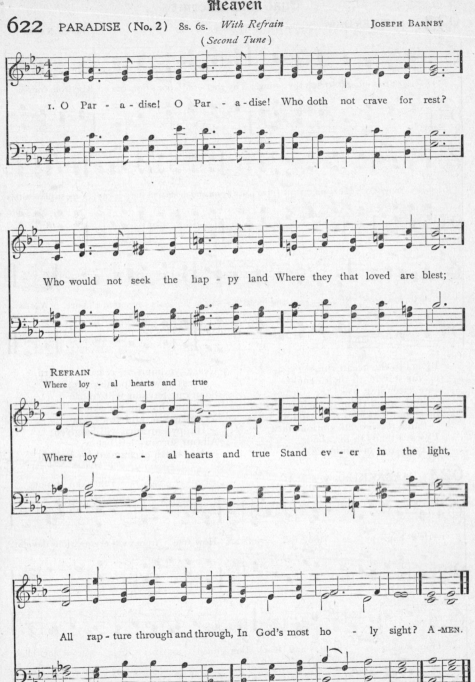

1. O Par - a - dise! O Par - a - dise! Who doth not crave for rest?

Who would not seek the hap - py land Where they that loved are blest;

REFRAIN
Where loy - al hearts and true

Where loy - al hearts and true Stand ev - er in the light,

All rap - ture through and through, In God's most ho - ly sight? A -MEN.

623 AMSTERDAM 7s. 6s. D. Irregular.

JAMES NARES

1. Rise, my soul, and stretch thy wings, Thy bet-ter por-tion trace; Rise from tran-si-to-ry things Toward heaven, thy na-tive place: Sun, and moon, and stars de-cay; Time shall soon this earth re-move; Rise, my soul, and haste a-way To seats pre-pared a-bove. A-MEN.

2 Rivers to the ocean run,
　　Nor stay in all their course;
Fire ascending seeks the sun;
　　Both speed them to their source:
So a soul that's born of God,
　　Pants to view his glorious face;
Upward tends to his abode,
　　To rest in his embrace.

3 Cease, ye pilgrims, cease to mourn,
　　Press onward to the prize;
Soon our Saviour will return
　　Triumphant in the skies:
Yet a season, and you know
　　Happy entrance will be given;
All our sorrows left below,
　　And earth exchanged for heaven.

ROBERT SEAGRAVE

624 HABAKKUK 8. 8. 6. D.

EDWARD HODGES

1. How hap-py is the pil-grim's lot, How free from ev-ery anx-ious thought, From world-ly hope and fear! Con-fined to nei-ther court nor cell,

Heaven

His soul dis-dains on earth to dwell, He on-ly so-journs here. A-MEN.

2 This happiness in part is mine,
Already saved from low design,
From every creature-love,
Blest with the scorn of finite good,
My soul is lightened of its load,
And seeks the things above.

3 There is my house and portion fair;
My treasure and my heart are there,
And my abiding home;

For me my elder brethren stay,
And angels beckon me away,
And Jesus bids me come.

4 I come, thy servant, Lord, replies,
I come to meet thee in the skies,
And claim my heavenly rest!
Now let the pilgrim's journey end;
Now, O my Saviour, Brother, Friend,
Receive me to thy breast!

JOHN WESLEY

625 VIGIL S. M.

GIOVANNI PARSELLO

1. "For-ev-er with the Lord!" A-men, so let it be!

Life from the dead is in that word, 'Tis im-mor-tal-i-ty. A-MEN.

2 Here in the body pent,
Absent from him I roam,
Yet nightly pitch my moving tent
A day's march nearer home.

3 "Forever with the Lord!"
Father, if 'tis thy will,
The promise of that faithful word,
E'en here to me fulfill.

4 So when my latest breath
Shall rend the veil in twain,
By death I shall escape from death,
And life eternal gain.

5 Knowing as I am known,
How shall I love that word,
And oft repeat before the throne,
"Forever with the Lord!"

JAMES MONTGOMERY

Time and Eternity

626 PATMOS 7. 6. 8. 6. D.

HENRY J. STORER

1. I saw the ho-ly cit-y, The New Je-ru-sa-lem,

Come down from heaven a bride a-dorned With jew-eled di-a-dem:

The flood of crys-tal wa-ters Flowed down the gold-en street;

And na-tions brought their hon-ors there, And laid them at her feet. A-MEN.

2 And there no sun was needed,
　Nor moon to shine by night,
God's glory did enlighten all,
　The Lamb himself, the light;
And there his servants serve him,
　And, life's long battle o'er,
Enthroned with him, their Saviour, King,
　They reign for evermore.

3 O great and glorious vision!
　The Lamb upon his throne;
O wondrous sight for man to see!
　The Saviour with his own:

To drink the living waters
　And stand upon the shore,
Where neither sorrow, sin, nor death
　Shall ever enter more.

4 O Lamb of God who reignest,
　Thou bright and morning Star,
Whose glory lightens that new earth
　Which now we see from far:
O worthy Judge Eternal,
　When thou dost bid us come,
Then open wide the gates of pearl
　And call thy servants home.

GODFREY THRING

627 BEYOND P. M. *With Refrain*   KARL P. HARRINGTON

1. Be - yond the smil -ing and the weep - ing, I shall be soon;

Be'- yond the wak- ing and the sleep -ing, Be - yond the sow-ing and the reap -ing,

REFRAIN

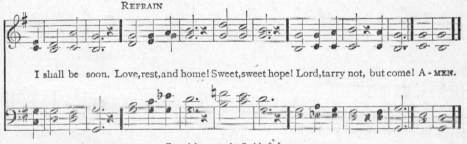

I shall be soon. Love, rest, and home! Sweet, sweet hope! Lord, tarry not, but come! A - MEN.

2 Beyond the blooming and the fading,
  I shall be soon;
Beyond the shining and the shading,
Beyond the hoping and the dreading,
  I shall be soon.

3 Beyond the rising and the setting,
  I shall be soon;
Beyond the calming and the fretting,
Beyond remembering and forgetting,
  I shall be soon.

4 Beyond the parting and the meeting,
  I shall be soon;
Beyond the farewell and the greeting,
Beyond the pulse's fever beating,
  I shall be soon.

5 Beyond the frost-chain and the fever,
  I shall be soon;
Beyond the rock-waste and the river,
Beyond the ever and the never,
  I shall be soon.

                                    HORATIUS BONAR

628 GOING HOME L. M. *With Refrain*

Arr. by WILLIAM McDONALD

1. My heaven-ly home is bright and fair: Nor pain nor death can en - ter there;

Its glit-tering towers the sun out-shine; That heaven-ly man - sion shall be mine.

REFRAIN

I'm go-ing home, I'm go-ing home, I'm go-ing home to die no more;

To die no more, to die no more, I'm go-ing home to die no more. A-MEN.

2. My Father's house is built on high,
Far, far above the starry sky.
When from this earthly prison free,
That heavenly mansion mine shall be.

3. While here, a stranger far from home,
Affliction's waves may round me foam;
Although, like Lazarus, sick and poor,
My heavenly mansion is secure.

4. Let others seek a home below,
Which flames devour, or waves o'erflow,
Be mine the happier lot to own
A heavenly mansion near the throne.

5. Then fail the earth, let stars decline,
And sun and moon refuse to shine,
All nature sink and cease to be,
That heavenly mansion stands for me.

WILLIAM HUNTER

Missions

629 RIGHINI 6. 6. 4. 6. 6. 6. 4.   VINCENZO RIGHINI

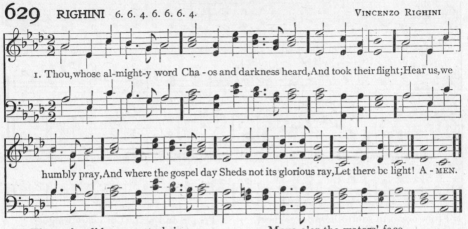

1. Thou, whose al-might-y word Cha-os and darkness heard, And took their flight; Hear us, we humbly pray, And where the gospel day Sheds not its glorious ray, Let there be light! A - MEN.

2 Thou who didst come to bring
On thy redeeming wing,
  Healing and sight,
Health to the sick in mind,
Sight to the inly blind;
O now, to all mankind,
  Let there be light!

3 Spirit of truth and love,
Life-giving, holy Dove,
  Speed forth thy flight;

Move o'er the waters' face
Bearing the lamp of grace;
And in earth's darkest place,
  Let there be light!

4 Holy and blessèd Three,
Glorious Trinity,
  Wisdom, Love, Might;
Boundless as ocean's tide
Rolling in fullest pride,
Through the world far and wide,
  Let there be light!

JOHN MARRIOTT

630 MIGDOL L. M.   LOWELL MASON

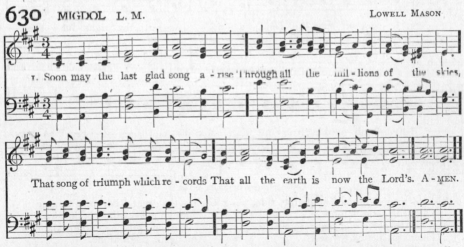

1. Soon may the last glad song a-rise Through all the mil-lions of the skies, That song of triumph which re-cords That all the earth is now the Lord's. A - MEN.

2 Let thrones, and powers, and kingdoms be
Obedient, mighty God, to thee;
And over land, and stream, and main,
Wave thou the scepter of thy reign,

3 O that the anthem now might swell,
And host to host the triumph tell,
That not one rebel heart remains,
But over all the Saviour reigns!

MRS. VOKES

Special Subjects and Occasions

631 DUKE STREET L. M.

JOHN HATTON

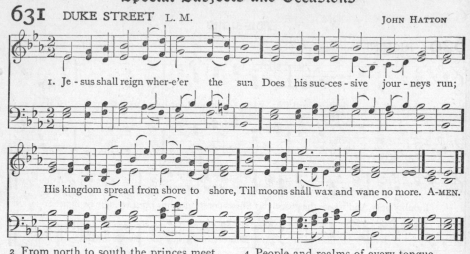

1. Je-sus shall reign wher-e'er the sun Does his suc-ces-sive jour-neys run;
His kingdom spread from shore to shore, Till moons shall wax and wane no more. A-MEN.

2 From north to south the princes meet
To pay their homage at his feet;
While western empires own their Lord,
And savage tribes attend his word.

3 To him shall endless prayer be made,
And endless praises crown his head;
His name like sweet perfume shall rise
With every morning sacrifice.

4 People and realms of every tongue
Dwell on his love with sweetest song,
And infant voices shall proclaim
Their early blessings on his name.

5 Let every creature rise and bring
Peculiar honors to our King;
Angels descend with songs again,
And earth repeat the loud Amen.

ISAAC WATTS

632 EVANSTON C. M.

KARL P. HARRINGTON

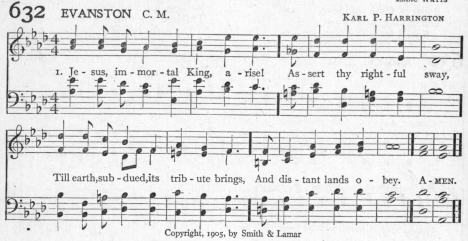

1. Je-sus, im-mor-tal King, a-rise! As-sert thy right-ful sway,
Till earth, sub-dued, its trib-ute brings, And dis-tant lands o-bey. A-MEN.

Copyright, 1905, by Smith & Lamar

2 Ride forth, victorious Conqueror, ride,
Till all thy foes submit,
And all the powers of hell resign
Their trophies at thy feet.

3 Send forth thy word and let it fly
The spacious earth around,
Till every soul beneath the sun
Shall hear the joyful sound.

4 O may the great Redeemer's name
Through every clime be known,
And heathen gods, forsaken, fall,
And Jesus reign alone!

5 From sea to sea, from shore to shore,
Be thou, O Christ, adored,
And earth with all her millions shout
Hosannas to the Lord!

A. C. HOBART SEYMOUR

633 THE KINGDOM COMING 6. 6. 8. 6. 6. 8. *With Refrain*

ROBERT M. McINTOSH

1. From all the dark pla - ces Of earth's hea - then ra - ces,

O see how the thick shad - ows fly! The voice of sal - va - tion

A - wakes ev - er - y na - tion, "Come o - ver and help us," they cry.

REFRAIN

The king-dom is com-ing, O tell ye the sto - ry, God's banner ex - alt - ed shall be!

The earth shall be full of His knowledge and glo-ry, As wa-ters that cov-er the sea! A - MEN.

2 The sunlight is glancing
   O'er armies advancing
      To conquer the kingdoms of sin;
   Our Lord shall possess them,
   His presence shall bless them,
      His beauty shall enter them in.

3 With shouting and singing,
   And jubilant ringing,
      Their arms of rebellion cast down,
   At last every nation,
   The Lord of salvation
      Their King and Redeemer shall crown.

MARY B. C. SLADE

634 TELL IT OUT P. M.

Arr. by IRA D. SANKEY

1. Tell it out a-mong the hea-then that the Lord is King; Tell it out! Tell it out! Tell it out a-mong the na-tions, bid them shout and sing; Tell it out! Tell it out! Tell it out with ad-o-ra-tion that he shall in-crease, That the might-y King of glo-ry is the King of Peace; Tell it out with ju-bi-la-tion, let the song ne'er cease, Tell it out! Tell it out! A-MEN.

450

2 Tell it out among the heathen that the Saviour reigns;
Tell it out! Tell it out!
Tell it out among the nations, bid them break their chains;
Tell it out! Tell it out!
Tell it out among the weeping ones that Jesus lives,
Tell it out among the weary ones what rest he gives,
Tell it out among the sinners that he still receives;
Tell it out! Tell it out!

3 Tell it out among the heathen, Jesus reigns above;
Tell it out! Tell it out!
Tell it out among the nations that his reign is love;
Tell it out! Tell it out!
Tell it out among the highways and the lanes at home,
Let it ring across the mountains and the ocean's foam,
Like the sound of many waters, let our glad shout come!
Tell it out! Tell it out!

FRANCES R. HAVERGAL

635 FIAT LUX 6. 6. 4. 6. 6. 6. 4.   JOHN B. DYKES

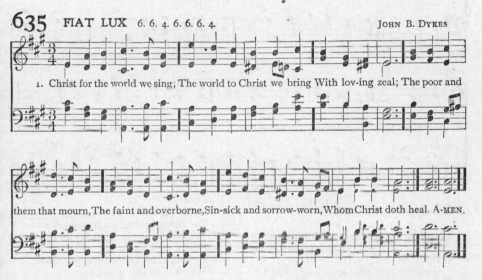

1. Christ for the world we sing; The world to Christ we bring With lov-ing zeal; The poor and them that mourn, The faint and overborne, Sin-sick and sorrow-worn, Whom Christ doth heal. A-MEN.

2 Christ for the world we sing;
The world to Christ we bring
With fervent prayer:
The wayward and the lost,
By restless passions tossed,
Redeemed at countless cost
From dark despair.

3 Christ for the world we sing;
The world to Christ we bring
With one accord;
With us the work to share,
With us reproach to dare,
With us the cross to bear,
For Christ our Lord.

4 Christ for the world we sing;
The world to Christ we bring
With joyful song;
The newborn souls, whose days
Reclaimed from error's ways,
Inspired with hope and praise,
To Christ belong.

SAMUEL WOLCOTT

636 ST. GEORGE'S, WINDSOR 7S. D.

GEORGE J. ELVEY

1. Watch-man, tell us of the night, What its signs of prom-ise are. Trav-eler, o'er yon mountain's height See that glo-ry-beaming star! Watchman, does its beauteous ray Aught of hope or joy fore-tell? Trav-eler, yes; it brings the day, Prom-ised day of Is-ra-el. A-MEN.

2 Watchman, tell us of the night;
   Higher yet the star ascends.
Traveler, blessedness and light,
   Peace and truth, its course portends.
Watchman, will its beams alone
   Gild the spot that gave them birth?
Traveler, ages are its own,
   See, it bursts o'er all the earth!

3 Watchman, tell us of the night,
   For the morning seems to dawn.
Traveler, darkness takes its flight;
   Doubt and terror are withdrawn.
Watchman, let thy wandering cease;
   Hie thee to thy quiet home!
Traveler, lo, the Prince of Peace,
   Lo, the Son of God is come!

JOHN BOWRING

636 WATCHMAN 7S. D. (*Second Tune*)

LOWELL MASON

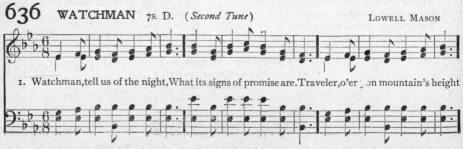

1. Watchman, tell us of the night, What its signs of promise are. Traveler, o'er yon mountain's height

See that glo-ry-beaming star! Watchman, does its beauteous ray Aught of hope or joy foretell?

Trav-eler, yes; it brings the day, Prom-ised day of Is-ra-el. A-MEN.

637 ST. BEES 7s.

JOHN B. DYKES

1. Has-ten, Lord, the glo-rious time, When, be-neath Mes-si-ah's sway,

Ev-ery na-tion, ev-ery clime, Shall the gos-pel call o-bey. A-MEN.

2 Mightiest kings his power shall own;
Heathen tribes his name adore;
Satan and his host o'erthrown,
Bound in chains, shall hurt no more.

3 Then shall wars and tumults cease,
Then be banished grief and pain;
Righteousness and joy and peace,
Undisturbed, shall ever reign.

4 Bless we, then, our gracious Lord;
Ever praise his glorious name;
All his mighty acts record,
All his wondrous love proclaim.

HARRIET AUBER

638 FABEN 8s. 7s. D.   JOHN H. WILCOX

1. Light of those whose dreary dwelling Borders on the shades of death, Come, and by thy love's re-

veal-ing, Dis-si-pate the clouds beneath: The new heaven and earth's Creator, In our deep-est

dark-ness rise, - Scattering all the night of na-ture, Pour-ing eyesight on ,our eyes. A-MEN.

2 Still we wait for thine appearing;
    Life and joy thy beams impart,
Chasing all our fears, and cheering
    Every poor, benighted heart:
Come, and manifest the favor
    God hath for our ransomed race;
Come, thou universal Saviour;
    Come, and bring the gospel grace.

3 Save us in thy great compassion,
    O thou mild, pacific Prince;
Give the knowledge of salvation,
    Give the pardon of our sins:
By thine all-restoring merit,
    Every burdened soul release;
Every weary, wandering spirit,
    Guide into thy perfect peace.

CHARLES WESLEY

638 LIGHT OF THE WORLD 8s. 7s. D.   FERDINAND H. HIMMEL
                  (*Second Tune*)

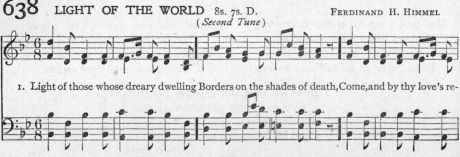

1. Light of those whose dreary dwelling Borders on the shades of death, Come, and by thy love's re-

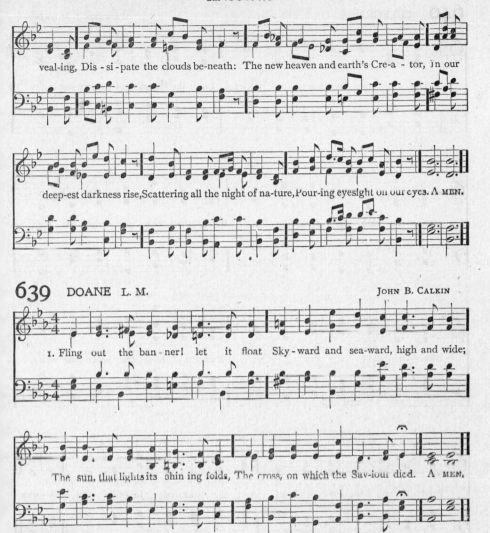

veal-ing, Dis - si - pate the clouds be-neath: The new heaven and earth's Cre-a - tor, In our

deep-est darkness rise, Scattering all the night of na-ture, Pour-ing eyesight on our eyes. A MEN.

639 DOANE L. M.

JOHN B. CALKIN

1. Fling out the ban - ner! let it float Sky - ward and sea - ward, high and wide;

The sun, that lights its shin-ing folds, The cross, on which the Sav-iour died. A MEN.

2 Fling out the banner! angels bend
    In anxious silence o'er the sign,
  And vainly seek to comprehend
    The wonder of the love divine.

3 Fling out the banner! heathen lands
    Shall see from far the glorious sight;
  And nations, crowding to be born,
    Baptize their spirits in its light.

4 Fling out the banner! sin-sick souls
    That sink and perish in the strife

3hall touch in faith its radiant hem,
    And spring immortal into life.

5 Fling out the banner! let it float
    Skyward and seaward, high and wide,
  Our glory, only in the cross;
    Our only hope, the Crucified!

6 Fling out the banner! wide and high,
    Seaward and skyward let it shine;
  Nor skill, nor might, nor merit ours;
    We conquer only in that sign.

GEORGE W. DOANE

640 CULFORD 7s. D.

Edward J. Hopkins

1. Go, ye mes-sen-gers of God! Like the beams of morn-ing fly,
Take the won-der-work-ing rod, Wave the ban-ner-cross on high:
Where the loft-y min-a-ret Gleams a-long the morn-ing skies,
Wave it till the cres-cent set, And the Star of Ja-cob rise! A-MEN.

2 Go to many a tropic isle
    In the bosom of the deep,
Where the skies forever smile
    And the oppressed forever weep:
O'er their gloomy night of care
    Pour the living light of heaven;
Chase away their dark despair,
    Bid them hope to be forgiven!

3 Where the golden gates of day
    Open on the palmy East,
Wide the bleeding cross display,
    Spread the gospel's richest feast:
Bear the tidings round the ball,
    Visit every soil and sea:
Preach the cross of Christ to all,
    Jesus' love is full and free!

Joshua Marsden

641 IBSTONE 6s.

MARIA TIDDEMAN

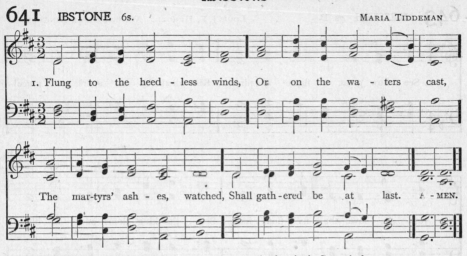

1. Flung to the heed - less winds, Or on the wa - ters cast,

The mar-tyrs' ash - es, watched, Shall gath-ered be at last. A - MEN.

2 And from that scattered dust,
  Around us and abroad,
Shall spring a plenteous seed
  Of witnesses for God.

3 The Father hath received
  Their latest living breath,

And vain is Satan's boast
  Of victory in their death:

4 Still, still, though dead, they speak,
  And, trumpet-tongued, proclaim,
To many a wakening land,
  The one availing name.

MARTIN LUTHER. Tr. by JOHN A. MESSENGER

642 EAGLEY C. M.

JAMES WALCH

1. The Lord will come and not be slow; His foot-steps can - not err;

Be - fore him right - eous - ness shall go, His roy - al har - bin - ger. A - MEN.

2 Mercy and truth, that long were missed,
  Now joyfully are met;
Sweet peace and righteousness have kissed,
  And hand in hand are set.

3 The nations all whom thou hast made
  Shall come, and all shall frame
To bow them low before thee, Lord!
  And glorify thy name.

4 Truth from the earth, like to a flower,
  Shall bud and blossom then,
And justice, from her heavenly bower,
  Look down on mortal men.

5 Thee will I praise, O Lord, my God!
  Thee honor and adore
With my whole heart; and blaze abroad
  Thy name for evermore!

JOHN MILTON

457

643 MESSIAH 7s. D. LOUIS J. F. HEROLD. Arr. by GEORGE KINGSLEY

1. See how great a flame as-pires, Kin-dled by a spark of grace!
Je - sus' love the na - tions fires, Sets the king-doms on a blaze:
To bring fire on earth he came; Kin - dled in some hearts it is:
O that all might catch the flame, All par-take the glo-rious bliss! A-MEN.

2 When he first the work begun,
   Small and feeble was his day:
Now the word doth swiftly run;
   Now it wins its widening way:
More and more it spreads and grows,
   Ever mighty to prevail;
Sin's strongholds it now o'erthrows,
   Shakes the trembling gates of hell.

3 Saw ye not the cloud arise,
   Little as a human hand?
Now it spreads along the skies,
   Hangs o'er all the thirsty land;
Lo! the promise of a shower
   Drops already from above;
But the Lord will shortly pour
   All the spirit of his love.

CHARLES WESLEY

644 ST. BONIFACE L. M.   JOSEPH BARNBY

1. Look from thy sphere of end-less day, O God of mer-cy and of might;

In pit-y look on those who stray, Be-night-ed, in this land of light. A-MEN.

2 In peopled vale, in lonely glen,
  In crowded mart, by stream or sea,
How many of the sons of men
  Hear not the message sent from thee!

3 Send forth thy heralds, Lord, to call
  The thoughtless young, the hardened old,
A scattered, homeless flock, till all
  Be gathered to thy peaceful fold.

4 Send them thy mighty word to speak,
  Till faith shall dawn, and doubt depart,
To awe the bold, to stay the weak,
  And bind and heal the broken heart.

5 Then all these wastes, a dreary scene,
  That make us sadden as we gaze,
Shall grow with living waters green,
  And lift to heaven the voice of praise.

Copyright, D. Appleton & Co.   WILLIAM C. BRYANT

645 HUMMEL C. M.   HEINRICH C. ZEUNER

1. Great God, the na-tions of the earth Are by cre-a-tion thine;

And in thy works, by all be-held, Thy ra-diant glo-ries shine, A-MEN.

2 But, Lord, thy greater love has sent
  Thy gospel to mankind,
Unveiling what rich stores of grace
  Are treasured in thy mind.

3 When, Lord, shall these glad tidings spread
  The spacious earth around,

Till every tribe and every soul
  Shall hear the joyful sound?

4 Smile, Lord, on each divine attempt
  To spread the gospel's rays,
And build on sin's demolished throne
  The temples of thy praise.

THOMAS GIBBONS

646 ST. GEORGE'S, WINDSOR 7s. D.

GEORGE J. ELVEY

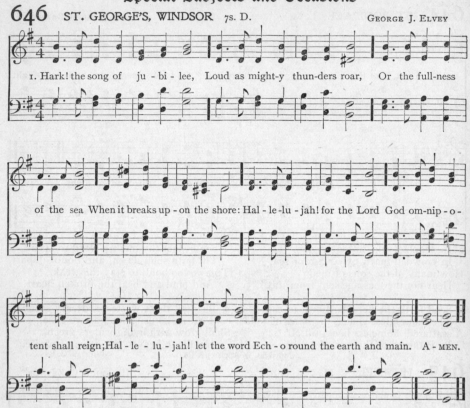

1. Hark! the song of ju - bi - lee, Loud as might-y thun-ders roar, Or the full-ness of the sea When it breaks up - on the shore: Hal - le - lu - jah! for the Lord God om-nip - o - tent shall reign; Hal - le - lu - jah! let the word Ech - o round the earth and main. A - MEN.

2 Hallelujah! hark! the sound,
  From the depths unto the skies,
Wakes above, beneath, around,
  All creation's harmonies:
See Jehovah's banner furled,
  Sheathed his sword; he speaks; 'tis done!
And the kingdoms of this world
  Are the kingdoms of his Son.

3 He shall reign from pole to pole
  With illimitable sway;
He shall reign, when, like a scroll,
  Yonder heavens have passed away:
Then the end; beneath his rod
  Man's last enemy shall fall;
Hallelujah! Christ in God,
  God in Christ, is all in all.

JAMES MONTGOMERY

647 ZION 8. 7. 8. 7. 4. 7.

THOMAS HASTINGS

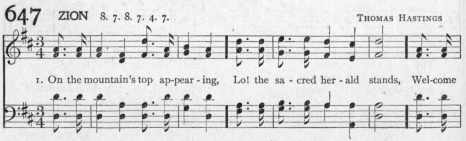

1. On the mountain's top ap-pear - ing, Lo! the sa - cred her - ald stands, Wel-come

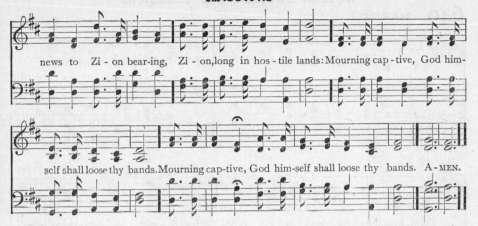

news to Zi-on bear-ing, Zi-on, long in hos-tile lands: Mourning cap-tive, God him-self shall loose thy bands. Mourning cap-tive, God him-self shall loose thy bands. A-MEN.

2 Has thy night been long and mournful?
  Have thy friends unfaithful proved?
  Have thy foes been proud and scornful,
  By thy sighs and tears unmoved?
    Cease thy mourning;
    Zion still is well beloved.

3 God, thy God, will now restore thee;
  He himself appears thy Friend;
  All thy foes shall flee before thee;

Here their boasts and triumphs end:
    Great deliverance
    Zion's King will surely send.

4 Peace and joy shall now attend thee;
  All thy warfare now is past;
  God thy Saviour will defend thee;
  Victory is thine at last:
    All thy conflicts
    End in everlasting rest.

THOMAS KELLY

648 SWABIA S. M. Old German Chorale. Arr. by WILLIAM H. HAVERGAL

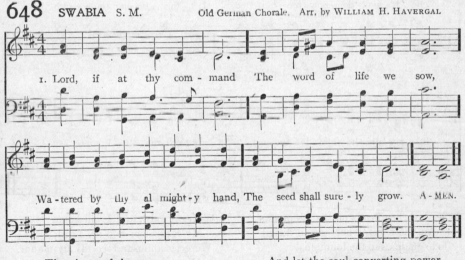

1. Lord, if at thy com-mand The word of life we sow,
Wa-tered by thy al-might-y hand, The seed shall sure-ly grow. A-MEN.

2 The virtue of thy grace
  A large increase shall give,
  And multiply the faithful race
  Who to thy glory live.

3 Now then the ceaseless shower
  Of gospel blessings send,

And let the soul-converting power
  Thy ministers attend.

4 On multitudes confer
  The heart-renewing love,
  And by the joy of grace prepare
  For fuller joys above.

CHARLES WESLEY

649

HARWELL 8s. 7s. D.

LOWELL MASON

1. Praise the Sav-iour, all ye na-tions, Praise him, all ye hosts a-bove;

Shout, with joy-ful ac-cla-ma-tions, His di-vine, vic-to-rious love;

Be his king-dom now pro-mo-ted, Let the earth her mon-arch know;

Be my all to him de-vot-ed, To my Lord my all I owe. A-MEN.

2 See how beauteous on the mountains
  Are their feet, whose grand design
Is to guide us to the fountains
  That o'erflow with bliss divine,
Who proclaim the joyful tidings
  Of salvation all around,
Disregard the world's deridings,
  And in works of love abound.

3 With my substance I will honor
  My Redeemer and my Lord;
Were ten thousand worlds my manor,
  All were nothing to his word:
While the heralds of salvation
  His abounding grace proclaim,
Let his friends, of every station,
  Gladly join to spread his fame.

BENJAMIN FRANCIS

Missions

650 ELLACOMBE 7s. 6s. D.   German

1. Hail, to the Lord's an-noint-ed, Great Da-vid's great-er Son!

Hail, in the time ap-point-ed, His reign on earth be-gun!

He comes to break op-pres-sion, To set the cap-tive free;

To take a-way trans-gres-sion, And rule in eq-ui-ty. A-MEN.

2 He comes with succor speedy
   To those who suffer wrong;
To help the poor and needy,
   And bid the weak be strong;
To give them songs for sighing,
   Their darkness turn to light,
Whose souls, condemned and dying,
   Were precious in his sight.

3 He shall come down like showers
   Upon the fruitful earth,
And love and joy, like flowers,
   Spring in his path to birth:

Before him, on the mountains,
   Shall peace, the herald, go,
And righteousness, in fountains,
   From hill to valley flow.

4 To him shall prayer unceasing,
   And daily vows ascend;
His kingdom still increasing,
   A kingdom without end:
The tide of time shall never
   His covenant remove;
His name shall stand forever;
   That name to us is Love.

JAMES MONTGOMERY

651 STANLEY L. M. D.

ARTHUR H. MANN

1. King-dom of light! whose morn-ing-star To Bethl'hem's man-ger led the way,

Not yet up-on our long-ing eyes Shines the full splendor of thy day:

Yet still a-cross the cen-turies falls, Sol-emn and sweet, our Lord's com-mand;

And still with stead-fast faith we cry, "Lo, the glad king-dom is at hand!" A-MEN.

2 Kingdom of heaven! whose dawn began
　With love's divine, incarnate breath,
Our hearts are slow to understand
　The lessons of that life and death:
Yet though with stammering tongues we tell
　Redemption's story, strange and sweet,
The world's Redeemer, lifted up,
　Shall draw the nations to his feet.

3 Kingdom of peace! whose music clear
　Swept through Judea's starlit skies,
Still the harsh sounds of human strife
　Break on thy heavenly harmonies:
Yet shall thy song of triumph ring
　In full accord, from land to land,
And men with angels learn to sing,
　"Behold, the kingdom is at hand!"

EMILY H. MILLER

652 DEVA 6s. 5s. D. *With Refrain*

EDWARD J. HOPKINS

1. Tell the bless-èd tid - ings, Chil-dren of the King, With your glad ho - san - nas Make the morn-ing ring: Songs of his sal - va - tion Nev-er-more should cease,

REFRAIN

Crown him with your prais-es, Hail him Prince of Peace! Round his throne of tri - umph Hap-py hosts at - tend, His the power and glo - ry, King-dom with-out end. A MEN.

2 Tell the blessèd tidings,
  Ye whose ears have heard;
Tell it to the captives
  Waiting for his word:
Tell the hungry nations,
  Longing to be fed,
Of the living water,
  And the heavenly bread.

REFRAIN
Mighty to deliver,
  Tender Guide and Friend,
His the power and glory,
  Kingdom without end.

3 Bear the blessèd tidings
  Over land and sea,
Lo, the morning breaketh,
  And the shadows flee!
Whosoever heareth
  Speed the news along,
Join with men and angels,
  In salvation's song.

REFRAIN
Christ the world's Redeemer,
  Saviour, Guide, and Friend!
Thine the power and glory,
  Kingdom without end!

EMILY H. MILLER

653 WEBB 7s. 6s. D.

GEORGE J. WEBB

1. The morn-ing light is break-ing, The dark-ness dis-ap-pears; The sons of earth are wak-ing To pen-i-ten-tial tears: Each breeze that sweeps the o-cean Brings tid-ings from a-far, Of na-tions in com-mo-tion, Pre-pared for Zi-on's war. A-MEN.

2 See heathen nations bending
　Before the God we love,
And thousand hearts ascending
　In gratitude above:
While sinners, now confessing,
　The gospel call obey,
And seek the Saviour's blessing,
　A nation in a day.

3 Blest river of salvation,
　Pursue thine onward way;
Flow thou to every nation,
　Nor in thy richness stay:
Stay not till all the lowly
　Triumphant reach their home:
Stay not till all the holy
　Proclaim, "The Lord is come!"

SAMUEL F. SMITH

654 TIDINGS P. M.

JAMES WALCH

1. O Zi-on, haste, thy mis-sion high ful-fill-ing, To tell to all the

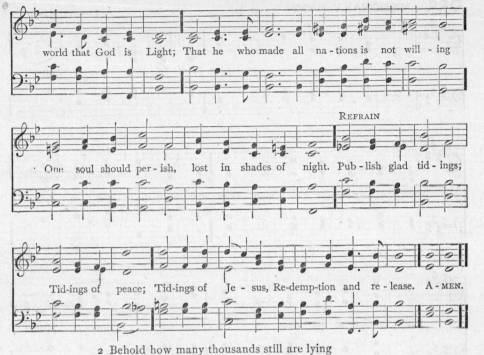

world that God is Light; That he who made all na-tions is not will-ing

One soul should per-ish, lost in shades of night. Pub-lish glad tid-ings;

REFRAIN

Tid-ings of peace; Tid-ings of Je-sus, Re-demp-tion and re-lease. A-MEN.

2 Behold how many thousands still are lying
   Bound in the darksome prison-house of sin,
   With none to tell them of the Saviour's dying,
   Or of the life he died for them to win.

3 'Tis thine to save from peril of perdition
   The souls for whom the Lord his life laid down;
   Beware lest, slothful to fulfill thy mission,
   Thou lose one jewel that should dock his crown.

4 Proclaim to every people, tongue, and nation
   That God, in whom they live and move, is love;
   Tell how he stooped to save his lost creation,
   And died on earth that man might live above.

5 Give of thy sons to bear the message glorious;
   Give of thy wealth to speed them on their way;
   Pour out thy soul for them in prayer victorious;
   And all thou spendest Jesus will repay.

6 He comes again; O Zion, ere thou meet him,
   Make known to every heart his saving grace;
   Let none whom he hath ransomed fail to greet him,
   Through thy neglect, unfit to see his face.
             Publish glad tidings;
                Tidings of peace;
             Tidings of Jesus,
             Redemption and release.

MARY A. THOMSON

467

655 MISSIONARY HYMN 7s. 6s. D.

LOWELL MASON

1. From Green-land's i-cy moun-tains, From In-dia's cor-al strand;
Where Af-ric's sun-ny foun-tains Roll down their gold-en sand:
From ma-ny an an-cient riv-er, From ma-ny a palm-y plain,
They call us to de-liv-er Their land from er-ror's chain. A-MEN.

2 What though the spicy breezes
  Blow soft o'er Ceylon's isle;
Though every prospect pleases,
  And only man is vile?
In vain with lavish kindness
  The gifts of God are strown;
The heathen in his blindness
  Bows down to wood and stone.

3 Shall we, whose souls are lighted
  With wisdom from on high,
Shall we to men benighted
  The lamp of life deny?

Salvation! O salvation!
  The joyful sound proclaim,
Till earth's remotest nation
  Has learned Messiah's name.

4 Waft, waft, ye winds, his story,
  And you, ye waters, roll,
Till, like a sea of glory,
  It spreads from pole to pole:
Till o'er our ransomed nature
  The Lamb for sinners slain,
Redeemer, King, Creator,
  In bliss returns to reign.

REGINALD HEBER

656 CHRIST CHURCH 6. 6. 6. 6. 8. 8. CHARLES STEGGALL

1. Great King of glo - ry, come, And with thy fa - vor crown This tem - ple as thy home, This peo- ple as thine own: Be - neath this roof, O deign to show How God can dwell with men be - low. A-MEN.

2 Here may thine ears attend
Our interceding cries,
And grateful praise ascend,
Like incense, to the skies:
Here may thy word melodious sound,
And spread celestial joys around.

3 Here may our unborn sons
And daughters sound thy praise,
And shine, like polished stones,
Through long-succeeding days:
Here, Lord, display thy saving power,
While temples stand and men adore.

4 Here may the listening throng
Receive thy truth in love;
Here Christians join the song
Of seraphim above;
Till all, who humbly seek thy face,
Rejoice in thy abounding grace.

BENJAMIN FRANCIS

657 NUREMBERG 7s.

JOHANN R. AHLE

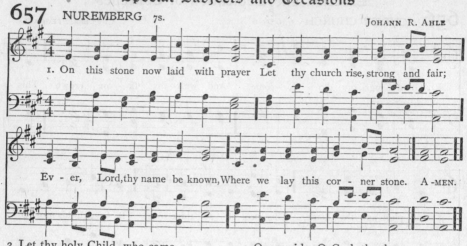

1. On this stone now laid with prayer Let thy church rise, strong and fair;

Ev - er, Lord, thy name be known, Where we lay this cor - ner stone. A-MEN.

2 Let thy holy Child, who came
Man from error to reclaim,
And for sinners to atone,
Bless, with thee, this corner stone.

3 May thy Spirit here give rest
To the heart by sin oppressed,
And the seeds of truth be sown,
Where we lay this corner stone.

4 Open wide, O God, thy door
For the outcast and the poor,
Who can call no house their own,
Where we lay this corner stone.

5 By wise master-builders squared,
Here be living stones prepared
For the temple near thy throne,
Jesus Christ its Corner Stone.

JOHN PIERPONT

658 ALSACE L. M.

From LUDWIG VAN BEETHOVEN

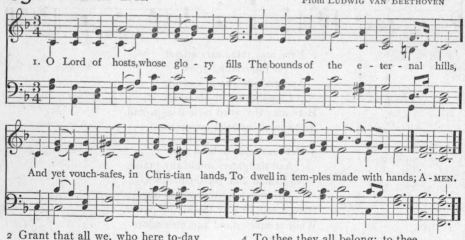

1. O Lord of hosts, whose glo - ry fills The bounds of the e - ter - nal hills,

And yet vouch-safes, in Chris-tian lands, To dwell in tem-ples made with hands; A-MEN.

2 Grant that all we, who here to-day
Rejoicing this foundation lay,
May be in very deed thine own,
Built on the precious Corner Stone.

3 Endue the creatures with thy grace
That shall adorn thy dwelling place;
The beauty of the oak and pine,
The gold and silver, make them thine.

4 To thee they all belong; to thee
The treasures of the earth and sea;
And when we bring them to thy throne
We but present thee with thine own.

5 The heads that guide endue with skill;
The hands that work preserve from ill;
That we, who these foundations lay,
May raise the topstone in its day.

JOHN M. NEALE

Erection and Dedication of Churches

659 DUNDEE C. M.   Scotch Psalter

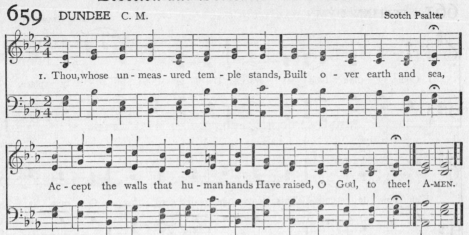

1. Thou, whose un-meas-ured tem-ple stands, Built o-ver earth and sea,

Ac-cept the walls that hu-man hands Have raised, O God, to thee! A-MEN.

2 Lord, from thine inmost glory send,
  Within these courts to bide,
The peace that dwelleth without end
  Serenely by thy side!

3 May erring minds that worship here
  Be taught the better way;

And they who mourn, and they who fear,
  Be strengthened as they pray.

4 May faith grow firm, and love grow warm,
  And pure devotion rise,
While round these hallowed walls the storm
  Of earthborn passion dies.

WILLIAM C. BRYANT

660 DUKE STREET L. M.   JOHN HATTON

1. The per-fect world, by Ad-am trod, Was the first tem-ple built by God;

His fi-at laid the cor-ner stone, And heaved its pil-lars one by one. A-MEN.

2 He hung its starry roof on high,
  The broad expanse of azure sky;
He spread its pavement, green and bright,
And curtained it with morning light.

3 The mountains in their places stood,
  The sea, the sky; and all was good;

And when its first pure praises rang,
The morning stars together sang.

4 Lord, 'tis not ours to make the sea,
  And earth, and sky, a house for thee;
But in thy sight our offering stands,
A humbler temple, made with hands.

NATHANIEL P. WILLIS

471

661 ITALIAN HYMN 6. 6. 4. 6. 6. 6. 4.

FELICE GIARDINI

1. Come, O thou God of grace, Dwell in this ho - ly place, E'en now de - scend! This tem - ple, reared to thee, O may it ev - er be Filled with thy maj - es - ty, Till time shall end! A-MEN.

2 Be in each song of praise
Which here thy people raise
    With hearts aflame!
Let every anthem rise
Like incense to the skies,
A joyful sacrifice,
    To thy blest name!

3 Speak, O eternal Lord,
Out of thy living word,
    O give success!
Do thou the truth impart
Unto each waiting heart;
Source of all strength thou art,
    Thy gospel bless!

4 To the great One and Three
Glory and praises be
    In love now given!
Glad songs to thee we sing,
Glad hearts to thee we bring,
Till we our God and King
    Shall praise in heaven!

WILLIAM E. EVANS

662 REGENT SQUARE 8s. 7s. 6l.

HENRY SMART

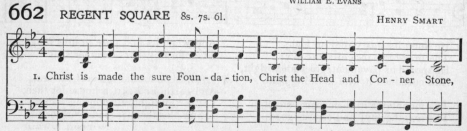

1. Christ is made the sure Foun - da - tion, Christ the Head and Cor - ner Stone,

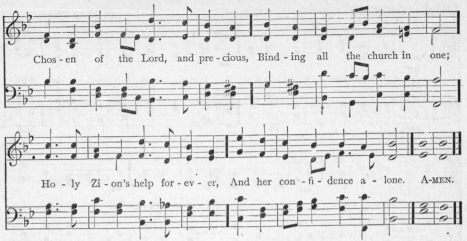

Chos-en of the Lord, and pre-cious, Bind-ing all the church in one;

Ho-ly Zi-on's help for-ev-er, And her con-fi-dence a-lone. A-MEN.

2 To this temple, where we call thee,
Come, O Lord of hosts, to-day:
With thy wonted loving-kindness,
Hear thy servants as they pray;
And thy fullest benediction
Shed within its walls alway.

3 Here vouchsafe to all thy servants
What they ask of thee to gain,
What they gain from thee forever
With the blessèd to retain,
And hereafter in thy glory
Evermore with thee to reign.

From the Latin. Tr. by JOHN M. NEALE

663 MILLER L. M.   CARL P. E. BACH. Arr. by EDWARD MILLER

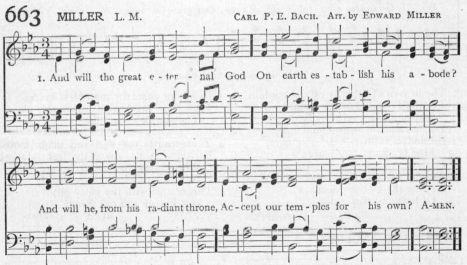

1. And will the great e-ter-nal God On earth es-tab-lish his a-bode?

And will he, from his ra-diant throne, Ac-cept our tem-ples for his own? A-MEN.

2 These walls we to thy honor raise;
Long may they echo with thy praise:
And thou, descending, fill the place
With choicest tokens of thy grace.

3 Here let the great Redeemer reign,
With all the graces of his train;

While power divine his word attends,
To conquer foes, and cheer his friends.

4 And in that great decisive day,
When God the nations shall survey,
May it before the world appear
That crowds were born to glory here.

PHILIP DODDRIDGE

664 SHORTLE 8. 8. 6. D.

CHARLES G. GOODRICH

1. O Lord, our God, al-might-y King, We fain would make this tem-ple ring With our a-dor-ing praise; And join-ing with the ransomed host, To Fa-ther, Son, and Ho-ly Ghost, Our grate-ful songs we raise, Our grate-ful songs we raise. A-MEN.

2 The heaven of heavens cannot contain
  Thy majesty, and in thy train
    Thy archangel veils his face;
  Yet curtained tent or temple fair,
  If humble, contrite hearts be there,
    May be thy resting place.

3 We sing thy wondrous works and ways;
  We sing the glorious displays
    Of love and power divine;

In all our past, thy matchless grace
Hath been vouchsafed within this place
  The glory e'er be thine.

4 These courts renewed and made more
For thine abode, low at thy feet   [meet
  With prayer, to thee we bring;
Hear and forgive; thy love distill;
This temple with thy glory fill;
  Our Father and our King!

MRS. F. K. STRATTON

664 LOS ANGELES 8. 8. 6. D. (*Second Tune*)

DAVID S. SMITH

1. O Lord, our God, al-might-y King, We fain would make this

Erection and Dedication of Churches

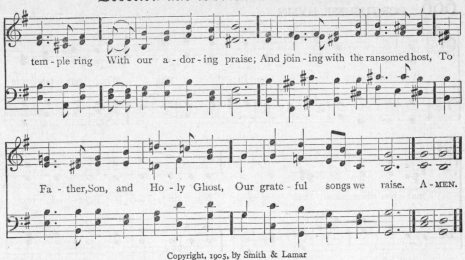

tem - ple ring With our a - dor - ing praise; And join - ing with the ransomed host, To

Fa - ther, Son, and Ho - ly Ghost, Our grate - ful songs we raise. A - MEN.

665   TEMPLE   C. M.

MARO L. BARTLETT

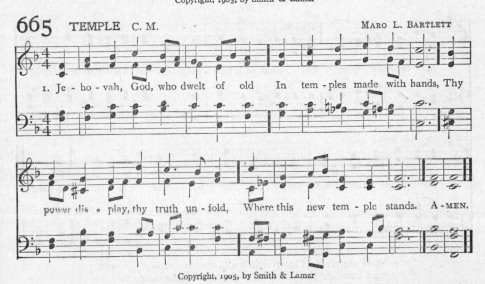

1. Je - ho - vah, God, who dwelt of old In tem - ples made with hands, Thy

power dis - play, thy truth un - fold, Where this new tem - ple stands. A - MEN.

2 Vouchsafe to meet thy children here,
  Nor ever hence depart;
From sorrow's eye wipe every tear,
  And bless each longing heart.

3 The rich man's gift, the widow's mite
  Are blended in these walls;
These altars welcome all alike
  Who heed God's gracious calls.

4 From things unholy and unclean
  We separate this place;

May naught here ever come between
  This people and thy face!

5 Now with this house we give to thee
  Ourselves, our hearts, our all,
The pledge of faith and loyalty,
  Held subject to thy call.

6 And when at last the blood-washed throng
  Is gathered from all lands,
We'll enter with triumphant song
  The house not made with hands.

LEWIS R. AMIS

666 PORTUGUESE HYMN 11s.

Composer Unknown

1. We rear not a tem-ple, like Ju-dah's of old, Whose por-tals were mar-ble, whose vault-ings were gold; No in-cense is light-ed, no vic-tims are slain, No mon-arch kneels pray-ing to hal-low the fane, No mon-arch kneels pray-ing to hal-low the fane. A-MEN.

2 More simple and lowly the walls that we raise,
And humbler the pomp of procession and praise,
Where the heart is the altar whence incense shall roll,
And Messiah the King who shall pray for the soul.

3 O Father, come in! but not in the cloud
Which filled the bright courts where thy chosen ones bowed;
But come in that Spirit of glory and grace,
Which beams on the soul and illumines the face.

4 O come in the power of thy life-giving word,
And reveal to each heart its Redeemer and Lord;
Till faith bring the peace to the penitent given,
And love fill the air with the fragrance of heaven.

HENRY WARE, Jr.

The Family

667 SABBATA C. M.

HENRY F. HEMY

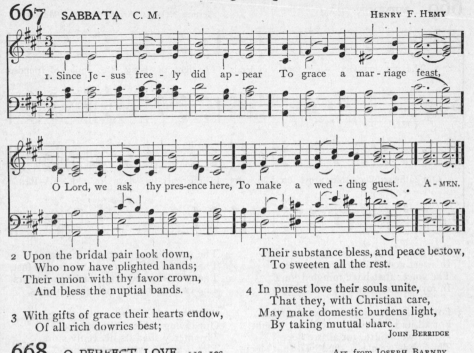

1. Since Jesus freely did appear To grace a marriage feast, O Lord, we ask thy presence here, To make a wedding guest. A-MEN.

2 Upon the bridal pair look down,
Who now have plighted hands;
Their union with thy favor crown,
And bless the nuptial bands.

3 With gifts of grace their hearts endow,
Of all rich dowries best;

Their substance bless, and peace bestow,
To sweeten all the rest.

4 In purest love their souls unite,
That they, with Christian care,
May make domestic burdens light,
By taking mutual share.

JOHN BERRIDGE

668 O PERFECT LOVE 11s. 10s.

Arr. from JOSEPH BARNBY

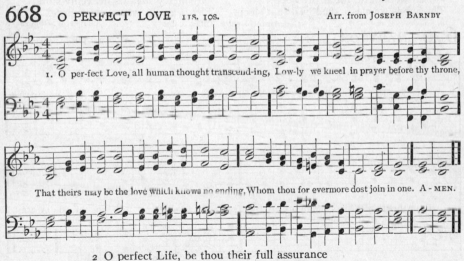

1. O perfect Love, all human thought transcending, Lowly we kneel in prayer before thy throne, That theirs may be the love which knows no ending, Whom thou for evermore dost join in one. A-MEN.

2 O perfect Life, be thou their full assurance
Of tender charity and steadfast faith,
Of patient hope and quiet, brave endurance,
With childlike trust that fears nor pain nor death.

3 Grant them the joy which brightens earthly sorrow;
Grant them the peace which calms all earthly strife,
And to life's day the glorious unknown morrow
That dawns upon eternal love and life.

DOROTHY F. BLOMFIELD

669 MENDON L. M.

German Melody. Arr. by LOWELL MASON

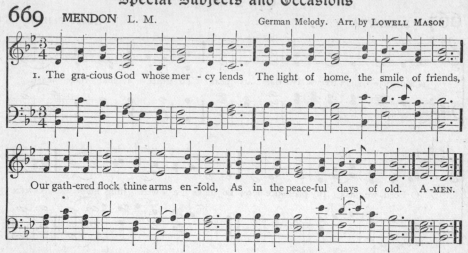

1. The gra-cious God whose mer - cy lends The light of home, the smile of friends,

Our gath-ered flock thine arms en-fold, As in the peace-ful days of old. A-MEN.

2 Wilt thou not hear us while we raise,
In sweet accord of solemn praise,
The voices that have mingled long
In joyous flow of mirth and song?

3 For all the blessings life has brought,
For all its sorrowing hours have taught,
For all we mourn, for all we keep,
The hands we clasp, the loved that sleep,

4 The noontide sunshine of the past,
These brief, bright moments fading fast,
The stars that gild our darkening years,
The twilight ray from holier spheres,

5 We thank thee, Father; let thy grace
Our loving circle still embrace,
Thy mercy shed its heavenly store,
Thy peace be with us evermore.

Copyright, Houghton, Mifflin & Co.　　　OLIVER W. HOLMES

670 MARYTON L. M.

H. PERCY SMITH

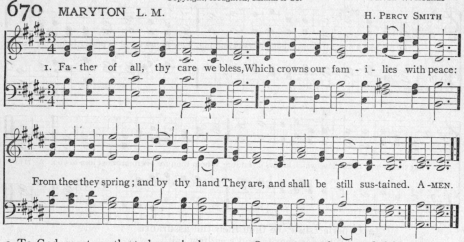

1. Fa-ther of all, thy care we bless, Which crowns our fam - i - lies with peace:

From thee they spring; and by thy hand They are, and shall be still sus-tained. A-MEN.

2 To God, most worthy to be praised,
Be our domestic altars raised;
Who, Lord of heaven, yet deigns to come
And sanctify our humblest home.

3 To thee may each united house
Morning and night present its vows;

Our servants there, and rising race,
Be taught thy precepts and thy grace.

4 So may each future age proclaim
The honors of thy glorious name,·
And each succeeding race remove
To join the family above.

PHILIP DODDRIDGE

671 ALVERSTROKE 11S. 10S.

JOSEPH BARNBY

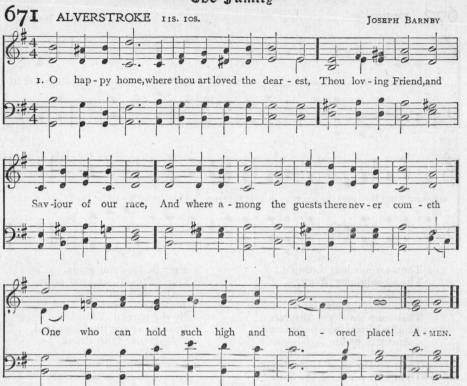

1. O hap-py home, where thou art loved the dear-est, Thou lov-ing Friend, and Sav-iour of our race, And where a-mong the guests there nev-er com-eth One who can hold such high and hon-ored place! A-MEN.

2 O happy home, where two in heart united
   In holy faith and blessèd hope are one,
Whom death a little while alone divideth,
   And cannot end the union here begun!

3 O happy home, whose little ones are given
   Early to thee, in humble faith and prayer,
To thee, their Friend, who from the heights of heaven
   Guides them, and guards with more than mother's care!

4 O happy home, where each one serves thee, lowly,
   Whatever his appointed work may be,
Till every common task seems great and holy,
   When it is done, O Lord, as unto thee!

5 O happy home, where thou art not forgotten
   When joy is overflowing, full, and free;
O happy home, where every wounded spirit
   Is brought, Physician, Comforter, to thee, —

6 Until at last, when earth's day's work is ended
   All meet thee in the blessèd home above,
From whence thou camest, where thou hast ascended,
   Thy everlasting home of peace and love!

CARL J. SPITTA. Tr. by Mrs. ALEXANDER

672 DORT 6. 6. 4. 6. 6. 6. 4.   LOWELL MASON

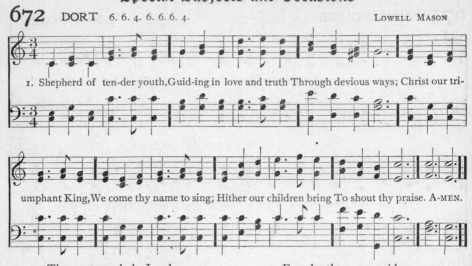

1. Shepherd of ten-der youth, Guid-ing in love and truth Through devious ways; Christ our tri-

umphant King, We come thy name to sing; Hither our children bring To shout thy praise. A-MEN.

2 Thou art our holy Lord,
The all-subduing Word,
    Healer of strife;
Thou didst thyself abase,
That from sin's deep disgrace
Thou mightest save our race,
    And give us life.

3 Thou art the great High Priest;
Thou hast prepared the feast
    Of heavenly love;
While in our mortal pain
None calls on thee in vain;
Help thou dost not disdain,
    Help from above.

4 Ever be thou our guide,
Our shepherd, and our pride,
    Our staff and song;
Jesus, thou Christ of God,
By thy perennial word
Lead us where thou hast trod,
    Make our faith strong.

5 So now, and till we die,
Sound we thy praises high,
    And joyful sing;
Infants, and the glad throng
Who to thy church belong,
Unite to swell the song
    To Christ our King.

CLEMENT of Alexandria. Tr. by HENRY M. DEXTER

673 CHILDREN'S OFFERINGS 7. 7. 5. D.   JOHN STAINER

1ST VOICE   *cres.*

1. Beau-teous are the flowers of earth, Flowers we bring with ho - ly mirth,

2D VOICE, *ad lib.*   *cres.*

1. Beau-teous are the flowers of earth, Flowers we bring with ho - ly mirth,

mf   *cres.*

Bright and sweet and gay; Will our Fa-ther deign to own

Bright and sweet and gay; Will our Fa-ther deign to own

Gifts we lay be-fore his throne, On this hap-py day? A-MEN.

Gifts we lay be-fore his throne, On this hap-py day? A-MEN.

2 Yes, he will; for all things bright
Are most precious in his sight,
And he loves to see
Children come with flowers for him,
Whom the flaming seraphim
Worship ceaselessly.

3 Yes, he will; for children's love
Makes this world like heaven above,
Where no evil reigns,
And where all unite to bring
Purest offerings, and sing
Love's unending strains.

4 Yes, he will; for hearts that turn
To the sick and poor, and learn
How to make them glad,
Shine like beacons on the strand
Of the far-off, happy land,
To the lost and sad.

5 So our lowly gifts to thee,
Lord of earth and sky and sea,
Thou wilt kindly take;
Every little flower we bring,
Every simple hymn we sing,
And not one forsake.

WILLIAM C. DIX

674 SAMUEL 6. 6. 6. 6. 8. 8.   ARTHUR S. SULLIVAN

1. Hushed was the eve-ning hymn, The tem-ple courts were dark, The lamp was burn-ing dim, Be-fore the sa-cred ark: When sud-den-ly a voice di-vine Rang through the si-lence of the shrine. A-MEN.

2 The old man, meek and mild,
    The priest of Israel, slept;
His watch the temple-child,
    The little Levite, kept;
And what from Eli's sense was sealed,
The Lord to Hannah's son revealed.

3 O give me Samuel's ear,
    The open ear, O Lord,
Alive and quick to hear
    Each whisper of thy word!
Like him to answer at thy call,
And to obey thee first of all.

4 O give me Samuel's heart,
    A lowly heart, that waits
Where in thy house thou art,
    Or watches at thy gates!
By day and night, a heart that still
Moves at the breathing of thy will.

5 O give me Samuel's mind,
    A sweet, unmurmuring faith,
Obedient and resigned
    To thee in life and death!
That I may read with childlike eyes
Truths that are hidden from the wise.

JAMES D. BURNS

675 CHILDREN'S PRAISE 7. 7. 7. 5. D.   JOSEPH BARNBY

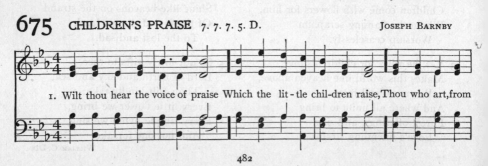

1. Wilt thou hear the voice of praise Which the lit-tle chil-dren raise, Thou who art, from

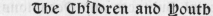

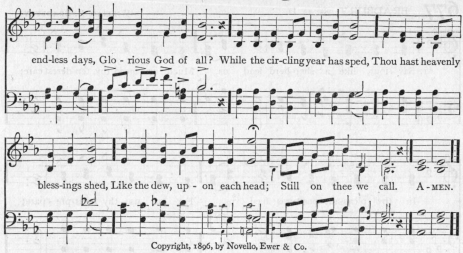

end-less days, Glo - rious God of all? While the cir-cling year has sped, Thou hast heavenly

bless-ings shed, Like the dew, up - on each head; Still on thee we call. A - MEN.

2 Still thy constant care bestow;
Let us each in wisdom grow,
And in favor while below,
  With the God above.
In our hearts the Spirit mild,
Which adorned the Saviour-child,
Gently soothe each impulse wild
  To the sway of love.

3 Thine example, kept in view,
Jesus, help us to pursue;
Lead us all our journey through
  By thy guiding hand;
And when life on earth is o'er,
Where the blest dwell evermore,
May we praise thee and adore,
  An unbroken band.

CAROLINE L. RICE

676   PERCIVALS   7s.

Composer Unknown

1. Sav - iour, teach me day by day, Love's sweet les - son to o - bey;

Sweet - er les - son can - not be, Lov - ing him who first loved me. A - MEN.

2 With a childlike heart of love,
At thy bidding may I move;
Prompt to serve and follow thee,
Loving him who first loved me.

3 Teach me all thy steps to trace,
Strong to follow in thy grace;
Learning how to love from thee;
Loving him who irst loved me.

4 Love in loving finds employ,
In obedience all her joy;
Ever new that joy will be,
Loving him who first loved me.

5 Thus may I rejoice to show
That I feel the love I owe;
Singing, till thy face I see,
Of his love who first loved me.

JANE E. LEESON

677 BRADBURY 8s. 7s. D.

WILLIAM B. BRADBURY

1. Sav - iour, like a shep-herd lead us, Much we need thy ten-derest care;

In thy pleas-ant pas-tures feed us, For our use thy folds pre - pare;

Bless-èd Je - sus, Bless - èd Je - sus! Thou hast bought us, thine we are,

Bless-èd Je - sus, Bless-èd Je - sus! Thou hast bought us, thine we are. A - MEN.

2 We are thine, do thou befriend us,
　Be the guardian of our way;
Keep thy flock, from sin defend us,
　Seek us when we go astray:
　　Blessèd Jesus!
Hear, O hear us, when we pray.

3 Thou hast promised to receive us,
　Poor and sinful though we be;
Thou hast mercy to relieve us,
　Grace to cleanse, and power to free:
　　Blessèd Jesus!
We will early turn to thee.

4 Early let us seek thy favor,
　Early let us do thy will;
Blessèd Lord and only Saviour,
　With thy love our bosoms fill:
　　Blessèd Jesus!
Thou hast loved us, love us still.

Author Unknown

The Children and Youth

678 SILOAM C. M.

ISAAC B. WOODBURY

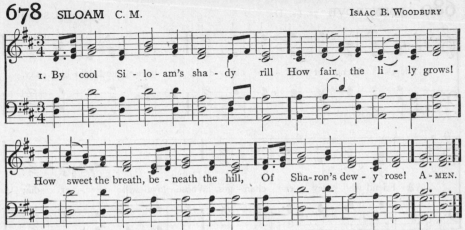

1. By cool Si - lo - am's sha - dy rill How fair the li - ly grows!

How sweet the breath, be - neath the hill, Of Sha - ron's dew - y rose! A - MEN.

2 Lo! such the child whose early feet
The paths of peace have trod;
Whose secret heart, with influence sweet,
Is upward drawn to God.

3 By cool Siloam's shady rill
The lily must decay;
The rose that blooms beneath the hill
Must shortly fade away.

4 And soon, too soon, the wintry hour
Of man's maturer age

Will shake the soul with sorrow's power,
And stormy passion's rage.

5 O Thou, whose infant feet were found
Within thy Father's shrine, [crowned,
Whose years, with changeless virtue
Were all alike divine;

6 Dependent on thy bounteous breath,
We seek thy grace alone,
In childhood, manhood, age, and death,
To keep us still thine own.

REGINALD HEBER

679 HUMMEL C. M.

HEINRICH C. ZEUNER

1. Ho - san - na! be the chil - dren's song, To Christ, the chil-dren's King;

His praise, to whom our souls be - long, Let all the children sing. A - MEN.

2 Hosanna! sound from hill to hill,
And spread from plain to plain,
While louder, sweeter, clearer still,
Woods echo to the strain.

3 Hosanna! on the wings of light,
O'er earth and ocean fly,

Till morn to eve, and noon to night,
And heaven to earth, reply.

4 Hosanna! then, our song shall be;
Hosanna to our King!
This is the children's jubilee;
Let all the children sing.

JAMES MONTGOMERY

680 EDENGROVE 7s. 6s. D.

SAMUEL SMITH

1. There's a Friend for lit-tle chil-dren A-bove the bright blue sky,
A Friend who nev-er chan-ges, Whose love will nev-er die;
Our earth-ly friends may fail us, And change with chang-ing years,
This Friend is al-ways wor-thy Of that dear name he bears. A-MEN.

2 There's a rest for little children
    Above the bright blue sky,
Who love the blessèd Saviour,
    And to the Father cry;
A rest from every turmoil,
    From sin and sorrow free,
Where every little pilgrim
    Shall rest eternally.

3 There's a home for little children
    Above the bright blue sky,
Where Jesus reigns in glory,
    A home of peace and joy;
No home on earth is like it,
    Nor can with it compare;
For every one is happy,
    Nor could be happier there.

4 There's a song for little children
    Above the bright blue sky,
A song that will not weary,
    Though sung continually;
A song which even angels
    Can never, never sing;
They know not Christ as Saviour,
    But worship him as King.

5 There's a crown for little children
    Above the bright blue sky,
And all who look for Jesus
    Shall wear it by and by;
All, all above is treasured,
    And found in Christ alone:
Lord, grant thy little children
    To know thee as their own.

ALBERT MIDLANE

681 ST. THERESA 6s. 5s. D. *With Refrain* ARTHUR S. SULLIVAN

1. Brightly gleams our banner, Pointing to the sky, Waving wanderers onward To their home on high. Journeying o'er the desert, Gladly thus we pray, And with hearts united Take our heavenward way. *Brightly gleams our banner, Pointing to the sky, Waving wanderers onward To their home on high. A-men.*

2 Jesus, Lord and Master,
  At thy sacred feet,
Here with hearts rejoicing
  See thy children meet;
Often have we left thee,
  Often gone astray;
Keep us, mighty Saviour,
  In the narrow way.

3 All our days direct us
  In the way we go;
Lead us on victorious
  Over every foe:

Bid thine angels shield us
  When the storm-clouds lower;
Pardon, Lord, and save us
  In the last dread hour.

4 Then with saints and angels
  May we join above,
Offering prayers and praises
  At thy throne of love;
When the toil is over,
  Then come rest and peace;
Jesus in his beauty;
  Songs that never cease.

THOMAS J. POTTER. Alt.

682 ATHENS P. M.

Greek Melody

1. I think when I read that sweet sto - ry of old, When Je - sus was here a - mong men, How he called lit - tle chil - dren as lambs to his fold, I should like to have been with him then. I wish that his hands had been placed on my head, That his arms had been thrown a-round me, That I might have seen his kind look when he said, Let the lit - tle ones come un - to me. A - MEN.

2 Yet still to his footstool in prayer I may go
　And ask for a share in his love;
　And if I thus earnestly seek him below,
　I shall see him and hear him above:
　In that beautiful place he has gone to prepare,
　For all who are washed and forgiven;
　And many dear children shall be with him there,
　For of such is the kingdom of heaven.

JEMIMA T. LUKE

683 ST. HILL 6s. 5s. D.

JOHN STAINER

1. Christ, who once a-mongst us As a child did dwell, Is the chil-dren's Sav-iour, And he loves us well; If we keep our prom-ise Made him at the font, He will be our Shep-herd, And we shall not want. A MEN

2 There it was they laid us
　In those tender arms,
Where the lambs are carried
　Safe from all alarms;
If we trust his promise,
　He will let us rest
In his arms forever,
　Leaning on his breast.

3 Though we may not see him
　For a little while,
We shall know he holds us,
　Often feel his smile;
Death will be to slumber
　In that sweet embrace,
And we shall awaken
　To behold his face.

4 He will be our Shepherd
　After as before,
By still heavenly waters
　Lead us evermore,
Make us lie in pastures
　Beautiful and green,
Where none thirst or hunger,
　And no tears are seen.

5 Jesus, our good Shepherd,
　Laying down thy life,
Lest thy sheep should perish
　In the cruel strife,
Help us to remember
　All thy love and care,
Trust in thee, and love thee
　Always, everywhere.

W. ST. HILL BOURNE

684 PALM SUNDAY L. M.

KARL P. HARRINGTON

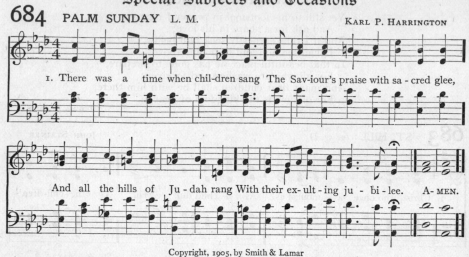

1. There was a time when chil-dren sang The Sav-iour's praise with sa-cred glee,

And all the hills of Ju-dah rang With their ex-ult-ing ju-bi-lee. A-MEN.

2 O to have joined their rapturous songs,
And swelled their sweet hosannas high,
And blessed him with our feeble tongues,
As he, the Man of grief, went by!

3 But Christ is now a glorious King,
And angels in his presence bow;
The humble songs that we can sing,
O will he, can he, hear them now?

4 He can, he will, he loves to hear
The notes which loving children raise:
Jesus, we come with trembling fear,
O teach our hearts and tongues to praise!

5 We join the hosts around thy throne,
Who once, like us, the desert trod;
And thus we make their song our own,
Hosanna to the Son of God!

THOMAS R. TAYLOR

685 MOORE 6s. 5s.

KARL P. HARRINGTON

1. Je-sus, meek and gen-tle, Son of God most high,

Pity-ing, lov-ing Sav-iour, Hear thy chil-dren's cry. A-MEN.

2 Give us holy freedom,
Fill our hearts with love;
Draw us, holy Jesus,
To the realms above.

3 Lead us on our journey,
Be thyself the way
Through the earthly darkness
To the heavenly day.

GEORGE R. PRYNNE

Education

686 CAMP L. M.

PETER C. LUTKIN

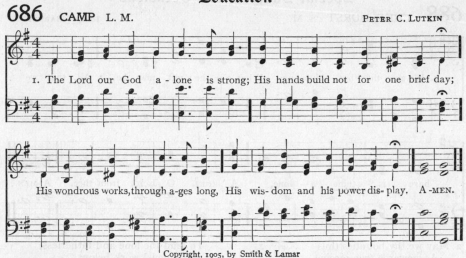

1. The Lord our God a-lone is strong; His hands build not for one brief day;

His wondrous works, through a-ges long, His wis-dom and his power dis-play. A-MEN.

2 His mountains lift their solemn forms,
  To watch in silence o'er the land;
  The rolling ocean, rocked with storms,
  Sleeps in the hollow of his hand.

3 Beyond the heavens he sits alone,
  The universe obeys his nod;
  The lightning-rifts disclose his throne,
  And thunders voice the name of God.

4 Thou sovereign God, receive this gift
  Thy willing servants offer thee;
  Accept the prayers that thousands lift,
  And let these halls thy temple be.

5 And let those learn, who here shall meet,
  True wisdom is with reverence crowned,
  And science walks with humble feet
  To seek the God that faith hath found.

CALEB T. WINCHESTER

687 PATTEN C. M.

PETER C. LUTKIN

1. Al-might-y Lord, with one ac-cord We of-fer thee our youth,

And pray that thou would'st give us now The war-fare of the truth. A-MEN.

2 Thy cause doth claim our souls by name,
  Because that we are strong;
  In all the land, one steadfast band,
  May we to Christ belong.

3 Let fall on every college hall
  The luster of thy cross;

That love may dare thy work to share
  And count all else as loss.

4 Our hearts be ruled, our spirits schooled
  Alone thy will to seek;
  And when we find thy blessèd mind,
  Instruct our lips to speak.

M. WOOLSEY STRYKER

688 CHISELHURST S. M.

JOSEPH BARNBY

1. We give thee but thine own, What-e'er the gift may be; All that we have is thine a - lone, A trust, O Lord, from thee. A-MEN.

2 May we thy bounties thus
As stewards true receive,
And gladly, as thou blessest us,
To thee our first fruits give.

3 O hearts are bruised and dead,
And homes are bare and cold,
And lambs for whom the Shepherd bled
Are straying from the fold!

4 To comfort and to bless,
To find a balm for woe,

To tend the lone and fatherless,
Is angels' work below.

5 The captive to release,
To God the lost to bring,
To teach the way of life and peace,—
It is a Christlike thing.

6 And we believe thy word,
Though dim our faith may be;
Whate'er for thine we do, O Lord,
We do it unto thee.

WILLIAM W. HOW

689 BARTHOLDY L. M.

FELIX MENDELSSOHN-BARTHOLDY

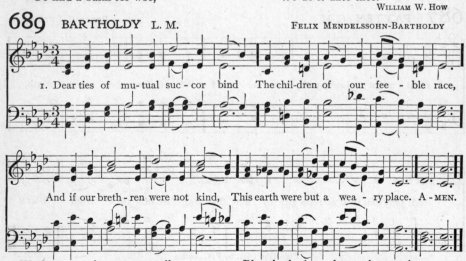

1. Dear ties of mu-tual suc - cor bind The chil-dren of our fee - ble race, And if our breth-ren were not kind, This earth were but a wea - ry place. A-MEN.

2 We lean on others as we walk
Life's twilight path, with pitfalls strewn;
And 'twere an idle boast to talk
Of treading that dim path alone.

3 Amid the snares misfortune lays
Unseen beneath the steps of all,

Blest is the love that seeks to raise,
And stay and strengthen those who fall;

4 Till, taught by Him who for our sake
Bore every form of life's distress,
With every passing year we make
The sum of human sorrow less.

WILLIAM C. BRYANT

690 DALEHURST C. M.

ARTHUR COTTMAN

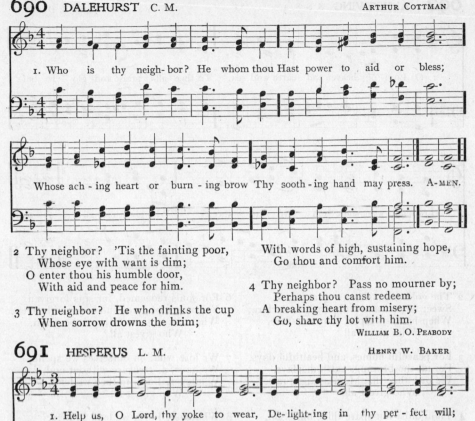

1. Who is thy neigh-bor? He whom thou Hast power to aid or bless;

Whose ach-ing heart or burn-ing brow Thy sooth-ing hand may press. A-MEN.

2 Thy neighbor? 'Tis the fainting poor,
Whose eye with want is dim;
O enter thou his humble door,
With aid and peace for him.

3 Thy neighbor? He who drinks the cup
When sorrow drowns the brim;

With words of high, sustaining hope,
Go thou and comfort him.

4 Thy neighbor? Pass no mourner by;
Perhaps thou canst redeem
A breaking heart from misery;
Go, share thy lot with him.

WILLIAM B. O. PEABODY

691 HESPERUS L. M.

HENRY W. BAKER

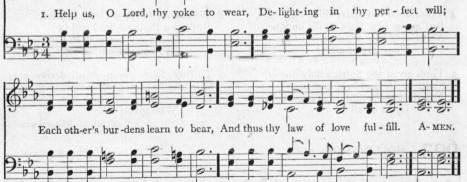

1. Help us, O Lord, thy yoke to wear, De-light-ing in thy per-fect will;

Each oth-er's bur-dens learn to bear, And thus thy law of love ful-fill. A-MEN.

2 He that hath pity on the poor
Lendeth his substance to the Lord;
And, lo! his recompense is sure,
For more than all shall be restored.

3 Teach us, with glad, ungrudging heart,
As thou hast blest our various store,

From our abundance to impart
A liberal portion to the poor.

4 To thee our all devoted be,
In whom we breathe and move and live;
Freely we have received from thee;
Freely may we rejoice to give.

THOMAS COTTERILL

692 ALMSGIVING 8.8.8.4.   JOHN B. DYKES

1. O Lord of heaven and earth and sea, To thee all praise and glo-ry be!

How shall we show our love to thee, Who giv-est all? A-MEN.

2 The golden sunshine, vernal air,
Sweet flowers and fruit thy love declare;
When harvests ripen, thou art there,
   Who givest all.

3 For peaceful homes, and healthful days,
For all the blessings earth displays,
We owe thee thankfulness and praise,
   Who givest all.

4 Thou didst not spare thine only Son,
But gav'st him for a world undone,
And freely with that blessèd One
   Thou givest all.

5 Thou giv'st the Spirit's holy dower,
Spirit of life and love and power,
And dost his sevenfold graces shower
   Upon us all.

6 For souls redeemed, for sins forgiven,
For means of grace and hopes of heaven,
What can to thee, O Lord, be given,
   Who givest all?

7 We lose what on ourselves we spend,
We have, as treasure without end,
Whatever, Lord, to thee we lend,
   Who givest all.

8 Whatever, Lord, we lend to thee,
Repaid a thousandfold will be;
Then gladly will we give to thee
   Who givest all.

9 To thee, from whom we all derive
Our life, our gifts, our power to give;
O may we ever with thee live,
   Who givest all!
                    CHRISTOPHER WORDSWORTH

693 HOLLINGSIDE 7s. D.   JOHN B. DYKES

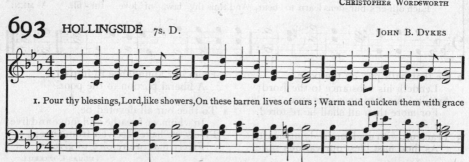

1. Pour thy blessings, Lord, like showers, On these barren lives of ours; Warm and quicken them with grace

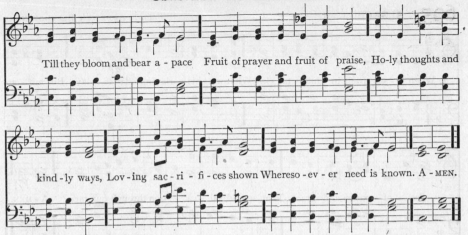

Till they bloom and bear a - pace Fruit of prayer and fruit of praise, Ho-ly thoughts and

kind-ly ways, Lov-ing sac-ri-fi-ces shown Whereso-ev-er need is known. A-MEN.

2 Chiefest, Lord, to-day may we
In the sick and suffering see,
Those whom thou would'st have us bless
With fraternal tenderness,
With our treasure freely poured,
With compassion's richer hoard,
With these ministries most dear
To thy stricken children here.

3 Heavy is the cross they bear,
But our love that cross can share;
Dark thy Providence must seem,
But our cheer can cast a gleam
On their lot; and in our turn
Holiest lessons we may learn,
Where thine own revealing light
Streams through pain's mysterious night.

Miss KIMBALL

694 PARKER. C. M.

KARL P. HARRINGTON

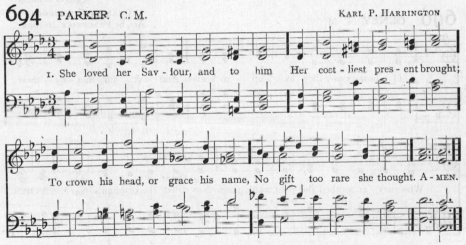

1. She loved her Sav-iour, and to him Her cost-liest pres-ent brought;

To crown his head, or grace his name, No gift too rare she thought. A-MEN.

2 So let the Saviour be adored,
And not the poor despised;
Give to the hungry from your hoard,
But all, give all to Christ.

3 Go, clothe the naked, lead the blind,
Give to the weary rest;

For sorrow's children comfort find,
And help for all distressed;

4 But give to Christ alone thy heart,
Thy faith, thy love supreme;
Then for his sake thine alms impart,
And so give all to him.

WILLIAM CUTTER

695 ALSACE L. M.

From LUDWIG VAN BEETHOVEN

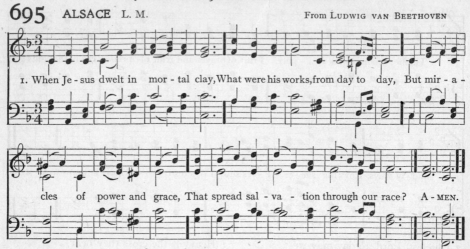

1. When Je-sus dwelt in mor-tal clay, What were his works, from day to day, But mir-a-cles of power and grace, That spread sal-va-tion through our race? A-MEN.

2 At his command, from rayless night
Redeemed, the blind receive their sight;
The deaf in rapture hear his voice,
The dumb in songs of praise rejoice.

3 Teach us, O Lord, to keep in view
Thy pattern, and thy steps pursue;

Let alms bestowed, let kindness done,
Be witnessed by each rolling sun.

4 Teach us to mark, from day to day,
In generous acts our radiant way,
Tread the same path our Saviour trod,
The path to glory and to God.

THOMAS GIBBONS

696 OLNEY C. M.

CHARLES F. GOUNOD
Arr. by FREDERICK BRIDGE

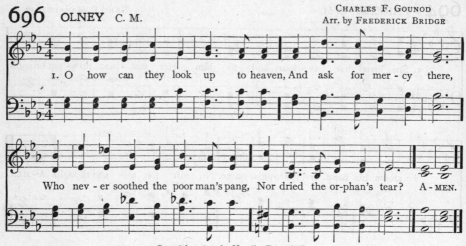

1. O how can they look up to heaven, And ask for mer-cy there, Who nev-er soothed the poor man's pang, Nor dried the or-phan's tear? A-MEN.

2 The dread omnipotence of heaven
We every hour provoke;
Yet still the mercy of our God
Withholds the avenging stroke:

3 And Christ was still the healing friend
Of poverty and pain;

And never did imploring soul
His garment touch in vain.

4 May we with humble effort take
Example from above;
And thence the active lesson learn
Of charity and love!

SIMON BROWNE

697 RESCUE THE PERISHING P. M. *With Refrain* WILLIAM H. DOANE

1. Res - cue the per - ish - ing, Care for the dy - ing, Snatch them in pit - y from

sin and the grave: Weep o'er the err - ing one, Lift up the fall - en,

REFRAIN

Tell them of Je - sus the might - y to save. Res - cue the per - ish - ing,

Care for the dy - ing; Je - sus is mer - ci - ful, Je - sus will save. A - MEN.

2 Though they are slighting him,
   Still he is waiting,
Waiting the penitent child to receive:
   Plead with them earnestly,
   Plead with them gently:
He will forgive if they only believe.

3 Down in the human heart,
   Crushed by the tempter,
Feelings lie buried that grace can restore:

Touched by a loving heart,
   Wakened by kindness, [more.
Chords that were broken will vibrate once

4 Rescue the perishing,
   Duty demands it; [vide:
Strength for thy labor the Lord will pro-
   Back to the narrow way
   Patiently win them;
Tell the poor wanderer a Saviour has died.

FANNY J. CROSBY

698 OWEN S. M.

JOSEPH E. SWEETSER

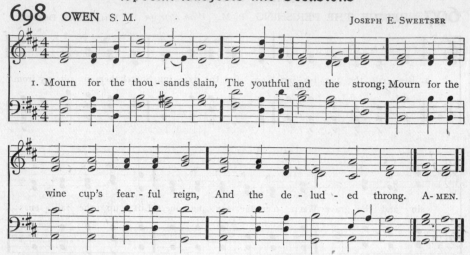

1. Mourn for the thou-sands slain, The youthful and the strong; Mourn for the
wine cup's fear-ful reign, And the de-lud-ed throng. A-MEN.

2 Mourn for the ruined soul—
  Eternal life and light
Lost by the fiery, maddening bowl,
  And turned to hopeless night.

3 Mourn for the lost; but call,
  Call to the strong, the free;

Rouse them to shun that dreadful fall,
And to the refuge flee.

4 Mourn for the lost; but pray,
  Pray to our God above,
To break the fell destroyer's sway,
  And show his saving love.

SETH C. BRACE

699 ST. MARK C. M.

HENRY J. GAUNTLETT

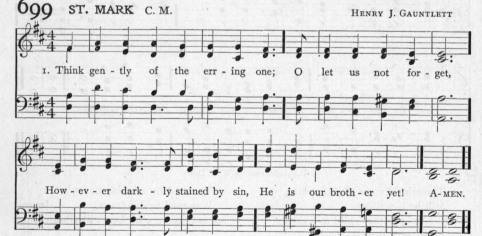

1. Think gen-tly of the err-ing one; O let us not for-get,
How-ev-er dark-ly stained by sin, He is our broth-er yet! A-MEN.

2 Heir of the same inheritance,
  Child of the selfsame God,
He hath but stumbled in the path
  We have in weakness trod.

3 Speak gently to the erring ones:
  We yet may lead them back,

With holy words, and tones of love,
From misery's thorny track.

4 Forget not, brother, thou hast sinned,
  And sinful yet may'st be;
Deal gently with the erring heart,
  As God hath dealt with thee.

Miss FLETCHER

700 WESTMINSTER C. M.　　　　　　　　　JAMES TURLE

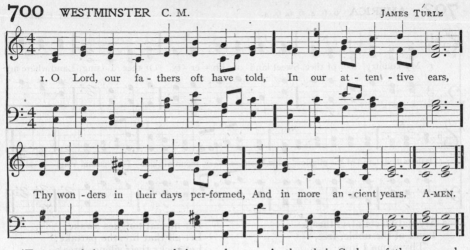

1. O Lord, our fa-thers oft have told, In our at-ten-tive ears,
Thy won-ders in their days per-formed, And in more an-cient years. A-MEN.

2 'Twas not their courage nor their sword
　To them salvation gave;
　'Twas not their number nor their strength
　That did their country save;

3 But thy right hand, thy powerful arm,
　Whose succor they implored,
　Thy providence protected them
　Who thy great name adored.

4 As thee their God our fathers owned,
　So thou art still our King;
　O, therefore, as thou didst to them,
　To us deliverance bring!

5 To thee the glory we ascribe,
　From whom salvation came;
　In God, our shield, we will rejoice,
　And ever bless thy name.
　　　　　　　　　　　　　TATE and BRADY

701 MANOAH C. M.　　　　　　From GIOACHINO A. ROSSINI

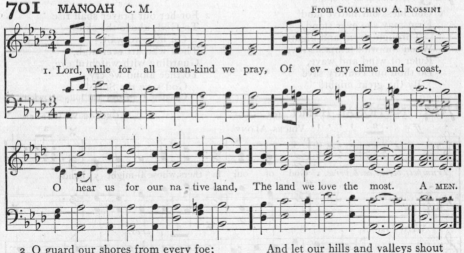

1. Lord, while for all man-kind we pray, Of ev-ery clime and coast,
O hear us for our na-tive land, The land we love the most. A MEN.

2 O guard our shores from every foe;
　With peace our borders bless,
　Our cities with prosperity,
　Our fields with plenteousness.

3 Unite us in the sacred love
　Of knowledge, truth, and thee;

And let our hills and valleys shout
　The songs of liberty.

4 Lord of the nations, thus to thee
　Our country we commend;
　Be thou her refuge and her trust,
　Her everlasting Friend.
　　　　　　　　　　　JOHN R. WREFORD

Special Subjects and Occasions

702 AMERICA 6. 6. 4. 6. 6. 6. 4.   HENRY CAREY

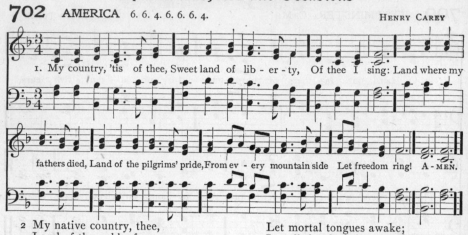

1. My country, 'tis of thee, Sweet land of lib - er - ty, Of thee I sing: Land where my fathers died, Land of the pilgrims' pride, From ev - ery mountain side Let freedom ring! A - MEN.

2 My native country, thee,
Land of the noble, free,
 Thy name I love;
I love thy rocks and rills,
Thy woods and templed hills;
My heart with rapture thrills,
 Like that above.

3 Let music swell the breeze,
And ring from all the trees
 Sweet freedom's song:

Let mortal tongues awake;
Let all that breathe partake;
Let rocks their silence break,
 The sound prolong.

4 Our fathers' God, to thee,
Author of liberty,
 To thee we sing;
Long may our land be bright
With freedom's holy light;
Protect us by thy might,
 Great God, our King.
          SAMUEL FRANCIS SMITH

703 6. 6. 4. 6. 6. 6. 4.

1 God bless our native land!
Firm may she ever stand,
 Through storm and night:
When the wild tempests rave,
Ruler of wind and wave,
Do thou our country save
 By thy great might!

2 For her our prayer shall rise
To God, above the skies;
 On him we wait:
Thou who art ever nigh,
Guarding with watchful eye,
To thee aloud we cry,
 God save the State!
  CHARLES T. BROOKS and JOHN S. DWIGHT

704 NATIONAL HYMN 10s.   GEORGE W. WARREN

Trumpets, before each verse. 1. God of our fa - thers, whose al-might - y hand Leads forth in beau - ty all the star - ry band Of shin - ing worlds in

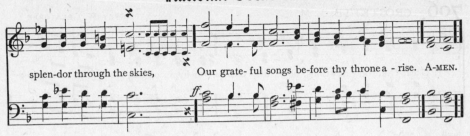

splen-dor through the skies, Our grate-ful songs be-fore thy throne a - rise. A-MEN.

2 Thy love divine hath led us in the past,
In this free land by thee our lot is cast;
Be thou our ruler, guardian, guide, and stay,
Thy word our law, thy paths our chosen way.

3 From war's alarms, from deadly pestilence,
Be thy strong arm our ever sure defense;
Thy true religion in our hearts increase,
Thy bounteous goodness nourish us in peace.

4 Refresh thy people on their toilsome way,
Lead us from night to never-ending day;
Fill all our lives with love and grace divine,
And glory, laud, and praise be ever thine.

DANIEL C. ROBERTS

705 BROOKFIELD L. M.

THOMAS B. SOUTHGATE

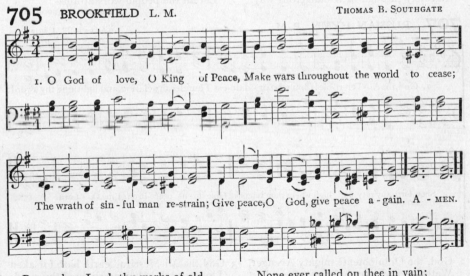

1. O God of love, O King of Peace, Make wars throughout the world to cease;
The wrath of sin-ful man re-strain; Give peace, O God, give peace a-gain. A - MEN.

2 Remember, Lord, thy works of old,
The wonders that our fathers told;
Remember not our sin's dark stain;
Give peace, O God, give peace again.

3 Whom shall we trust but thee, O Lord?
Where rest but on thy faithful word?

None ever called on thee in vain;
Give peace, O God, give peace again.

4 Where saints and angels dwell above,
All hearts are knit in holy love;
O bind us in that heavenly chain;
Give peace, O God, give peace again.

HENRY W. BAKER

706 GROSTETTE L. M.

HENRY W. GREATOREX

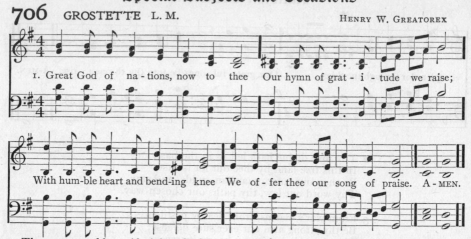

1. Great God of na-tions, now to thee Our hymn of grat - i - tude we raise; With hum-ble heart and bend-ing knee We of - fer thee our song of praise. A-MEN.

2 Thy name we bless, Almighty God,
For all the kindness thou hast shown
To this fair land the pilgrims trod,
This land we fondly call our own.

3 Here freedom spreads her banner wide
And casts her soft and hallowed ray;
Here thou our fathers' steps didst guide
In safety through their dangerous way.

4 We praise thee that the gospel's light
Through all our land its radiance sheds,
Dispels the shades of error's night,
And heavenly blessings round us spreads.

5 Great God, preserve us in thy fear;
In danger still our guardian be;
O spread thy truth's bright precepts here;
Let all the people worship thee.

ALFRED A. WOODHULL

707 RUSSIAN HYMN P. M.

ALEXIS T. LWOFF

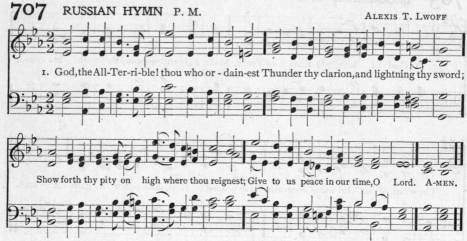

1. God, the All-Ter-ri-ble! thou who or - dain-est Thunder thy clarion, and lightning thy sword; Show forth thy pity on high where thou reignest; Give to us peace in our time, O Lord. A-MEN.

2 God, the Omnipotent! mighty Avenger,
Watching invisible, judging unheard;
Save us in mercy, O save us from danger;
Give to us peace in our time, O Lord.

3 God, the All-Merciful! earth hath forsaken
Thy ways all holy, and slighted thy word;
Let not thy wrath in its terror awaken;
Give to us pardon and peace, O Lord.

4 So will thy people, with thankful devotion,
Praise him who saved them from peril and sword,
Shouting in chorus, from ocean to ocean,
Peace to the nations, and praise to the Lord.

HENRY F. CHORLEY

708 DEVENTER L. M.

BERTHOLD TOURS

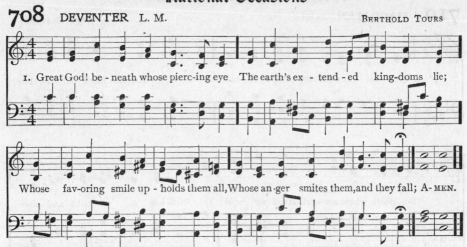

1. Great God! be-neath whose pierc-ing eye The earth's ex-tend-ed king-doms lie;
Whose fav-oring smile up-holds them all, Whose an-ger smites them, and they fall; A-MEN.

2 We bow before thy heavenly throne;
Thy power we see, thy greatness own;
Yet, cherished by thy milder voice,
Our bosoms tremble and rejoice.

3 Thy kindness to our fathers shown
Their children's children long shall own;
To thee, with grateful hearts, shall raise
The tribute of exulting praise.

4 Led on by thine unerring aid,
Secure the paths of life we tread;
And, freely as the vital air,
Thy first and noblest bounties share.

5 Great God, our Guardian, Guide, and
O still thy sheltering arm extend; [Friend!
Preserved by thee for ages past,
For ages let thy kindness last!

WILLIAM ROSCOE. Alt.

709 ASCHAM 8s. 7s.

EDMUND S. CARTER

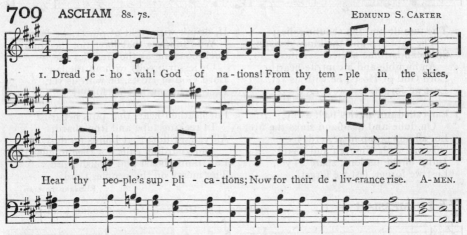

1. Dread Je-ho-vah! God of na-tions! From thy tem-ple in the skies,
Hear thy peo-ple's sup-pli-ca-tions; Now for their de-liv-erance rise. A-MEN.

2 Lo! with deep contrition turning,
In thy holy place we bend;
Hear us, fasting, praying, mourning;
Hear us, spare us, and defend.

3 Though our sins, our hearts confounding,
Long and loud for vengeance call,

Thou hast mercy more abounding;
Jesus' blood can cleanse them all.

4 Let that mercy veil transgression;
Let that blood our guilt efface:
Save thy people from oppression;
Save from spoil thy holy place.

THOMAS COTTERILL

503

710 MAGDALEN 8s. 6l.

JOHN STAINER

1. God of our fa-thers, known of old, Lord of our far-flung bat-tle line,

Be-neath whose aw-ful hand we hold Do-min-ion o-ver palm and pine:

VOICES IN UNISON   IN HARMONY

Lord God of Hosts, be with us yet, Lest we for-get, lest we for-get! A-MEN.

2 The tumult and the shouting dies;
   The captains and the kings depart;
Still stands thine ancient sacrifice,
   An humble and a contrite heart:
Lord God of Hosts, be with us yet,
Lest we forget, lest we forget!

3 Far-called our navies melt away,
   On dune and headland sinks the fire;
Lo, all our pomp of yesterday
   Is one with Nineveh and Tyre!
Judge of the nations, spare us yet,
Lest we forget, lest we forget!

4 If, drunk with sight of power, we loose
   Wild tongues that have not thee in awe,
Such boasting as the Gentiles use
   Or lesser breeds without the law:
Lord God of Hosts, be with us yet,
Lest we forget, lest we forget!

5 For heathen heart that puts her trust
   In reeking tube and iron shard;
All valiant dust that builds on dust,
   And guarding calls not thee to guard:
For frantic boast and foolish word,
Thy mercy on thy people, Lord!

RUDYARD KIPLING

711 MESSIAH 7s. D.

LOUIS J. F. HEROLD. Arr. by GEORGE KINGSLEY

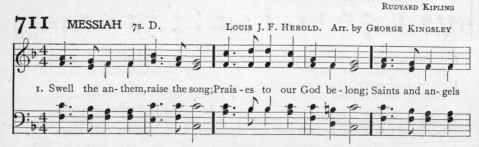

1. Swell the an-them, raise the song; Prais-es to our God be-long; Saints and an-gels

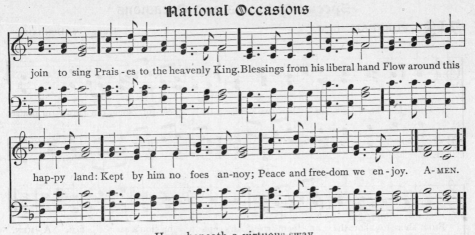

join to sing Prais - es to the heavenly King. Blessings from his liberal hand Flow around this

hap-py land: Kept by him no foes an-noy; Peace and free-dom we en - joy. A - MEN.

2 Here, beneath a virtuous sway
May we cheerfully obey;
Never feel oppression's rod,
Ever own and worship God.
Hark! the voice of nature sings
Praises to the King of kings;
Let us join the choral song,
And the grateful notes prolong.

NATHAN STRONG. Alt.

712 OLIVARIUS L. M.

PETER C. LUTKIN

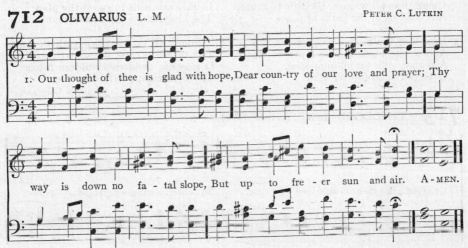

1. Our thought of thee is glad with hope, Dear coun-try of our love and prayer; Thy

way is down no fa - tal slope, But up to free - er sun and air. A - MEN.

2 Tried as by furnace fires, and yet
    By God's grace only stronger made;
In future tasks before thee set
    Thou shalt not lack the old-time aid.

3 Great, without seeking to be great
    By fraud or conquest; rich in gold,
But richer in the large estate
    Of virtue which thy children hold.

4 With peace that comes of purity,
    And strength to simple justice due,
So runs our loyal dream of thee.
    God of our fathers! make it true.

5 O land of lands! to thee we give
    Our love, our trust, our service free;
For thee thy sons shall nobly live,
    And at thy need shall die for thee.

JOHN G. WHITTIER

713 PURITAN L. M.

HENRY M. DUNHAM

Slow

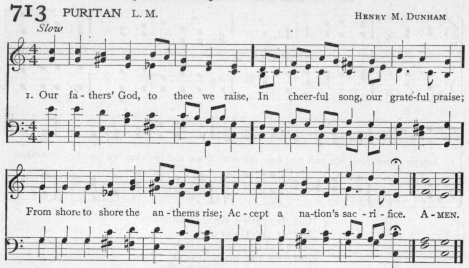

1. Our fa-thers' God, to thee we raise, In cheer-ful song, our grate-ful praise;
From shore to shore the an-thems rise; Ac-cept a na-tion's sac-ri-fice. A-MEN.

2 Incline our hearts with godly fear
To seek thy face, thy word revere;
Cause thou all wrongs, all strife to cease,
And lead us in the paths of peace.

3 Here may the weak a welcome find,
And wealth increase with lowly mind;
A refuge, still, for all oppressed,
O be our land forever blest!

4 Thy wisdom, Lord, thy guidance lend,
Where'er our widening bounds extend;
Inspire our wills to speed thy plan:
The kingdom of the Son of man!

5 Through all the past thy truth we trace,
Thy ceaseless care, thy signal grace;
O may our children's children prove
Thy sovereign, everlasting love.

BENJAMIN COPELAND

713 THEODORE L. M. (*Second Tune*)

PETER C. LUTKIN

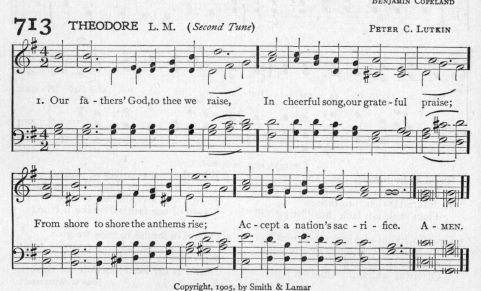

1. Our fa-thers' God, to thee we raise, In cheerful song, our grate-ful praise;
From shore to shore the anthems rise; Ac-cept a nation's sac-ri-fice. A-MEN.

714 REX REGUM C. M. D. JOHN STAINER

1. O King of kings, O Lord of hosts, whose throne is lift - ed high

A - bove the na - tions of the earth, the ar - mies of the sky,

The spir - its of the per - fect - ed may give their no - bler songs;

And we, thy chil - dren, wor - ship thee, to whom all praise be - longs. A - MEN.

2 Thy hand has hid within our fields treasures of countless worth;
The light, the suns of other years, shine from the depths of earth;
The very dust, inbreathed by thee, the clods all cold and dead,
Wake into beauty and to life, to give thy children bread.

3 Thou who hast sown the sky with stars, setting thy thoughts in gold,
Hast crowned our nation's life, and ours, with blessings manifold;
Thy mercies have been numberless; thy love, thy grace, thy care,
Were wider than our utmost need, and higher than our prayer.

4 O King of kings, O Lord of hosts, our fathers' God and ours!
Be with us in the future years; and if the tempest lowers,
Look through the cloud with light of love, and smile our tears away
And lead us through the brightening years to heaven's eternal day.

HENRY BURTON

715 ALL SAINTS L. M. WILLIAM KNAPP

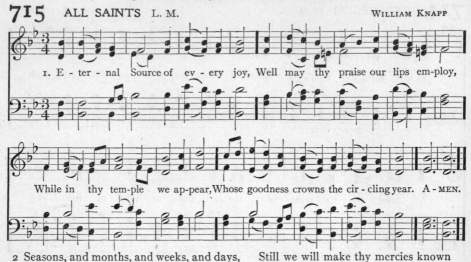

1. E - ter - nal Source of ev - ery joy, Well may thy praise our lips em-ploy,

While in thy tem-ple we ap-pear, Whose goodness crowns the cir - cling year. A - MEN.

2 Seasons, and months, and weeks, and days,
Demand successive songs of praise;
Still be the cheerful homage paid,
With opening light and evening shade.

3 Here in thy house shall incense rise,
And circling Sabbaths bless our eyes,

Still we will make thy mercies known
Around thy board, around our own.

4 O may our more harmonious tongue
In worlds unknown pursue the song;
And in those brighter courts adore,
Where days and years revolve no more!

PHILIP DODDRIDGE

716 ST. ANSELM 7s. 6s. D. JOSEPH BARNBY

1. We plow the fields and scat-ter The good seed on the land, But it is fed and wa-tered

By God's al-might-y hand; He sends the snow in win - ter, The warmth to swell the grain,

The breez - es and the sun - shine, And soft re - fresh - ing rain. A - MEN.

The Seasons

2 He only is the Maker
   Of all things near and far;
   He paints the wayside flower,
   He lights the evening-star;
   The winds and waves obey him,
   By him the birds are fed;
   Much more to us, his children,
   He gives our daily bread.

3 We thank thee, then, O Father,
   For all things bright and good,
   The seedtime and the harvest,
   Our life, our health, our food;
   Accept the gifts we offer
   For all thy love imparts,
   And, what thou most desirest,
   Our humble, thankful hearts.

MATTHIAS CLAUDIUS. Tr. by JANE M. CAMPBELL

717 ST. GEORGE'S, WINDSOR 7s. D.

GEORGE J. ELVEY

1. Come, ye thankful people, come, Raise the song of harvest-home: All is safe-ly gathered in,

Ere the winter storms be-gin; God, our Ma-ker, doth pro-vide For our wants to be sup-plied:

Come to God's own tem-ple, come, Raise the song of har-vest-home. A-MEN.

2 All the world is God's own field,
   Fruit unto his praise to yield;
   Wheat and tares together sown,
   Unto joy or sorrow grown;
   First the blade, and then the ear,
   Then the full corn shall appear:
   Lord of harvest, grant that we
   Wholesome grain and pure may be.

3 For the Lord our God shall come,
   And shall take his harvest home;
   From his field shall in that day
   All offenses purge away;

Give his angels charge at last
In the fire the tares to cast;
But the fruitful ears to store
In his garner evermore.

4 Even so, Lord, quickly come
   To thy final harvest-home;
   Gather thou thy people in,
   Free from sorrow, free from sin;
   There, forever purified,
   In thy presence to abide:
   Come, with all thine angels, come,
   Raise the glorious harvest-home.

HENRY ALFORD

Dorologies

718   L. M.

PRAISE God, from whom all blessings flow;
Praise him, all creatures here below;
Praise him above, ye heavenly host;
Praise Father, Son, and Holy Ghost.

THOMAS KEN

719   C. M.

Now let the Father, and the Son,
  And Spirit, be adored;
Where there are works to make him known,
  Or saints to love the Lord.

ISAAC WATTS

720   C. M.

To Father, Son, and Holy Ghost,
  The God whom we adore,
Be glory, as it was, is now,
  And shall be evermore.

TATE and BRADY

721   C. M.

THE God of mercy be adored,
  Who calls our souls from death,
Who saves by his redeeming word,
  And new-creating breath;
To praise the Father, and the Son,
  And Spirit all-divine,
The One in Three, and Three in One,
  Let saints and angels join.

ISAAC WATTS

722   S. M.

To God, the Father, Son,
  And Spirit, One in Three,
Be glory, as it was, is now,
  And shall forever be.

JOHN WESLEY

723   8s. 7s. D.

LORD, dismiss us with thy blessing,
  Bid us now depart in peace;
Still on heavenly manna feeding,
  Let our faith and love increase:

Fill each breast with consolation;
  Up to thee our hearts we raise:
When we reach our blissful station,
  Then we'll give thee nobler praise.

ROBERT HAWKER

724   8. 7. 8. 7. 4. 7.

GREAT Jehovah! we adore thee,
  God the Father, God the Son,
God the Spirit, joined in glory
  On the same eternal throne:
    Endless praises
To Jehovah, Three in One!

WILLIAM GOODE

725   7s.

SING we to our God above,
Praise eternal as his love;
Praise him, all ye heavenly host,—
Father, Son, and Holy Ghost.

CHARLES WESLEY

726   7. 6. 7. 6. 7. 8. 7. 6.

FATHER, Son, and Holy Ghost,
  Thy Godhead we adore,
Join we with the heavenly host,
  To praise thee evermore!
Live, by earth and heaven adored,
  The Three in One, the One in Three;
Holy, holy, holy Lord,
  All glory be to thee!

CHARLES WESLEY

727   6. 6. 4. 6. 6. 6. 4.

To God, the Father, Son,
And Spirit, Three in One,
  All praise be given!
Crown him, in every song;
To him your hearts belong:
Let all his praise prolong,
  On earth, in heaven!

EDWIN F. HATFIELD

Chants and Occasional Pieces

DIRECTIONS FOR CHANTING

1 CHANTS consist of two distinct divisions: one portion is recited, the other portion is sung.

2 The words from the commencement of each verse and half verse up to the accented syllable, which is printed in italics, are called the Recitation, and should be recited smoothly, and without undue haste.

3 On reaching the accented syllable, and beginning with it, the *music* of the chant commences, in strict time (*a tempo*), the upright strokes corresponding to the bars. The Recitation must therefore be considered as *outside* the chant, and may be of any length. The note on which the Recitation is made is called the Reciting-note.

4 If there is no syllable after that which is accented, the accented syllable must be held for one whole bar or measure.

5 Marks of punctuation must be attended to, as in good *reading*.

6 As the accent holds the position of the first beat of the first bar, it is unnecessary to sing it louder than any of the words recited; its position, musically, will give it quite enough emphasis.

7 Final *ed* is always to be pronounced as a separate syllable.

728 VENITE, EXULTEMUS DOMINO Psalm 95

1 O COME, let us *sing* | unto · the | Lord ‖ let us heartily re*joice* in the | strength of | our sal- | vation.

2 Let us come before his *pres*ence | with thanks- | giving ‖ and *show* ourselves | glad in | him with | psalms.

3 For the *Lord* is a | great — | God ‖ and a *great* | King a- | bove all | gods.

4 In his hand are all the *cor*ners | of the | earth ‖ and the *strength* of the | hills is | his — | also.

5 The sea is *his* | and he | made it ‖ and his *hands* pre- | pared · the | dry — | land.

6 O come, let us *wor*ship and | fall — | down ‖ and *kneel* be- |fore the | Lord our | Maker.

7 For *he* is the | Lord our | God ‖ and we are the people of his pasture, *and* the | sheep of | his — | hand.

8 O worship the *Lord* in the | beauty · of | holiness ‖ let the whole *earth* | stand in | awe of | him.

9 * For he cometh, for he *com*eth to | judge the | earth ‖ and with righteousness to judge the *world*, and the | peo-ple | with his | truth.

Glory be to the *Fa*ther | and · to the | Son ‖ *and* | to the | Ho-ly | Ghost;

As it was in the beginning, is *now*, and | ev-er | shall be ‖ *world* without | end. — | A- — | men.

Chants and Occasional Pieces

729 TE DEUM LAUDAMUS

HENRY LAWES

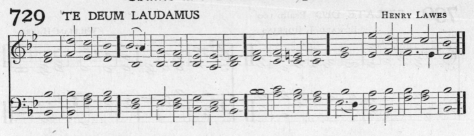

1 WE *praise* | thee, O | God ‖ we ac*know*ledge | thee to | be the | Lord.
2 All the *earth* doth | wor-ship | thee ‖ *the* | Fa-ther | ev-er- | lasting.
3 To thee all *Angels* | cry a- | loud ‖ the *Heavens* and | all the | Powers there- | in.
4 To thee Cheru*bim* and | Ser-a- | phim ‖ *con-* | tin-ual- | ly do | cry,
5 *H*oly | Ho-ly | Ho-ly ‖ *Lord* | God of | Sab-a- | oth;
6 Heaven and earth are *full* of the | Maj es- | ty ‖ *of* | thy — | Glo- — | ry.
7 The glorious *com*pany | of · the A- | postles ‖ *praise* | — — | — — | thee.
8 The goodly *fel*lowship | of the | Prophets ‖ *praise* | — — | — — | thee.
9 The *noble* | army · of | Martyrs ‖ *praise* | — — | — — | thee.
10 The holy *Church* throughout | all the | world ‖ *doth* ac- | knowl- — | edge — | thee.
11 *The* | Fa- — | ther ‖ *of* an | in- · finite | Maj-es- | ty;
12 *Thine* a- | dor- · able, true ‖ *and* | on- — | — ly | Son;
13 * *Al*so the | Holy | Ghost ‖ *the* | Com- — | fort- — | er.
14 *Thou* art the | King of | Glory ‖ *O* | — — | — — | Christ.
15 Thou art the ever- | last-ing | Son ‖ *of* | — the | Fa- — | ther.

* Last half of chant

ROBERT COOKE

16 When thou tookest upon *thee* to de- | liv-er | man ‖ thou didst humble thy*self* to be | born — | of a | Virgin.
17 When thou hadst over*come* the | sharpness · of | death ‖ thou didst open the *King*dom of | Heaven · to | all be- | lievers.
18 Thou sittest at the *right* | hand of | God ‖ *in* the | Glo-ry | of the | Father.
19 We be*lieve* that | thou shalt | come ‖ *to* | be — | our — | Judge.
20 We therefore *pray* thee | help thy | servants ‖ whom thou hast re*deemed* | with thy | pre-cious | blood.
21 Make them to be *num*bered | with thy | Saints ‖ *in* | glo-ry | ev-er- | lasting.
22 O *Lord* | save thy | people ‖ *and* | bless thine | her-it- | age.
23 *Gov-* | — ern | them ‖ *and* | lift them | up for- | ever.

Return to chant in B♭ at the top of page

24 *Day* | by — | day ‖ *we* | mag-ni- | fy — | thee;
25 *And* we | worship · thy | Name ‖ *ever* | world with- | out — | end.
26 *Vouch-* | safe, O | Lord ‖ to *keep* us this | day with- | out — | sin.
27 O *Lord,* · have | mercy · up- | on us ‖ *have* | mercy · up- | on — | us.
28 O Lord, let thy *mercy* | be up- | on us ‖ *as* our | trust — | is in | thee.
29 O Lord, in *thee* | have I | trusted ‖ *let* me | nev-er | be con- | founded.

730 JUBILATE DEO Psalm 100

EDWARD J. HOPKINS

WILLIAM HAYES

HENRY ALDRICH

B. COOKE

HENRY ALDRICH

THOMAS NORRIS

1 O BE joyful in the *Lord* | all ye | lands ‖ serve the Lord with gladness, and come be-*fore* his | pres-ence | with a | song.

2 Be ye sure that the Lord he is God; it is he that hath made us, *and* not | we our- | selves ‖ we are his people, *and* the | sheep of | his — | pasture.

3 O go your way into his gates with thanksgiving, and *into* his | courts with | praise ‖ be thankful unto *him,* and | speak good | of his | Name.

4 For the Lord is gracious, his *mercy* is | ev-er- | lasting ‖ and his truth endureth from *gener-* | ation · to | gen-er- | ation.

Glory be to the *Father* | and · to the | Son ‖ *and* | to the | Ho-ly | Ghost;

As it was in the beginning, is *now,* and | ever | shall be ‖ *world* without | end. — | A-— | men.

731 MAGNIFICAT Luke 1. 46-55

GEORGE A. MACFARREN   EDWARD J. HOPKINS

W. H. COOKE   HENRY HILES

CHARLES E. KETTLE

HENRY SMART

1 My soul doth *magni-* | fy the | Lord ‖ and my spirit *hath* re- | joiced · in | God my | Saviour.

2 *For* he | hath re- | garded ‖ the *lowli-* | ness of | his hand- | maiden.

3 *For* be- | hold, from | henceforth ‖ *all* gener- | ations · shall | call me | blessed.

4 For he that is *mighty* hath | magni- · fied | me ‖ *and* | ho-ly | is his | name.

5 And his *mercy* is on | them that | fear him ‖ *through-* | out all | gen-er- | ations.

6 He hath showed *strength* | with his | arm ‖ he hath scattered the proud in the imagi- | na-tion | of their | hearts.

7 He hath put down the *mighty* | from their | seat ‖ and *hath* ex- | alted · the | humble · and | meek.

8 He hath filled the *hun*gry with | good — | things ‖ and the *rich* he hath | sent — | empty · a- | way.

9 * He remembering his mercy hath *hol*pen his | servant | Israel ‖ as he promised to our forefathers, *A*braham | and his | seed,for- | ever.

Glory be to the *Fa*ther | and · to the | Son ‖ *and* | to the | Ho-ly | Ghost;

As it was in the beginning, is *now*, and | ev-er | shall be ‖ *world* without | end. — | A- — | men.

* Last half of double chant

732 DEUS MISEREATUR Psalm 67

HENRY ALDRICH   THOMAS PURCELL

THOMAS ATTWOOD

From LUDWIG VAN BEETHOVEN

1 GOD be merciful *unto* | us and | bless us ‖ and show us the light of his countenance, *and* be | merci- ˙ ful | un-to | us;

2 That thy *way* may be | known up -˙on | earth ‖ Thy *saving* | health a- | mong all | nations.

3 Let the people *praise* | thee, O | God ‖ *yea* let | all the | peo-ple | praise thee.

4 O let the nations re*joice* | and be | glad ‖ for thou shalt judge the folk righteously, and *govern* the | nations ˙ up- | on — | earth.

5 Let the people *praise* | thee, O | God ‖ *yea* let | all the | peo-ple | praise thee.

6 Then shall the *earth* bring | forth her | increase ‖ and God, even our own *God*, shall | give — | us his | blessing.

7 * *God* shall | bless — | us ‖ and all the *ends* of the | world shall | fear — | him.

Glory be to the *Father* | and ˙ to the | Son ‖ *and* | to the | Ho-ly | Ghost;

As it was in the beginning, is *now*, and | ev-er | shall be ‖ *world* without | end. — | A- — | men.

* Last half of double chant

733 NUNC DIMITTIS Luke 2. 29-32

JOSEPH BARNBY   JAMES TURLE

TONUS REGIUS (Gregorian)

Composer Unknown

1 LORD, now lettest thou thy *servant* de- | part in | peace ‖ *ac-* | cord ing | to thy | word.

2 *For* mine | eyes have | seen ‖ *thy* | — sal- | va- — | tion,

3 *Which* thou | hast pre- | pared ‖ *before* the | face of | all — | people;

4 To be a *light* to | lighten the | Gentiles ‖ and to be the *glo-ry* | of thy | people | Is-rael.

Glory be to the *Father* | and · to the | Son ‖ *and* | to the | Ho-ly | Ghost;

As it was in the beginning, is *now*, and | ev-er | shall be ‖ *world* without | end. — | A- — | men.

734 INVOCATION SENTENCE   KARL P. HARRINGTON

IN UNISON OR HARMONY

The Lord is in his ho-ly temple; let all the earth keep si-lence be-fore him.

735 THE LORD'S PRAYER

VINCENT NOVELLO

C. A. WICKES

WILLIAM CROFT

L. T. DOWNES

OUR Father who art in heaven, *hal*lowed | be thy | name. ‖ Thy kingdom come. Thy will be *done* in | earth · as it | is in | heaven.

Give us this *day* our | daily | bread; ‖ And forgive us our trespasses, as we forgive *them* that | tres- · pass a- | gainst — | us.

And lead us not into temptation, but de*liver* | us from | evil; ‖ For thine is the kingdom, and the power, and the glory, for- | ever. | A- — | men.

736 MY GOD, MY FATHER

ARTHUR H. D. TROYTE

1. My God, my Father, while I stray Far from my home on life's rough way,

O teach me from my heart to say, "Thy will be done!" A-MEN.

2 Though dark my path and sad my lot,
Let me be still and murmur not,
And breathe the prayer divinely taught,
"Thy will be done!"

3 What though in lonely grief I sigh
For friends beloved, no longer nigh!
Submissive still would I reply,
"Thy will be done!"

4 Though thou hast called me to resign
What most I prized, it ne'er was mine:

I have but yielded what was thine;
Thy will be done!

5 Let but my fainting heart be blest
With thy sweet Spirit for its guest,
My God, to thee I leave the rest:
Thy will be done!

6 Renew my will from day to day;
Blend it with thine, and take away
All that now makes it hard to say,
"Thy will be done!"

CHARLOTTE ELLIOTT

518

737 GLORIA PATRI

CHARLES MEINEKE

Glo-ry be to the Fa-ther, and to the Son, and to the Ho-ly Ghost; As it was in the be-gin-ning, is now, and ev-er shall be, world without end. A-men, A-men.

737 GLORIA PATRI (*Second Tune*)

HENRY W. GREATOREX

Glo-ry be to the Fa-ther, and to the Son, and to the Ho-ly Ghost; As it was in the be-gin-ning, is now, and ev-er shall be, world without end. A-men, A-men.

738   THE TEN COMMANDMENTS

GOD spake these words, and said: I am the Lord thy God: Thou shalt have none other gods before me.

Lord, have mercy upon us, and incline our hearts to keep this law.

Thou shalt not make unto thee any graven image, or any likeness of any thing that is in heaven above, or that is in the earth beneath, or that is in the water under the earth: thou shalt not bow down thyself to them, nor serve them: for I the Lord thy God am a jealous God, visiting the iniquity of the fathers upon the children unto the third and fourth generation of them that hate me; and showing mercy unto thousands of them that love me, and keep my commandments.

Lord, have mercy upon us, and incline our hearts to keep this law.

Thou shalt not take the name of the Lord thy God in vain; for the Lord will not hold him guiltless that taketh his name in vain.

Lord, have mercy upon us, and incline our hearts to keep this law.

Remember the sabbath day, to keep it holy.   Six days shalt thou labor, and do all thy work: but the seventh day is the sabbath of the Lord thy God: in it thou shalt not do any work, thou, nor thy son, nor thy daughter, thy manservant, nor thy maidservant, nor thy cattle, nor thy stranger that is within thy gates: for in six days the Lord made heaven and earth, the sea, and all that in them is, and rested the seventh day: wherefore the Lord blessed the sabbath day, and hallowed it.

Lord, have mercy upon us, and incline our hearts to keep this law.

Honor thy father and thy mother: that thy days may be long upon the land which the Lord thy God giveth thee.

Lord, have mercy upon us, and incline our hearts to keep this law.

Thou shalt not kill.

Lord, have mercy upon us, and incline our hearts to keep this law.

Thou shalt not commit adultery.

Lord, have mercy upon us, and incline our hearts to keep this law.

Thou shalt not steal.

Lord, have mercy upon us, and incline our hearts to keep this law.

Thou shalt not bear false witness against thy neighbor.

Lord, have mercy upon us, and incline our hearts to keep this law.

Thou shalt not covet thy neighbor's house, thou shalt not covet thy neighbor's wife, nor his manservant, nor his maidservant, nor his ox, nor his ass, nor any thing that is thy neighbor's.

Lord, have mercy upon us, and write all these thy laws in our hearts, we beseech thee.

738 RESPONSES TO THE COMMANDMENTS

No. 1 — *After 9 Commandments* — WALTER B. GILBERT

Lord, have mer-cy up-on us, and in-cline our hearts to keep this law.

After the 10th

us, and write all these thy laws in our hearts, we be-seech thee.

No. 2 — *After 9 Commandments* — CHARLES GOUNOD

Lord, have mer-cy up-on us, and in-cline our hearts to keep this law.

After the 10th — *Piu lento*

us, and write all these thy laws in our hearts, we be-seech thee.

No. 3 — *After 9 Commandments* — EDWARD HODGES

Lord, have mer-cy up-on us, and in-cline our hearts to keep this law.

After the 10th

on us, and write all these thy laws in our hearts, we be-seech thee.

739 OFFERTORY SENTENCE   JOSEPH BARNBY

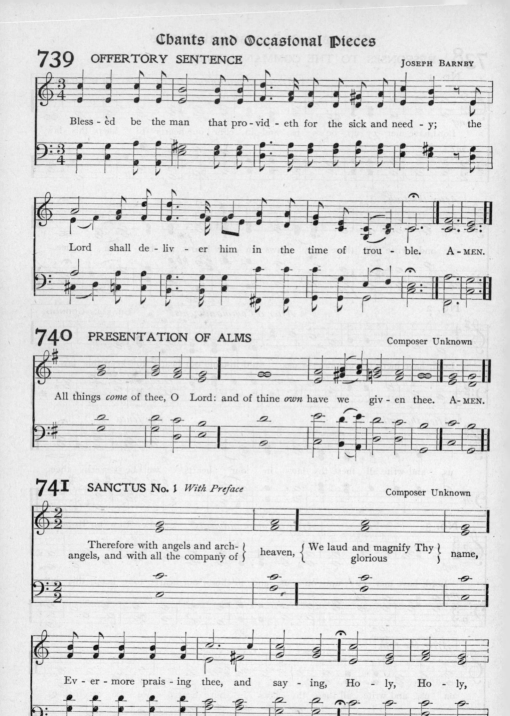

Bless - èd be the man that pro - vid - eth for the sick and need - y; the

Lord shall de - liv - er him in the time of trou - ble. A - MEN.

740 PRESENTATION OF ALMS   Composer Unknown

All things *come* of thee, O Lord: and of thine *own* have we giv - en thee. A - MEN.

741 SANCTUS No. 1 *With Preface*   Composer Unknown

Therefore with angels and arch- } angels, and with all the company of } heaven, { We laud and magnify Thy } glorious { name,

Ev - er - more prais - ing thee, and say - ing, Ho - ly, Ho - ly,

Ho - ly Lord God of Hosts, Heaven and earth are full of thy glo - ry: Glo - ry be to thee, O Lord, Most High. A-MEN.

SANCTUS No. 2

CARL F. PRICE

Ho - ly, .. Ho - ly, .. Ho - ly .. Lord God of Hosts, Heaven and earth are full of thy glo - ry: Glo - ry be to thee, O Lord, Most High. A - - men, A - - men, A - - men.

742 GLORIA IN EXCELSIS

Old Chant

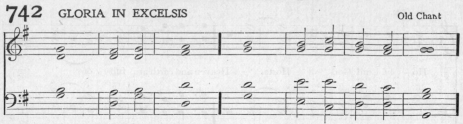

1 GLORY *be* to | God on | high ‖ and on *earth* | peace, good | will · toward | men.
2 We praise thee, we bless *thee*, we | wor-ship | thee ‖ we glorify thee, we give *thanks* to | thee for | thy great | glory.

3 O Lord *God* | Heaven- · ly | King ‖ *God* the | Fa-ther | Al- — | mighty.
4 O Lord, the only begotten *Son* | Je-sus | Christ ‖ O Lord God, Lamb of *God* | Son — | of the | Father,

5 That takest a*way* the | sins · of the | world ‖ have *mer*cy up- | on — | us.
6 Thou that takest a*way* the | sins · of the | world ‖ have *mer*cy up- | on — | us.
7 Thou that takest a*way* the | sins · of the | world ‖ *re-* | ceive our | prayer.
8 Thou that sittest at the right *hand* of | God the | Father ‖ have *mer*cy up- | on — | us.

A - MEN.

9 For thou *only* | art — | holy ‖ *thou* | on-ly | art the | Lord.
10 Thou only, O *Christ*, with the | Ho-ly | Ghost ‖ art most *high* in the | glory · of | God the | Father.

743 TOO LATE 10s. Words by ALFRED TENNYSON   Miss LINDSA

SOPRANO SOLO OR DUET. Vs. 1, 2, 3

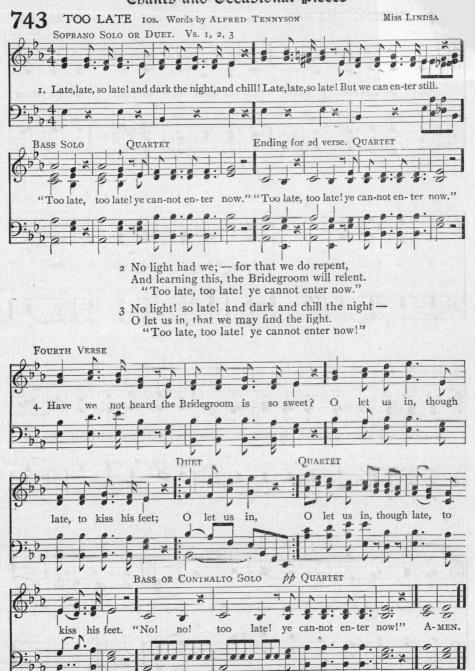

1. Late, late, so late! and dark the night, and chill! Late, late, so late! But we can en-ter still.

BASS SOLO   QUARTET   Ending for 2d verse. QUARTET

"Too late, too late! ye can-not en-ter now." "Too late, too late! ye can-not en-ter now."

2 No light had we; — for that we do repent,
And learning this, the Bridegroom will relent.
"Too late, too late! ye cannot enter now."

3 No light! so late! and dark and chill the night —
O let us in, that we may find the light.
"Too late, too late! ye cannot enter now!"

FOURTH VERSE

4. Have we not heard the Bridegroom is so sweet? O let us in, though

DUET   QUARTET

late, to kiss his feet; O let us in, O let us in, though late, to

BASS OR CONTRALTO SOLO *pp* QUARTET

kiss his feet. "No! no! too late! ye can-not en-ter now!" A-MEN.

CROSSING THE BAR   Words by ALFRED TENNYSON   JOSEPH BARNBY

Sun - set and eve - ning-star, And one clear call for me! And may there

be no moan-ing of the bar, When I put out to sea, . .

But such a tide as mov-ing seems a - sleep, Too full for sound and foam,

rall.

When that which drew from out the bound-less deep Turns a - gain home.

... Twi - light and eve - ning bell, And aft - er that the dark!

Twi - - - - - light and eve - ning bell,

And may there be no sad - ness of fare-well, When I em - bark;

cres - - cen - - - - - do rit.

For, though from out our bourne of time and place The flood may bear me far,

f

I hope to see my Pi - lot face to face When I have crossed the bar. A - MEN.

745 LANIER P. M.

PETER C. LUTKIN

1. In - to the woods my Mas - ter went, Clean for-spent, for - spent;

In - to the woods my Mas - ter came, For-spent with love and shame. But the

ol - ives they were not blind to him, The lit - tle gray leaves were kind to him, The

thorn-tree had a mind to him, When in - to the woods he came. A - MEN.

Copyright, 1905, by Smith & Lamar

2 Out of the woods my Master went,
And he was well content;
Out of the woods my Master came,
Content with death and shame.
When death and shame would woo him last,
From under the trees they drew him last,
'Twas on a tree they slew him last,
When out of the woods he came.

Copyright, 1884, 1891, by Mary D. Lanier

SIDNEY LANIER

746 MARYLEBONE L. M. 6l. Words by CHARLES WESLEY   Music by C. HUBERT H. PARRY

In age and fee - ble-ness ex - treme,
fee - ble - ness ex - treme,
Who shall a help - less worm re - deem? Je - sus, my on - ly hope thou art, .. Strength of my fail - ing flesh and heart, O could I catch one smile from thee, And drop in - to e - ter - ni - ty! A - - men, A - men.

747 DIES IRAE L. M. 3l. Tr. from Latin by W. J. Irons — John B. Dykes

1. Day of Wrath! O day of mourn-ing! See ful-filled the proph-ets' warning,
Heaven and earth in ash-es burn-ing! 2. O what fear man's bos-om rend-eth,
When from heaven the Judge descendeth, On whose sen-tence all de-pend - eth!

ff 3 Wondrous sound the trumpet flingeth;
Through earth's sepulchers it ringeth;
All before the throne it bringeth.

f 4 Death is struck, and nature quaking,
All creation is awaking,
To its Judge an answer making.

mf 5 Lo! the Book exactly worded,
Wherein all hath been recorded:
Thence shall judgment be awarded.

mf 6 When the Judge his seat attaineth,
And each hidden deed arraigneth,
Nothing unavenged remaineth.

p 7 What shall I, frail man, be pleading?
Who for me be interceding,
When the just are mercy needing?

f 8 King of Majesty tremendous,
Who dost free salvation send us,
dim Fount of pity, then befriend us!

mf 9 Think, good Jesu, my salvation
Cost thy wondrous Incarnation;
dim Leave me not to reprobation!

p 10 Faint and weary, thou hast sought me,
On the Cross of suffering bought me.
Shall such grace be vainly brought me?

mf 11 Righteous Judge! for sin's pollution
Grant thy gift of absolution,
Ere that day of retribution.

p 12 Guilty, now I pour my moaning,
All my shame with anguish owning;
Spare, O God, thy suppliant groaning!

cr 13 Thou the sinful woman savedst;
mf Thou the dying thief forgavest;
And to me a hope vouchsafest.

p 14 Worthless are my prayers and sighing,
cr Yet, good Lord, in grace complying,
mf Rescue me from fires undying!

15. With thy fa-vored sheep O place me! Nor a-mong the goats a-base me;

rall.

But to thy right hand up-raise me. 16. While the wick-ed are con-found-ed,

Doomed to flames of woe unbound-ed, Call me with thy saints sur-round - ed.

17. Low I kneel, with heart-sub-mis-sion, See, like ash - es, my con-tri-tion; Help me in my

last con-di-tion. 18. Ah! that day of tears and mourning! From the dust of earth re-turn-ing

Man for judg-ment must pre-pare him; 19. Spare, O God, in mer-cy spare him!

Lord, all - pity-ing, Je - su blest, Grant us thine e - ter - nal rest. A-MEN.

Chants and Occasional Pieces

748 THE LORD BLESS YOU AND KEEP YOU

PETER C. LUTKIN

532

Alphabetical Index of Tunes

Alphabetical Index of Tunes

Alphabetical Index of Tunes

535

Alphabetical Index of Tunes

Metrical Index

Chants and Occasional Pieces

Index of Chants and Occasional Pieces

Index of Composers

Composers

Index of Authors of Hymns

Authors of Hymns

Authors of Hymns

First Lines of Stanzas

First Lines of Stanzas

First Lines of Hymns

First Lines of Hymns

551

First Lines of Hymns

Chants and Occasional Pieces

First Lines of Chants and Occasional Pieces

The Psalter

For Responsive Readings
in the Sunday Services

Note

The verses printed in Roman are to be read by the Minister

The verses printed in Italic are to be read by the People

THIS Psalter, in accordance with the order of the General Conference, is printed in parallelism after the Hebrew original; and the Hebrew meter, so far as known, is carefully considered in combining portions of separate Psalms into a single reading. The text used is the Authorized Version, except where slight changes were necessary to preserve the parallelism or meter, or render more perfectly the original meaning, and in these cases the emendations are conformed to the character and quality of the version endeared by centuries of use. The Imprecatory Psalms, as well as imprecations contained in other parts of the book, are omitted, as in the Select Psalms prepared by John Wesley.

The selections were made and edited by Professor Robert W. Rogers, D.D., of Drew Theological Seminary.

The Psalter

First Sunday
Morning

Praise the Lord from the heavens:
Praise him in the heights.

Praise ye him, all his angels:
Praise ye him, all his hosts.

Praise ye him, sun and moon:
Praise him, all ye stars of light.

Praise him, ye heavens of heavens,
And ye waters above the heavens.

Let them praise the name of the
Lord:
For he commanded, and they were
created.

He established them forever and
ever:
He made a decree which shall not
pass.

Praise the Lord from the earth,
Ye dragons, and all deeps:

Fire and hail, snow and vapor;
Stormy wind, fulfilling his word:

Mountains and all hills;
Fruitful trees and all cedars:

Beasts and all cattle;
Creeping things and flying fowl:

Kings of the earth and all people;
Princes and all judges of the earth:

Young men and maidens;
Old men and children:

Let them praise the name of the
Lord;
For his name alone is excellent:

His glory is above the earth and
the heavens.

He also exalteth the horn of his
people,
He is the praise of all his saints;
Of the children of Israel, a people
near unto him.

Sing unto the Lord a new song,
And his praise in the assembly of
the saints.

Let Israel rejoice in him that made
him:
Let the children of Zion be joyful
in their King.

Evening

How amiable are thy tabernacles,
O Lord of hosts!

My soul longeth, yea, fainteth
For the courts of the Lord;

My heart and my flesh cry out
Unto the living God.

Yea, the sparrow hath found a house,
And the swallow a nest for herself,
Where she may lay her young,

Even thine altars, O Lord of hosts,
My King, and my God.

Blessed are they that dwell in thy
house:
They will be still praising thee.

They go from strength to strength,
They appear before God in Zion.

O Lord God of hosts, hear my
prayer:
Give ear, O God of Jacob.

Behold, O God our shield,
And look upon the face of thine anointed.

> *For a day in thy courts is better than a thousand.*
> *I had rather be a doorkeeper in the house of my God,*
> *Than to dwell in the tents of wickedness.*

For the Lord God is a sun and a shield:
The Lord will give grace and glory:
No good thing will he withhold from them that walk uprightly.

> *O Lord of hosts,*
> *Blessed is the man that trusteth in thee.*

Second Sunday
Morning

I waited patiently for the Lord;
And he inclined unto me, and heard my cry.

> *He brought me up out of a horrible pit, out of the miry clay,*
> *And set my feet upon a rock, and established my goings.*

And he hath put a new song in my mouth,
Even praise unto our God:

> *Many shall see it, and fear,*
> *And shall trust in the Lord.*

Blessed is the man that maketh the Lord his trust,
And respecteth not the proud, nor such as turn aside to lies.

> *Many, O Lord my God, are the wonderful works thou hast done,*
> *And thy thoughts which are to usward.*

If I would declare and speak of them,
They are more than can be numbered.

> *Sacrifice and offering thou didst not desire,*
> *Burnt offering and sin offering hast thou not required.*

Then I said, Lo, I am come;
In the volume of the book it is written of me:

> *I delight to do thy will, O my God;*
> *Yea, thy law is within my heart.*

I have preached righteousness in the great congregation;
Lo, I have not refrained my lips,
O Lord, thou knowest.

> *I have not hid thy righteousness within my heart;*
> *I have declared thy faithfulness and thy salvation.*

Withhold not thou thy tender mercies from me, O Lord:
Let thy loving-kindness and thy truth continually preserve me.

> *For innumerable evils have compassed me about,*
> *Mine iniquities have overtaken me, so that I am not able to look up.*

They are more in number than the hairs of my head,
Therefore my heart faileth me.

> *Be pleased, O Lord, to deliver me:*
> *O Lord, make haste to help me.*

Let all those that seek thee rejoice and be glad in thee:
Let such as love thy salvation say continually,
The Lord be magnified.

> *But I am poor and needy;*
> *Yet the Lord thinketh upon me.*

Thou art my help and my deliverer;
Make no tarrying, O my God.

Evening

God is our refuge and strength,
A very present help in trouble.

*Therefore will we not fear, though
the earth be removed,
And though the mountains shake
in the midst of the sea;*

Though the waters thereof roar and
be troubled,
Though the mountains shake with
the swelling thereof.

*There is a river, whose streams
make glad the city of God,
The holy place of the tabernacles
of the Most High.*

God is in the midst of her; she shall
not be moved:
God shall help her, and that right
early.

*The heathen raged, the kingdoms
were moved:
He uttered his voice, the earth
melted.*

The Lord of hosts is with us;
The God of Jacob is our refuge.

*Come, behold the works of the
Lord,
What signs he hath made in the
earth.*

He maketh wars to cease unto the
end of the earth;
He breaketh the bow, and cutteth
the spear in sunder;
He burneth the chariot in the
fire.

*Be still, and know that I am
God:
I will be exalted among the na-
tions,
I will be exalted in the earth.*

The Lord of hosts is with us;
The God of Jacob is our refuge.

· Third Sunday
Morning

As the hart panteth after the
water brooks,
So panteth my soul after thee, O
God.

*My soul thirsteth for God, for the
living God:
When shall I come and appear
before God?*

My tears have been my food day
and night,
While they continually say unto
me, Where is thy God?

*When I remember these things I
pour out my soul within me,
For I had gone with the multitude,
I went with them to the house of
God,
With the voice of joy and praise, a
multitude keeping holyday.*

Why art thou cast down, O my
soul?
And why art thou disquieted within
me?

*Hope thou in God; for I shall yet
praise him
For the help of his countenance.*

O my God, my soul is cast down
within me:
Therefore will I remember thee from
the land of the Jordan,
And the Hermons, from the hill
Mizar,

*Deep calleth unto deep at the noise
of thy waterfalls:
All thy waves and thy billows are
gone over me.*

Yet the Lord will command his
loving-kindness in the daytime;
And in the night his song shall be
with me,

Even a prayer unto the God of my life.

I will say unto God my rock, Why hast thou forgotten me?
Why go I mourning because of the oppression of the enemy?

As with a sword in my bones, mine enemies reproach me,
While they continually say unto me, Where is thy God?

Why art thou cast down, O my soul?
And why art thou disquieted within me?

Hope thou in God; for I shall yet praise him,
Who is the health of my countenance, and my God.

Judge me, O God, and plead my cause against an ungodly nation:
Oh deliver me from the deceitful and unjust man.

For thou art the God of my strength; why dost thou cast me off?
Why go I mourning because of the oppression of the enemy?

Oh send out thy light and thy truth; let them lead me:
Let them bring me unto thy holy hill, And to thy tabernacles.

Then will I go unto the altar of God,
Unto God my exceeding joy;
And upon the harp will I praise thee, O God, my God.

Why art thou cast down, O my soul?
And why art thou disquieted within me?

Hope thou in God; for I shall yet praise him,
Who is the health of my countenance, and my God.

Evening

Hear my prayer, O Lord; give ear to my supplications:
In thy faithfulness answer me, and in thy righteousness.

And enter not into judgment with thy servant;
For in thy sight shall no man living be justified.

For the enemy hath persecuted my soul;
He hath smitten my life down to the ground:
He hath made me to dwell in dark places, as those that have been long dead.

Therefore is my spirit overwhelmed within me;
My heart within me is desolate.

I remember the days of old;
I meditate on all thy works;
I muse on the work of thy hands.

I stretch forth my hands unto thee:
My soul thirsteth after thee, as a thirsty land.

Hear me speedily, O Lord; my spirit faileth:
Hide not thy face from me,
Lest I be like unto them that go down into the pit.

Cause me to hear thy loving-kindness in the morning;
For in thee do I trust:

Cause me to know the way wherein I should walk;
For I lift up my soul unto thee.

Deliver me, O Lord, from mine enemies:
I flee unto thee to hide me.

Teach me to do thy will;
For thou art my God:
Thy Spirit is good;
Lead me in the land of uprightness.

Quicken me, O Lord, for thy name's sake:
In thy righteousness bring my soul out of trouble.
For I am thy servant.

Fourth Sunday
Morning

Fret not thyself because of evil-doers,
Neither be thou envious against the workers of iniquity.

For they shall soon be cut down like the grass,
And wither as the green herb.

Trust in the Lord, and do good;
So shalt thou dwell in the land, and verily thou shalt be fed.

Delight thyself also in the Lord;
And he shall give thee the desires of thy heart.

Commit thy way unto the Lord;
Trust also in him, and he shall bring it to pass.

And he shall make thy righteousness as the light,
And thy judgment as the noonday.

Rest in the Lord, and wait patiently for him:
Fret not thyself because of him who prospereth in his way,
Because of the man who bringeth wicked devices to pass.

Cease from anger, and forsake wrath:
Fret not thyself in any wise to do evil.

For evildoers shall be cut off;
But those that wait upon the Lord, they shall inherit the earth.

For yet a little while, and the wicked shall not be:

Yea, thou shalt diligently consider his place, and it shall not be.

But the meek shall inherit the earth,
And shall delight themselves in the abundance of peace.

The wicked plotteth against the just,
And gnasheth upon him with his teeth.

The Lord shall laugh at him;
For he seeth that his day is coming.

Better is a little that the righteous hath
Than the riches of many wicked.

For the arms of the wicked shall be broken;
But the Lord upholdeth the righteous.

The Lord knoweth the days of the upright;
And their inheritance shall be forever.

They shall not be ashamed in the evil time;
And in the days of famine they shall be satisfied.

But the wicked shall perish,
And the enemies of the Lord shall be as the fat of lambs:
They shall consume; in smoke shall they consume away.

The wicked borroweth, and payeth not again,
But the righteous showeth mercy, and giveth.

For such as are blessed of him shall inherit the land;
And they that are cursed of him shall be cut off.

The steps of a good man are ordered of the Lord,
And he delighteth in his way.

Evening

Depart from evil, and do good;
And dwell for evermore.

For the Lord loveth justice,
And forsaketh not his saints;

They are preserved forever:
But the seed of the wicked shall be cut off.

The righteous shall inherit the
land,
And dwell therein forever.

The mouth of the righteous speaketh wisdom,
And his tongue talketh of judgment.

The law of his God is in his heart;
None of his steps shall slide.

The wicked watcheth the righteous,
And seeketh to slay him.

The Lord will not leave him in his
hand,
Nor condemn him when he is
judged.

Wait on the Lord, and keep his way,
And he shall exalt thee to inherit the land:
When the wicked are cut off, thou shalt see it.

I have seen the wicked in great
power,
And spreading himself like a
green bay tree.

Yet he passéd away, and, lo, he was not:
Yea, I sought him, but he could not be found.

Mark the perfect man, and behold
the upright;
For the end of that man is peace.

But the transgressors shall be destroyed together:

The end of the wicked shall be cut off.

But the salvation of the righteous
is of the Lord:
He is their strength in the time of
trouble.

And the Lord shall help them, and deliver them:
He shall deliver them from the wicked, and save them,
Because they trust in him.

Fifth Sunday
Morning

I will bless the Lord at all times:
His praise shall continually be in my mouth.

My soul shall make her boast in
the Lord.
The humble shall hear thereof, and
be glad.

Oh magnify the Lord with me,
And let us exalt his name together.

I sought the Lord, and he heard
me,
And delivered me from all my
fears.

They looked unto him, and were lightened;
And their faces were not ashamed.

This poor man cried, and the Lord
heard him,
And saved him out of all his
troubles.

The angel of the Lord encampeth round about them that fear him,
And delivereth them.

Oh taste and see that the Lord is
good:
Blessed is the man that trusteth
in him.

Oh fear the Lord, ye his saints;
For there is no want to them that
fear him.

The young lions do lack, and suf-
fer hunger;
But they that seek the Lord shall
not want any good thing.

Come, ye children, hearken unto
me:
I will teach you the fear of the Lord.

What man is he that desireth life,
And loveth many days, that he may
see good?

Keep thy tongue from evil,
And thy lips from speaking guile.

Depart from evil, and do good;
Seek peace, and pursue it.

The eyes of the Lord are toward the
righteous,
And his ears are open unto their cry.

The face of the Lord is against
them that do evil,
To cut off the remembrance of
them from the earth.

The righteous cry, and the Lord
heareth,
And delivereth them out of all their
troubles.

The Lord is nigh unto them that
are of a broken heart,
And saveth such as be of a con-
trite spirit.

Many are the afflictions of the
righteous;
But the Lord delivereth him out of
them all.

He keepeth all his bones:
Not one of them is broken.

Evil shall slay the wicked;
And they that hate the righteous
shall be desolate.

The Lord redeemeth the soul of
his servants;
And none of them that trust in him
shall be desolate.

Evening

Praise ye the Lord.
Praise the Lord, O my soul.

While I live will I praise the Lord:
I will sing praises unto my God
while I have any being.

Put not your trust in princes,
Nor in the son of man, in whom
there is no help.

His breath goeth forth, he re-
turneth to his earth;
In that very day his thoughts
perish.

Happy is he that hath the God of
Jacob for his help,
Whose hope is in the Lord his God:

Who made heaven and earth,
The sea, and all that in them is;

Who keepeth truth forever;
Who executeth justice for the op-
pressed;
Who giveth food to the hungry.

The Lord looseth the prisoners;
The Lord openeth the eyes of the
blind;

The Lord raiseth up them that are
bowed down;
The Lord loveth the righteous;

The Lord preserveth the sojourners;
He relieveth the fatherless and
widow;
But the way of the wicked he turn-
eth upside down.

The Lord will reign forever,
Thy God, O Zion, unto all generations.

Praise ye the Lord.

Sixth Sunday
Morning

I will praise thee, O Lord, with my whole heart;
I will show forth all thy marvelous works.

I will be glad and rejoice in thee;
I will sing praise to thy name, O thou Most High.

When mine enemies turn back,
They shall fall and perish at thy presence.

For thou hast maintained my right and my cause;
Thou satest in the throne judging right.

Thou hast rebuked the heathen,
Thou hast destroyed the wicked;
Thou hast put out their name forever and ever.

The enemy are come to an end, they are desolate forever;
And the cities which thou hast overthrown,
Their very memorial is perished.

But the Lord shall endure forever:
He hath prepared his throne for judgment;

And he shall judge the world in righteousness,
He shall minister judgment to the peoples in uprightness.

The Lord also will be a refuge for the oppressed,
A refuge in times of trouble;

And they that know thy name will put their trust in thee;
For thou, Lord, hast not forsaken them that seek thee.

Sing praises to the Lord, which dwelleth in Zion:
Declare among the people his doings.

When he maketh inquisition for blood he remembereth them;
He forgetteth not the cry of the humble.

Have mercy upon me, O Lord;
Consider my trouble which I suffer of them that hate me,

Thou that liftest me up from the gates of death;
That I may show forth all thy praise.

In the gates of the daughter of Zion
I will rejoice in thy salvation.

The heathen are sunk down in the pit that they made:
In the net which they hid is their own foot taken.

The Lord hath made himself known, he hath executed judgment:
The wicked is snared in the work of his own hands.

The wicked shall be turned into Hell,
Even all the nations that forget God.

For the needy shall not alway be forgotten,
Nor the expectation of the poor perish forever.

Arise, O Lord; let not man prevail:
Let the heathen be judged in thy sight.

Put them in fear, O Lord:
Let the nations know themselves to be but men.

Evening

Why do the heathen rage,
And the people imagine a vain thing?

The kings of the earth set themselves,
And the rulers take counsel together,
Against the Lord, and against his
anointed, saying,

Let us break their bonds asunder,
And cast away their cords from us.

He that sitteth in the heavens shall
laugh:
The Lord shall have them in de-
rision.

Then shall he speak unto them in his wrath,
And vex them in his sore displeasure:

Yet I have set my king
Upon my holy hill of Zion.

I will declare the decree:
The Lord hath said unto me, Thou art my son;
This day have I begotten thee.

Ask of me, and I shall give thee
the heathen for thine inheritance,
And the uttermost parts of the
earth for thy possession.

Thou shalt break them with a rod of iron;
Thou shalt dash them in pieces like a potter's vessel.

Now therefore be wise, O ye kings:
Be instructed, ye judges of the earth.

Serve the Lord with fear,
And rejoice with trembling.

Kiss the Son, lest he be angry, and
ye perish from the way,
When his wrath is kindled but a
little.

Blessed are all they that put their trust in him.

Seventh Sunday
Morning

I will lift up mine eyes unto the hills:
From whence shall my help come?

My help cometh from the Lord,
Which made heaven and earth.

He will not suffer thy foot to be moved:
He that keepeth thee will not slumber.

Behold, he that keepeth Israel
Shall neither slumber nor sleep.

The Lord is thy keeper:
The Lord is thy shade upon thy right hand.

The sun shall not smite thee by
day,
Nor the moon by night.

The Lord shall preserve thee from all evil;
He shall preserve thy soul.

The Lord shall preserve thy going
out and thy coming in
From this time forth and for ever-
more.

I was glad when they said unto me,
Let us go unto the house of the Lord.

Our feet shall stand
Within thy gates, O Jerusalem.

Jerusalem is builded
As a city that is compact together;

Whither the tribes go up, the tribes
of the Lord,
Unto the testimony of Israel,
To give thanks unto the name of
the Lord.

For there are set thrones for judgment,
The thrones of the house of David.

9

Pray for the peace of Jerusalem:
They shall prosper that love thee.

Peace be within thy walls,
And prosperity within thy palaces.

For my brethren and companions'
sakes,
I will now say, Peace be within thee.

For the sake of the house of Jehovah our God
I will seek thy good.

Evening

Hear me when I call,
O God of my righteousness;

Thou hast enlarged me when I was
in distress:
Have mercy upon me, and hear
my prayer.

O ye sons of men, how long will ye
turn my glory into shame?
How long will ye love vanity, and
seek after falsehood?

But know that the Lord hath set
apart for himself him that is
godly:
The Lord will hear when I call
unto him.

Stand in awe, and sin not:
Commune with your own heart
upon your bed, and be still.

Offer the sacrifices of righteousness,
And put your trust in the Lord.

Many there be that say, Who will
show us any good?
Lord, lift thou up the light of thy
countenance upon us.

Thou hast put gladness in my
heart,
More than they have when their
grain and their new wine are increased.

In peace will I both lay me down
and sleep;
For thou, Lord, only makest me
dwell in safety.

Behold, bless ye the Lord, all ye
servants of the Lord,
Which by night stand in the house
of the Lord.

Lift up your hands to the sanctuary,
And bless ye the Lord.

The Lord bless thee out of Zion;
Even he that made heaven and
earth.

Eighth Sunday
Morning

O Lord my God, in thee do I put
my trust:
Save me from all them that persecute me, and deliver me,

Lest they tear my soul like a lion,
Rending it in pieces, while there
is none to deliver.

O Lord my God, if I have done this;
If there be iniquity in my hands;

If I have rewarded evil unto him
that was at peace with me
(Yea, I have delivered him that
without cause was mine adversary);

Let the enemy persecute my soul,
and take it;
Yea, let him tread my life down to
the earth,
And lay mine honor in the dust.

Arise, O Lord, in thine anger;
Lift up thyself against the rage of
mine enemies,
And awake for me; thou hast commanded judgment.

And let the congregation of the
peoples compass thee about;
And over them return thou on high.

The Lord shall judge the people:
Judge me, O Lord, according to
my righteousness, and to mine in-
tegrity that is in me.

Oh let the wickedness of the wicked
come to an end, but establish thou
the just:
For the righteous God trieth the
minds and hearts.

My defense is of God,
Which saveth the upright in heart.

God is a righteous judge,
Yea, a God that hath indignation
every day.

If a man turn not, he will whet
his sword;
He hath bent his bow, and made
it ready;

He hath also prepared for him the
instruments of death;
He ordaineth his arrows against
the persecutors.

Behold, he travaileth with iniquity;
Yea, he hath conceived mischief,
and brought forth falsehood.

He hath made a pit, and digged it,
And is fallen into the ditch which
he made.

His mischief shall return upon his
own head,
And his violence shall come down
upon his own pate

I will praise the Lord according to
his righteousness,
And will sing praise to the name of
the Lord Most High.

Evening

O Lord, rebuke me not in thine
anger,
Neither chasten me in thy hot displeasure.

Have mercy upon me, O Lord; for
I am weak:
O Lord, heal me; for my bones are
vexed.

My soul also is sore vexed:
And thou, O Lord, how long?

Return, O Lord, deliver my soul:
Save me for thy mercies' sake.

For in death there is no remembrance of thee:
In the grave who shall give thee
thanks?

I am weary with my groaning;
All the night make I my bed to
swim;
I water my couch with my tears.

Mine eye is consumed because of
grief;
It waxeth old because of all mine
enemies.

Depart from me, all ye workers of
iniquity;
For the Lord hath heard the voice
of my weeping.

The Lord hath heard my supplication;
The Lord will receive my prayer.

All mine enemies shall be put to
shame and sore troubled:
They shall turn back, they shall be
put to shame suddenly.

Ninth Sunday
Morning

The Lord hear thee in the day of
trouble;
The name of the God of Jacob defend thee;

Send thee help from the sanctuary,
And strengthen thee out of Zion;

Remember all thy offerings,
And accept thy burnt sacrifice;

Grant thee thy heart's desire,
And fulfill all thy counsel.

We will rejoice in thy salvation,
And in the name of our God we will
set up our banners:
The Lord fulfill all thy petitions.

Now know I that the Lord saveth
his anointed;
He will hear him from his holy
heaven
With the saving strength of his
right hand.

Some trust in chariots, and some
in horses;
But we will remember the name of
the Lord our God.

They are brought down and fallen;
But we are risen, and stand up-
right.

Save, Lord:
Let the King hear us when we
call.

The king shall joy in thy strength,
O Lord;
And in thy salvation how greatly
shall he rejoice!

Thou hast given him his heart's
desire,
And hast not withholden the re-
quest of his lips.

For thou meetest him with the
blessings of goodness:
Thou settest a crown of pure gold
on his head.

He asked life of thee, thou gavest
it him,
Even length of days forever and
ever.

His glory is great in thy salva-
tion:
Honor and majesty hast thou laid
upon him.

For thou hast made him most
blessed forever:
Thou hast made him glad with joy
in thy presence.

For the king trusteth in the Lord;
And through the mercy of the Most
High he shall not be moved.

Be thou exalted, O Lord, in thine
own strength:
So will we sing and praise thy
power.

Evening

The earth is the Lord's, and the
fullness thereof;
The world, and they that dwell
therein.

For he hath founded it upon the
seas,
And established it upon the floods.

Who shall ascend into the hill of the
Lord?
And who shall stand in his holy
place?

He that hath clean hands, and a
pure heart;
Who hath not lifted up his soul
unto falsehood,
And hath not sworn deceitfully.

He shall receive the blessing from
the Lord,
And righteousness from the God of
his salvation.

This is the generation of them that
seek him,
That seek thy face, O Jacob.

Lift up your heads, O ye gates;
And be ye lifted up, ye everlasting
doors:
And the King of glory shall come in.

Who is this King of glory?

The Lord strong and mighty,
The Lord mighty in battle.

Lift up your heads, O ye gates;
Even lift them up, ye everlasting
doors:
And the King of glory shall come
in.

Who is this King of glory?

The Lord of hosts,
He is the King of glory.

Tenth Sunday
Morning

Unto thee, O Lord, do I lift up my
soul.
O my God, in thee have I trusted,

Let me not be ashamed;
Let not mine enemies triumph
over me.

Yea, let none that wait on thee be
ashamed:
Let them be ashamed which transgress without cause.

Show me thy ways, O Lord;
Teach me thy paths.

Lead me in thy truth, and teach
me;
For thou art the God of my salvation;
On thee do I wait all the day.

Remember, O Lord, thy tender
mercies and thy loving-kindnesses;
For they have been ever of old.

Remember not the sins of my
youth, nor my transgressions:
According to thy mercy remember
thou me,
For thy goodness' sake, O Lord.

Good and upright is the Lord:
Therefore will he teach sinners in
the way.

The meek will he guide in judgment;

And the meek will he teach his
way.

All the paths of the Lord are mercy
and truth
Unto such as keep his covenant
and his testimonies.

For thy name's sake, O Lord,
Pardon mine iniquity, for it is
great.

What man is he that feareth the
Lord?
Him shall he teach in the way that
he shall choose.

His soul shall dwell at ease;
And his seed shall inherit the earth.

The secret of the Lord is with them
that fear him;
And he will show them his cove-
nant.

Mine eyes are ever toward the
Lord;
For he shall pluck my feet out of the
net.

Turn thee unto me, and have
mercy upon me;
For I am desolate and afflicted.

The troubles of my heart are enlarged:
Oh bring thou me out of my distresses.

Look upon mine affliction and my
pain;
And forgive all my sins.

Oh keep my soul, and deliver me:
Let me not be ashamed, for I put
my trust in thee.

Let integrity and uprightness pre-
serve me,
For I wait for thee.

Redeem Israel, O God,
Out of all his troubles.

Evening

Judge me, O Lord, for I have walked in mine integrity:
I have trusted also in the Lord without wavering.

Examine me, O Lord, and prove me;
Try my reins and my heart.

For thy loving-kindness is before mine eyes;
And I have walked in thy truth.

I have not sat with vain persons;
Neither will I go in with dissemblers.

I hate the congregation of evil-doers,
And will not sit with the wicked.

I will wash my hands in innocency:
So will I compass thine altar, O Lord;

That I may publish with the voice of thanksgiving,
And tell of all thy wondrous works.

Lord, I have loved the habitation of thy house,
And the place where thine honor dwelleth.

Gather not my soul with sinners,
Nor my life with bloody men;

In whose hands is mischief,
And their right hand is full of bribes.

But as for me, I will walk in mine integrity:
Redeem me, and be merciful unto me.

My foot standeth in an even place:
In the congregations will I bless the Lord.

Eleventh Sunday

Morning

Lord, how are mine adversaries increased!
Many are they that rise up against me.

Many there be which say of my soul,
There is no help for him in God.

But thou, O Lord, art a shield for me;
My glory, and the lifter up of my head.

I cried unto the Lord with my voice,
And he heard me out of his holy hill.

I laid me down and slept;
I awaked; for the Lord sustained me.

I will not be afraid of ten thousands of the people
That have set themselves against me round about.

Arise, O Lord; save me, O my God:
For thou hast smitten all mine enemies upon the cheek bone;
Thou hast broken the teeth of the ungodly.

Salvation belongeth unto the Lord:
Thy blessing be upon thy people.

Thy mercy, O Lord, is in the heavens;
Thy faithfulness reacheth unto the clouds.

Thy righteousness is like the great mountains;
Thy judgments are a great deep:
O Lord, thou preservest man and beast.

How excellent is thy loving-kindness, O God!
Therefore the children of men put their trust under the shadow of thy wings.

They shall be abundantly satisfied with the fatness of thy house;
And thou shalt make them drink of the river of thy pleasures.

For with thee is the fountain of life:
In thy light shall we see light.

Oh continue thy loving-kindness unto them that know thee,
And thy righteousness to the upright in heart.

Let not the foot of pride come against me,
And let not the hand of the wicked remove me.

There are the workers of iniquity fallen:
They are cast down, and shall not be able to rise.

Evening

Give ear to my words, O Lord,
Consider my meditation.

Hearken unto the voice of my cry, my King, and my God;
For unto thee will I pray.

My voice shalt thou hear in the morning, O Lord;
In the morning will I direct my prayer unto thee, and will look up.

For thou art not a God that hath pleasure in wickedness:
Neither shall evil dwell with thee.

The foolish shall not stand in thy sight:
Thou hatest all workers of iniquity.

Thou shalt destroy them that speak lies:
The Lord will abhor the bloody and deceitful man.

But as for me, in the abundance of thy mercy will I come into thy house:
In thy fear will I worship toward thy holy temple.

Lead me, O Lord, in thy righteousness because of mine enemies;
Make thy way straight before my face.

Let all those that put their trust in thee rejoice,
Let them ever shout for joy, because thou defendest them:

Let them also that love thy name be joyful in thee.
For thou wilt bless the righteous;
O Lord, thou wilt compass him with favor as with a shield.

By terrible things thou wilt answer us in righteousness,
O God of our salvation;

Thou that art the confidence of all the ends of the earth,
And of them that are afar off upon the sea.

Twelfth Sunday
Morning

The heavens declare the glory of God;
And the firmament showeth his handiwork.

Day unto day uttereth speech,
And night unto night showeth knowledge.

There is no speech nor language;
Their voice is not heard.

Their line is gone out through all the earth,
And their words to the end of the world.

In them hath he set a tabernacle for the sun,
Which is as a bridegroom coming out of his chamber,
And rejoiceth as a strong man to run a race.

His going forth is from the end of the heavens,
And his circuit unto the ends of it;
And there is nothing hid from the heat thereof.

O Lord, our Lord,
How excellent is thy name in all the earth,

Who hast set thy glory above the heavens!
Out of the mouth of babes and sucklings hast thou ordained strength,

Because of thine enemies,
That thou mightest still the enemy and the avenger.

When I consider thy heavens, the work of thy fingers,
The moon and the stars, which thou hast ordained;

What is man, that thou art mindful of him?
And the son of man, that thou visitest him?

For thou hast made him a little lower than the angels,
And hast crowned him with glory and honor.

Thou madest him to have dominion over the works of thy hands;
Thou hast put all things under his feet:

All sheep and oxen,
Yea, and the beasts of the field,

The fowl of the air, and the fish of the sea,
Whatsoever passeth through the paths of the seas.

O Lord, our Lord,
How excellent is thy name in all the earth.

Evening

In the Lord put I my trust:
How say ye to my soul,
Flee as a bird to your mountain;

For, lo, the wicked bend the bow,
They make ready their arrow upon the string,
That they may shoot in darkness at the upright in heart;

If the foundations be destroyed,
What can the righteous do?

The Lord is in his holy temple;
The Lord's throne is in heaven;

His eyes behold, his eyelids try, the children of men.
The Lord trieth the righteous;

But the wicked and him that loveth violence his soul hateth.
Upon the wicked he shall rain snares;
Fire and brimstone and an horrible tempest shall be the portion of their cup.

For the righteous Lord loveth righteousness:
The upright shall behold his countenance.

Help, Lord; for the godly man ceaseth;
For the faithful fail from among the children of men.

They speak vanity every one with his neighbor:
With flattering lips, and with a double heart, do they speak.

The Lord shall cut off all flattering lips,
The tongue that speaketh proud things;

Who have said, With our tongue will we prevail;
Our lips are our own: who is lord over us?

For the oppression of the poor,
For the sighing of the needy,
Now will I arise, saith the Lord;
I will set him in the safety he panteth for.

The words of the Lord are pure words;
As silver tried in a furnace on the earth,
Purified seven times.

Thou wilt keep them, O Lord,
Thou shalt preserve them from this generation forever.

The wicked walk on every side,
When vileness is exalted among the sons of men.

Thirteenth Sunday
Morning

Hear the right, O Lord, attend unto my cry;
Give ear unto my prayer, that goeth not out of feigned lips.

Let my sentence come forth from thy presence;
Let thine eyes look upon equity.

Thou hast proved my heart; thou hast visited me in the night;
Thou hast tried me, and findest nothing;

I am purposed that my mouth shall not transgress.
As for the works of men, by the word of thy lips
I have kept me from the paths of the destroyer.

My steps have held fast to thy paths,
My feet have not slipped.

I have called upon thee, for thou wilt hear me, O God:
Incline thine ear unto me, and hear my speech.

Show thy marvelous loving-kindness,
O thou that savest by thy right hand them which put their trust in thee
From those that rise up against them.

Keep me as the apple of the eye;
Hide me under the shadow of thy wings,

Deliver my soul from the wicked by thy sword;
From men by thy hand, O Lord,

From men of the world, whose portion is in this life,
And whose belly thou fillest with thy treasure:

They are satisfied with children,
And leave the rest of their substance to their babes.

Consider and hear me, O Lord my God:
Lighten mine eyes, lest I sleep the sleep of death;

Lest mine enemy say, I have prevailed against him;
Lest mine adversaries rejoice when I am moved.

But I have trusted in thy mercy;
My heart shall rejoice in thy sal-
vation.

I will sing unto the Lord,
Because he hath dealt bountifully
with me.

As for me, I shall behold thy face
in righteousness;
I shall be satisfied, when I awake,
with thy likeness.

Evening

Why standest thou afar off, O
Lord?
Why hidest thou thyself in times of
trouble?

The wicked in his pride doth per-
secute the poor;
Let them be taken in the devices
that they have imagined.

For the wicked boasteth of his
heart's desire,
And blesseth the covetous whom
the Lord abhorreth.

The wicked, in the pride of his
countenance, will not seek after God.
God is not in all his thoughts.
His ways are always grievous;

Thy judgments are far above out
of his sight:
As for all his enemies, he puffeth
at them.

Arise, O Lord; O God, lift up thy
hand:
Forget not the humble.

Wherefore doth the wicked con-
temn God,
And say in his heart, Thou wilt not
require it?

The poor committeth himself unto
thee;
Thou art the helper of the fatherless.

Break thou the arm of the wicked;
And as for the evil man, seek out
his wickedness till thou find none.

The Lord is King forever and ever:
The heathen are perished out of
his land.

Lord, thou hast heard the desire
of the humble:
Thou wilt prepare their heart, thou
wilt cause thine ear to hear;

To judge the fatherless and the
oppressed,
That man of the earth may no
more oppress.

Fourteenth Sunday
Morning

I love thee, O Lord, my strength.

The Lord is my rock, and my
fortress, and my deliverer;
My God, my strength, in whom I
will trust;
My shield, and the horn of my
salvation, my high tower.

I will call upon the Lord, who is
worthy to be praised:
So shall I be saved from mine
enemies.

The sorrows of death compassed
me,
And the •floods of ungodliness
made me afraid.

The sorrows of hell compassed me;
The snares of death came upon me.

In my distress I called upon the
Lord,
And cried unto my God:

He heard my voice out of his temple,
And my cry before him came into
his ears.

Then the earth shook and trembled;
The foundations also of the moun-
tains quaked
And were shaken, because he was
wroth.

There went up a smoke out of his
nostrils,
And fire out of his mouth devoured:
Coals were kindled by it.

He bowed the heavens also, and
came down;
And thick darkness was under his
feet.

And he rode upon a cherub, and did
fly;
Yea, he did fly upon the wings of
the wind.

He made darkness his secret place,
his pavilion round about him,
Darkness of waters, thick clouds
of the skies.

At the brightness before him his
thick clouds passed,
Hailstones and coals of fire.

The Lord also thundered in the
heavens,
And the Most High uttered his
voice,
Hailstones and coals of fire.

Yea, he sent out his arrows, and
scattered them;
And he shot out lightnings, and
discomfited them.

Then the channels of waters were
seen,
And the foundations of the world
were laid bare.

At thy rebuke, O Lord,
At the blast of the breath of thy
nostrils.

He sent from on high, he took me;
He drew me out of many waters.

He delivered me from my strong
enemy,
And from them which hated me;
for they were too strong for me.

They came upon me in the day of
my calamity;
But the Lord was my stay.

He brought me forth also into a
large place;
He delivered me, because he delighted in me.

Evening

The fool hath said in his heart,
There is no God.
They are corrupt, they have done
abominable works;
There is none that doeth good.

The Lord looked down from heaven
upon the children of men,
To see if there were any that did
understand,
That did seek after God.

They are all gone aside; they are
together become filthy;
There is none that doeth good, no,
not one.

Have all the workers of iniquity
no knowledge,
Who eat up my people as they eat
bread,
And call not upon the Lord?

There were they in great fear;
For God is in the generation of the
righteous.

Ye put to shame the counsel of the
poor,
Because the Lord is his refuge.

The Lord is my shepherd; I shall
not want.
He maketh me to lie down in green
pastures;

He leadeth me beside still waters.
He restoreth my soul:
He leadeth me in the paths of
righteousness for his name's sake.

Yea, though I walk through the
valley of the shadow of death,
I will fear no evil; for thou art with
me;
Thy rod and thy staff, they comfort me.

Thou preparest a table before me
in the presence of mine enemies:
Thou anointest my head with oil;
My cup runneth over.

Surely goodness and mercy shall
follow me all the days of my
life;
And I will dwell in the house of
the Lord forever.

Fifteenth Sunday
Morning

The Lord rewarded me according
to my righteousness;
According to the cleanness of my
hands hath he recompensed me.

For I have kept the ways of the
Lord,
And have not wickedly departed
from my God.

For all his judgments were before
me,
And I put not away his statutes
from me.

I was also upright before him,
And I kept myself from mine in-
iquity.

Therefore hath the Lord recompensed me according to my righteousness,
According to the cleanness of my
hands in his eyesight.

With the merciful thou wilt show
thyself merciful;
With an upright man thou wilt
show thyself upright;

With the pure thou wilt show thyself pure;
And with the froward thou wilt
show thyself froward.

For thou wilt save the afflicted
people;
But wilt bring down high looks.

For thou wilt light my candle:
The Lord my God will lighten my
darkness.

As for God, his way is perfect:
He is a shield unto all them that
take refuge in him.

For who is God, save the Lord?
And who is a rock, save our
God?

It is God that girdeth me with
strength,
And maketh my way perfect.

He maketh my feet like hinds' feet:
And setteth me upon my high
places.

He teacheth my hands to war;
So that mine arms do bend a bow
of brass.

Thou hast also given me the shield
of thy salvation;
And thy right hand hath holden
me up,
And thy gentleness hath made me
great.

Thou hast enlarged my steps under
me,
And my feet did not slip.

The Lord liveth; and blessed be my
rock;
And let the God of my salvation be
exalted.

It is God that executeth vengeance for me,
And subdueth peoples under me.

He delivereth me from mine enemies;
Yea, thou liftest me up above those that rise up against me;
Thou deliverest me from the violent man.

Therefore I will give thanks unto thee, O Lord, among the heathen,
And will sing praises unto thy name.

Great deliverance giveth he to his king,
And showeth mercy to his anointed,
To David and to his seed, for evermore.

Evening

The Lord is my light and my salvation;
Whom shall I fear?

The Lord is the strength of my life;
Of whom shall I be afraid?

When the wicked came upon me to eat up my flesh,
Even mine adversaries and my foes, they stumbled and fell.

Though a host should encamp against me,
My heart shall not fear:

Though war should rise against me,
In this will I be confident.

One thing have I asked of the Lord, that will I seek after:
That I may dwell in the house of the Lord all the days of my life,

To behold the beauty of the Lord,
And to inquire in his temple.

For in the time of trouble he shall hide me in his pavilion:
In the secret of his tabernacle he shall hide me:

He shall lift me up upon a rock.
And now shall my head be lifted up above mine enemies round about me;

Therefore will I offer in his tabernacle sacrifices of joy;
I will sing, yea, I will sing praises unto the Lord.

Hear, O Lord, when I cry with my voice:
Have mercy also upon me, and answer me.

When thou saidst, Seek ye my face; my heart said unto thee,
Thy face, Lord, will I seek.

Hide not thy face from me;
Put not thy servant away in anger:

Thou hast been my help;
Leave me not, neither forsake me, O God of my salvation.

When my father and my mother forsake me,
Then the Lord will take me up.

Teach me thy way, O Lord;
And lead me in a plain path,
Because of mine enemies.

Deliver me not over unto the will of mine enemies:
For false witnesses are risen up against me,
And such as breathe out cruelty.

I had fainted, unless I had believed to see the goodness of the Lord
In the land of the living.

Wait on the Lord:
Be of good courage, and he shall strengthen thy heart;
Wait, I say, on the Lord.

Sixteenth Sunday
Morning

My God, my God, why hast thou forsaken me?
Why art thou so far from helping me, and from the words of my roaring?

O my God, I cry in the daytime, but thou hearest not;
And in the night season, and am not silent.

But thou art holy,
O thou that inhabitest the praises of Israel.

Our fathers trusted in thee:
They trusted, and thou didst deliver them.

They cried unto thee, and were delivered:
They trusted in thee, and were not confounded.

But I am a worm, and no man;
A reproach of men, and despised of the people.

All they that see me laugh me to scorn:
They shoot out the lip, they shake the head, saying,

He trusted on the Lord, that he would deliver him:
Let him deliver him, seeing he delighted in him.

Be not far from me; for trouble is near;
For there is none to help.

Many bulls have compassed me;
Strong bulls of Bashan have beset me round.

They gape upon me with their mouths,
As a ravening and a roaring lion.

I am poured out like water,
And all my bones are out of joint:

My heart is like wax;
It is melted within me.

My strength is dried up like a potsherd;
And my tongue cleaveth to my jaws;

And thou hast brought me into the dust of death.
For dogs have compassed me:

The assembly of the wicked have inclosed me;
They pierced my hands and my feet.
I may count all my bones.
They look and stare upon me;

They part my garments among them,
And upon my vesture do they cast lots.

But be not thou far off, O Lord:
O thou my strength, haste thee to help me.

Deliver my soul from the sword,
My darling from the power of the dog.

Save me from the lion's mouth;
Yea, from the horns of the wild oxen thou hast heard me.

I will declare thy name unto my brethren:
In the midst of the assembly will I praise thee.

Evening

Ye that fear the Lord, praise him;
All ye the seed of Jacob, glorify him;

And stand in awe of him, all ye the seed of Israel.
For he hath not despised nor abhorred the affliction of the afflicted;

Neither hath he hid his face from him;
But when he cried unto him, he heard.

My praise shall be of thee in the great congregation:
I will pay my vows before them that fear him.

The meek shall eat and be satisfied;
They shall praise the Lord that seek after him:
Let your heart live forever.

All the ends of the world shall remember and turn unto the Lord;
And all the kindreds of the nations shall worship before thee.

For the kingdom is the Lord's;
And he is the governor among the nations.

A seed shall serve him;
It shall be told of the Lord unto the next generation.

They shall come and shall declare his righteousness
Unto a people that shall be born, that he hath done this.

We have heard with our ears, O God,
Our fathers have told us.

What work thou didst in their days,
In the times of old.

Thou didst drive out the heathen with thy hand;
But them thou didst plant:

Thou didst afflict the peoples;
But them thou didst spread abroad.

For they got not the land in possession by their own sword,
Neither did their own arm save them;

But thy right hand, and thine arm, and the light of thy countenance,
Because thou wast favorable unto them.

Thou art my King, O God:
Command deliverance for Jacob.

Seventeenth Sunday
Morning

In thee, O Lord, do I put my trust;
Let me never be put to shame:

Deliver me in thy righteousness.
Bow down thine ear unto me; deliver me speedily:

Be thou to me a strong rock,
A house of defense to save me.

For thou art my rock and my fortress;
Therefore for thy name's sake lead me and guide me.

Pull me out of the net that they have hidden for me;
For thou art my strength.

Into thy hand I commend my spirit:
Thou hast redeemed me, O Lord, God of truth.

I will be glad and rejoice in thy mercy;
For thou hast considered my trouble:

Thou hast known my soul in adversities;
And thou hast not shut me up into the hand of the enemy;

Thou hast set my feet in a large place.
And I trusted in thee, O Lord:

I said, Thou art my God.
My times are in thy hand;

Deliver me from the hand of mine enemies, and from them that persecute me.
Make thy face to shine upon thy servant:

Save me for thy mercies' sake.
Let me not be ashamed, O Lord; for I have called upon thee:

Oh how great is thy goodness, Which thou hast laid up for them that fear thee,

Which thou hast wrought for them that trust in thee,
Before the sons of men!

Thou shalt hide them in the secret of thy presence:
Thou shalt keep them secretly in a pavilion from the strife of tongues.

Blessed be the Lord;
For he hath showed me his marvelous kindness in a strong city.

As for me, I said in my haste, I am cut off from before thine eyes:

Nevertheless thou heardest the voice of my supplications,
When I cried unto thee.

Oh love the Lord, all ye his saints: The Lord preserveth the faithful, And plentifully rewardeth the proud doer.

Be of good courage, and he shall strengthen your heart,
All ye that hope in the Lord.

Evening

Give unto the Lord, O ye mighty, Give unto the Lord glory and strength.

Give unto the Lord the glory due unto his name;
Worship the Lord in the beauty of holiness.

The voice of the Lord is upon the waters:
The God of glory thundereth,
The Lord is upon many waters.

The voice of the Lord is powerful;
The voice of the Lord is full of majesty.

The voice of the Lord breaketh the cedars;
Yea, the Lord breaketh the cedars of Lebanon.

He maketh them also to skip like a calf;
Lebanon and Sirion like a young wild ox.

The voice of the Lord divideth the flames of fire.
The voice of the Lord shaketh the wilderness;
The Lord shaketh the wilderness of Kadesh.

The voice of the Lord maketh the hinds to calve,
And strippeth the forests bare:
And in his temple doth every one speak of his glory.

The Lord sitteth upon the flood;
Yea, the Lord sitteth King forever.

The Lord will give strength unto his people;
The Lord will bless his people with peace.

Oh praise the Lord, all ye nations;
Praise him, all ye peoples.

For his mercy is great toward us;
And the truth of the Lord endureth forever.

Praise ye the Lord.

Eighteenth Sunday
Morning

Rejoice in the Lord, O ye righteous:
Praise is comely for the upright.

Praise the Lord with the harp:
Sing unto him with the psaltery
of ten strings.

Sing unto him a new song;
Play skillfully with a loud noise.

For the word of the Lord is right;
And all his works are done in
truth.

He loveth righteousness and judgment:
The earth is full of the goodness of
the Lord.

By the word of the Lord were the
heavens made,
And all the host of them by the
breath of his mouth.

He gathereth the waters of the sea
together as a heap:
He layeth up the depth in storehouses.

Let all the earth fear the Lord:
Let all the inhabitants of the world
stand in awe of him.

For he spake, and it was done;
He commanded, and it stood fast.

The Lord bringeth the counsel of
the heathen to naught;
He maketh the devices of the peo-
ple to be of none effect.

The counsel of the Lord standeth
forever,
The thoughts of his heart to all generations.

Blessed is the nation whose God is
the Lord,
The people whom he hath chosen
for his own inheritance.

The Lord looketh from heaven;
He beholdeth all the sons of
men;

From the place of his habitation
he looketh forth
Upon all the inhabitants of the
earth,

He that fashioneth the hearts of
them all,
That considereth all their works.

There is no king saved by the mul-
titude of a host:
A mighty man is not delivered by
much strength.

A horse is a vain thing for safety;
Neither shall he deliver any by his
great strength.

Behold, the eye of the Lord is upon
them that fear him,
Upon them that hope in his
mercy;

To deliver their soul from death,
And to keep them alive in famine.

Our soul waiteth for the Lord:
He is our help and our shield.

For our heart shall rejoice in
him,
Because we have trusted in his holy
name.

Let thy mercy, O Lord, be upon
us,
According as we have hoped in
thee.

Evening

Blessed is he whose transgression
is forgiven,
Whose sin is covered.

Blessed is the man unto whom the
Lord imputeth not iniquity,
And in whose spirit there is no
guile.

When I kept silence, my bones waxed old
Through my roaring all the day long.

For day and night thy hand was heavy upon me:
My moisture is turned into the drought of summer.

I acknowledged my sin unto thee,
And mine iniquity have I not hid:

I said, I will confess my transgressions unto the Lord;
And thou forgavest the iniquity of my sin.

For this shall every one that is godly pray unto thee in a time when thou mayest be found:
Surely in the floods of great waters they shall not come nigh unto him.

Thou art my hiding place; thou shalt preserve me from trouble;
Thou shalt compass me about with songs of deliverance.

I will instruct thee and teach thee in the way which thou shalt go:
I will guide thee with mine eye.

Be ye not as the horse, or as the mule, which have no understanding;
Whose mouth must be held in with bit and bridle,
Else it will not come near unto thee.

Many sorrows shall be to the wicked;
But he that trusteth in the Lord, mercy shall compass him about.

Be glad in the Lord, and rejoice, ye righteous;
And shout for joy, all ye that are upright in heart.

Nineteenth Sunday
Morning

I will bless the Lord at all times:
His praise shall continually be in my mouth.

My soul shall make her boast in the Lord:
The humble shall hear thereof, and be glad.

Oh magnify the Lord with me,
And let us exalt his name together.

I sought the Lord, and he heard me,
And delivered me from all my fears.

They looked unto him, and were lightened;
And their faces were not ashamed.

This poor man cried, and the Lord heard him,
And saved him out of all his troubles.

The angel of the Lord encampeth round about them that fear him,
And delivereth them.

Oh taste and see that the Lord is good:
Blessed is the man that trusteth in him.

Oh fear the Lord, ye his saints;
For there is no want to them that fear him.

The young lions do lack, and suffer hunger;
But they that seek the Lord shall not want any good thing.

Come, ye children, hearken unto me:
I will teach you the fear of the Lord.

What man is he that desireth life,
And loveth many days, that he
may see good?

Keep thy tongue from evil,
And thy lips from speaking guile.

Depart from evil, and do good;
Seek peace, and pursue it.

The eyes of the Lord are upon
the righteous,
And his ears are open unto their
cry.

The face of the Lord is against
them that do evil,
To cut off the remembrance of
them from the earth.

The righteous cry, and the Lord
heareth,
And delivereth them out of all their
troubles.

The Lord is nigh unto them that
are of a broken heart,
And saveth such as be of a con-
trite spirit.

Many are the afflictions of the
righteous:
But the Lord delivereth him out
of them all.

He keepeth all his bones:
Not one of them is broken.

Evil shall slay the wicked:
And they that hate the righteous
shall be desolate.

The Lord redeemeth the soul of
his servants:
And none of them that trust in him
shall be desolate.

Evening

I said, I will take heed to my ways,
That I sin not with my tongue.

I will keep my mouth with a bridle,
While the wicked is before me.

I was dumb with silence, I held my
peace, even from good;
And my sorrow was stirred.

My heart was hot within me;
While I was musing the fire
burned;
Then spake I with my tongue:

Lord, make me to know mine end,
And the measure of my days, what
it is;
That I may know how frail I am.

Behold, thou hast made my days
as an handbreadth;
And mine age is as nothing before
thee:

Verily every man at his best state
is altogether vanity.
Surely every man walketh in a
vain show;

Surely they are disquieted in vain:
He heapeth up riches, and knoweth
eth not who shall gather them.

And now, Lord, what wait I for?
My hope is in thee.

Deliver me from all my trans-
gressions:
Make me not the reproach of the
foolish.

I was dumb, I opened not my
mouth;
Because thou didst it.

Remove thy stroke away from me:
I am consumed by the blow of thy
hand.

When thou with rebukes dost correct man for iniquity,
Thou makest his beauty to consume away like a moth:
Surely every man is vanity.

Hear my prayer, O Lord, and
give ear unto my cry;
Hold not thy peace at my tears:

For I am a stranger with thee,
A sojourner, as all my fathers were.

*Oh spare me, that I may recover
strength,
Before I go hence, and be no more.*

Twentieth Sunday
Morning

Plead my cause, O Lord, with them
that strive with me:
Fight thou against them that fight
against me.

*Take hold of shield and buckler,
And stand up for my help.*

Draw out also the spear, and stop
the way against them that persecute me:
Say unto my soul, I am thy salvation.

*And my soul shall be joyful in the
Lord:
It shall rejoice in his salvation.*

All my bones shall say, Lord, who
is like unto thee,
Which deliverest the poor from him
that is too strong for him,
Yea, the poor and the needy from
him that spoileth him?

*I will give thee thanks in the great
assembly:
I will praise thee among much
people.*

Let not them that are mine enemies
wrongfully rejoice over me;
Neither let them wink with the eye
that hate me without a cause.

*For they speak not peace;
But they devise deceitful words
against them that are quiet in the
land.*

Thou hast seen it, O Lord; keep
not silence:
O Lord, be not far from me.

*Stir up thyself, and awake to my
judgment.
Even unto my cause, my God and
my Lord.*

Judge me, O Lord my God, according to thy righteousness;
And let them not rejoice over
me.

*Let them shout for joy, and be
glad, that favor my righteous cause:
Yea, let them say continually, Let
the Lord be magnified,
Which hath pleasure in the prosperity of his servant.*

And my tongue shall talk of thy
righteousness
And of thy praise all the day
long.

*O Israel, hope in the Lord;
For with the Lord there is mercy,
And with him is plenteous re-
demption.*

And he will redeem Israel
From all his iniquities.

Evening

Great is the Lord, and greatly to
be praised,
In the city of our God, in his holy
mountain.

*Beautiful for situation, the joy of
the whole earth,
Is mount Zion, on the sides of the
north,
The city of the great King.*

God is known in her palaces for a
refuge.
For, lo, the kings assembled,
They passed by together.

*They saw it, and so they mar-
veled;
They were troubled, and hasted
away.*

Trembling took hold of them there,
Pain, as of a woman in travail.

Thou breakest the ships of Tar-
shish
With an east wind.

As we have heard, so have we seen
In the city of the Lord of hosts, in
the city of our God:
God will establish it forever.

We have thought of thy loving-
kindness, O God,
In the midst of thy temple.

According to thy name, O God,
So is thy praise unto the ends of the
earth:
Thy right hand is full of righteousness.

Let mount Zion rejoice,
Let the daughters of Judah be
glad,
Because of thy judgments.

Walk about Zion, and go round
about her;
Number the towers thereof;

Mark ye well her bulwarks;
Consider her palaces:
That ye may tell it to the genera-
tion following.

For this God is our God forever
and ever:
He will be our guide even unto
death.

Twenty=first Sunday
Morning

Forever, O Lord,
Thy word is settled in heaven.

Thy faithfulness is unto all gen-
erations:
Thou hast established the earth,
and it abideth.

They continue this day according
to thine ordinances;
For all things are thy servants.

Unless thy law had been my de-
light,
I should then have perished in
mine affliction.

I will never forget thy precepts;
For with them thou hast quickened
me.

I am thine, save me;
For I have sought thy precepts.

The wicked have waited for me, to
destroy me;
But I will consider thy testimonies.

I have seen an end of all perfec-
tion;
But thy commandment is exceed-
ing broad.

Oh how love I thy law!
It is my meditation all the day.

Thy commandments make me
wiser than mine enemies;
For they are ever with me.

I have more understanding than
all my teachers;
For thy testimonies are my meditation.

I understand more than the aged,
Because I have kept thy precepts.

I have refrained my feet from
every evil way,
That I might observe thy word.

I have not departed from thine
ordinances;
For thou hast taught me.

How sweet are thy words unto my
taste!
Yea, sweeter than honey to my
mouth!

Through thy precepts I get understanding:
Therefore I hate every false way.

Thy word is a lamp unto my feet,
And light unto my path.

I have sworn, and have confirmed it,
That I will observe thy righteous ordinances.

I am afflicted very much:
Quicken me, O Lord, according unto thy word.

Accept, I beseech thee, the freewill offerings of my mouth, O Lord,
And teach me thine ordinances.

My soul is continually in my hand;
Yet do I not forget thy law.

The wicked have laid a snare for me;
Yet have I not gone astray from thy precepts.

Thy testimonies have I taken as a heritage forever;
For they are the rejoicing of my heart.

I have inclined my heart to perform thy statutes
Forever, even unto the end.

Evening

O Lord, rebuke me not in thy wrath;
Neither chasten me in thy hot displeasure.

For thine arrows stick fast in me,
And thy hand presseth me sore.

There is no soundness in my flesh because of thine anger;
Neither is there any rest in my bones because of my sin.

For mine iniquities are gone over my head:
As a heavy burden they are too heavy for me.

I am troubled and bowed down greatly;
I go mourning all the day long.
I am faint and sore broken.

Lord, all my desire is before thee;
And my groaning is not hid from thee.

My heart panteth, my strength faileth me:
As for the light of mine eyes, it also is gone from me.

But I, as a deaf man, heard not;
And I was as a dumb man that openeth not his mouth.

Thus I was as a man that heareth not,
And in whose mouth are no reproofs.

For in thee, O Lord, do I hope:
Thou wilt hear, O Lord my God.

For I am ready to halt,
And my sorrow is continually before me.

For I will declare mine iniquity;
I will be sorry for my sin.

Forsake me not, O Lord:
O my God, be not far from me.

Make haste to help me,
O Lord, my salvation.

Twenty=second Sunday
Morning

Hear this, all ye people;
Give ear, all ye inhabitants of the world,

Both low and high,
Rich and poor together.

My mouth shall speak wisdom;
And the meditation of my heart shall be of understanding.

I will incline mine ear to a parable:
I will open my dark saying upon the harp.

Wherefore should I fear in the days of evil,
When iniquity at my heels compasseth me about?

They that trust in their wealth,
And boast themselves in the multitude of their riches;

None of them can by any means redeem his brother,
Nor give to God a ransom for him,

That he should still live alway,
That he should not see corruption.

For he shall see it. Wise men die;
Likewise the fool and the brutish perish,
And leave their wealth to others.

Their inward thought is, that their houses shall continue forever,
And their dwelling places to all generations;
They call their lands after their own names.

Nevertheless man being in honor abideth not:
He is like the beasts that perish.
This their way is their folly:
Yet their posterity approve their sayings.

Like sheep they are laid in the grave;
Death shall be their shepherd:
And the upright shall have dominion over them in the morning;

And their beauty shall consume in the grave,
That there be no dwelling for it.

But God will redeem my soul from the power of the grave;
For he shall receive me.

Be not thou afraid when one is made rich,
When the glory of his house is increased:

For when he dieth he shall carry nothing away;
His glory shall not descend after him.

Though while he lived he blessed his soul
(And men praise thee, when thou doest well to thyself),

He shall go to the generation of his fathers;
They shall never see the light.

Man that is in honor, and understandeth not,
Is like the beasts that perish.

Evening

Oh clap your hands, all ye people;
Shout unto God with the voice of triumph.

For the Lord Most High is terrible;
He is a great King over all the earth.

He subdueth the people under us,
And the nations under our feet.

He shall choose our inheritance for us,
The excellency of Jacob whom he loved.

God is gone up with a shout,
The Lord with the sound of a trumpet.

Sing praises to God, sing praises:
Sing praises unto our King, sing
praises.

For God is the King of all the
earth:
Sing ye praises with understanding.

God reigneth over the heathen:
God sitteth upon his holy throne.

The princes of the peoples are
gathered together
Even the people of the God of
Abraham;

For the shields of the earth belong
unto God:
He is greatly exalted.

Save me, O God, by thy name,
And judge me by thy strength.

Hear my prayer, O God;
Give ear to the words of my mouth.

For strangers are risen up against
me,
And oppressors have sought after
my soul:
They have not set God before them.

Behold, God is my helper:
The Lord is of them that uphold
my soul.

With a freewill offering will I sacri-
fice unto thee:
I will give thanks unto thy name,
O Lord, for it is good.

Twenty-third Sunday
Morning

The Mighty God, the Lord, hath
spoken,
And called the earth from the rising
of the sun unto the going down
thereof.

Out of Zion, the perfection of
beauty,
God hath shined forth.

Our God shall come, and shall not
keep silence:
A fire shall devour before him,
And it shall be very tempestuous
round about him.

He shall call to the heavens above,
And to the earth, that he may
judge his people:

Gather my saints together unto
me,
Those that have made a covenant
with me by sacrifice.

And the heavens shall declare his
righteousness;
For God is judge himself.

Hear, O my people, and I will
speak;
O Israel, and I will testify unto
thee:
I am God, even thy God.

Not for sacrifices will I reprove
thee;
And thy burnt offerings are con-
tinually before me.

I will take no bullock out of thy
house,
Nor he-goats out of thy folds.

For every beast of the forest is
mine,
And the cattle upon a thousand
hills.

I know all the fowls of the mountains;
And the wild beasts of the field are
mine.

If I were hungry, I would not tell
thee;
For the world is mine, and the
fullness thereof.

Will I eat the flesh of bulls,
Or drink the blood of goats?

Offer unto God the sacrifice of thanksgiving;
And pay thy vows unto the Most High;

And call upon me in the day of trouble:
I will deliver thee, and thou shalt glorify me.

But unto the wicked God saith,
What hast thou to do to declare my statutes,
And that thou shouldest take my covenant in thy mouth,

Seeing that thou hatest instruction,
And castest my words behind thee?

When thou sawest a thief, thou consentedst with him,
And hast been partaker with adulterers.

Thou givest thy mouth to evil,
And thy tongue frameth deceit.

Thou sittest and speakest against thy brother;
Thou slanderest thine own mother's son.

These things hast thou done, and I kept silence;
Thou thoughtest that I was altogether such a one as thyself:
But I will reprove thee, and set them in order before thine eyes.

Now consider this, ye that forget God,
Lest I tear you in pieces, and there be none to deliver:

Whoso offereth praise glorifieth me;
And to him that ordereth his way aright
Will I show the salvation of God.

Evening

Be merciful unto me, O God; for man would swallow me up:
He fighting daily oppresseth me.

Mine enemies would daily swallow me up;
For they be many that fight against me,
O thou Most High.

What time I am afraid,
I will trust in thee.

In God I will praise his word:
In God I have put my trust, I will not fear
What flesh can do unto me.

Every day they wrest my words:
All their thoughts are against me for evil.

They gather themselves together, they hide themselves,
They mark my steps,
When they wait for my soul.

Thou numberest my wanderings:
Put thou my tears into thy bottle;
Are they not in thy book?

Then shall mine enemies turn back in the day that I call:
This I know, that God is for me.

In God I will praise his word:
In the Lord I will praise his word.

In God have I put my trust, I will not be afraid
What man can do unto me.

Thy vows are upon me, O God:
I will render praises unto thee.

For thou hast delivered my soul from death:
Wilt not thou deliver my feet from falling,

That I may walk before God
In the light of the living?

*Be merciful unto me, O God, be
merciful unto me;
For my soul trusteth in thee:*

Yea, in the shadow of thy wings
will I make my refuge,
Until these calamities be overpast.

*I will cry unto God Most High,
Unto God that performeth all
things for me.*

Be thou exalted, O God, above the
heavens;
Let thy glory be above all the earth.

Twenty=fourth Sunday
Morning

Have mercy upon me, O God, according to thy loving-kindness:
According unto the multitude of
thy tender mercies blot out my
transgressions.

*Wash me thoroughly from mine
iniquity,
And cleanse me from my sin.*

For I acknowledge my transgressions;
And my sin is ever before me.

*Against thee, thee only, have I
sinned,
And done that which is evil in thy
sight;*

That thou mayest be justified when
thou speakest,
And be clear when thou judgest.

*Behold, I was shapen in iniquity;
And in sin did my mother conceive me.*

Behold, thou desirest truth in the
inward parts;
And in the hidden part thou shalt
make me to know wisdom.

*Purge me with hyssop, and I shall
be clean:
Wash me, and I shall be whiter
than snow.*

Make me to hear joy and gladness,
That the bones which thou hast
broken may rejoice.

*Hide thy face from my sins,
And blot out all mine iniquities.*

Create in me a clean heart, O
God;
And renew a right spirit within
me.

*Cast me not away from thy presence;
And take not thy holy Spirit from
me.*

Restore unto me the joy of thy
salvation;
And uphold me with thy free Spirit.

*Then will I teach transgressors thy
ways;
And sinners shall be converted
unto thee.*

Deliver me from bloodguiltiness, O
God, thou God of my salvation;
And my tongue shall sing aloud of
thy righteousness.

*O Lord, open thou my lips;
And my mouth shall show forth
thy praise.*

For thou desirest not sacrifice;
else would I give it:
Thou delightest not in burnt offering.

*The sacrifices of God are a broken
spirit:
A broken and a contrite heart, O
God, thou wilt not despise.*

Do good in thy good pleasure unto
Zion:
Build thou the walls of Jerusalem.

Then shalt thou be pleased with the sacrifices of righteousness,
With burnt offering and whole burnt offering:
Then shall they offer bullocks upon thine altar.

Evening

Lord, who shall abide in thy tabernacle?
Who shall dwell in thy holy hill?

He that walketh uprightly, and worketh righteousness,
And speaketh the truth in his heart;

He that backbiteth not with his tongue,
Nor doeth evil to his neighbor,
Nor taketh up a reproach against his neighbor;

In whose eyes a vile person is contemned,
But who honoreth them that fear the Lord;
He that sweareth to his own hurt, and changeth not;

He that putteth not out his money to usury,
Nor taketh reward against the innocent.
He that doeth these things shall never be moved.

O God, thou art my God; early will I seek thee:
My soul thirsteth for thee, my flesh longeth for thee,
In a dry and weary land, where no water is;

To see thy power and thy glory,
So as I have seen thee in the sanctuary.

Because thy loving-kindness is better than life,
My lips shall praise thee.

Thus will I bless thee while I live:
I will lift up my hands in thy name.

My soul shall be satisfied as with marrow and fatness;
And my mouth shall praise thee with joyful lips;

When I remember thee upon my bed,
And meditate on thee in the night watches.

Because thou hast been my help,
Therefore in the shadow of thy wings will I rejoice.

My soul followeth hard after thee:
Thy right hand upholdeth me.

But the King shall rejoice in God:
Every one that sweareth by him shall glory;
But the mouth of them that speak lies shall be stopped.

Twenty-fifth Sunday
Morning

Blessed are the undefiled in the way,
Who walk in the law of the Lord.

Blessed are they that keep his testimonies,
That seek him with the whole heart.

Yea, they do no iniquity;
They walk in his ways.

Thou hast commanded us thy precepts,
That we should observe them diligently.

Oh that my ways were established
To observe thy statutes!

Then shall I not be ashamed,
When I have respect unto all thy commandments.

I will praise thee with uprightness of heart,
When I learn thy righteous judgments.

I will keep thy statutes:
Oh forsake me not utterly.

Wherewithal shall a young man cleanse his way?
By taking heed thereto according to thy word.

With my whole heart have I sought thee:
Oh let me not wander from thy commandments.

Thy word have I laid up in my heart,
That I might not sin against thee.

Blessed art thou, O Lord:
Teach me thy statutes.

With my lips have I declared
All the judgments of thy mouth.

I have rejoiced in the way of thy testimonies,
As much as in all riches.

I will meditate in thy precepts,
And have respect unto thy ways.

I will delight myself in thy statutes:
I will not forget thy word.

Deal bountifully with thy servant, that I may live;
So will I observe thy word.

Open thou mine eyes, that I may behold
Wondrous things out of thy law.

I am a stranger in the earth:
Hide not thy commandments from me.

My soul breaketh for the longing
That it hath unto thine ordinances at all times.

Thy testimonies also are my delight
And my counselors.

Evening

Praise waiteth for thee, O God, in Zion;
And unto thee shall the vow be performed.

O thou that hearest prayer,
Unto thee shall all flesh come.

Iniquities prevail against me:
As for our transgressions, thou shalt purge them away.

Blessed is the man whom thou choosest, and causest to approach unto thee,
That he may dwell in thy courts:

We shall be satisfied with the goodness of thy house,
Even of thy holy temple.

By terrible things thou wilt answer us in righteousness,
O God of our salvation,

Thou that art the confidence of all the ends of the earth,
And of them that are afar off upon the sea:

Which by his strength setteth fast the mountains,
Being girded about with power;

Which stilleth the roaring of the seas,
The noise of their waves,
And the tumult of the peoples.

They also that dwell in the uttermost parts are afraid at thy tokens:
Thou makest the outgoings of the morning and evening to rejoice.

Thou visitest the earth, and waterest it,
Thou greatly enrichest it;

The river of God is full of water:
Thou providest them corn, when
thou hast so prepared the earth.

Thou waterest its ridges abundantly;
Thou settlest the furrows thereof:

Thou makest it soft with showers;
Thou blessest the springing thereof.

Thou crownest the year with thy
goodness;
And thy paths drop fatness.

They drop upon the pastures of
the wilderness;
And the little hills rejoice on every
side.

The pastures are clothed with
flocks;
The valleys also are covered over
with corn;
They shout for joy, they also sing.

Twenty=sixth Sunday
Morning

Make a joyful noise unto God, all
ye lands:

Sing forth the honor of his name:
Make his praise glorious.

Say unto God, How terrible are thy
works!
Through the greatness of thy power
shall thine enemies submit themselves unto thee.

All the earth shall worship thee,
And shall sing unto thee;
They shall sing to thy name.

Come, and see the works of God;
He is terrible in his doing toward
the children of men.

He turned the sea into dry land;
They went through the river on
foot:
There did we rejoice in him.

He ruleth by his power forever;
His eyes behold the nations:
Let not the rebellious exalt themselves.

Oh bless our God, ye people,
And make the voice of his praise
to be heard;

Which holdeth our soul in life,
And suffereth not our feet to be
moved.

For thou, O God, hast proved us:
Thou hast tried us, as silver is
tried.

Thou broughtest us into the net;
Thou laidst a sore burden upon
our loins.

Thou hast caused men to ride
over our heads;
We went through fire and through
water;
But thou broughtest us out into a
wealthy place.

God be merciful unto us, and bless
us,
And cause his face to shine upon us;

That thy way may be known upon
earth,
Thy saving health among all nations.

Let the people praise thee, O God;
Let all the people praise thee.

Oh let the nations be glad and
sing for joy;
For thou shalt judge the peoples
righteously,
And govern the nations upon earth.

Let the people praise thee, O God;
Let all the people praise thee.

Then shall the earth yield her
increase:
God, even our own God, shall bless
us.

God shall bless us;
And all the ends of the earth shall
fear him.

Evening

Unto thee, O God, do we give
thanks;
Unto thee do we give thanks: for
that thy name is near
Thy wondrous works declare.

*When I shall receive the congre-
gation
I will judge uprightly.*

The earth and all the inhabitants
thereof are dissolved:
I have set up the pillars of it.

*I said unto the fools, Deal not
foolishly:
And to the wicked, Lift not up
the horn:*

Lift not up your horn on high;
Speak not with a stiff neck.

*For neither from the east, nor
from the west,
Nor yet from the south, cometh
promotion.*

But God is the judge:
He putteth down one, and setteth
up another.

*For in the hand of the Lord there
is a cup, and the wine is red;
It is full of mixture, and he
poureth out of the same:
But the dregs thereof, all the wicked
of the earth shall drain them, and
drink them.*

But I will declare forever,
I will sing praises to the God of
Jacob.

*All the horns of the wicked also
will I cut off;
But the horns of the righteous shall
be exalted.*

If I regard iniquity in my heart,
The Lord will not hear me:

*But verily God hath heard me;
He hath attended to the voice of
my prayer.*

Blessed be God,
Which hath not turned away my
prayer,
Nor his mercy from me.

Twenty=seventh Sunday
Morning

Let God arise, let his enemies be
scattered;
Let them also that hate him flee
before him.

*As smoke is driven away, so drive
them away:
As wax melteth before the fire,
So let the wicked perish at the
presence of God.*

But let the righteous be glad; let
them exult before God:
Yea, let them exceedingly rejoice.

*Sing unto God, sing praises to his
name:
Extol him that rideth upon the
heavens
By his name Jehovah, and rejoice
ye before him.*

A father of the fatherless, and a
judge of the widows,
Is God in his holy habitation.

*God setteth the solitary in families:
He bringeth out those which are
bound with chains:
But the rebellious dwell in a dry
land.*

O God, when thou wentest forth
before thy people,
When thou didst march through
the wilderness;

The earth shook,
The heavens also dropped at the
presence of God:
Yon Sinai was moved at the
presence of God, the God of Israel.

Thou, O God, didst send a plentiful rain,
Thou didst confirm thine inheritance, when it was weary.

Thy congregation hath dwelt therein:
Thou, O God, hast prepared of thy goodness for the poor.

Blessed be the Lord, who daily loadeth us with benefits,
Even the God who is our salvation.

God is unto us a God of deliverances;
And unto God the Lord belongeth escape from death.

Thy God hath commanded thy strength:
Strengthen, O God, that which thou hast wrought for us.

Sing unto God, ye kingdoms of the earth;
Oh sing praises unto the Lord;

To him that rideth upon the heaven of heavens, which were of old;
Lo, he doth send his voice, a mighty voice.

Ascribe ye strength unto God:
His excellency is over Israel,
And his strength is in the clouds.

O God, thou art terrible out of thy holy places:
The God of Israel, he giveth strength and power unto his people.

Evening

In Judah is God known:
His name is great in Israel.

In Salem also is his tabernacle,
And his dwelling place in Zion.

There he brake the arrows of the bow;
The shield, and the sword, and the battle.

Glorious art thou and excellent,
From the mountains of prey.

The stout-hearted are made a spoil,
They have slept their sleep;
And none of the men of might have found their hands.

At thy rebuke, O God of Jacob,
Both chariot and horse are cast into a dead sleep.

Thou, even thou, art to be feared;
And who may stand in thy sight when once thou art angry?

Thou didst cause judgment to be heard from heaven;
The earth feared, and was still,

When God arose to judgment,
To save all the meek of the earth.

Surely the wrath of man shall praise thee:
The remainder of wrath shalt thou restrain.

Vow, and pay unto the Lord your God:
Let all that be round about him bring presents unto him that ought to be feared.

He shall cut off the spirit of princes:
He is terrible to the kings of the earth.

Twenty=eighth Sunday
Morning

Save me, O God;
For the waters are come in unto my soul.

I sink in deep mire, where there is no standing:
I am come into deep waters, where the floods overflow me.

I am weary of my crying; my throat is dried:
Mine eyes fail while I wait for my God.

O God, thou knowest my foolishness;
And my sins are not hid from thee.

Let not them that wait for thee be ashamed for my sake, O Lord God of hosts:
Let not those that seek thee be confounded for my sake, O God of Israel.

Because for thy sake I have borne reproach;
Shame hath covered my face.

I am become a stranger unto my brethren,
And an alien unto my mother's children.

For the zeal of thy house hath eaten me up;
And the reproaches of them that reproached thee are fallen upon me.

When I wept, and chastened my soul with fasting,
That was to my reproach.

But as for me, my prayer is unto thee, O Lord, in an acceptable time:
O God, in the multitude of thy mercy,
Hear me in the truth of thy salvation.

Deliver me out of the mire, and let me not sink:
Let me be delivered from them that hate me, and out of the deep waters.

Let not the waterflood overflow me,
Neither let the deep swallow me up;
And let not the pit shut her mouth upon me.

Hear me, O Lord; for thy lovingkindness is good:
According to the multitude of thy tender mercies turn thou unto me.

And hide not thy face from thy servant;
For I am in distress; hear me speedily.

Draw nigh unto my soul, and redeem it:
Deliver me because of mine enemies.

Thou knowest my reproach, and my shame, and my dishonor:
Mine adversaries are all before thee.

Reproach hath broken my heart; and I am full of heaviness:
And I looked for some to take pity, but there was none;
And for comforters, but I found none.

But I am poor and sorrowful:
Let thy salvation, O God, set me up on high.

I will praise the name of God with a song,
And will magnify him with thanksgiving.

Evening

Lord, thou hast been favorable unto thy land;
Thou hast brought back the captivity of Jacob.

Thou hast forgiven the iniquity of thy people;
Thou hast covered all their sin.

Thou hast taken away all thy wrath;
Thou hast turned thyself from the fierceness of thine anger.

Turn us, O God of our salvation,
And cause thine indignation to-
ward us to cease.

Wilt thou be angry with us forever?
Wilt thou draw out thine anger to all generations?

Wilt thou not revive us again,
That thy people may rejoice in
thee?

Show us thy mercy, O Lord,
And grant us thy salvation.

I will hear what God the Lord will
speak;
For he will speak peace unto his
people, and to his saints:
But let them not turn again to folly.

Surely his salvation is nigh them that fear him,
That glory may dwell in our land.

Mercy and truth are met together;
Righteousness and peace have
kissed each other.

Truth shall spring out of the earth;
And righteousness hath looked down from heaven.

Yea, the Lord shall give that which
is good;
And our land shall yield its in-
crease.

Righteousness shall go before him,
And shall set us in the way of his steps.

Twenty=ninth Sunday
Morning

In thee, O Lord, do I put my trust:
Let me never be put to confusion.

Deliver me in thy righteousness,
and rescue me:
Incline thine ear unto me, and
save me.

Be thou my strong habitation, whereunto I may continually resort:
Thou hast given commandment to save me;

For thou art my rock and my
fortress.
Deliver me, O my God, out of the
hand of the wicked,
Out of the hand of the unrighteous
and cruel man.

For thou art my hope, O Lord God:
Thou art my trust from my youth.

I am as a wonder unto many;
But thou art my strong refuge.

My mouth shall be filled with thy praise,
And with thy honor all the day.

Cast me not off in the time of old age;
Forsake me not when my strength
faileth.

O God, be not far from me;
O my God, make haste to help me.

But I will hope continually,
And will praise thee yet more and
more.

My mouth shall show forth thy righteousness,
And thy salvation all the day;

I will go in the strength of the
Lord God:
I will make mention of thy right-
eousness, even of thine only.

O God, thou hast taught me from my youth;
And hitherto have I declared thy wondrous works.

Now also when I am old and gray-headed, O God, forsake me not,
Until I have showed thy strength unto this generation,
Thy power to every one that is to come.

Thy righteousness also, O God, is very high;
Thou who hast done great things, O God, who is like unto thee?

Thou, who hast showed me great and sore troubles,
Shalt quicken me again,
And shalt bring me up again from the depths of the earth.

Thou shalt increase my greatness, And turn again and comfort me.

I will also praise thee with the psaltery,
Even thy truth, O my God:

Unto thee will I sing with the harp, O thou Holy One of Israel.

My lips shall greatly rejoice when I sing unto thee;
And my soul, which thou hast redeemed.

Evening

He that dwelleth in the secret place of the Most High
Shall abide under the shadow of the Almighty.

I will say of the Lord, He is my refuge and my fortress;
My God, in him will I trust.

Surely he shall deliver thee from the snare of the fowler,
And from the noisome pestilence.

He shall cover thee with his feathers,
And under his wings shalt thou trust:

His truth shall be thy shield and buckler.

Thou shalt not be afraid for the terror by night,
Nor for the arrow that flieth by day;

Nor for the pestilence that walketh in darkness,
Nor for the destruction that wasteth at noonday.

A thousand shall fall at thy side, And ten thousand at thy right hand;
But it shall not come nigh thee.

Only with thine eyes shalt thou behold,
And see the reward of the wicked.

For thou, O Lord, art my refuge!
Thou hast made the Most High thy habitation;

There shall no evil befall thee,
Neither shall any plague come nigh thy dwelling.

For he shall give his angels charge over thee,
To keep thee in all thy ways.

They shall bear thee up in their hands,
Lest thou dash thy foot against a stone.

Thou shalt tread upon the lion and adder:
The young lion and the dragon shalt thou trample under foot.

Because he hath set his love upon me, therefore will I deliver him:
I will set him on high, because he hath known my name.

He shall call upon me, and I will answer him;
I will be with him in trouble:
I will deliver him, and honor him.

With long life will I satisfy him,
And show him my salvation.

Thirtieth Sunday
Morning

Give the king thy judgments, O God,
And thy righteousness unto the king's son.

He shall judge thy people with righteousness,
And thy poor with judgment.

The mountains shall bring peace to the people,
And the little hills, by righteousness.

He shall judge the poor of the people,
He shall save the children of the needy,
And shall break in pieces the oppressor.

They shall fear thee as long as the sun endureth,
And so long as the moon, throughout all generations.

He shall come down like rain upon the mown grass,
As showers that water the earth.

In his days shall the righteous flourish,
And abundance of peace, so long as the moon endureth.

He shall have dominion also from sea to sea,
And from the River unto the ends of the earth.

They that dwell in the wilderness shall bow before him;
And his enemies shall lick the dust.

The kings of Tarshish and of the isles shall bring presents:

The kings of Sheba and Seba shall offer gifts.

Yea, all kings shall fall down before him;
All nations shall serve him.

For he shall deliver the needy when he crieth,
And the poor, that hath no helper.

He shall have pity on the poor and needy,
And the souls of the needy he shall save.

He shall redeem their soul from deceit and violence;
And precious shall their blood be in his sight:

And he shall live; and to him shall be given of the gold of Sheba:
Prayer also shall be made for him continually;
And daily shall he be praised.

There shall be a handful of corn in the earth upon the top of the mountains;
The fruit thereof shall shake like Lebanon:
And they of the city shall flourish like grass of the earth.

His name shall endure forever;
His name shall be continued as long as the sun:

And men shall be blessed in him;
All nations shall call him blessed.

Blessed be the Lord God, the God of Israel,
Who only doeth wondrous things:

And blessed be his glorious name forever;
And let the whole earth be filled with his glory.

Evening

It is a good thing to give thanks
unto the Lord,
And to sing praises unto thy name,
O Most High;

*To show forth thy loving-kindness
in the morning,
And thy faithfulness every night,*

Upon an instrument of ten strings,
and upon the psaltery;
Upon the harp with a solemn sound.

*For thou, Lord, hast made me glad
through thy work:
I will triumph in the works of thy
hands.*

How great are thy works, O Lord!
Thy thoughts are very deep.

*A brutish man knoweth not;
Neither doth a fool understand this:*

When the wicked spring as the
grass,
And when all the workers of iniquity do flourish;

*It is that they shall be destroyed
forever.
But thou, O Lord, art on high for
evermore.*

For, lo, thine enemies, O Lord,
For, lo, thine enemies shall perish;
All the workers of iniquity shall be
scattered.

*But my horn hast thou exalted like
the horn of a wild ox:
I shall be anointed with fresh oil.*

Mine eye also shall see my desire
on mine enemies,
Mine ears shall hear my desire of
the wicked that rise up against me.

*The righteous shall flourish like
the palm tree:
He shall grow like a cedar in
Lebanon.*

Those that be planted in the house
of the Lord;
They shall flourish in the courts of
our God.

*They shall still bring forth fruit in
old age;
They shall be fat and flourishing:*

To show that the Lord is upright;
He is my rock, and there is no unrighteousness in him.

Thirty=first Sunday
Morning

Truly God is good to Israel,
Even to such as are of a clean
heart.

*But as for me, my feet were almost
gone;
My steps had well nigh slipped.*

For I was envious at the foolish,
When I saw the prosperity of the
wicked.

*For there are no pangs in their
death;
But their strength is firm.*

They are not in trouble as other
men;
Neither are they plagued like other
men.

*Verily in vain have I cleansed my
heart,
And washed my hands in innocency;*

For all the day long have I been
plagued,
And chastened every morning.

*If I had said, I will speak thus;
Behold, I had been faithless to the
generation of thy children.*

When I thought to know this,
It was too painful for me;

*Until I went into the sanctuary of
God,
And considered their latter end.*

Surely thou settest them in slippery places:
Thou castest them down to destruction.

*How are they become a desolation
in a moment!
They are utterly consumed with
terrors.*

As a dream when one awaketh,
So, O Lord, when thou awakest,
thou shalt despise their image.

*For my heart was grieved,
And I was pricked in my reins:*

So foolish was I, and ignorant;
I was as a beast before thee.

*Nevertheless I am continually with
thee:
Thou hast holden my right hand.*

Thou shalt guide me with thy
counsel,
And afterward receive me to
glory.

*Whom have I in heaven but
thee?
And there is none upon earth that
I desire besides thee.*

My flesh and my heart faileth;
But God is the strength of my
heart and my portion forever.

*For, lo, they that are far from thee
shall perish:
Thou hast destroyed all them that
go a whoring from thee.*

But it is good for me to draw near
unto God:
I have made the Lord God my
refuge,
That I may tell of all thy works.

Evening

Oh sing unto the Lord a new
song:
Sing unto the Lord, all the earth.

*Sing unto the Lord, bless his
name;
Show forth his salvation from day
to day.*

Declare his glory among the heathen,
His marvelous works among all
people.

*For great is the Lord, and greatly
to be praised:
He is to be feared above all gods.*

For all the gods of the nations are
idols;
But the Lord made the heavens.

*Honor and majesty are before him:
Strength and beauty are in his
sanctuary.*

Give unto the Lord, ye kindreds of
the peoples,
Give unto the Lord glory and
strength.

*Give unto the Lord the glory due
unto his name:
Bring an offering, and come into
his courts.*

Oh worship the Lord in the beauty
of holiness:
Fear before him, all the earth.

*Say among the heathen, the Lord
reigneth:
The world also is established that
it cannot be moved:
He shall judge the people righteously.*

Let the heavens rejoice, and let the
earth be glad;
Let the sea roar, and the fullness
thereof;

Let the field be joyful, and all that is therein;
Then shall all the trees of the wood rejoice

Before the Lord; for he cometh,
For he cometh to judge the earth:

He shall judge the world with righteousness,
And the people with his truth.

Thirty=second Sunday
Morning

I cried unto God with my voice,
Even unto God with my voice; and he gave ear unto me.

In the day of my trouble I sought the Lord:
My hand was stretched out in the night, and slacked not;
My soul refused to be comforted.

I remembered God, and was troubled:
I complained, and my spirit was overwhelmed.

Thou holdest mine eyes waking:
I am so troubled that I cannot speak.

I have considered the days of old,
The years of ancient times.

I call to remembrance my song in the night:
I commune with mine own heart;
And my spirit maketh diligent search.

Will the Lord cast off forever?
And will he be favorable no more?

Is his mercy clean gone forever?
Doth his promise fail for evermore?

Hath God forgotten to be gracious?

Hath he in anger shut up his tender mercies?

And I said, This is my infirmity;
But I will remember the years of the right hand of the Most High.

I will remember the works of the Lord;
For I will remember thy wonders of old.

I will meditate also of all thy work,
And talk of thy doings.

Thy way, O God, is in the sanctuary:
Who is a great god like unto God?

Thou art the God that doest wonders:
Thou hast declared thy strength among the people.

Thou hast with thine arm redeemed thy people,
The sons of Jacob and Joseph.

The waters saw thee, O God;
The waters saw thee, they were afraid:

The depths also were troubled.
The clouds poured out water;

The skies sent out a sound:
Thine arrows also went abroad.

The voice of thy thunder was in the heaven;
The lightnings lightened the world:
The earth trembled and shook.

Thy way was in the sea,
And thy path in the great waters,
And thy footsteps were not known.

Thou leddest thy people like a flock,
By the hand of Moses and Aaron.

Evening

Sing aloud unto God our strength:
Make a joyful noise unto the God
of Jacob.

*Take a Psalm, and bring hither
the timbrel,
The pleasant harp with the psaltery.*

Blow the trumpet at the new moon,
At the full moon, on our feast
day.

*For it is a statute for Israel,
And a law of the God of Jacob.*

He appointed it in Joseph for a
testimony,
When he went out over the land of
Egypt,
Where I heard a language that I
knew not.

*I removed his shoulder from the
burden:
His hands were freed from the
basket.*

Thou calledst in trouble, and I de-
livered thee;
I answered thee in the secret place
of thunder;
I proved thee at the waters of
Meribah.

*Hear, O my people, and I will
testify unto thee:
O Israel, if thou wouldest hearken
unto me!*

There shall no strange god be in
thee;
Neither shalt thou worship any
foreign god.

*I am the Lord thy God,
Which brought thee out of the land
of Egypt:
Open thy mouth wide, and I will
fill it.*

But my people would not hearken
to my voice;
And Israel would none of me.

*So I let them go after the stubborn-
ness of their heart,
That they might walk in their own
counsels.*

Oh that my people would hearken
unto me,
That Israel would walk in my
ways!

*He would feed them also with the
finest of the wheat;
And with honey out of the rock
would I satisfy thee.*

Thirty-third Sunday

Morning

Bow down thine ear, O Lord, and
hear me;
For I am poor and needy.

*Preserve my soul; for I am holy:
O thou my God, save thy servant
that trusteth in thee.*

Be merciful unto me, O Lord;
For unto thee do I cry all the day
long.

*Rejoice the soul of thy servant;
For unto thee, O Lord, do I lift
up my soul.*

For thou, Lord, art good, and
ready to forgive,
And plenteous in mercy unto all
them that call upon thee.

*Give ear, O Lord, unto my prayer;
And attend unto the voice of my
supplications.*

In the day of my trouble I will call
upon thee;
For thou wilt answer me.

Among the gods there is none like
unto thee, O Lord;
Neither are there any works like
unto thy works.

All nations whom thou hast made
shall come and worship before thee,
O Lord;
And they shall glorify thy name.

*For thou art great, and doest won-
drous things:
Thou art God alone.*

Teach me thy way, O Lord; I will
walk in thy truth:
Unite my heart to fear thy name.

*I will praise thee, O Lord my God,
with my whole heart;
And I will glorify thy name for
evermore.*

For great is thy mercy toward
me;
And thou hast delivered my soul
from the lowest hell.

*Thou, O Lord, art a God merci-
ful and gracious,
Slow to anger, and plenteous in
mercy and truth.*

Oh turn unto me, and have mercy
upon me;
Give thy strength unto thy servant,
And save the son of thy handmaid.

*Show me a token for good,
That they which hate me may see it,
and be ashamed,
Because thou, Lord, hast helped
me, and comforted me.*

Evening

How long, O Lord? wilt thou forget
me forever?
How long wilt thou hide thy face
from me?

How long shall I take counsel in
my soul,
Having sorrow in my heart all the
day?

How long shall mine enemy be
exalted over me?
Consider and hear me, O Lord my
God:
Lighten mine eyes, lest I sleep the
sleep of death;

*Lest mine enemy say, I have pre-
vailed against him;
Lest mine adversaries rejoice when
I am moved.*

But I have trusted in thy mercy;
My heart shall rejoice in thy salvation.

*I will sing unto the Lord,
Because he hath dealt bountifully
with me.*

The Lord loveth the gates of Zion
More than all the dwellings of
Jacob.

*Glorious things are spoken of thee,
O city of God.*

I will make mention of Rahab and
Babylon as among them that know
me:
Behold, Philistia, and Tyre, with
Ethiopia:
This one was born there.

*Yea, of Zion it shall be said,
This one and that one was born
in her;
And the Most High himself shall
establish her.*

The Lord shall count, when he
writeth up the people,
This one was born there.

*As well the singers as the players
shall say
All my fountains are in thee.*

Thirty=fourth Sunday
Morning

I will sing of the mercies of the Lord
forever:
With my mouth will I make known
thy faithfulness to all generations.

*For I have said, Mercy shall be
built up forever;
Thy faithfulness shalt thou establish in the very heavens.*

I have made a covenant with my
chosen,
I have sworn unto David my servant:

*Thy seed will I establish for-
ever,
And build up thy throne to all
generations.*

And the heavens shall praise thy
wonders, O Lord;
Thy faithfulness also in the congregation of the saints.

*For who in the heaven can be com-
pared unto the Lord?
Who among the sons of the mighty
is like unto the Lord?*

A God greatly to be feared in the
assembly of the saints,
And to be had in reverence of all
them that are about him.

*O Lord God of hosts,
Who is a strong Lord, like unto
thee?
And thy faithfulness is round
about thee.*

Thou rulest the raging of the sea:
When the waves thereof arise, thou
stillest them.

*The heavens are thine, the earth
also is thine:
The world and the fullness thereof,
thou hast founded them.*

The north and the south, thou hast
created them:
Tabor and Hermon rejoice in thy
name.

*Thou hast a mighty arm;
Strong is thy hand, and high is
thy right hand.*

Justice and judgment are the habitation of thy throne:
Mercy and truth shall go before thy
face.

*Blessed is the people that know the
joyful sound:
They shall walk, O Lord, in the
light of thy countenance.*

In thy name shall they rejoice all
the day;
And in thy righteousness shall they
be exalted.

*For thou art the glory of their
strength;
And in thy favor our horn shall
be exalted.*

For the Lord is our defense;
And the Holy One of Israel is our
King.

Evening

I have found David my servant;
With my holy oil have I anointed
him:

*With whom my hand shall be es-
tablished;
Mine arm also shall strengthen
him.*

The enemy shall not exact from
him,
Nor the son of wickedness afflict
him.

*And I will beat down his foes
before him,
And plague them that hate him.*

But my faithfulness and my mercy shall be with him;
And in my name shall his horn be exalted.

I will set his hand also on the sea,
And his right hand on the rivers.

He shall cry unto me, Thou art my Father,
My God, and the Rock of my salvation.

I also will make him my firstborn,
The highest of the kings of the earth.

My mercy will I keep for him for evermore;
And my covenant shall stand fast with him.

His seed also will I make to endure forever,
And his throne as the days of heaven.

If his children forsake my law,
And walk not in my judgments;

If they break my statutes,
And keep not my commandments;

Then will I visit their transgression with the rod,
And their iniquity with stripes.

But my loving-kindness will I not utterly take from him,
Nor suffer my faithfulness to fail.

My covenant will I not break,
Nor alter the thing that is gone out of my lips.

Once have I sworn by my holiness:
I will not lie unto David:

His seed shall endure forever,
And his throne as the sun before me.

It shall be established forever as the moon,
And as a faithful witness in heaven.

Thirty-fifth Sunday
Morning

Lord, thou hast been our dwelling place
In all generations.

Before the mountains were brought forth,
Or ever thou hadst formed the earth and the world,
Even from everlasting to everlasting, thou art God.

Thou turnest man to destruction,
And sayest, Return, ye children of men.

For a thousand years in thy sight
Are but as yesterday when it is past,
And as a watch in the night.

Thou carriest them away as with a flood; they are as a sleep:
In the morning they are like grass which groweth up.

In the morning it flourisheth, and groweth up;
In the evening it is cut down, and withereth.

For we are consumed by thine anger,
And by thy wrath are we troubled.

Thou hast set our iniquities before thee,
Our secret sins in the light of thy countenance.

For all our days are passed away in thy wrath:
We spend our years as a tale that is told.

*The days of our years are three-
score years and ten,
And if by reason of strength they
be fourscore years;*

Yet is their strength labor and sorrow;
For it is soon cut off, and we fly
away.

*Who knoweth the power of thine
anger?
Even according to thy fear, so is thy
wrath.*

So teach us to number our days,
That we may apply our hearts
unto wisdom.

*Return, O Lord; how long?
And let it repent thee concerning
thy servants.*

Oh satisfy us early with thy mercy,
That we may rejoice and be glad
all our days.

*Make us glad according to the
days wherein thou hast afflicted us,
And the years wherein we have
seen evil.*

Let thy work appear unto thy servants,
And thy glory unto their children.

*And let the beauty of the Lord our
God be upon us;
And establish thou the work of our
hands upon us;
Yea, the work of our hands es-
tablish thou it.*

Evening

The Lord reigneth; let the earth
rejoice;
Let the multitude of isles be glad.

*Clouds and darkness are round
about him:
Righteousness and judgment are
the habitation of his throne.*

A fire goeth before him,
And burneth up his enemies round
about.

*His lightnings lightened the world:
The earth saw, and trembled.*

The hills melted like wax at the
presence of the Lord,
At the presence of the Lord of the
whole earth.

*The heavens declare his righteous-
ness,
And all the people see his glory.*

Let all them be put to shame that
serve graven images,
That boast themselves of idols:
Worship him, all ye gods.

*Zion heard and was glad,
And the daughters of Judah re-
joiced,
Because of thy judgments, O Lord.*

For thou, Lord, art most high
above all the earth:
Thou art exalted far above all
gods.

*O ye that love the Lord, hate evil:
He preserveth the souls of his
saints;
He delivereth them out of the hand
of the wicked.*

Light is sown for the righteous,
And gladness for the upright in
heart.

*Be glad in the Lord, ye righteous;
And give thanks at the remembrance of his holiness.*

Thirty=sixth Sunday
Morning

O Lord God to whom vengeance
belongeth,
Thou God to whom vengeance belongeth, show thyself.

Lift up thyself, thou Judge of the earth:
Render to the proud their reward.

Lord, how long shall the wicked,
How long shall the wicked triumph?

They utter and speak hard things:
All the workers of iniquity boast themselves.

And they say, The Lord shall not see,
Neither shall the God of Jacob regard it.

Understand, ye brutish among the people;
And ye fools, when will ye be wise?

He that planted the ear, shall he not hear?
He that formed the eye, shall he not see?

He that chastiseth the heathen, shall not he correct,
Even he that teacheth man knowledge?

The Lord knoweth the thoughts of man,
That they are vanity.

Blessed is the man whom thou chastenest, O Lord,
And teachest out of thy law;

That thou mayest give him rest from the days of adversity,
Until the pit be digged for the wicked.

For the Lord will not cast off his people,
Neither will he forsake his inheritance.

But judgment shall return unto righteousness;
And all the upright in heart shall follow it.

Unless the Lord had been my help,
My soul had almost dwelt in silence.

When I said, My foot slippeth;
Thy mercy, O Lord, held me up.

In the multitude of my thoughts within me
Thy comforts delight my soul.

Shall the throne of iniquity have fellowship with thee,
Which frameth mischief by a law?

They gather themselves together against the soul of the righteous,
And condemn the innocent blood.

But the Lord hath been my defense,
And my God the rock of my refuge.

And he shall bring upon them their own iniquity,
And shall cut them off in their own wickedness;
The Lord our God shall cut them off.

Evening

Oh sing unto the Lord a new song;
For he hath done marvelous things:
His right hand, and his holy arm,
hath gotten him the victory.

The Lord hath made known his salvation:
His righteousness hath he openly showed in the sight of the heathen.

He hath remembered his mercy and his truth toward the house of Israel:
All the ends of the earth have seen the salvation of our God.

Make a joyful noise unto the Lord, all the earth:
Break forth and sing for joy, yea, sing praises.

Sing praises unto the Lord with the harp;
With the harp and the voice of melody.

With trumpets and sound of cornet
Make a joyful noise before the Lord, the King.

Let the sea roar, and the fullness thereof;
The world, and they that dwell therein;

Let the floods clap their hands;
Let the hills sing for joy together
Before the Lord; for he cometh to judge the earth:

He shall judge the world with righteousness,
And the peoples with equity.

Make a joyful noise unto God, all ye lands:
Sing forth the honor of his name:
Make his praise glorious.

Say unto God, How terrible are thy works!
Through the greatness of thy power shall thine enemies submit themselves unto thee.

All the earth shall worship thee,
And shall sing unto thee;
They shall sing to thy name.

Thirty=seventh Sunday
Morning

Hear my prayer, O Lord,
And let my cry come unto thee.

Hide not thy face from me in the day of my distress:
Incline thine ear unto me;
In the day when I call answer me speedily.

For my days are consumed like smoke,
And my bones are burned as a firebrand.

My heart is smitten and withered like grass,
For I forget to eat my bread.

By reason of the voice of my groaning
My bones cleave to my skin.

But thou, O Lord, shalt endure forever;
And thy remembrance unto all generations.

Thou shalt arise, and have mercy upon Zion;
For it is time to favor her,
Yea, the set time is come.

For thy servants take pleasure in her stones,
And have pity upon her dust.

So the heathen shall fear the name of the Lord,
And all the kings of the earth thy glory.

When the Lord shall build up Zion;
He shall appear in his glory;

He will regard the prayer of the destitute,
And not despise their prayer.

This shall be written for the generation to come;
And the people which shall be created shall praise the Lord.

For he hath looked down from the height of his sanctuary;
From heaven did the Lord behold the earth;

To hear the groaning of the prisoner;
To loose those that are appointed to death;

To declare the name of the Lord in Zion,
And his praise in Jerusalem;

> When the people are gathered together,
> And the kingdoms, to serve the Lord.

He weakened my strength in the way;
He shortened my days.

> I said, O my God, take me not away in the midst of my days:
> Thy years are throughout all generations.

Of old hast thou laid the foundation of the earth;
And the heavens are the work of thy hands.

> They shall perish, but thou shalt endure;
> Yea, all of them shall wax old like a garment;
> As a vesture shalt thou change them, and they shall be changed:

But thou art the same,
And thy years shall have no end.

> The children of thy servants shall continue,
> And their seed shall be established before thee.

Evening

The Lord reigneth; let the people tremble:
He sitteth between the cherubim; let the earth be moved.

> The Lord is great in Zion;
> And he is high above all the people.

Let them praise thy great and terrible name:
For it is holy.

> The king's strength also loveth judgment;
> Thou dost establish equity;
> Thou executest judgment and righteousness in Jacob.

Exalt ye the Lord our God,
And worship at his footstool:
For he is holy.

> Moses and Aaron among his priests,
> And Samuel among them that call upon his name;

They called upon the Lord, and he answered them.
He spake unto them in the pillar of cloud:

> They kept his testimonies,
> And the ordinance that he gave them.

Thou answeredst them, O Lord our God:
Thou wast a God that forgavest them,
Though thou tookest vengeance of their doings.

> Exalt the Lord our God,
> And worship at his holy hill;
> For the Lord our God is holy.

I will sing of mercy and judgment:
Unto thee, O Lord, will I sing.

> I will behave myself wisely in a perfect way:
> Oh when wilt thou come unto me?

I will walk within my house with a perfect heart.
I will set no wicked thing before mine eyes:

> I hate the work of them that turn aside;
> It shall not cleave unto me.

A froward heart shall depart from me:
I will know no evil thing.

Thirty=eighth Sunday
Morning

Bless the Lord, O my soul;
And all that is within me, bless his holy name.

Bless the Lord, O my soul,
And forget not all his benefits:

Who forgiveth all thine iniquities;
Who healeth all thy diseases;

Who redeemeth thy life from destruction;
Who crowneth thee with loving-kindness and tender mercies;

Who satisfieth thy mouth with good things,
So that thy youth is renewed like the eagle's.

The Lord executeth righteous acts,
And judgments for all that are oppressed.

He made known his ways unto Moses,
His acts unto the children of Israel.

The Lord is merciful and gracious,
Slow to anger, and plenteous in mercy.

He will not always chide;
Neither will he keep his anger forever.

He hath not dealt with us after our sins,
Nor rewarded us according to our iniquities.

For as the heaven is high above the earth,
So great is his mercy toward them that fear him.

As far as the east is from the west,
So far hath he removed our transgressions from us.

Like as a father pitieth his children,
So the Lord pitieth them that fear him.

For he knoweth our frame;
He remembereth that we are dust.

As for man, his days are as grass;
As a flower of the field, so he flourisheth.

For the wind passeth over it, and it is gone;
And the place thereof shall know it no more.

But the mercy of the Lord is from everlasting to everlasting upon them that fear him,
And his righteousness unto children's children;

To such as keep his covenant,
And to those that remember his precepts to do them.

The Lord hath prepared his throne in the heavens;
And his kingdom ruleth over all.

Bless the Lord, ye his angels,
That excel in strength, that do his commandments,
Hearkening unto the voice of his word.

Bless ye the Lord, all ye his hosts,
Ye ministers of his, that do his pleasure.

Bless the Lord, all his works,
In all places of his dominion:
Bless the Lord, O my soul.

Evening

The Lord reigneth; he is clothed with majesty;
The Lord is clothed with strength; he hath girded himself therewith:
The world also is established, that it cannot be moved.

Thy throne is established of old:
Thou art from everlasting.

The floods have lifted up, O Lord,
The floods have lifted up their voice;
The floods lift up their waves.

More than the voices of many
waters,
The mighty billows of the sea,
Is the Lord mighty on high.

Thy testimonies are very sure:
Holiness becometh thy house,
O Lord, for evermore.

When Israel went out of Egypt,
The house of Jacob from a people
of strange language;

Judah became his sanctuary,
And Israel his dominion.

The sea saw it, and fled;
The Jordan was driven back.

The mountains skipped like rams,
And the little hills like lambs.

What aileth thee, O thou sea, that
thou fleddest?
Thou Jordan, that thou wast
driven back?

Ye mountains, that ye skipped like
rams;
And ye little hills, like lambs?

Tremble, thou earth, at the presence
of the Lord,
At the presence of the God of Jacob,

Which turned the rock into a pool
of water,
The flint into a fountain of waters.

Thirty=ninth Sunday
Morning

Bless the Lord, O my soul.

O Lord my God, thou art very great;
Thou art clothed with honor and
majesty:

Who coverest thyself with light as
with a garment;
Who stretchest out the heavens like
a curtain;
Who layeth the beams of his
chambers in the waters;

Who maketh the clouds his chariot;
Who walketh upon the wings of
the wind;

Who maketh winds his messengers;
Flames of fire his ministers;

Who laid the foundations of the
earth,
That it should not be moved forever.

Thou coveredst it with the deep as
with a garment;
The waters stood above the mountains.

At thy rebuke they fled;
At the voice of thy thunder they
hasted away

(The mountains rose, the valleys
sank down)
Unto the place which thou hadst
founded for them.

Thou hast set a bound that they
may not pass over;
That they turn not again to cover
the earth.

He sendeth forth springs into the
valleys;
They run among the hills;

They give drink to every beast of
the field;
The wild asses quench their thirst.

By them the fowls of the heaven
have their habitation;
They sing among the branches.

He watereth the mountains from
his chambers:
The earth is filled with the fruit
of thy works.

He causeth the grass to grow for the cattle,
And herb for the service of man;

That he may bring forth food out of the earth,
And wine that maketh glad the heart of man,

And oil to make his face to shine,
And bread that strengtheneth man's heart.

The trees of the Lord are filled with sap,
The cedars of Lebanon, which he hath planted;

Where the birds make their nests:
As for the stork, the fir trees are her house.

The high mountains are for the wild goats;
The rocks are a refuge for the conies.

He appointed the moon for seasons:
The sun knoweth his going down.

Evening

Bless the Lord, O my soul.

O Lord my God, thou art very great;
Thou art clothed with honor and majesty:

Thou makest darkness, and it is night,
Wherein all the beasts of the forest creep forth.

The young lions roar after their prey,
And seek their meat from God.

The sun ariseth, they get them away,
And lay them down in their dens.

Man goeth forth unto his work
And to his labor until the evening.

O Lord, how manifold are thy works!
In wisdom hast thou made them all:
The earth is full of thy riches.

Yonder is the sea, great and wide,
Wherein are things creeping innumerable,
Both small and great beasts.

There go the ships;
There is leviathan, whom thou hast formed to play therein.

These wait all upon thee,
That thou mayest give them their meat in due season.

That thou givest unto them, they gather;
Thou openest thy hand, they are filled with good.

Thou hidest thy face, they are troubled;
Thou takest away their breath, they die,
And return to their dust.

Thou sendest forth thy Spirit, they are created;
And thou renewest the face of the earth.

The glory of the Lord shall endure forever;
The Lord shall rejoice in his works:

He looketh on the earth, and it trembleth;
He toucheth the hills, and they smoke.

I will sing unto the Lord as long as I live:
I will sing praise to my God while I have my being.

My meditation of him shall be sweet:
I will be glad in the Lord.

Fortieth Sunday
Morning

Oh give thanks unto the Lord, call upon his name;
Make known among the people his deeds.

Sing unto him, sing psalms unto him;
Talk ye of all his wondrous works.

Glory ye in his holy name:
Let the heart of them rejoice that seek the Lord.

Seek the Lord and his strength;
Seek his face evermore.

Remember his marvelous works that he hath done,
His wonders, and the judgments of his mouth,

O ye seed of Abraham his servant,
Ye children of Jacob, his chosen ones.

He is the Lord our God:
His judgments are in all the earth.

He hath remembered his covenant forever,
The word which he commanded to a thousand generations,

The covenant which he made with Abraham,
And his oath unto Isaac,

And confirmed the same unto Jacob for a law,
To Israel for an everlasting covenant,

Saying, Unto thee will I give the land of Canaan,
The lot of your inheritance;

When they were but a few men in number,

Yea, very few, and strangers in it.

When they went from one nation to another,
From one kingdom to another people.

He suffered no man to do them wrong;
Yea, he reproved kings for their sakes,

Saying, Touch not mine anointed ones,
And do my prophets no harm.

And he called for a famine upon the land;
He brake the whole staff of bread.

He sent a man before them;
Joseph was sold for a servant:

His feet they hurt with fetters:
He was laid in chains of iron,

Until the time that his word came to pass,
The word of the Lord tried him.

The king sent and loosed him;
Even the ruler of peoples, and let him go free.

He made him lord of his house;
And ruler of all his substance;

To bind his princes at his pleasure,
And teach his elders wisdom.

Israel also came into Egypt;
And Jacob sojourned in the land of Ham.

And he increased his people greatly,
And made them stronger than their adversaries.

That they might keep his statutes,
And observe his laws.
Praise ye the Lord.

Evening

The Lord said unto my lord, Sit thou at my right hand,
Until I make thine enemies thy footstool.

The Lord shall send forth the rod of thy strength out of Zion:
Rule thou in the midst of thine enemies.

Thy people offer themselves willingly
In the day of thy power, in the beauties of holiness.

Out of the womb of the morning
Thou hast the dew of thy youth.

The Lord hath sworn, and will not repent:
Thou art a priest forever
After the order of Melchizedek.

The Lord at thy right hand
Shall strike through kings in the day of his wrath.

He shall judge among the heathen,
He shall fill the places with dead bodies;
He shall wound the heads over many countries.

He shall drink of the brook in the way:
Therefore shall he lift up the head.

I cried with my voice unto the Lord;
With my voice unto the Lord did I make supplication.

I pour out my complaint before him;
I show before him my trouble.

When my spirit was overwhelmed within me,
Thou knewest my path.

In the way wherein I walked
Have they hidden a snare for me.

Look on my right hand, and see;
For there is no man that knoweth me:

Refuge hath failed me;
No man careth for my soul.

I cried unto thee, O Lord;
I said, Thou art my refuge,
My portion in the land of the living.

Attend unto my cry;
For I am brought very low:

Deliver me from my persecutors;
For they are stronger than I.

Bring my soul out of prison,
That I may praise thy name:

The righteous shall compass me about;
For thou shalt deal bountifully with me.

Forty-first Sunday

Morning

Oh give thanks unto the Lord; for he is good;
For his mercy endureth forever.

Let the redeemed of the Lord say so,
Whom he hath redeemed from the hand of the enemy,

And gathered out of the lands,
From the east and from the west,
From the north and from the south.

They wandered in the wilderness in a solitary way;
They found no city to dwell in.

Hungry and thirsty,
Their soul fainted in them.

Then they cried unto the Lord in their trouble,
And he delivered them out of their distresses,

He led them also by a straight way,
That they might go to a city of habitation.

Oh that men would praise the Lord
for his goodness,
And for his wonderful works to
the children of men!

For he satisfieth the longing soul,
And filleth the hungry soul with goodness.

Such as sit in darkness and in the
shadow of death,
Being bound in affliction and iron,

Because they rebelled against the words of God,
And contemned the counsel of the Most High:

Therefore he brought down their
heart with labor;
They fell down, and there was none
to help.

Then they cried unto the Lord in their trouble,
And he saved them out of their distresses.

He brought them out of darkness
and the shadow of death,
And brake their bands in sunder.

Oh that men would praise the Lord for his goodness,
And for his wonderful works to the children of men!

For he hath broken the gates of
brass,
And cut the bars of iron in sunder.

Fools because of their transgression,
And because of their iniquities, are afflicted.

Their soul abhorreth all manner
of meat;
And they draw near unto the gates
of death.

Then they cry unto the Lord in their trouble,
And he saveth them out of their distresses.

He sent his word, and healed
them,
And delivered them from their
destructions.

Oh that men would praise the Lord for his goodness,
And for his wonderful works to the children of men!

And let them offer the sacrifices of
thanksgiving,
And declare his works with re-
joicing.

Evening

My heart is fixed, O God;
I will sing, yea, I will sing praises, even with my glory.

Awake, psaltery and harp:
I myself will awake right early.

I will praise thee, O Lord, among the people;
And I will sing praises unto thee among the nations.

For thy mercy is great above the
heavens;
And thy truth reacheth unto the
clouds.

Be thou exalted, O God, above the heavens,
And thy glory above all the earth.

That thy beloved may be deliv-
ered,
Save with thy right hand, and an-
swer me.

God hath spoken in his holiness: I will rejoice;
I will divide Shechem, and mete out the valley of Succoth.

Gilead is mine; Manasseh is mine;
Ephraim also is the strength of my
head;
Judah is my scepter.

Who will bring me into the strong
city?
Who will lead me unto Edom?

Hast not thou cast us off, O God?
And thou goest not forth, O God,
with our hosts.

Give us help from trouble;
For vain is the help of man.

Through God we shall do valiantly:
For he it is that shall tread down
our enemies.

Forty=second Sunday
Morning

They that go down to the sea in
ships,
That do business in great waters;

These see the works of the Lord,
And his wonders in the deep.

For he commandeth, and raiseth
the stormy wind,
Which lifteth up the waves thereof.

They mount up to the heaven, they
go down again to the depths:
Their soul is melted because of
trouble.

They reel to and fro, and stagger
like a drunken man,
And are at their wits' end

Then they cry unto the Lord in
their trouble,
And he bringeth them out of their
distresses.

He maketh the storm a calm,
So that the waves thereof are
still.

Then are they glad because they be
quiet;
So he bringeth them unto their de-
sired haven.

Oh that men would praise the Lord
for his goodness,
And for his wonderful works to the
children of men!

Let them exalt him also in the
congregation of the people,
And praise him in the assembly of
the elders.

He turneth rivers into a wilderness,
And the water springs into dry
ground;

A fruitful land into barrenness,
For the wickedness of them that
dwell therein.

He turneth the wilderness into a
pool of water,
And a dry ground into water
springs.

And there he maketh the hungry to
dwell,
That they may prepare a city for
habitation,

And sow fields, and plant vineyards,
Which may yield fruits of increase.

He blesseth them also, so that they
are multiplied greatly;
And he suffereth not their cattle to
decrease.

Again, they are diminished and
brought low
Through oppression, affliction, and
sorrow.

He poureth contempt upon princes,
And causeth them to wander in
the wilderness, where there is no
way.

Yet setteth he the poor on high from affliction,
And maketh him families like a flock.

The righteous shall see it, and rejoice;
And all iniquity shall stop her mouth.

Whoso is wise will observe these things;
Even they shall understand the loving-kindnesses of the Lord.

Evening

Teach me, O Lord, the way of thy statutes;
And I shall keep it unto the end.

Give me understanding, and I shall keep thy law;
Yea, I shall observe it with my whole heart.

Make me to go in the path of thy commandments;
For therein do I delight.

Incline my heart unto thy testimonies,
And not to covetousness.

Turn away mine eyes from beholding vanity,
And quicken thou me in thy way.

Confirm unto thy servant thy word,
Which tendeth unto the fear of thee.

Turn away my reproach which I fear;
For thy judgments are good.

Behold, I have longed after thy precepts:
Quicken me in thy righteousness.

Let thy mercies also come unto me, O Lord,
Even thy salvation, according to thy word,

So shall I have an answer for him that reproacheth me;
For I trust in thy word.

And take not the word of truth utterly out of my mouth;
For I have hoped in thy judgments.

So shall I keep thy law continually
Forever and ever.

And I will walk at liberty;
For I seek thy precepts.

I will also speak of thy testimonies before kings,
And will not be ashamed.

And I will delight myself in thy commandments,
Which I have loved.

I will lift up my hands also unto thy commandments, which I have loved;
And I will meditate in thy statutes.

Forty=third Sunday
Morning

Praise ye the Lord.
I will praise the Lord with my whole heart,
In the assembly of the upright, and in the congregation.

The works of the Lord are great,
Sought out of all them that have pleasure therein.

His work is honorable and glorious;
And his righteousness endureth forever.

He hath made his wonderful works to be remembered:
The Lord is gracious and full of compassion,

He hath given meat unto them that fear him:
He will ever be mindful of his covenant.

> He hath showed his people the power of his works,
> That he may give them the heritage of the heathen.

The works of his hands are truth and justice;
All his commandments are sure.

> They stand fast forever and ever;
> They are done in truth and uprightness.

He hath sent redemption unto his people;
He hath commanded his covenant forever:
Holy and reverend is his name.

> The fear of the Lord is the beginning of wisdom;
> A good understanding have all they that do his commandments:
> His praise endureth forever.

Praise ye the Lord.
Blessed is the man that feareth the Lord,
That delighteth greatly in his commandments.

> His seed shall be mighty upon earth:
> The generation of the upright shall be blessed.

Wealth and riches shall be in his house;
And his righteousness endureth forever.

> Unto the upright there ariseth light in the darkness:
> He is gracious, and full of compassion, and righteous.

A good man showeth favor and lendeth;
He will guide his affairs with discretion.

> For he shall never be moved;
> The righteous shall be in everlasting remembrance.

He shall not be afraid of evil tidings:
His heart is fixed, trusting in the Lord.

> He hath dispersed, he hath given to the poor;
> His righteousness endureth forever:
> His horn shall be exalted with honor.

The wicked shall see it, and be grieved;
He shall gnash with his teeth, and melt away:
The desire of the wicked shall perish.

Evening

Unto thee do I lift up mine eyes,
O thou that dwellest in the heavens.

> Behold, as the eyes of servants look unto the hand of their master,
> As the eyes of a maid unto the hand of her mistress;

So our eyes look unto the Lord our God,
Until he have mercy upon us.

> Have mercy upon us, O Lord, have mercy upon us;
> For we are exceedingly filled with contempt.

Our soul is exceedingly filled
With the scorning of those that are at ease,
And with the contempt of the proud.

*If it had not been the Lord who
was on our side,
Let Israel now say,
If it had not been the Lord who
was on our side,
When men rose up against us;*

Then they had swallowed us up
alive,
When their wrath was kindled
against us:

*Then the waters had overwhelmed
us,
The stream had gone over our soul;
Then the proud waters had gone
over our soul.*

Blessed be the Lord,
Who hath not given us as a prey to
their teeth.

*Our soul is escaped as a bird out
of the snare of the fowlers:
The snare is broken, and we are
escaped.*

Our help is in the name of the
Lord,
Who made heaven and earth.

Forty=fourth Sunday
Morning

Not unto us, O Lord, not unto us,
But unto thy name give glory,
For thy mercy, and for thy truth's
sake.

*Wherefore should the heathen say,
Where is now their God?*

But our God is in the heavens:
He hath done whatsoever he
pleased.

*Their idols are silver and gold,
The work of men's hands.*

They have mouths, but they speak
not;
Eyes have they, but they see not;

*They have ears, but they hear not;
Noses have they, but they smell not;*

They have hands, but they handle
not;
Feet have they, but they walk not;
Neither speak they through their
throat.

*They that make them are like unto
them;
Yea, every one that trusteth in them.*

O Israel, trust thou in the Lord:
He is their help and their shield.

*O house of Aaron, trust ye in the
Lord:
He is their help and their shield.*

Ye that fear the Lord, trust in the
Lord:
He is their help and their shield.

*The Lord hath been mindful of us;
he will bless us:
He will bless the house of Israel;*

He will bless the house of Aaron.
He will bless them that fear the
Lord,
Both small and great.

*The Lord increase you more and
more,
You and your children.*

Blessed are ye of the Lord,
Which made heaven and earth.

*The heavens are the heavens of the
Lord;
But the earth hath he given to the
children of men.*

The dead praise not the Lord,
Neither any that go down into
silence;

*But we will bless the Lord
From this time forth and for ever-
more.
Praise ye the Lord.*

Evening

They that trust in the Lord
Are as mount Zion, which cannot
be moved, but abideth forever.

*As the mountains are round about
Jerusalem,
So the Lord is round about his
people
From this time forth and for ever-
more.*

For the scepter of wickedness shall
not rest upon the lot of the righteous;
Lest the righteous put forth their
hands unto iniquity.

*Do good, O Lord, unto those that
be good,
And to them that are upright in
their hearts.*

But as for such as turn aside unto
their crooked ways,
The Lord shall lead them forth
with the workers of iniquity.
Peace be upon Israel.

*When the Lord brought back those
that returned to Zion,
We were like unto them that
dream.*

Then was our mouth filled with
laughter,
And our tongue with singing:

*Then said they among the heathen,
The Lord hath done great things
for them.*

The Lord hath done great things
for us,
Whereof we are glad.

*Turn again our captivity, O Lord,
As the streams in the South.*

They that sow in tears shall reap
in joy.

He that goeth forth and weepeth,
bearing seed for sowing,
Shall doubtless come again with
joy, bringing his sheaves with him.

Forty=fifth Sunday
Morning

I love the Lord, because he hath
heard
My voice and my supplications.

*Because he hath inclined his ear
unto me,
Therefore will I call upon him as
long as I live.*

The sorrows of death compassed
me,
And the pains of hell gat hold upon
me:
I found trouble and sorrow.

*Then called I upon the name of
the Lord:
O Lord, I beseech thee, deliver my
soul.*

Gracious is the Lord, and righteous;
Yea, our God is merciful.

*The Lord preserveth the simple:
I was brought low, and he saved
me,*

Return unto thy rest, O my soul;
For the Lord hath dealt bountifully with thee.

*For thou hast delivered my soul
from death,
Mine eyes from tears,
And my feet from falling.*

I will walk before the Lord
In the land of the living.
I believed, therefore have I spoken:

*I was greatly afflicted:
I said in my haste,
All men are liars.*

What shall I render unto the Lord
For all his benefits toward me?

I will take the cup of salvation,
And call upon the name of the
Lord.

I will pay my vows unto the Lord
Now in the presence of all his
people.

Precious in the sight of the Lord
Is the death of his saints.

O Lord, truly I am thy servant:
I am thy servant, the son of thy
handmaid;
Thou hast loosed my bonds.

I will offer to thee the sacrifice of
thanksgiving,
And will call upon the name of the
Lord.

I will pay my vows unto the
Lord
Now in the presence of all his peo-
ple,

In the courts of the Lord's house,
In the midst of thee, O Jerusa-
lem.
Praise ye the Lord.

Evening

Out of the depths have I cried unto
thee, O Lord.

Lord, hear my voice:
Let thine ears be attentive
To the voice of my supplications.

If thou, Lord, shouldest mark iniquities,
O Lord, who could stand?

But there is forgiveness with thee,
That thou mayest be feared.

I wait for the Lord, my soul doth
wait,
And in his word do I hope.

My soul waiteth for the Lord
More than watchmen wait for the
morning;
Yea, more than watchmen for the
morning.

O Israel, hope in the Lord;
For with the Lord there is mercy,
And with him is plenteous redemp-
tion.

And he will redeem Israel
From all his iniquities.

Lord, my heart is not haughty, nor
mine eyes lofty;
Neither do I exercise myself in
great matters,
Or in things too wonderful for me.

Surely I have stilled and quieted
my soul;
Like a weaned child with his
mother,
Like a weaned child is my soul
within me.

O Israel, hope in the Lord
From this time forth and for evermore.

Forty=sixth Sunday
Morning

Oh give thanks unto the Lord; for
he is good;
For his mercy endureth forever.

Let Israel now say,
That his mercy endureth forever.

Let the house of Aaron now say,
That his mercy endureth forever.

Let them now that fear the Lord
say,
That his mercy endureth forever.

Out of my distress I called upon the
Lord:
The Lord answered me and set me
in a large place.

The Lord is on my side; I will not fear:
What can man do unto me?

It is better to trust in the Lord
Than to put confidence in man.

It is better to trust in the Lord
Than to put confidence in princes.

The Lord is my strength and song;
And he is become my salvation.

The voice of rejoicing and salvation is in the tents of the righteous:
The right hand of the Lord doeth valiantly.

The right hand of the Lord is exalted:
The right hand of the Lord doeth valiantly.

I shall not die, but live,
And declare the works of the Lord.

The Lord hath chastened me sore;
But he hath not given me over unto death.

Open to me the gates of righteousness:
I will enter into them, I will praise the Lord.

This is the gate of the Lord;
The righteous shall enter into it.

I will praise thee; for thou hast heard me,
And art become my salvation.

The stone which the builders rejected
Is become the head of the corner.

This is the Lord's doing;
It is marvelous in our eyes.

This is the day which the Lord hath made;
We will rejoice and be glad in it.

Save now, we beseech thee, O Lord:
O Lord, we beseech thee, send now prosperity.

Blessed be he that cometh in the name of the Lord:
We have blessed you out of the house of the Lord.

Thou art my God, and I will praise thee:
Thou art my God, I will exalt thee.

Oh give thanks unto the Lord; for he is good;
For his mercy endureth forever.

Evening

Lord, remember for David
All his affliction;

How he sware unto the Lord,
And vowed unto the Mighty One of Jacob:

Surely I will not come into the tabernacle of my house,
Nor go up into my bed;

I will not give sleep to mine eyes,
Or slumber to mine eyelids;

Until I find out a place for the Lord,
A habitation for the Mighty One of Jacob.

Lo, we heard of it in Ephrathah:
We found it in the field of the wood.

We will go into his tabernacles;
We will worship at his footstool.

Arise, O Lord, into thy resting place;
Thou, and the ark of thy strength.

Let thy priests be clothed with righteousness;
And let thy saints shout for joy.

For thy servant David's sake
Turn not away the face of thine
anointed.

The Lord hath sworn unto David
in truth;
He will not turn from it:
Of the fruit of thy body will I set
upon thy throne.

If thy children will keep my
covenant
And my testimony that I shall
teach them,
Their children also shall sit upon
thy throne for evermore.

For the Lord hath chosen Zion;
He hath desired it for his habitation.

This is my resting place forever:
Here will I dwell; for I have de-
sired it.

I will abundantly bless her pro-
vision:
I will satisfy her poor with bread.

Her priests also will I clothe with
salvation;
And her saints shall shout aloud
for joy.

There will I make the horn of David
to bud:
I have ordained a lamp for mine
anointed.

Forty=seventh Sunday
Morning

Praise ye the Lord.
Praise ye the name of the Lord;

Praise him, O ye servants of the
Lord,
Ye that stand in the house of the
Lord,
In the courts of the house of our
God.

Praise ye the Lord; for the Lord is
good:
Sing praises unto his name; for it is
pleasant.

For the Lord hath chosen Jacob
unto himself,
And Israel for his own possession.

For I know that the Lord is great,
And that our Lord is above all
gods.

Whatsoever the Lord pleased, that
hath he done,
In heaven and in earth, in the seas
and in all deeps;

Who causeth the vapors to ascend
from the ends of the earth;
Who maketh lightnings for the
rain;
Who bringeth forth the wind out
of his treasuries;

Who smote the firstborn of Egypt,
Both of man and beast;

Who sent signs and wonders into
the midst of thee, O Egypt,
Upon Pharaoh, and upon all his
servants;

Who smote many nations,
And slew mighty kings,

Sihon king of the Amorites,
And Og king of Bashan,
And all the kingdoms of Canaan.

And gave their land for a heritage,
A heritage unto Israel his people.

Thy name, O Lord, endureth forever;
Thy memorial, O Lord, throughout
all generations.

For the Lord will judge his peo-
ple,
And repent himself concerning his
servants.

The idols of the heathen are silver and gold,
The work of men's hands.

They have mouths, but they speak not;
Eyes have they, but they see not;

They have ears, but they hear not;
Neither is there any breath in their mouths.

They that make them shall be like unto them;
Yea, every one that trusteth in them.

O house of Israel, bless ye the Lord:
O house of Aaron, bless ye the Lord:

O house of Levi, bless ye the Lord:
Ye that fear the Lord, bless ye the Lord.

Blessed be the Lord out of Zion,
Which dwelleth at Jerusalem.
Praise ye the Lord.

Evening

Hear my prayer, O Lord; give ear to my supplications:
In thy faithfulness answer me, and in thy righteousness.

And enter not into judgment with thy servant;
For in thy sight shall no man living be justified.

For the enemy hath persecuted my soul;
He hath smitten my life down to the ground:
He hath made me to dwell in darkness, as those that have been long dead.

Therefore is my spirit overwhelmed within me;
My heart within me is desolate.

I remember the days of old;
I meditate on all thy works;
I muse on the work of thy hands.

I spread forth my hands unto thee:
My soul thirsteth after thee, as a weary land.

Make haste to answer me, O Lord; my spirit faileth:
Hide not thy face from me,
Lest I be like unto them that go down into the pit.

Cause me to hear thy loving-kindness in the morning;
For in thee do I trust:

Cause me to know the way wherein I should walk;
For I lift up my soul unto thee.

Deliver me, O Lord, from mine enemies:
I flee unto thee to hide me.

Teach me to do thy will;
For thou art my God:

Thy Spirit is good;
Lead me in the land of uprightness.

Quicken me, O Lord, for thy name's sake:
In thy righteousness bring my soul out of trouble.

Forty=eighth Sunday
Morning

O Lord, thou hast searched me, and known me.

Thou knowest my downsitting and mine uprising;
Thou understandest my thought afar off.

Thou searchest out my path and my lying down,
And art acquainted with all my ways.

For there is not a word in my tongue,
But, lo; O Lord, thou knowest it altogether.

Thou hast beset me behind and before,
And laid thine hand upon me.

Such knowledge is too wonderful for me;
It is high, I cannot attain unto it.

Whither shall I go from thy Spirit?
Or whither shall I flee from thy presence?

If I ascend up into heaven, thou art there;
If I make my bed in hell, behold, thou art there.

If I take the wings of the morning,
And dwell in the uttermost parts of the sea;

Even there shall thy hand lead me,
And thy right hand shall hold me.

If I say, Surely the darkness shall cover me,
And the light about me shall be night;

Yea, the darkness hideth not from thee,
But the night shineth as the day:
The darkness and the light are both alike to thee.

I will praise thee; for I am fearfully and wonderfully made:

Marvelous are thy works;
And that my soul knoweth right well.

How precious also are thy thoughts unto me, O God!
How great is the sum of them!

If I should count them, they are more in number than the sand:
When I awake, I am still with thee.

Surely thou wilt slay the wicked, O God:
Depart from me therefore, ye bloodthirsty men.

For they speak against thee wickedly,
And thine enemies take thy name in vain.

Search me, O God, and know my heart:
Try me, and know my thoughts;

And see if there be any wicked way in me,
And lead me in the way everlasting.

Evening

Blessed be the Lord my strength,
Which teacheth my hands to war,
And my fingers to fight:

My goodness, and my fortress,
My high tower, and my deliverer;

My shield, and he in whom I take refuge;
Who subdueth my people under me.

Lord, what is man, that thou takest knowledge of him?
Or the son of man, that thou makest account of him?

Man is like to vanity:
His days are as a shadow that passeth away.

Bow thy heavens, O Lord, and come down:
Touch the mountains, and they shall smoke.

Cast forth lightning, and scatter them;
Send out thine arrows, and discomfit them.

Stretch forth thy hand from above;
Rescue me, and deliver me out of great waters,

Out of the hand of aliens;
Whose mouth speaketh vanity,
And whose right hand is a right
hand of falsehood.

*I will sing a new song unto thee,
O God:
Upon a psaltery of ten strings will
I sing praises unto thee.*

Thou art he that giveth salvation
unto kings;
Who delivereth David his servant
from the hurtful sword.

*Rescue me, and deliver me out of
the hand of aliens,
Whose mouth speaketh vanity,
And whose right hand is a right
hand of falsehood.*

When our sons shall be as plants
grown up in their youth,
And our daughters as corner stones
hewn after the fashion of a palace;

*When our garners are full, af-
fording all manner of store,
And our sheep bring forth thousands and ten thousands in our
fields;*

When our oxen are well laden;
When there is no breaking in, and
no going forth,
And no outcry in our streets:

*Happy is the people that is in such
a case;
Yea, happy is the people whose
God is the Lord.*

Forty=ninth Sunday
Morning

I will extol thee, my God, O King;
And I will bless thy name forever
and ever.

*Every day will I bless thee;
And I will praise thy name forever and ever.*

Great is the Lord, and greatly to
be praised;
And his greatness is unsearchable.

*One generation shall praise thy
works to another,
And shall declare thy mighty
acts.*

Of the glorious majesty of thine
honor,
And of thy wondrous works, will I
meditate.

*And men shall speak of the might
of thy terrible acts;
And I will declare thy greatness.*

They shall utter the memory of thy
great goodness,
And shall sing of thy righteousness.

*The Lord is gracious, and full of
compassion;
Slow to anger, and of great mercy.*

The Lord is good to all;
And his tender mercies are over all
his works.

*All thy works shall praise thee, O
Lord;
And thy saints shall bless thee.*

They shall speak of the glory of thy
kingdom,
And talk of thy power;

*To make known to the sons of men
his mighty acts,
And the glorious majesty of his
kingdom.*

Thy kingdom is an everlasting
kingdom,
And thy dominion endureth
throughout all generations.

*The Lord upholdeth all that fall,
And raiseth up all those that be
bowed down.*

The eyes of all wait for thee;
And thou givest them their food in
due season.

Thou openest thine hand,
And satisfiest the desire of every
living thing.

The Lord is righteous in all his ways,
And holy in all his works.

The Lord is nigh unto all them
that call upon him,
To all that call upon him in truth.

He will fulfill the desire of them
that fear him;
He also will hear their cry and will
save them.

The Lord preserveth all them that
love him;
But all the wicked will he destroy.

My mouth shall speak the praise of
the Lord;
And let all flesh bless his holy name
forever and ever.

Evening

God is my King of old,
Working salvation in the midst of
the earth.

Thou didst divide the sea by thy
strength:
Thou brakest the heads of the
dragons in the waters.

Thou brakest the heads of leviathan in pieces;
Thou gavest him to be food to the
people inhabiting the wilderness.

Thou didst cleave fountain and
flood:
Thou driedst up mighty rivers.

The day is thine, the night also is
thine:
Thou hast prepared the light and
the sun.

Thou hast set all the borders of the
earth:
Thou hast made summer and win-
ter.

Remember this, that the enemy
hath reproached, O Lord,
And that a foolish people hath
blasphemed thy name.

Oh deliver not the soul of thy turtle-
dove unto the wild beast:
Forget not the life of thy poor for-
ever.

Have respect unto the covenant;
For the dark places of the earth
are full of the habitations of violence.

Oh let not the oppressed return
ashamed:
Let the poor and needy praise thy
name.

Arise, O God, plead thine own
cause:
Remember how the foolish man reproacheth thee all the day.

Forget not the voice of thine ad-
versaries:
The tumult of those that rise up
against thee ascendeth continually.

O Lord God of hosts, hear my
prayer,
Give ear, O God of Jacob.

O Lord of hosts,
Blessed is the man that trusteth in
thee.

Fiftieth Sunday
Morning

Praise ye the Lord;
For it is good to sing praises unto
our God;
For it is pleasant, and praise is
comely.

The Lord doth build up Jerusalem;
He gathereth together the outcasts
of Israel.

He healeth the broken in heart,
And bindeth up their wounds.

He counteth the number of the
stars;
He calleth them all by their names.

Great is our Lord, and mighty in
power;
His understanding is infinite.

The Lord lifteth up the meek:
He casteth the wicked down to the
ground.

Sing unto the Lord with thanksgiving;
Sing praises upon the harp unto
our God,

Who covereth the heavens with
clouds,
Who prepareth rain for the earth,
Who maketh grass to grow upon
the mountains.

He giveth to the beast his food,
And to the young ravens which cry.

He delighteth not in the strength
of the horse:
He taketh no pleasure in the legs
of a man.

The Lord taketh pleasure in them
that fear him,
In those that hope in his mercy.

Praise the Lord, O Jerusalem;
Praise thy God, O Zion.

For he hath strengthened the bars
of thy gates;
He hath blessed thy children within
thee.

He maketh peace in thy borders;
He filleth thee with the finest of the
wheat,

He sendeth forth his commandment upon earth;
His word runneth very swiftly.

He giveth snow like wool;
He scattereth the hoarfrost like
ashes.

He casteth forth his ice like morsels:
Who can stand before his cold?

He sendeth out his word, and
melteth them:
He causeth his wind to blow, and
the waters flow.

He showeth his word unto Jacob,
His statutes and his ordinances
unto Israel.

He hath not dealt so with any
nation;
And as for his ordinances, they
have not known them.
Praise ye the Lord.

Evening

O God, the heathen are come into
thine inheritance;

Thy holy temple have they defiled;
They have laid Jerusalem in
heaps.

The dead bodies of thy servants
have they given to be food unto the
birds of the heavens,
The flesh of thy saints unto the
beasts of the earth.

Their blood have they shed like
water round about Jerusalem;
And there was none to bury them.

We are become a reproach to our
neighbors,
A scoffing and derision to them that
are round about us.

How long, O Lord? wilt thou be
angry forever?
Shall thy jealousy burn like fire?

Remember not against us the iniquities of our forefathers:
Let thy tender mercies speedily meet us;
For we are brought very low.

*Help us, O God of our salvation,
for the glory of thy name;
And deliver us, and forgive our
sins, for thy name's sake.*

Wherefore should the heathen say,
Where is their God?
Let the avenging of thy servants' blood that is shed
Be known among the nations before our eyes.

*Let the sighing of the prisoner
come before thee:
According to the greatness of thy
power preserve thou those that are
appointed to die;*

So we thy people and sheep of thy pasture
Will give thee thanks forever:
We will show forth thy praise to all generations.

Fifty=first Sunday
Morning

Give ear, O Shepherd of Israel,
Thou that leadest Joseph like a flock;
Thou that sittest between the cherubim, shine forth.

*Before Ephraim and Benjamin
and Manasseh, stir up thy might,
And come to save us.*

Turn us again, O God;
And cause thy face to shine, and we shall be saved.

*O Lord God of hosts,
How long wilt thou be angry
against the prayer of thy people?*

Thou hast fed them with the bread of tears,
And givest them tears to drink in large measure.

*Thou makest us a strife unto our
neighbors;
And our enemies laugh among
themselves.*

Turn again, O God of hosts;
And cause thy face to shine, and we shall be saved.

*Thou broughtest a vine out of
Egypt:
Thou didst drive out the heathen,
and plantedst it.*

Thou preparedst room before it,
And it took deep root, and filled the land.

*The hills were covered with the
shadow of it,
And the boughs thereof were like
the goodly cedars.*

It sent out its boughs unto the sea,
And its branches unto the River.

*Why hast thou broken down its
hedges,
So that all they that pass by the
way do pluck it?*

The boar out of the wood doth waste it,
And the wild beasts of the field feed on it.

*Turn again, we beseech thee, O God
of hosts:
Look down from heaven, and behold, and visit this vine,*

And the stock which thy right hand planted,
And the branch that thou madest strong for thyself.

It is burned with fire, it is cut down:
They perish at the rebuke of thy
countenance.

Let thy hand be upon the man of
thy right hand,
Upon the son of man whom thou
madest strong for thyself.

So will we not go back from thee:
Quicken thou us, and we will call
upon thy name.

Turn again, O Lord God of hosts;
Cause thy face to shine, and we
shall be saved.

Evening

The Lord reigneth; let the people
tremble:
He sitteth between the cherubim;
let the earth be moved.

The Lord is great in Zion;
And he is high above all the peoples.

Let them praise thy great and
terrible name:
For it is holy.

The king's strength also loveth
judgment;
Thou dost establish equity;
Thou executest judgment and right-
eousness in Jacob.

Exalt ye the Lord our God,
And worship at his footstool:
For he is holy.

Moses and Aaron among his
priests,
And Samuel among them that call
upon his name;

They called upon the Lord, and he
answered them.
He spake unto them in the pillar
of cloud:
They kept his testimonies,
And the ordinance that he gave
them.

Thou answeredst them, O Lord our
God:
Thou wast a God that forgavest
them,
Though thou tookest vengeance of
their doings.

Exalt ye the Lord our God,
And worship at his holy hill;
For the Lord our God is holy.

Make a joyful noise unto the Lord,
all ye lands.

Serve the Lord with gladness:
Come before his presence with
singing.

Know ye that the Lord, he is God:
It is he that hath made us, and we
are his;
We are his people, and the sheep
of his pasture.

Enter into his gates with thanks-
giving,
And into his courts with praise:

Give thanks unto him, and bless his
name.
For the Lord is good; his mercy
endureth forever,
And his truth unto all generations.

Fifty=second Sunday
Morning

Give ear, O my people, to my law:
Incline your ears to the words of
my mouth.

I will open my mouth in a parable;
I will utter dark sayings of old,

Which we have heard and known,
And our fathers have told us.

We will not hide them from their
children,
Telling to the generation to come
the praises of the Lord,
And his strength, and his won-
drous works that he hath done.

For he established a testimony in Jacob,
And appointed a law in Israel,

Which he commanded our fathers,
That they should make them known
to their children;

That the generation to come might know them, even the children that should be born;
Who should arise and tell them to their children,

That they might set their hope in
God,
And not forget the works of God,
But keep his commandments,

And might not be as their fathers,
A stubborn and rebellious generation,

A generation that set not their
heart aright,
And whose spirit was not steadfast
with God.

Marvelous things did he in the sight of their fathers,
In the land of Egypt, in the field of Zoan.

He divided the sea, and caused
them to pass through;
And he made the waters to stand
as a heap.

In the daytime also he led them with a cloud,
And all the night with a light of fire.

He clave rocks in the wilderness,
And gave them drink abundantly
as out of the depths.

He brought streams also out of the rock,
And caused waters to run down like rivers.

Yet went they on still to sin against
him,

To rebel against the Most High in
the desert.

And they tempted God in their heart
By asking food according to their desire.

Yea, they spake against God;
They said, Can God prepare a
table in the wilderness?

Behold, he smote the rock, so that waters gushed out,
And streams overflowed;

Can he give bread also?
Will he provide flesh for his peo-
ple?

Therefore the Lord heard, and was wroth;
And a fire was kindled against Jacob,
And anger also went up against Israel;

Because they believed not in God,
And trusted not in his salva-
tion.

Yet he commanded the skies above,
And opened the doors of heaven;

And he rained down manna upon
them to eat,
And gave them food from heaven.

Man did eat the bread of the mighty:
He sent them food to the full.

And they remembered that God
was their rock,
And the Most High God their
Redeemer.

Evening

Praise ye the Lord.
Oh give thanks unto the Lord; for he is good;
For his mercy endureth forever.

Who can utter the mighty acts of
the Lord,
Or show forth all his praise?

Blessed are they that keep justice,
And he that doeth righteousness at
all times.

Remember me, O Lord, with the favor that thou bearest unto thy people;
Oh visit me with thy salvation,

That I may see the prosperity of
thy chosen,
That I may rejoice in the gladness
of thy nation,
That I may glory with thine inheritance.

We have sinned with our fathers,
We have committed iniquity, we
have done wickedly.

Our fathers understood not thy
wonders in Egypt;
They remembered not the multitude of thy mercies,
But were rebellious at the sea, even
at the Red Sea.

Nevertheless he saved them for his
name's sake,
That he might make his mighty
power to be known.

He rebuked the Red Sea also, and
it was dried up:
So he led them through the depths,
as through a wilderness.

And he saved them from the hand
of him that hated them,
And redeemed them from the hand
of the enemy.

And the waters covered their enemies;
There was not one of them left.

Then believed they his words;
They sang his praise.

Save us, O Lord our God,
And gather us from among the
heathen,

To give thanks unto thy holy
name,
And to triumph in thy praise.

Blessed be the Lord, the God of
Israel,
From everlasting even to ever-
lasting.

And let all the people say, Amen.
Praise ye the Lord.

Fifty=third Sunday
Morning

Praise ye the Lord.
Praise, O ye servants of the Lord,
Praise the name of the Lord.

Blessed be the name of the Lord
From this time forth and for evermore.

From the rising of the sun unto the
going down of the same
The Lord's name is to be praised.

The Lord is high above all nations,
And his glory above the heavens.

Who is like unto the Lord our
God,
That hath his seat on high,

That humbleth himself to behold
The things that are in heaven and
in the earth?

He raiseth up the poor out of the
dust,
And lifteth up the needy out of the
dunghill;

That he may set him with princes,
Even with the princes of his people.

He maketh the barren woman to
keep house,
And to be a joyful mother of children.
Praise ye the Lord.

I will praise thee with my whole heart:
Before the gods will I sing praises unto thee.

I will worship toward thy holy temple,
And praise thy name for thy loving-kindness and for thy truth:
For thou hast magnified thy word above all thy name.

In the day that I cried thou answeredst me,
Thou strengthenedst me with strength in my soul.

All the kings of the earth shall praise thee, O Lord,
For they have heard the words of thy mouth.

Yea, they shall sing of the ways of the Lord;
For great is the glory of the Lord.

For though the Lord is high, yet hath he respect unto the lowly;
But the proud he knoweth from afar.

Though I walk in the midst of trouble, thou wilt revive me;
Thou shalt stretch forth thy hand against the wrath of mine enemies,
And thy right hand shall save me.

The Lord will perfect that which concerneth me:
Thy mercy, O Lord, endureth forever;
Forsake not the works of thine own hands.

Evening

Many a time have they afflicted me from my youth up,
Let Israel now say,

Many a time have they afflicted me from my youth up:
Yet they have not prevailed against me.

The plowers plowed upon my back;
They made long their furrows.

The Lord is righteous:
He hath cut asunder the cords of the wicked.

Let them be put to shame and turned backward,
All they that hate Zion.

Let them be as the grass upon the housetops;
Which withereth before it groweth up;

Wherewith the reaper filleth not his hand,
Nor he that bindeth sheaves, his bosom:

Neither do they that go by say,
The blessing of the Lord be upon you;
We bless you in the name of the Lord.

Blessed is every one that feareth the Lord,
That walketh in his ways.

For thou shalt eat the labor of thy hands:
Happy shalt thou be, and it shall be well with thee.

Thy wife shall be as a fruitful vine,
In the innermost parts of thy house;

Thy children like olive plants,
Round about thy table.

Behold, thus shall the man be blessed
That feareth the Lord.

The Lord shall bless thee out of Zion:
And thou shalt see the good of Jerusalem all the days of thy life.

Yea, thou shalt see thy children's children.
Peace be upon Israel.

Readings for Special Days

First Reading
Christmas

The people that walked in darkness have seen a great light.
They that dwell in the land of the shadow of death, upon them hath the light shined.

Thou hast multiplied the nation, thou hast increased their joy:
They joy before thee according to the joy in harvest, as men rejoice when they divide the spoil.

For the yoke of his burden, and the staff of his shoulder,
The rod of his oppressor, thou hast broken as in the day of Midian.

For unto us a child is born, unto us a Son is given:
And the government shall be upon his shoulder:

And his name shall be called Wonderful, Counselor,
Mighty God, Everlasting Father, Prince of Peace.

Of the increase of his government and peace there shall be no end,
Upon the throne of David, and upon his kingdom.

To establish it and to uphold it with justice and with righteousness
From henceforth and forever. The zeal of the Lord of hosts will perform this.

And there shall come forth a shoot out of the stock of Jesse,
And a branch out of his roots shall bear fruit;

And the spirit of the Lord shall rest upon him,
The spirit of wisdom and understanding;

The spirit of counsel and might,
The spirit of knowledge and of the fear of the Lord.

And he shall not judge after the sight of his eyes, [his ears;
Neither decide after the hearing of

But with righteousness shall he judge the poor,
And decide with equity for the meek of the earth;

And he shall smite the oppressor with the rod of his mouth
And with the breath of his lips shall he slay the wicked.

And righteousness shall be the girdle of his waist,
And faithfulness the girdle of his loins.

And the wolf shall dwell with the lamb,
And the leopard shall lie down with the kid;

And the calf and the young lion and the fatling together;
And a little child shall lead them.

And the cow and the bear shall feed;
Their young ones shall lie down together;
And the lion shall eat straw like the ox.

And the sucking child shall play on the hole of the asp,
And the weaned child shall put his hand on the adder's den.

They shall not hurt nor destroy in all my holy mountain;
For the earth shall be full of the knowledge of the Lord,
As the waters cover the sea.

Second Reading
Palm Sunday

Rejoice greatly, O daughter of Zion;
Shout, O daughter of Jerusalem:

Behold thy King cometh unto thee;
He is just and having salvation;

Lowly, and riding upon an ass,
Even upon a colt, the foal of an ass.

And he shall speak peace unto the nations:
And his dominion shall be from sea to sea,
And from the River to the ends of the earth.

Thou art fairer than the children of
men;
Grace is poured into thy lips:
Therefore God hath blessed thee
forever.

*Gird thy sword upon thy thigh, O
mighty one,
Thy glory and thy majesty.*

And in thy majesty ride on prosper-
ously,
Because of truth and meekness and
righteousness.

*Thy throne, O God, is forever and ever.
A scepter of equity is the scepter of
thy kingdom.*

O thou that tellest good tidings to Zion,
Get thee up into the high mountain.

*O thou that tellest good tidings to
Jerusalem
Lift up thy voice with strength;*

Lift it up, be not afraid;
Say unto the cities of Judah, Behold
your God.

*How beautiful upon the mountains
are the feet of him that bringeth good
tidings,
That publisheth peace, that bringeth
good tidings of good, that publisheth
salvation;
That sayeth unto Zion, Thy God
reigneth.*

Third Reading
Good Friday

Who hath believed our report?
And to whom hath the arm of the
Lord been revealed?

*For he shall grow up before him as a
tender plant,
And as a root out of a dry ground:*

He hath no form nor comeliness,
And when we shall see him there is
no beauty that we should desire him.

*He is despised and rejected of men;
A man of sorrows, and acquainted
with grief:*

And as one from whom men hide the
face

He was despised, and we esteemed
him not.

*Surely he hath borne our griefs
And carried our sorrows:*

Yet we did esteem him stricken,
Smitten of God and afflicted.

*But he was wounded for our trans-
gressions,
He was bruised for our iniquities.*

The chastisement of our peace was
upon him,
And with his stripes we are healed.

*All we like sheep have gone astray;
We have turned every one to his own
way;*

And the Lord hath laid on him
The iniquity of us all.

*He was oppressed, yet he humbled
himself
And opened not his mouth.*

As a lamb that is led to the slaugh-
ter,
And as a sheep that before her
shearers is dumb;
So he opened not his mouth.

*By oppression and judgment he was
taken away;
And as for his generation, who
among them considered,*

That he was cut off out of the land of
the living?
For the transgression of my people
was he stricken.

*And he made his grave with the
wicked,
And with the rich in his death;*

Although he had done no violence,
Neither was any deceit in his mouth,
Yet it pleased the Lord to bruise
him:
He hath put him to grief.

Fourth Reading
Easter

Now is Christ risen from the dead,
And become the first fruits of them
that slept.

For since by man came death,
By man came also the resurrection
of the dead.

For as in Adam all die,
Even so in Christ shall all be made
alive.

But some man will say, How are the
dead raised up?
And with what body do they come?

All flesh is not the same flesh: but
there is one flesh of men,
Another flesh of beasts, another of
fishes, and another of birds.

There are also celestial bodies and
bodies terrestrial:
But the glory of the celestial is one,
and the glory of the terrestrial is
another.

There is one glory of the sun, and
another glory of the moon,
And another glory of the stars, for one
star differeth from another in glory.

So also is the resurrection of the dead.

It is sown in corruption;
It is raised in incorruption:

It is sown in dishonor;
It is raised in glory:

It is sown in weakness;
It is raised in power:

It is sown a natural body;
It is raised a spiritual body.

There is a natural body,
There is a spiritual body.

The first man Adam was made a
living soul;
The last Adam was made a quick-
ening spirit.

Behold I show you a mystery;
We shall not all sleep, but we shall all
be changed,

For this corruptible must put on
incorruption,
And this mortal must put on im-
mortality.

Thanks be to God, which giveth us
the victory
Through our Lord Jesus Christ.

Therefore, be ye steadfast, unmovable,
Always abounding in the work of the
Lord.

Forasmuch as ye know that your labor
Is not in vain in the Lord.

Fifth Reading
The Nation

Hear, O Israel:
The Lord our God is one Lord:

And thou shalt love the Lord thy God
With all thine heart, and with all thy
soul, and with all thy might.

And these words, which I command
thee this day,
Shall be in thine heart:

And thou shalt teach them diligently
unto thy children,
And thou shalt talk of them when
thou sittest in thy house;

And when thou walkest by the way,
And when thou liest down, and when
thou risest up.

And thou shalt bind them for a sign
upon thine hand,
And they shall be as frontlets be-
tween thine eyes.

And thou shalt write them upon the
posts of thy house
And on thy gates.

And it shall be, when the Lord thy
God shall have brought thee
Into the land which he sware unto
thy fathers,
To Abraham, to Isaac, and to Jacob,

To give thee great and goodly cities,
Which thou buildest not,

And houses full of good things
Which thou filledst not,

And wells digged
Which thou diggedst not,

Vineyards and olive trees
Which thou plantedst not,

When thou shalt have eaten and be
full,
Beware lest thou forget the Lord.

*Behold the days come, saith the Lord,
That I will make a new covenant
with the house of Israel.*

I will put my law in their inward
parts,
And in their heart will I write it.

*And I will be their God,
And they shall be my people.*

And they shall teach no more every
man his neighbor,
And every man his brother, saying,
Know the Lord;

*For they shall all know me,
From the least unto the greatest,
Saith the Lord.*

Blessed be the Lord, the God of our
fathers,
From everlasting even to everlasting.

Sixth Reading
Thanksgiving Day

Praise ye the Lord;
For it is good to sing praises unto our
God;
For it is pleasant, and praise is comely.

*Sing unto the Lord with thanks-
giving;
Sing praises upon the harp unto
our God.*

Who covereth the heaven with clouds,
Who prepareth rain for the earth,
Who maketh grass to grow upon the
mountains.

*He giveth to the beast his food
And to the young ravens which cry.*

Praise the Lord, O Jerusalem,
Praise thy God, O Zion.

*For he hath strengthened the bars of
thy gates,
He hath blessed thy children within
thee.*

He maketh peace in thy borders;
He filleth thee with the finest of the
wheat.

*Happy art thou, O Israel;
Who is like unto thee, a people saved
by the Lord?*

And Israel dwelleth in safety,
And full of the blessing of the Lord.

*The eternal God is thy dwelling
place,
And underneath are the everlasting
arms.*

O give thanks unto the Lord;
Sing unto him, sing praises unto
him,

*For the precious things of heaven,
for the dew,
And for the deep that coucheth beneath.*

And for the precious fruits brought
forth by the sun,
And for the precious things put forth
by the moon,

*And for the chief things of the
ancient mountains,
And for the precious things of the
everlasting hills,
And for the precious things of the
earth and its fullness.*

Let everything that hath breath
praise the Lord;
Praise ye the Lord.

Seventh Reading
Missions

Arise, shine; for thy light is come,
And the glory of the Lord is risen
upon thee.

*For behold darkness shall cover the
earth,
And gross darkness the peoples.*

But upon thee shall the Lord arise,
And his glory shall be seen upon
thee.

*And nations shall come to thy light,
And kings to the brightness of thy
rising.*

Lift up thine eyes round about, and
see.
They all gather themselves together,
they come to thee.

*Who are these that fly as a cloud,
And as doves to their windows?*

Surely the isles shall wait for me
And the ships of Tarshish first,

To bring thy sons from far,
Their silver and gold with them,

Unto the name of the Lord thy God,
And to the Holy One of Israel,
For he hath glorified thee.

Thy gates also shall be open con-
tinually,
They shall not be shut day nor night;

That men may bring unto thee the
wealth of the nations
And their kings led with them.

The glory of Lebanon shall come
unto thee,
The fir tree, the pine tree, and the
box together,

To beautify the place of my sanctuary,
And that I may make the place of my
feet glorious.

In the latter days it shall come to
pass
That the mountain of the Lord's
house shall be established in the top
of the mountains,
And it shall be exalted above the hills.

And peoples shall flow to it,
And many nations shall go and say:

· *Come and let us go up to the moun-*
tain of the Lord
And to the house of the God of
Jacob;

And he will teach us his ways,
And we will walk in his paths.

Eighth Reading
Education

Surely there is a mine for silver
And a place for gold which they refine.

Iron is taken out of the earth,
And brass is molten out of the stone.

Man setteth an end to darkness
And searchest out to the furthest
bound
The stones of thick darkness, and of
the shadow of death:

He putteth forth his hand upon the
flinty rock;
He overturneth the mountains by the
roots.

He cutteth out channels among the
rocks;
And his eye seeth every precious thing.

He bindeth the streams that they
trickle not;
And the thing that is hid bringeth he
forth to light.

But where shall wisdom be found?
And where is the place of understanding?

Man knoweth not the price thereof;
Neither is it found in the land of the
living.

The deep saith, It is not in me;
And the sea saith, It is not with me.

It cannot be gotten for gold,
Neither shall silver be weighed for
the price thereof.

It cannot be valued with the gold of
Ophir,
With the precious onyx or sapphire.
Whence then cometh wisdom?
And where is the place of understand-
ing?

Doth not wisdom cry,
And understanding put forth her
voice?

In the top of high places by the way,
Where the paths meet, she standeth;

Beside the gates, at the entry of the
city,
At the coming in of the doors, she
crieth aloud:

Receive instruction, and not silver:
And knowledge rather than choice
gold.

For wisdom is better than rubies;
And all things that may be desired
are not to be compared unto her.

Behold the fear of the Lord, that is
wisdom,
And to depart from evil is understanding.

The Ritual

Baptism

[Let every adult person and the parents of every child to be baptized, have the choice of either sprinkling, pouring, or immersion.]

[We will on no account whatever make a charge for administering Baptism.]

Order for the Administration of Baptism to Infants

The Minister, coming to the Font, which is to be filled with pure Water, shall use the following:

DEARLY BELOVED, forasmuch as all men are conceived and born in sin, and that our Saviour Christ saith, Except a man be born of water and of the Spirit he cannot enter into the kingdom of God; I beseech you to call upon God the Father, through our Lord Jesus Christ, that having, of his bounteous mercy, redeemed *this child* by the blood of his Son, he will grant that *he*, being baptized with water, may also be baptized with the Holy Ghost, be received into Christ's holy Church, and become *a lively Member* of the same.

Then shall the Minister say:

Let us pray.

Almighty and Everlasting God, who of thy great mercy hast condescended to enter into covenant relations with man, wherein thou hast included children as partakers of its gracious benefits, declaring that of such is thy kingdom; and in thy ancient Church didst appoint divers baptisms, figuring thereby the renewing of the Holy Ghost; and by thy well-beloved Son Jesus Christ gavest commandment to thy holy Apostles to go into all the world and disciple all nations, baptizing them in the name of the Father, and of the Son, and of the Holy Ghost: we beseech thee, that of thine infinite mercy thou wilt look upon *this child*: wash *him* and sanctify *him;* that *he*, being saved by thy grace, may be received into Christ's holy Church, and being steadfast in faith, joyful through hope, and rooted in love, may so overcome the evils of this present world that finally *he* may attain to everlasting life, and reign with thee, world without end, through Jesus Christ our Lord. *Amen.*

O Merciful God, grant that all carnal affections may die in *him*, and that all things belonging to the Spirit may live and grow in *him*. *Amen.*

Grant that *he* may have power and strength to have victory, and to triumph against the devil, the world, and the flesh. *Amen.*

Grant that whosoever is dedicated to thee by our office and ministry may also be endued with heavenly virtues, and everlastingly rewarded through thy mercy, O blessed Lord God, who dost live and govern all things, world without end. *Amen.*

Almighty, Everliving God, whose most dearly beloved Son Jesus Christ, for the forgiveness of our sins, did shed out of his most precious side both water and blood, regard, we beseech thee, our supplications. Sanctify this water for this Holy Sacrament; and grant that *this child*, now to be baptized, may receive the fullness of thy grace, and ever remain in the number of thy faithful and elect children, through Jesus Christ our Lord. *Amen.*

Then shall the Minister address the Parents or Guardians as follows:

Dearly Beloved, forasmuch as *this child is* now presented by you for Christian Baptism, you must remember that it is your part and duty to see that *he* be taught, as soon as *he* shall be able to learn, the nature and end of this Holy Sacrament. And that *he* may know these things the better, you shall call upon *him* to give reverent attendance upon the appointed means of grace, such as the ministry of the word, and the public and private worship of God; and further, you shall provide that *he* shall read the Holy Scriptures, and learn the Lord's Prayer, the Ten Commandments, the Apostles' Creed, the Catechism, and all other things which a Christian ought to know and believe to his soul's health, in order that *he* may be brought up to lead a virtuous and holy life, remembering always that

Baptism doth represent unto us that inward purity which disposeth us to follow the example of our Saviour Christ; that as he died and rose again for us, so should we, who are baptized, die unto sin and rise again unto righteousness, continually mortifying all corrupt affections, and daily proceeding in all virtue and godliness.

Do you therefore solemnly engage to fulfill these duties, so far as in you lies, the Lord being your helper?

Ans. **We do.**

Then shall the People stand up, and the Minister shall say:

Hear the words of the Gospel, written by St. Mark. [Chap. 10. 13-16.]

They brought young children to Christ, that he should touch them. And his disciples rebuked those that brought them. But when Jesus saw it, he was much displeased, and said unto them, Suffer the little children to come unto me, and forbid them not; for of such is the kingdom of God. Verily I say unto you, Whosoever shall not receive the kingdom of God as a little child, he shall not enter therein. And he took them up in his arms, put his hands upon them, and blessed them.

Then the Minister shall take the Child into his hands, and say to the friends of the Child:

Name this child.

And then, naming it after them, he shall sprinkle or pour Water upon it, or, if desired, immerse it in Water, saying:

N., I baptize thee in the name of the Father, and of the Son, and of the Holy Ghost. *Amen.*

Then shall the Minister offer the following Prayer, the People kneeling:

O God of infinite mercy, the Father of all the faithful seed, be pleased to grant unto *this child* an understanding mind and a sanctified heart. May thy providence lead *him* through the dangers, temptations, and ignorance of *his* youth, that *he* may never run into folly, nor into the evils of an unbridled appetite. We pray thee so to order the course of *his* life that, by good education, by holy examples, and by thy restraining and renewing grace, *he* may be led to serve thee faithfully all *his* days; so that, when *he has* glorified thee in *his* generation, and *has* served the Church on earth, *he* may be received into thine eternal kingdom, through Jesus Christ our Lord. *Amen.*

Almighty and Most Merciful Father, let thy loving mercy and compassion descend upon *these*, thy *servant* and *handmaid*, the parents [or guardians] of *this child*. Grant unto *them*, we beseech thee, thy Holy Spirit, that *they* may, like Abraham, command *their* houschold to keep the way of the Lord. Direct *their* actions, and sanctify *their* hearts, words, and purposes, that *their* whole family may be united to our Lord Jesus Christ in the bands of faith, obedience, and charity; and that they all, being in this life thy holy children by adoption and grace, may be admitted into the Church of the firstborn in heaven, through the merits of thy dear Son, our Saviour and Redeemer. *Amen.*

Then may the Minister offer extemporary Prayer.

Then shall be said, all kneeling:

Our Father who art in heaven, hallowed be thy name. Thy kingdom come. Thy will be done in earth, as it is in heaven. Give us this day our daily bread: and forgive us our trespasses, as we forgive them that trespass against us: and lead us not into temptation, but deliver us from evil: for thine is the kingdom, and the power, and the glory, forever. *Amen.*

Order for the Administration of Baptism to such as are of Riper Years

DEARLY BELOVED, forasmuch as all men are conceived and born in sin; and that which is born of the flesh is flesh, and they that are in the flesh cannot please God, but live in sin, committing many actual transgressions; and our Saviour Christ saith, Except a man be born of water and of the Spirit he cannot enter into the kingdom of God: I beseech you to call upon God the Father, through our Lord Jesus Christ, that of his bounteous goodness he will grant to *these persons* that which by nature *they* cannot have; that *they*, being baptized with water, may also be baptized with the Holy Ghost, and, being received into Christ's holy Church, may continue lively *Members* of the same.

Then shall the Minister say:

Let us pray.

Almighty and Immortal God, the aid of all that need, the helper of all that flee to thee for succor, the life of them that believe, and the resurrection of the dead: we call upon thee for *these persons*, that *they*, coming to thy Holy Baptism, may also be filled with thy Holy Spirit. Receive *them*, O Lord, as thou hast promised by thy well-beloved Son, saying, Ask, and ye shall receive; seek, and ye shall find; knock, and it shall be opened unto you: so give now unto us that ask; let us that seek, find; open the gate unto us that knock; that *these persons* may enjoy the everlasting benediction of thy heavenly washing, and may come to the eternal kingdom which thou hast promised, by Christ our Lord. *Amen.*

Then shall the People stand up, and the Minister shall say:

Hear the words of the Gospel, written by St. John. [Chap. 3. 1–8.]

There was a man of the Pharisees, named Nicodemus, a ruler of the Jews: the same came to Jesus by night, and said unto him, Rabbi, we know that thou art a teacher come from God; for no man can do these miracles that thou doest, except God be with him. Jesus answered and said unto him, Verily, verily, I say unto thee, Except a man be born again, he cannot see the kingdom of God. Nicodemus saith unto him, How can a man be born when he is old? Can he enter the second time into his mother's womb, and be born? Jesus answered, Verily, verily, I say unto thee, Except a man be born of water and of the Spirit, he cannot enter into the kingdom of God. That which is born of the flesh is flesh; and that which is born of the Spirit is spirit. Marvel not that I said unto thee, Ye must be born again. The wind bloweth where it listeth, and thou hearest the sound thereof, but canst not tell whence it cometh, and whither it goeth: so is everyone that is born of the Spirit.

Then the Minister shall speak to the Persons to be baptized on this wise:

Well Beloved, who *have* come hither desiring to receive Holy Baptism, you have heard how the Congregation hath prayed that our Lord Jesus Christ would vouchsafe to receive you, to bless you, and to give you the kingdom of heaven, and everlasting life. And our Lord Jesus Christ hath promised in his holy word to grant all those things that we have prayed for: which promise he for his part will most surely keep and perform.

Wherefore, after this promise made by Christ, you must also faithfully, for your part, promise in the presence of this whole Congregation, that you will renounce the devil and all his works, and constantly believe God's holy word, and obediently keep his commandments.

Then shall the Minister demand of each of the Persons to be baptized:

Quest. Dost thou renounce the devil and all his works, the vain pomp and glory of the world, with all covetous desires of the same, and the carnal desires of the flesh, so that thou wilt not follow nor be led by them?

Ans. I renounce them all.

Quest. Dost thou believe in God the Father Almighty, Maker of heaven and earth:

And in Jesus Christ, his only begotten Son our Lord; and that he was conceived by the Holy Ghost, born of the Virgin Mary; that he suffered under Pontius Pilate, was crucified, dead, and buried; that he rose again the third day; that he ascended into heaven, and sitteth at the right hand of God the Father Almighty; and from thence shall come again at the end of the world, to judge the quick and the dead?

And dost thou believe in the Holy Ghost; the holy catholic* Church, the communion of saints; the forgiveness of sins; the resurrection of the body; and everlasting life after death?

Ans. All this I steadfastly believe.

Quest. Wilt thou be baptized in this faith?

Ans. Such is my desire.

* The one universal Church of Christ.

Quest. Wilt thou then obediently keep God's holy will and commandments, and walk in the same all the days of thy life?

Ans. I will endeavor so to do, God being my helper.

Then shall the Minister say:

O Merciful God, grant that all carnal affections may die in *these persons*, and that all things belonging to the Spirit may live and grow in *them*. *Amen*.

Grant that *they* may have power and strength to have victory, and triumph against the devil, the world, and the flesh. *Amen*.

Grant that *they*, being here dedicated to thee by our office and ministry, may also be endued with heavenly virtues, and everlastingly rewarded through thy mercy, O blessed Lord God, who dost live, and govern all things, world without end. *Amen*.

Almighty, Everliving God, whose most dearly beloved Son Jesus Christ, for the forgiveness of our sins, did shed out of his most precious side both water and blood; and gave commandment to his disciples that they should go teach all nations, and baptize them in the name of the Father, and of the Son, and of the Holy Ghost; regard, we beseech thee, our supplications; and grant that the *persons* now to be baptized may receive the fullness of thy grace, and ever remain in the number of thy faithful and elect children, through Jesus Christ our Lord. *Amen*.

Then shall the Minister ask the name of each Person to be baptized, and shall sprinkle or pour Water upon him (or, if he shall desire it, shall immerse him in Water), saying:

N., I baptize thee in the name of the Father, and of the Son, and of the Holy Ghost. *Amen*.

Then shall be said the Lord's Prayer, all kneeling:

Our Father who art in heaven, hallowed be thy name. Thy kingdom come. Thy will be done in earth, as it is in heaven. Give us this day our daily bread: and forgive us our trespasses, as we forgive them that trespass against us: and lead us not into temptation, but deliver us from evil: for thine is the kingdom, and the power, and the glory, forever. *Amen*.

Then may the Minister conclude with extemporary Prayer.

Reception of Members

Form for Receiving Persons into the Church as Probationers

Those who are to be received into the Church as Probationers shall be called forward by name, and the Minister, addressing the Congregation, shall say:

DEARLY BELOVED BRETHREN, that none may be admitted hastily into the Church, we receive all persons seeking fellowship with us on profession of faith into a preparatory membership on trial; in which proof may be made, both to themselves and to the Church, of the sincerity and depth of their convictions and of the strength of their purpose to lead a new life.

The persons here present desire to be so admitted. You will hear their answers to the questions put to them, and if you make no objection they will be received.

It is needful, however, that you be reminded of your responsibility, as having previously entered this holy fellowship, and as now representing the Church into which they seek admission. Remembering their inexperience, and how much they must learn in order to become good soldiers of Jesus Christ, see to it that they find in you holy examples of life, and loving help in the true serving of their Lord and ours. I beseech you so to order your own lives that these new disciples may take no detriment from you, but that it may ever be cause for thanksgiving to God that they were led into this fellowship.

Then addressing the Persons seeking Admission on Probation, the Minister shall say:

Dearly Beloved, you have, by the grace of God, made your decision to follow Christ and to serve him. Your confidence in so doing is not to be based on any notion of fitness or worthiness in yourselves, but solely on the merits of our Lord Jesus Christ, and on his death and intercession for us.

That the Church may know your purpose, you will answer the questions I am now to ask you.

Have you an earnest desire to be saved from your sins?

Ans. **I have.**

Will you guard yourselves against all things contrary to the teaching of God's word, and endeavor to lead a holy life, following the commandments of God?

Ans. **I will endeavor so to do.**

Are you purposed to give reverent attendance upon the appointed means of grace in the ministry of the word, and in the private and public worship of God?

Ans. **I am so determined, with the help of God.**

No objection being offered, the Minister shall then announce that the Candidates are admitted as Probationers and shall assign them to classes.

Then shall the Minister offer extemporary Prayer.

Form for Receiving Persons into the Church after Probation

On the day appointed, all that are to be received into the Church shall be called forward, and the Minister, addressing the Congregation, shall say:

DEARLY BELOVED BRETHREN, the Scriptures teach us that the Church is the household of God, the body of which Christ is the head; and that it is the design of the Gospel to bring together in one all who are in Christ. The fellowship of the Church is the communion that its Members enjoy one with another. The ends of this fellowship are, the maintenance of sound doctrine and of the ordinances of Christian worship, and the exercise of that power of godly admonition and discipline which Christ has committed to his Church for the promotion of holiness. It is the duty of all men to unite in this fellowship; for it is only those that "be planted in the house of the Lord" that "shall flourish in the courts of our God." Its more particular duties are, to promote peace and unity; to bear one another's burdens; to prevent each other's stumbling; to seek the intimacy of friendly society among themselves; to continue steadfast in the faith and worship of the Gospel; and to pray and sympathize with each other. Among its privileges are, peculiar incitements to holiness from the hearing of God's word and sharing in Christ's ordinances; the being placed under the watchful care of Pastors; and the enjoyment of the blessings which are promised only to those who are of the Household of Faith. Into this holy fellowship the *persons* before you, who *have* already received the Sacrament of Baptism, and *have* been under the care of *proper leaders* for six months on Trial, *come* seeking admission. We now propose, in the fear of God, to question *them* as to *their* faith and purposes, that you may know that *they* are proper *persons* to be admitted into the Church.

Then, addressing the Applicants for Admission, the Minister shall say:

Dearly Beloved, you are come hither seeking the great privilege of union with the Church our Saviour has purchased with his own blood. We rejoice in the grace of God vouchsafed unto you in that he has called you to be his *followers*, and that thus far you have run well. You have heard how blessed are the privileges, and how solemn are the duties, of membership in Christ's Church; and before you are fully admitted thereto, it is proper that you do here publicly renew your vows, confess your faith, and declare your purpose, by answering the following questions:

Do you here, in the presence of God and of this Congregation, renew the solemn promise contained in the Baptismal Covenant, ratifying and confirming the same, and acknowledging *yourselves* bound faithfully to observe and keep that Covenant?

Ans. **I do.**

Have you saving faith in the Lord Jesus Christ?

Ans. **I trust I have.**

Do you believe in the Doctrines of the Holy Scriptures as set forth in the Articles of Religion of the Methodist Episcopal Church?

Ans. **I do.**

Will you cheerfully be governed by the Rules of the Methodist Episcopal Church, hold sacred the Ordinances of God, and endeavor, as much as in you lies, to promote the welfare of your brethren and the advancement of the Redeemer's kingdom?

Ans. I will.

Will you contribute of your earthly substance, according to your ability, to the support of the Gospel and the various benevolent enterprises of the Church?

Ans. I will.

Then the Minister, addressing the Church, shall say:

Brethren, *these persons* having given satisfactory responses to our inquiries, have any of you reason to allege why *they* should not be received into Full membership in the Church?

No objections being alleged, the Minister shall say to the Candidates:

We welcome you to the communion of the Church of God; and, in testimony of our Christian affection and the cordiality with which we receive you, I hereby extend to you the right hand of fellowship: and may God grant that you may be a faithful and useful Member of the Church militant till you are called to the fellowship of the Church triumphant, which is "without fault before the throne of God."

Then shall the Minister offer extemporary Prayer.

The Lord's Supper

[Whenever practicable, let none but the pure, unfermented juice of the grape be used in administering the Lord's Supper.]

[Let persons who have scruples concerning the receiving of the Sacrament of the Lord's Supper kneeling be permitted to receive it either standing or sitting.]

[No person shall be admitted to the Lord's Supper among us who is guilty of any practice for which we would exclude a Member of our Church.]

Order for the Administration of the Lord's Supper

The Elder shall say one or more of these Sentences, during the reading of which the Persons appointed for that purpose shall receive the Alms for the Poor:

LET your light so shine before men, that they may see your good works, and glorify your Father which is in heaven. [Matt. 5. 16.]

Lay not up for yourselves treasures upon earth, where moth and rust doth corrupt, and where thieves break through and steal: but lay up for yourselves treasures in heaven, where neither moth nor rust doth corrupt, and where thieves do not break through nor steal. [Matt. 6. 19, 20.]

Whatsoever ye would that men should do to you, do ye even so to them: for this is the law and the prophets. [Matt. 7. 12.]

Not every one that saith unto me, Lord, Lord, shall enter into the kingdom of heaven; but he that doeth the will of my Father which is in heaven. [Matt. 7. 21.]

Zaccheus stood, and said unto the Lord; Behold, Lord, the half of my goods I give to the poor; and if I have taken anything from any man by false accusation, I restore him fourfold. [Luke 19. 8.]

He which soweth sparingly shall reap also sparingly; and he which soweth bountifully shall reap also bountifully. Every man according as he purposeth in his heart, so let him give; not grudgingly, or of necessity: for God loveth a cheerful giver. [2 Cor. 9. 6, 7.]

As we have therefore opportunity, let us do good unto all men, especially unto them who are of the household of faith. [Gal. 6. 10.]

Godliness with contentment is great gain; for we brought nothing into this world, and it is certain we can carry nothing out. [1 Tim. 6. 6, 7.]

Charge them that are rich in this world, that they be not high-minded, nor trust in uncertain riches, but in the living God, who giveth us richly all things to enjoy; that they do good, that they be rich in good works, ready to distribute, willing to communicate; laying up in store for themselves a good foundation against the time to come, that they may lay hold on eternal life. [1 Tim. 6. 17–19.]

God is not unrighteous to forget your work and labor of love, which ye have showed toward his name, in that ye have ministered to the saints, and do minister. [Heb. 6. 10.]

To do good and to communicate forget not; for with such sacrifices God is well pleased. [Heb. 13. 16.]

Whoso hath this world's good, and seeth his brother have need, and shutteth up his bowels of compassion from him, how dwelleth the love of God in him? [1 John 3. 17.]

He that hath pity upon the poor lendeth unto the Lord; and that which he hath given will he pay him again. [Prov. 19. 17.]

Blessed is he that considereth the poor: the Lord will deliver him in time of trouble. [Psa. 41. 1.]

Thou shalt open thine hand wide unto thy brother, to thy poor. [Deut. 15. 11.]

After which the Elder shall give the following Invitation, the People standing:

If any man sin, we have an advocate with the Father, Jesus Christ the righteous: and he is the propitiation for our sins: and not for ours only, but also for the sins of the whole world.

Wherefore ye that do truly and earnestly repent of your sins, and are in love and charity with your neighbors, and intend to lead a new life, following the commandments of God, and walking from henceforth in his holy ways, draw near with faith, and take this Holy Sacrament to your comfort; and, devoutly kneeling, make your humble confession to Almighty God.

Then shall this general Confession be made by the Minister in the name of all those who are minded to receive the Holy Communion, both he and all the People devoutly kneeling, and saying:

Almighty God, Father of our Lord Jesus Christ, Maker of all things, Judge of all men, we acknowledge and bewail our manifold sins and wickedness, which we from time to time most grievously have committed, by thought, word, and deed, against thy Divine Majesty, provoking most justly thy wrath and indignation against us. We do earnestly repent, and are heartily sorry for these our misdoings; the remembrance of them is grievous unto us. Have mercy upon us, have mercy upon us, most merciful Father; for thy Son, our Lord Jesus Christ's sake, forgive us all that is past; and grant that we may ever hereafter serve and please thee in newness of life, to the honor and glory of thy name, through Jesus Christ our Lord. Amen.

Then shall the Elder say:

Almighty God, our heavenly Father, who of thy great mercy hast promised forgiveness of sins to all them that with hearty repentance and true faith turn unto thee, have mercy upon us; pardon and deliver us from all our sins; confirm and strengthen us in all goodness; and bring us to everlasting life, through Jesus Christ our Lord. *Amen.*

The Collect:

Almighty God, unto whom all hearts are open, all desires known, and from whom no secrets are hid, cleanse the thoughts of our hearts by the inspiration of thy Holy Spirit, that we may perfectly love thee, and worthily magnify thy holy name through Jesus Christ our Lord. Amen.

Then shall the Elder say:

We do not presume to come to this thy table, O merciful Lord, trusting in our own righteousness, but in thy manifold and great mercies. We are not worthy so much as to gather up the crumbs under thy table. But thou art the same Lord, whose property is always to have mercy. Grant us, therefore, gracious Lord, so to eat the flesh of thy dear Son Jesus Christ, and to drink his blood, that we may live and grow thereby; and that, being washed through his most precious blood, we may evermore dwell in him, and he in us. *Amen.*

Then the Elder shall offer the Prayer of Consecration, as followeth:

Almighty God, our heavenly Father, who of thy tender mercy didst give thine only Son Jesus Christ to suffer death upon the cross for our redemption; who made there, by his oblation of himself once offered, a full, perfect, and sufficient sacrifice, oblation, and satisfaction for the sins of the whole world; and did institute, and in his holy Gospel command us to continue, a perpetual memory of his precious death until his coming again: hear us, O merciful Father, we most humbly beseech thee, and grant that we, receiving these thy creatures of bread and wine, according to thy Son our Saviour Jesus Christ's holy institution, in remembrance of his death and passion, may be partakers of his most

The Lord's Supper

blessed body and blood; who, in the same night that he was betrayed, took bread; (1) and when he had given thanks, he broke it, and gave it to his disciples, saying, Take, eat; this is my body which is given for you; do this in remembrance of me.

(1) Here the Elder may take the plate of bread in his hand.

Likewise after supper he took (2) the cup; and when he had given thanks, he gave it to them, saying, Drink ye all of this; for this is my blood of the New Testament, which is shed for you, and for many, for the remission of sins; do this, as oft as ye shall drink it, in remembrance of me. *Amen.*

(2) Here he may take the cup in his hand.

Then shall the Minister receive the Communion in both kinds, and proceed to deliver the same to the other Ministers, if any be present; after which he shall say:

It is very meet, right, and our bounden duty that we should at all times and in all places give thanks unto thee, O Lord, holy Father, Almighty, Everlasting God.

Therefore with angels and archangels, and with all the company of heaven, we laud and magnify thy glorious name, evermore praising thee, and saying, Holy, Holy, Holy, Lord God of Hosts, heaven and earth are full of thy glory. Glory be to thee, O Lord most high! *Amen.*

The Minister shall then proceed to administer the Communion to the People in order, kneeling, into their uncovered hands; and when he delivereth the Bread, he shall say:

The body of our Lord Jesus Christ, which was given for *thee*, preserve *thy* soul and *body* unto everlasting life. Take and eat this in remembrance that Christ died for *thee*; and feed on him in *thy heart* by faith, with thanksgiving.

And the Minister that delivereth the Cup shall say:

The blood of our Lord Jesus Christ, which was shed for *thee*, preserve *thy* soul and *body* unto everlasting life. Drink this in remembrance that Christ's blood was shed for *thee*, and be thankful.

[If the Consecrated bread or wine shall be all spent before all have communed, the Elder may Consecrate more by repeating the prayer of Consecration.]

[When all have communed, the Minister shall return to the Lord's table and place upon it what remaineth of the Consecrated elements, covering the same with a fair linen cloth.]

Then shall the Elder say the Lord's Prayer; the People kneeling, and repeating after him every petition:

Our Father who art in heaven, hallowed be thy name. Thy kingdom come. Thy will be done in earth, as it is in heaven. Give us this day our daily bread: and forgive us our trespasses, as we forgive them that trespass against us: and lead us not into temptation, but deliver us from evil: for thine is the kingdom, and the power, and the glory, forever. *Amen.*

After which shall be said as followeth:

O Lord our heavenly Father, we thy humble servants desire thy Fatherly goodness mercifully to accept this our sacrifice of praise and thanksgiving; most humbly beseeching thee to grant, that, by the merits and death of thy Son Jesus Christ, and through faith in his blood, we and thy whole Church may obtain forgiveness of our sins, and all other benefits of his passion. And here we offer and present unto thee, O Lord, ourselves, our souls and bodies, to be a reasonable, holy, and lively sacrifice unto thee; humbly beseeching thee that all we who are partakers of this Holy Communion may be filled with thy grace and heavenly benediction. And although we be unworthy, through our manifold sins, to offer unto thee any sacrifice, yet we beseech thee to accept this our bounden duty and service; not weighing our merits, but pardoning our offenses, through Jesus Christ our Lord; by whom, and with whom, in the unity of the Holy Ghost, all honor and glory be unto thee, O Father Almighty, world without end. *Amen.*

Then shall be said or sung:

Glory be to God on high, and on earth peace, good will toward men! We praise thee, we bless thee, we worship thee, we glorify thee, we give thanks to thee for thy great glory, O Lord God, heavenly King, God the Father Almighty!

O Lord, the only begotten Son Jesus Christ; O Lord God, Lamb of God, Son of the Father, that takest away the sins of the world, have mercy upon us. Thou that takest away the sins of the world, have mercy upon us. Thou that takest away the sins of the world, receive our prayer. Thou that sittest at the right hand of God the Father, have mercy upon us. For thou only art holy; thou only art the Lord; thou only, O Christ, with the Holy Ghost, art most high in the glory of God the Father. *Amen.*

The Ritual

Then the Elder, if he see it expedient, may put up an extemporary Prayer; and afterward shall let the People depart with this Blessing:

The peace of God, which passeth all understanding, keep your hearts and minds in the knowledge and love of God, and of his Son Jesus Christ our Lord: and the blessing of God Almighty, the Father, the Son, and the Holy Ghost, be among you, and remain with you always. *Amen.*

N. B.—If the Elder is straitened for time in the usual administration of the Holy Communion, he may omit any part of the service except the Invitation, the Confession, and the Prayer of Consecration; and its administration to the Sick he may omit any part of the service except the Confession, the Prayer of Consecration, and the usual sentences in delivering the Bread and Wine, closing with the Lord's Prayer, *extempore* supplication, and the Benediction.

Matrimony
Form for the Solemnization of Matrimony
[The parts in brackets throughout may be used or not at discretion.]

At the day and time appointed for the Solemnization of Matrimony, the persons to be married—having been qualified according to law—standing together, the Man on the right hand and the Woman on the left, the Minister shall say:

DEARLY BELOVED, we are gathered together here in the sight of God, and in the presence of these witnesses, to join together this man and this woman in holy Matrimony; which is an honorable estate, instituted of God in the time of man's innocency, signifying unto us the mystical union that exists between Christ and his Church; which holy estate Christ adorned and beautified with his presence, and first miracle that he wrought, in Cana of Galilee, and is commended by Saint Paul to be honorable among all men; and therefore is not by any to be entered into unadvisedly, but reverently, discreetly, and in the fear of God.

Into which holy estate these two persons present come now to be joined. Therefore if any can show just cause why they may not lawfully be joined together, let him now speak, or else hereafter forever hold his peace.

[*And also speaking unto the persons that are to be married, the Minister shall say:*

I require and charge you both, that if either of you know any impediment why you may not be lawfully joined together in Matrimony, you do now confess it: for be ye well assured, that so many as are coupled together otherwise than God's word doth allow, are not joined together by God, neither is their Matrimony lawful.]

If no impediment be alleged, then shall the Minister say unto the Man:

M., wilt thou have this woman to be thy wedded wife, to live together after God's ordinance in the holy estate of Matrimony? Wilt thou love her, comfort her, honor and keep her, in sickness and in health; and forsaking all other, keep thee only unto her, so long as ye both shall live?

The Man shall answer:

I will.

Then shall the Minister say unto the Woman:

N., wilt thou have this man to be thy wedded husband, to live together after God's ordinance in the holy estate of Matrimony? Wilt thou love, honor, and keep him, in sickness and in health; and forsaking all other, keep thee only unto him, so long as ye both shall live?

The Woman shall answer:

I will.

[*Then the Minister shall cause the Man with his right hand to take the Woman by her right hand, and say after him as followeth:*

I, M., take thee N., to be my wedded wife, to have and to hold, from this day forward, for better, for worse, for richer, for poorer, in sickness and in health, to love and to cherish, till death us do part, according to God's holy ordinance; and thereto I plight thee my faith.

Then shall they loose their hands, and the Woman, with her right hand taking the Man by his right hand, shall likewise say after the Minister:

I, N., take thee M., to be my wedded husband, to have and to hold, from this day forward, for better, for worse, for richer, for poorer, in sickness and in health, to love and to cherish, till death us do part, according to God's holy ordinance; and thereto I plight thee my faith.]

Burial of the Dead

Then shall the Minister pray thus:

O Eternal God, Creator and Preserver of all mankind, Giver of all spiritual grace, the Author of everlasting life: send thy blessing upon these thy servants, this man and this woman, whom we bless in thy name; that as Isaac and Rebecca lived faithfully together, so these persons may surely perform and keep the vow and covenant between them made, and may ever remain in perfect love and peace together, and live according to thy laws, through Jesus Christ our Lord. *Amen.*

[*If the parties desire it, the Man shall here hand a Ring to the Minister, who shall return it to him, and direct him to place it on the third finger of the Woman's left hand. And the Man shall say to the Woman, repeating after the Minister:*

With this ring I thee wed, and with my worldly goods I thee endow, in the name of the Father, and of the Son, and of the Holy Ghost. *Amen.*]

Then shall the Minister join their right hands together, and say:

Forasmuch as *M.* and *N.* have consented together in holy wedlock, and have witnessed the same before God and this company, and thereto have pledged their faith either to other, and have declared the same by joining of hands; I pronounce that they are husband and wife together, in the name of the Father, and of the Son, and of the Holy Ghost. Those whom God hath joined together, let no man put asunder. *Amen.*

And the Minister shall add this blessing:

God, the Father, the Son, and the Holy Ghost, bless, preserve, and keep you; the Lord mercifully with his favor look upon you, and so fill you with all spiritual benediction and grace that ye may so live together in this life that in the world to come ye may have life everlasting. *Amen.*

Then shall the Minister offer the following Prayer:

O God of Abraham, God of Isaac, God of Jacob, bless this man and this woman, and sow the seed of eternal life in their hearts, that whatsoever in thy holy word they shall profitably learn, they may indeed fulfill the same. Look, O Lord, mercifully on them from heaven, and bless them: as thou didst send thy blessings upon Abraham and Sarah to their great comfort, so vouchsafe to send thy blessings upon this man and this woman, that they, obeying thy will, and always being in safety under thy protection, may abide in thy love unto their lives' end, through Jesus Christ our Lord.

Almighty God, who at the beginning didst create our first parents, Adam and Eve, and didst sanctify and join them together in marriage, pour upon these persons the riches of thy grace, sanctify and bless them, that they may please thee both in body and soul, and live together in holy love unto their lives' end. *Amen.*

Here the Minister may use extemporary Prayer.

Then the Minister shall repeat the Lord's Prayer:

Our Father who art in heaven, hallowed be thy name. Thy kingdom come. Thy will be done in earth, as it is in heaven. Give us this day our daily bread: and forgive us our trespasses, as we forgive them that trespass against us: and lead us not into temptation, but deliver us from evil: for thine is the kingdom, and the power, and the glory, forever. *Amen.*

Burial of the Dead

[We will on no account whatever make a charge for burying the dead.]

Form for the Burial of the Dead

The Minister, going before the Corpse shall say:

I AM the resurrection, and the life: he that believeth in me, though he were dead, yet shall he live: and whosoever liveth and believeth in me shall never die. [John 11. 25, 26.]

I know that my Redeemer liveth, and that he shall stand at the latter day upon the earth: and though after my skin worms destroy this body, yet in my flesh shall I see God: whom I shall see for myself, and mine eyes shall behold, and not another. [Job 19. 25–27.]

We brought nothing into this world, and it is certain we can carry nothing out. The Lord gave, and the Lord hath taken away; blessed be the name of the Lord. [1 Tim. 6. 7; Job 1. 21.]

In the House or Church may be read one or both of the following Psalms, or some other suitable portion of the Holy Scriptures:

Psalm 39:

I said, I will take heed to my ways, that I sin not with my tongue: I will keep my mouth with a bridle, while the wicked is before me. I was dumb with silence, I held my peace, even from good; and my sorrow was stirred. My heart was hot within me; while I was musing the fire burned: then spake I with my tongue, Lord, make me to know mine end, and the measure of my days, what it is; that I may know how frail I am. Behold, thou hast made my days as a handbreadth; and mine age is as nothing before thee: verily every man at his best state is altogether vanity. Surely every man walketh in a vain show: surely they are disquieted in vain: he heapeth up riches, and knoweth not who shall gather them. And now, Lord, what wait I for? my hope is in thee. Deliver me from all my transgressions: make me not the reproach of the foolish. I was dumb, I opened not my mouth; because thou didst it. Remove thy stroke away from me; I am consumed by the blow of thine hand. When thou with rebukes dost correct man for iniquity, thou makest his beauty to consume away like a moth: surely every man is vanity. Hear my prayer, O Lord, and give ear unto my cry; hold not thy peace at my tears: for I am a stranger with thee, and a sojourner, as all my fathers were. O spare me, that I may recover strength, before I go hence, and be no more.

Psalm 90:

Lord, thou hast been our dwelling place in all generations. Before the mountains were brought forth, or ever thou hadst formed the earth and the world, even from everlasting to everlasting, thou art God. Thou turnest man to destruction; and sayest, Return, ye children of men. For a thousand years in thy sight are but as yesterday when it is past, and as a watch in the night. Thou carriest them away as with a flood; they are as a sleep: in the morning they are like grass which groweth up. In the morning it flourisheth, and groweth up; in the evening it is cut down, and withereth. For we are consumed by thine anger, and by thy wrath are we troubled. Thou hast set our iniquities before thee, our secret sins in the light of thy countenance. For all our days are passed away in thy wrath: we spend our years as a tale that is told. The days of our years are threescore years and ten; and if by reason of strength they be fourscore years, yet is their strength labor and sorrow; for it is soon cut off, and we fly away. Who knoweth the power of thine anger? even according to thy fear, so is thy wrath. So teach us to number our days, that we may apply our hearts unto wisdom. Return, O Lord, how long? and let it repent thee concerning thy servants. O satisfy us early with thy mercy; that we may rejoice and be glad all our days. Make us glad according to the days wherein thou hast afflicted us, and the years wherein we have seen evil. Let thy work appear unto thy servants, and thy glory unto their children. And let the beauty of the Lord our God be upon us: and establish thou the work of our hands upon us; yea, the work of our hands establish thou it.

Then may follow the reading of the Epistle, as follows:

1 Corinthians 15. 41–58:

There is one glory of the sun, and another glory of the moon, and another glory of the stars; for one star differeth from another star in glory. So also is the resurrection of the dead. It is sown in corruption, it is raised in incorruption: it is sown in dishonor, it is raised in glory: it is sown in weakness, it is raised in power: it is sown a natural body, it is raised a spiritual body. There is a natural body, and there is a spiritual body. And so it is written,

The first man Adam was made a living soul; the last Adam was made a quickening spirit. Howbeit that was not first which is spiritual, but that which is natural; and afterward that which is spiritual. The first man is of the earth, earthy: the second man is the Lord from heaven. As is the earthy, such are they also that are earthy: and as is the heavenly, such are they also that are heavenly. And as we have borne the image of the earthy, we shall also bear the image of the heavenly. Now this I say, brethren, that flesh and blood cannot inherit the kingdom of God; neither doth corruption inherit incorruption. Behold, I show you a mystery; We shall not all sleep, but we shall all be changed, in a moment, in the twinkling of an eye, at the last trump: for the trumpet shall sound, and the dead shall be raised incorruptible, and we shall be changed. For this corruptible must put on incorruption, and this mortal must put on immortality. So when this corruptible shall have put on incorruption, and this mortal shall have put on immortality, then shall be brought to pass the saying that is written, Death is swallowed up in victory. O death, where is thy sting? O grave, where is thy victory? The sting of death is sin; and the strength of sin is the law. But thanks be to God, which giveth us the victory through our Lord Jesus Christ. Therefore, my beloved brethren, be ye steadfast, unmovable, always abounding in the work of the Lord, forasmuch as ye know that your labor is not in vain in the Lord.

At the grave, when the Corpse is laid in the Earth, the Minister shall say:

Man that is born of a woman hath but a short time to live, and is full of misery. He cometh up, and is cut down like a flower: he fleeth as it were a shadow, and never continueth in one stay.

In the midst of life we are in death: of whom may we seek for succor, but of thee, O Lord, who for our sins art justly displeased?

Yet, O Lord God most holy, O Lord most mighty, O holy and most merciful Saviour, deliver us not into the bitter pains of eternal death.

Thou knowest, Lord, the secrets of our hearts; shut not thy merciful ears to our prayers, but spare us, Lord most holy; O God most mighty, O holy and merciful Saviour, thou most worthy Judge eternal, suffer us not at our last hour for any pains of death to fall from thee.

Then, while the Earth shall be cast upon the Body by some standing by, the Minister shall say:

Forasmuch as it hath pleased Almighty God, in his wise providence, to take out of the world the soul of the departed, we therefore commit *his* body to the ground, earth to earth, ashes to ashes, dust to dust; looking for the general resurrection in the last day, and the life of the world to come, through our Lord Jesus Christ; at whose second coming in glorious majesty to judge the world, the earth and the sea shall give up their dead; and the corruptible bodies of those who sleep in him shall be changed and made like unto his own glorious body; according to the mighty working whereby he is able to subdue all things unto himself.

Then shall be said:

I heard a voice from heaven saying unto me, Write, From henceforth blessed are the dead who die in the Lord: Even so, saith the Spirit; for they rest from their labors.

Then shall the Minister say:
Lord, have mercy upon us.

Christ, have mercy upon us.

Lord, have mercy upon us.

Then the Minister may offer this Prayer:

Almighty God, with whom do live the spirits of those who depart hence in the Lord, and with whom the souls of the faithful, after they are delivered from the burden of the flesh, are in joy and felicity: we give thee hearty thanks for the good examples of all those thy servants, who, having finished their course in faith, do now rest from their labors. And we beseech thee, that we, with all those who are departed in the true faith of thy holy name, may have our perfect consummation and bliss, both in body and soul, in thy eternal and everlasting glory, through Jesus Christ our Lord. *Amen.*

The Collect:

O Merciful God, the Father of our Lord Jesus Christ, who is the resurrection and the life; in whom whosoever believeth shall live, though he die, and whosoever liveth and believeth in him shall not die eternally: we meekly beseech thee, O Father, to raise us from the death of sin unto the life of righteousness; that when we shall depart this life we may rest in him; and at the general resurrection on the last day may be found acceptable in thy sight, and receive that blessing which thy well-beloved Son shall then pronounce to all that love and fear thee, saying, Come, ye blessed children of my Father, receive the kingdom prepared for you from the beginning of the world. Grant this, we beseech thee, O Merciful Father, through Jesus Christ our Mediator and Redeemer. *Amen.*

Our Father who art in heaven, hallowed be thy name. Thy kingdom come. Thy will be done in earth, as it is in heaven. Give us this day our daily bread: and forgive us our trespasses, as we forgive them that trespass against us: and lead us not into temptation, but deliver us from evil: for thine is the kingdom, and the power, and the glory, forever. *Amen.*

The grace of our Lord Jesus Christ, and the love of God, and the fellowship of the Holy Ghost, be with us all evermore. *Amen.*

96